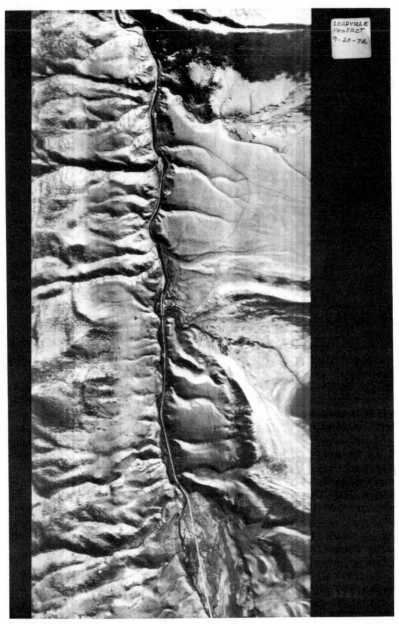

Thermal infrared imagery of a section of the Arkansas River
south of Leadville, Colorado showing drainage patterns of its
tributaries. The grey tone of this photograph indicates the
relative temperature of this ground feature with white representing a warm object and black, a cold object. South is at
the top of the photograph.

ENVIRONMENTAL IMPACT
ON
RIVERS

(RIVER MECHANICS Ⅲ)

Edited and Published by

HSIEH WEN SHEN

Professor of Civil Engineering, Colorado State University

H.W. Shen, P.O. Box 606, Fort Collins, Colorado
U.S.A. 80521

ENVIRONMENTAL IMPACT ON RIVERS

Library of Congress Catalog Card Number 70-168730

Thermal effluent from a power plant on the Missouri River.
The temperature of the effluent at a point about 500 feet
below the outfall was about 3°C warmer than the receiving
water. Flow is from left to right.

FOREWARD

This book is based essentially on the lecture notes delivered at the second week of the Second Institute on River Mechanics, Colorado State University, July 31 - August 11, 1972. Most of the lectures delivered at the first week of this institute are included in River Mechanics Vol. I, edited by myself and published in 1971. A main emphasis for the First Institute on River Mechanics, 1970, was hydraulic structures and a main emphasis for the Second Institute on River Mechanics was environmental inputs.

The purpose of this book is to describe current knowledge on various aspects of alluvial rivers. It is intended to present a rather comprehensive collection of information related to river mechanics and to be used as a reference book as well as a textbook for practicing engineers, scientists, administrators, planners, professors and students.

Hense, efforts have been made to present various authors' physical interpretations on particular subjects. The chapters, in general, are interrelated yet stand by themselves with minimum dependence on other chapters. Some duplication from chapter to chapter is permitted to reduce the need for continued cross-references. Concluding each chapter is a list of references. Notations used in each chapter are different. This book is not intended to be used as a design manual, although suggestions are sometimes given to aid design.

Chapter 1 discusses the effect of the changes of sediment bed material size, energy slope, kinematic viscosity (in terms of temperature) on sediment and flow discharges. It also gives detail analysis on the long term river systems response related to certain perturbations such as increase or decrease of sediment size, sediment load, flow discharge and others.

Chapter 2 presents i) some of the available suggested methods of estimating as well as predicting flow resistance over alluvial resistances, ii) some of the difficulties in analyzing alluvial bed form resistance, and iii) a few recent studies on the statistical properties of bed forms.

The effect of regulation on flow retardation can be divided into three parts: i) tall vegetation on the order of flow depths, ii) short vegetation on the order of normal boundary roughness and, iii) vegetated on the order of 20 to 80 percent flow depth. Chapter 3 presents i) the knowledge of roughness of short vegetation (either rigid or flexible), ii) flow measurements around a single cylinder (tall vegetation) in open channel flow, iii) flow resistance due to multiple cylinders in open channel flow and iv) application of iii) to flow retardation and sediment yields of various groups of cylinders.

Chapter 4 gives an analysis of the investigations on a portion of Rhine River, one of the most important rivers in Western Europe. It includes discussion on flume experiments, systematic river measurements, bed load sampler, bed load sediment transport rates, and the river behavior.

Chapter 5 describes regime problems of river formed in sediment. It discusses various terminologies used in river regime studies and certain interrelationships among the various variables such as depth, width, discharge, slope and sediment sizes with and without dunes. Many working graphs together with procedures of applying them to different situations are also given.

Natural mixing processes in rivers are discussed in Chapter 6. It begins with a derivation of diffusion equation. The many available simplified models with their solutions are discussed next. The current knowledge on longitudinal, vertical and transverse dispersion processes in natural rivers and laboratory flumes are well described in detail.

Chapter 7 reviews the sources of waste heat; the biologic effects and the synergistic effects of waste heat discharges into rivers; and the non-thermal effects of cooling water systems. It also discusses the various available methods such as site selection, intake and discharge design, and closed-cycle cooling to prevent or reduce damage due to cooling water discharges into river systems.

Chapter 8 described the mechanisms of heat transfer in non-stratified open-channel flows. It presents the formulation of three- two-, and one-space dimension heat transfer equations in open channel flow. The exchange of energy across an air-water interface is discussed in great detail. Comparison of observed and calculated temperature distribution in the Potomac River, Dan River, and North Platte River are given in the discussion of two dimensional heat equation.

Some effects of wastes on natural waters are presented in Chapter 9. It discusses waste pollutants, water pollution control policies, waste assimilative capacities, thermal pollution, eutrophication, and mercury in the aquatic environment. The main purpose of this chapter is to describe the various water quality problems in relation to wastes discharged into rivers.

Chapter 10 describes heated surface discharges into flowing ambiant streams and lakes. Discussions are given for false analytical concepts, which include physical basis, characteristics of warm water discharges, near field calculations, and far field calculations. The potential, the analysis, and the results of both hydraulic modeling and field investigations are given.

Fish behavior related to thermal pollution is discussed in Chapter 11. Basic problems of temperature acclimatior in fish are first described. The known thermal death points of fish related to acclimation temperatures for various fishes are given in a table. Next the voluntary response of fish to thermal loading and other environmental changes is discussed. The available and possible techniques for recording fish response to thermal stress are given. A research study in Yellowstone Park for fish behavior related to thermal pollution is discussed.

Chapter 12 deals with agricultural impact on water quality in western rivers. The related water quality problems and the major problem areas are described.

Dispersion of contaminants attached to sediment bed load is analyzed in Chapter 13. The theoretical development is based on the current but available knowledge that the stop lengths of sediment particles movement are gamma distributed. The movements of the peak and centroid are theoretically developed. The iso-concentration contours for two particular cases are presented to illustrate the methods.

Chapter 14 discusses the behavior of cohesive material from a soil engineer's viewpoint. Types of cohesive soils, the physio-chemical properties, effects of chemical elements, temperature, organic content, surface textures, and others on the erodibility of cohesive soil are described.

The upslope erosion analysis is discussed in Chapter 15. A detailed analysis on the well known "Universal Soil Loss Equation" which was developed by the same author is given in detail.

Chapter 16 deals with the application of remote sensing to river mechanics. It first discusses the basic techniques in remote sensing and then shows the potential application of remote sensing to river mechanics.

The possible variations to be encountered in suspended sediment sampling is discussed in Chapter 17. The current available theoretical analysis together with experimental evidence are given.

Chapter 18 gives a rather comprehensive analysis of fish facilities at river development projects. It discusses fish ladders, fishlocks, mechanical lifting of fish, fish passage during construction, passage through highway drainage structures, downstream migrants, and artificial propagation of fish.

Basic river basin and water resources plannings are discussed in Chapter 19. It gives the various aspects of the problems facing the planners and also describes the many technical tools for river basin and water resources plannings.

Chapter 20 discusses the historical, current, and future developments for Rederal guide lines of water resource project evaluation. This chapter is authored by the person who was the chariman of the committee to develop these guide lines.

Appendix A gives thoughts on river basin planning for an engineering consultant's viewpoint.

Appendix B gives an abstract of a lecture on sediment and phosophorous content of stream flows.

Appendix C presents a table of contents for River Mechanics Volumes I and II.

Hsieh Wen Shen
Fort Collins, Colorado
September, 1972

TABLE OF CONTENTS

Volume III

TABLE OF CONTENTS - (Continued)

Volume III - (Continued)

Chapter 1

RIVER RESPONSE

by

Julio Santos-Cayade, Ingeniero, Ph. D., Santo Domingo,
        Dominican Republic, former Graduate Student,
        Colorado State University, Fort Collins, Colorado

D. B. Simons, Associate Dean for Engineering Research, Professor
        of Civil Engineering, College of Engineering,
        Colorado State University, Fort Collins, Colorado

Chapter 1

RIVER RESPONSE

1.1 INTRODUCTION

The discussion of river morphology and river response requires identification of cause and effect relations. Dependent and independent variables must be kept constantly in mind to avoid confusion and misunderstanding. The identification of dependent and independent variables acting on a river is closely related to the length of time considered. A river system can be looked upon from the geological point of view, in which case the duration of time extends for millions of years. When a river is studied in geologic time, the initial relief, geology and paleoclimate are important independent variables. In the geologic time frame of reference the fluvial system in an open system undergoing continued change, there is no equilibrium state. The fluvial system is adjusting continuously to the effects of the erosion cycle (Davis, 1899).

The engineer is concerned with shorter time durations, on the order of ten to one hundred years. Such time durations are denoted,graded or engineering time. When a river system is looked upon from the engineering time frame of reference, the cause and effect relations vary with respect to geologic time. In engineering time, for example, the relief at the start of the erosion cycle may not be relevant, the geologic period is also irrelevant from the engineering point of view. Geology (lithology and structure) are independent variables in engineering time. In addition, when a river system is looked upon in engineering time, new variables that were indeterminate in geologic time, gain definite importance. Of special interest are the independent variables water and sediment discharge, and the dependent variable channel morphology. Here the fluvial system is an open system in or adjusting toward dynamic equilibrium.

In the engineering perspective most streams flow in channels that may vary locally with space and time but over an extended reach the streams display somewhat constant dimensional characteristics. Such streams have been described as in regime or graded. Blench (1957) defines regime as meaning "average values of the quantities considered as constituting regime (width, depth, velocity, meander pattern, water and sediment discharge, bed material and slope) do not show a definite trend over some interval."

Mackin (1948) defines a graded stream as one "in which, over a period of years, slope and channel characteristics are delicately adjusted to provide, with available discharge, just the velocity required for the transportation of the (sediment) load supplied from the drainage basin."

The independent variables water and sediment discharge must constitute a stationary time series in order to produce constant

channel dimensions constituting regime, that is with no definite
trend over some interval. The delicate equilibrium established
between water-sediment discharge, and slope-channel geometry is
altered when trends or changes are introduced in the water and/
or sediment discharge time series of a graded stream. Then the
river system adjusts toward a new channel geometry and slope
that will be in dynamic equilibrium with the modified water and
sediment time series. If the modified time series reaches a
stationary state so will the slope and channel characteristics.
The river system responds to changes in water and sediment discharge. However, the river system response is manifested with
a time lag in reference to permanent changes in the water and
sediment time series.

To infer future system responses, future changes in channel morphology of individual rivers must be studied. Once
future changes in channel morphology of individual rivers are
known, the interaction between rivers constituting the system
can be investigated and the river system response can be approximated. Since water and sediment discharge are independent
variables producing dynamic equilibrium of a graded stream, the
logical approach to study future changes in channel morphology
is to investigate how the variables affected by water and sediment discharge change, due to changes in water and sediment
discharge.

The relationships derived provide an initial step toward
the analysis of river system response to water resources development that affect the water and sediment discharge characteristics of the river system. In addition, immediate applications of the relationships are found in the prediction of
possible future changes of river stage and form resulting from
significant variations in water and sediment discharge characteristics of the river.

1.2 RELATIVE INFLUENCE OF VARIABLES ON SEDIMENT AND WATER
DISCHARGE

Relative influence of the hydraulic variables on the
sediment discharge will be studied, using Einstein's bed load
function (1950) and Colby's (1964) relationships. Einstein's
bed load function was chosen because it is "the most detailed
and comprehensive treatment, from the point of fluid mechanics,
that is presently available" (graf, 1971). Colby's (1964)
relationships were chosen because of the large amount and range
of data used in their development.

Einstein's bed load function has been programmed by
shulits and Hill (1968) to give only the bed load. To obtain
the total bed material load, Shulits and Hill's Fortran program
was completed by including Einstein's Figs. 1-1 and 1-2, giving
I_1, and I_2, and the fall velocities of the bed material particles. The program was further modified to use the average
measured velocity instead of Keulegan's computed velocity.

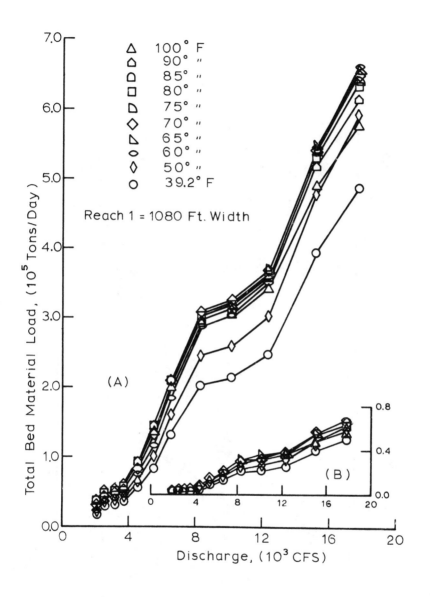

Fig. 1-1   Kinematic viscosity variation effects.
Rio Grande near Bernalillo.   Reach 1.

1-3

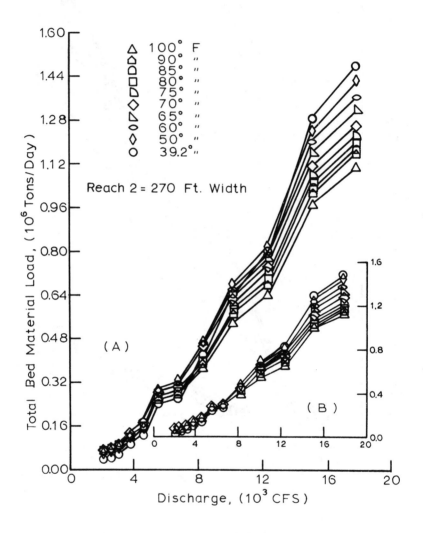

Fig. 1-2   Kinematic viscosity variation effects.
Rio Grande near Bernalillo.   Reach 2.

1-4

The data required to compute the total bed material discharge using Einstein's relations are:
    S = energy slope
    D65 = size of bed material for which 65 percent is finer
    D35 = size of bed material for which 35 percent is finer
    ν = kinematic viscosity
    n_W = Manning's wall friction coefficient
    A = cross sectional area
    PB = wetted perimeter of the bed
    PW = wetted perimeter of the banks
    DIM = size of the bed material, geometric mean
    PD = percentage of bed material of size   DIM
    G = acceleration of gravity
    SS = specific weight
    V = average velocity.
To study the relative influence of variables on sediment
and water discharges, the data taken on the Rio Grande near
Bernalillo are used. These data consisted basically of water
discharge, top width, cross sectional area and gage height
measurements. The measurements were taken by the U. S. Geological Survey at the gaging station on the Rio Grande near
Bernalillo over a period extending from October 1, 1940 to
October 1, 1970. In the analysis the average water temperature
was assumed equal to 70°F, the average bed material size distribution was taken from Nordin (1964), and the average energy
gradient of the channel was assumed equal to 0.00095 ft/ft.
The applicability of the results depends on the reliability of
the writer's modified Einstein bed load function and Colby's
relationships rather than on the choice of data.
    Now consider the variation of the average values of energy
slope, bed material size, and kinematic viscosity, one at a
time in order to obtain their variations with the sediment and
water discharges and with river stage. These computations were
done using the modified Einstein bed load function.
    The energy slope was varied from 0.7S to 1.5S, in which
S is the average bed slope assumed to be equal to the average
energy slope. Further, the kinematic viscosity was varied to
correspond with variations in temperature from 39.2° to 100°F
inclusive. The variation of D65, D35, DIM, and PD was accomplished by using the average bed material distribution given
by Nordin (1964) and shifting the curve representing the average bed material distribution along a line parallel to the
abscissa drawn through D50. The water and sediment discharges
were computed independently for each variation of the variables
and for three subreaches of the Rio Grande of different width
near Bernalillo. The computed water and sediment discharges
were plotted in Figs. 1-1 through 1-9.
    Figures 1-1 through 1-9 show the variation of sediment dis-
charge due to changes in bed material size, in slope and in
kinematic viscosity for any given water discharge. Figures 1-7,
1-8, and 1-9 show that when the bed material becomes finer, the

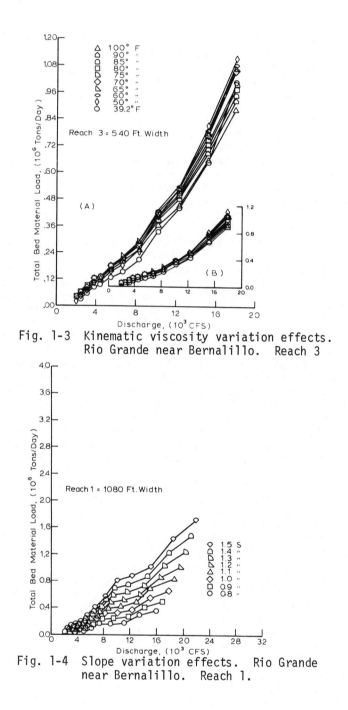

Fig. 1-3   Kinematic viscosity variation effects.
Rio Grande near Bernalillo.   Reach 3

Fig. 1-4   Slope variation effects.   Rio Grande
near Bernalillo.   Reach 1.

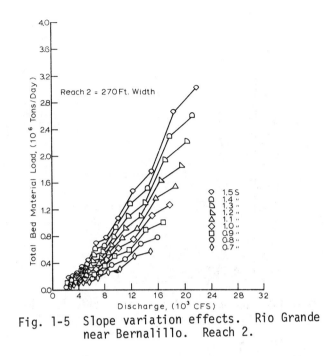

Fig. 1-5 Slope variation effects. Rio Grande
near Bernalillo. Reach 2.

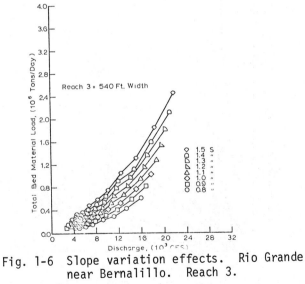

Fig. 1-6 Slope variation effects. Rio Grande
near Bernalillo. Reach 3.

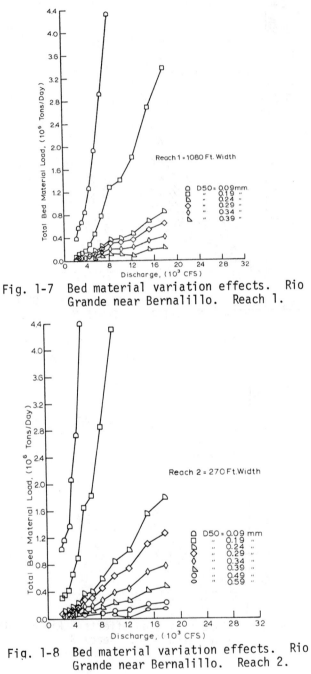

Fig. 1-7   Bed material variation effects.   Rio
Grande near Bernalillo.   Reach 1.

Fig. 1-8   Bed material variation effects.   Rio
Grande near Bernalillo.   Reach 2.

sediment discharge increases considerably. The second most important variable affecting sediment discharge is the slope variation, see Figs. 1-4, 1-5, and 1-6. Kinematic viscosity is third in importance, Figs. 1-1, 1-2, and 1-3. The effects of variables on sediment discharge were studied over approximately the same range of variation for each variable. Since the slope varies from 0.7S to 1.5S, it experiences an increase of 214%. The kinematic viscosity varies from 0.00000739 sq. ft. per sec. to 0.00001684 sq. ft. per sec., an increase of 224%. The median diameter of bed material, if only its variation from 0.19 mm. to 0.39 mm. is considered, increases 205%.

Figure 1-10 shows the variation of the sediment discharge due to changes in the depth of flow for any given discharge, computed using Colby's (1964) relationships. The values of depth of flow in Fig. 1-10, were varied from 1.0 to 10.0 ft, the median diameter of the bed material was maintained constant equal to 0.30 mm, the water temperature was assumed constant and the concentration of fine sediment was assumed less than 10.000 ppm. The channel width was maintained constant. In Fig. 1-10 the curves for constant depth of flow show a steep slope. This indicates that the capacity of the stream to transport sands increases very fast for a small increase of discharge at constant depth. Similar figures could be developed for other sizes of bed material, and they could be modified to include the effect of wash load and viscosity effects if one desired to do so.

1.3 PREDICTION OF LONG TERM RIVER CHANGES

Figures 1-1 through 1-10 presented in the preceding paragraphs, and the water and sediment transport relationships that they represent, i.e., Einstein (modified), Colby and Manning's equations will be used to determine the direction of change of hydraulic variables when the channel forming water and sediment discharges are varied.

It is important to notice that the Einstein, Colby and Manning's equations apply to a cross section or reach and differ from some of the available geomorphic equations that have been derived by considering a reach or total length of river. These equations also differ from other geomorphic equations that have been derived by gathering and analyzing data at a cross section or reach over long periods of time. Further, these equations deal with depth of flow, width of flow and energy slope instead of channel depth, channel width and channel slope as considered in most geomorphic equations.

The interdependency of top width, depth of flow, energy slope, bed material size and kinematic viscosity on the water and sediment discharge allows the establishment of the relative influence of these variables on the stage-discharge relationship. Information concerning the interdependency of top width, depth of flow, energy slope, bed material size and kinematic

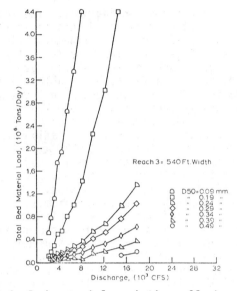

Fig. 1-9   Bed material variation effects.   Rio
Grande near Bernalillo.   Reach 3.

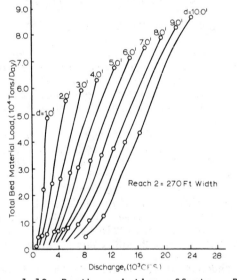

Fig. 1-10   Depth variation effects.   Rio
Grande near Bernalillo.   Reach 2.

viscosity with water and sediment discharges will be used to establish the direction of variation of hydraulic variables, as a consequence of changes imposed on the water and bed material discharge.

Neither Einstein's bed load function (1950) nor Colby's (1964) relationships directly take into account the width of the cross section, except when transforming the sediment discharge per foot of width to the total river width. The influence of the width, nevertheless, indirectly enters any method of estimating transport, since it affects the depth of flow for a given water discharge and energy slope. Therefore, although the total bed material load is linearly and directly proportional to the width, Fig. 1-11 shows an increase in total bed material load as the width decreases, due to its indirect effect on the depth. This effect can be demonstrated.

From Manning's discharge equation for wide rivers:

$$Q = \frac{1.486}{n} W d^{5/3} S^{1/2} \qquad (1-1)$$

The relation for depth is:

$$d = \left(\frac{nQ}{1.486 \, W \, S^{1/2}}\right)^{3/5} \qquad (1-2)$$

This relation shows that for n and S constant

$$d \sim \frac{1}{W^{3/5}} , \qquad (1-3)$$

and since

$$V \sim d^{2/3} , \qquad (1-4)$$

$$V \sim \frac{1}{W^{2/5}} , \qquad (1-5)$$

and from Colby,

$$Q_s \sim V^6 ; \qquad (1-6)$$

therefore,

$$Q_s \sim \frac{1}{W^{12/5}} . \qquad (1-7)$$

In Fig. 1-1, both influences are combined:

$$Q_s \sim W \cdot W^{-12/5} = W^{-7/5} \tag{1-8}$$

In Eq. 1-8, W represents the direct influence of width on Q_s, while $W^{-12/5}$ represents the indirect influence of W on the depth of flow. Equation 1-8 explains the inverse relation apparent in Fig. 1-12. The exponent in Eq. 1-8 is to be taken as a guideline only.

According to Einstein and Manning's equations:

$$W \sim [Q , Q_s] \ . \tag{1-9}$$

Equation 1-9 shows that equal variations in Q and Q_s have the same effect on the width.

The four possible combinations of variations of total bed material discharge, Q_s, and water discharge, Q_w, are an increase in water and total bed material discharge, $Q_s^+ Q_w^+$; a decrease in total bed material discharge and increase in water discharge, $Q_s^- Q_w^+$; an increase in total bed material discharge and a decrease in water discharge, $Q_s^+ Q_w^-$; and a decrease in water and total bed material discharge, $Q_s^- Q_w^-$. Figures 1-1 through 1-10 will be used to develop relations that indicate river response to changes in water and sediment discharge over engineering time.

A tributary entering a main stream may increase the total bed material discharge and water discharge in the main river from Q_s and Q_w to Q_s^+ and Q_w^+ . Looking at Figs. 1-4 through 1-6, it can be seen in each figure that the river experiences a decrease or increase in energy slope depending on the relative increase in Q_s . If the increase in Q_s , i. e., from Q_s to Q_s^+ is small the energy slope may decrease, for a large increase in Q_s the energy slope will increase. In summary, an increase in total bed material load and water discharge with respect to the original conditions, expressed as Q_s^+ and Q_w^+ , may cause either a decrease or an increase in energy slope.

$$Q_s^+ Q_w^+ \sim S^\pm \tag{1-10}$$

Figures 1-7 through 1-9 show that an increase of total bed material discharge and water discharge from Q_s and Q_w to

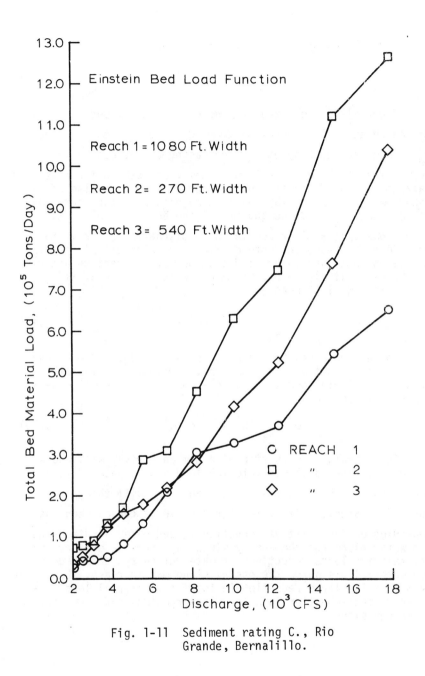

Fig. 1-11 Sediment rating C., Rio Grande, Bernalillo.

Q_S^+ and Q_W^+, can be obtained by either increasing or decreasing the bed material size. Therefore Eq. 1-10 can be extended to include D50 in the following form.

$$Q_S^+ \; Q_W^+ \sim S^\pm \; D50^\pm \tag{1-11}$$

Figure 1-10 shows that an increase of total bed material discharge and water discharge from Q_S and Q_W to Q_S^+ and Q_W^+ can be achieved by either increasing or decreasing the depth of flow. Figure 1-10 indicates that both an increase or decrease of the depth of flow can occur. The direction of change will depend on the relative magnitude of the increases in Q_S and Q_W and the quality of the bed material. Figure 1-10 shows that an increase in water discharge is likely to produce an increase in depth of flow. A relatively larger increase in total bed material discharge with respect to water discharge is likely to produce a decrease in depth of flow. Therefore, Eq. 1-11 becomes:

$$Q_S^+ \; Q_W^+ \sim S^\pm \; D50^\pm \; d^\pm \; . \tag{1-12}$$

To include width in the above equation, Eq. 1-9 must be considered. Equation 1-9 shows that for increases in both total bed material and water discharges, the width will increase. Therefore:

$$Q_S^+ \; Q_W^+ \sim S^\pm \; D50^\pm \; d^\pm \; W^+ \; . \tag{1-13}$$

In general, construction of a dam on a river will cause a decrease in the total bed material load and in water discharge downstream of the dam, i. e., Q_S and Q_W will change to Q_S^- and Q_W^-. Studying Figs. 1-4 through 1-6 it can be seen that depending on the relative reduction in bed material discharge and water discharge the energy slope may increase or decrease. For relative large reductions in water discharge compared to bed material discharge the energy slope may increase. Conversely a relative large reduction in total bed material load compared to the reduction in water discharge, may cause a decrease in energy slope.

$$Q_S^- \; Q_W^- \sim S^\pm \tag{1-14}$$

Figures 1-7 through 1-9 show that a decrease of total bed material discharge and water discharge from Q_S and Q_W to

1-14

Q_S^- and Q_W^- can result from either a decrease or an increase in bed material size. Hence:

$$Q_S^- \, Q_W^- \sim S^{\pm} \, D50^{\pm} \, . \qquad (1\text{-}15)$$

Figure 1-10 shows that a decrease of total bed material discharge and water discharge from Q_S and Q_W to Q_S^- and Q_W^- can result from either an increase or decrease in the depth of flow. Figure 1-10 shows that a small decrease in water discharge accompanied by a large decrease in total bed material load will cause an increase in depth of flow. For a larger decrease in water discharge the depth of flow may decrease. Therefore:

$$Q_S^- \, Q_W^- \sim S^{\pm} \, D50^{\pm} \, d^{\pm} \, . \qquad (1\text{-}16)$$

Equation 1-9 indicates that for reductions in total bed material discharge and water discharge, the width will decrease. Hence:

$$Q_S^- \, Q_W^- \sim S^{\pm} \, D50^{\pm} \, d^{\pm} \, W^- \, . \qquad (1\text{-}17)$$

Consider the situation where a diversion from one river into another is so designed that it will cause an increase in water discharge from Q_W to Q_W^+ , but a relative decrease in total bed material discharge from Q_S to Q_S^- . Figures 1-4 through 1-6 show that a decrease in total bed material load and an increase in water discharge, that is, a variation from Q_S and Q_W to Q_S^- and Q_W^- , will result in a decrease in energy slope.

$$Q_S^- \, Q_W^+ \sim S^- \qquad (1\text{-}18)$$

Figure 1-10 shows that a decrease of total bed material discharge and an increase in water discharge will result in an increase in depth of flow. Then:

$$Q_S^- \, Q_W^+ \sim S^- \, d^+ \, . \qquad (1\text{-}19)$$

Equation 1-9 indicates that for a reduction in total bed material discharge and an increase in water discharge, the width may increase or decrease.

$$Q_s^- \ Q_w^+ \sim S^- \ d^+ \ W^\pm \qquad (1\text{-}20)$$

However, it should be recognized that the chance for a decrease in W is practically zero. Therefore, the minus sign in the above equation could, for most cases, be deleted.

An increase in land use, cultivation or climatic change can cause an increase in total bed material discharge from Q_s to Q_s^+ , and a decrease in water discharge from Q_w to Q_w^- . Figures 1-4 through 1-6 show that an increase in total bed material load and a decrease in water discharge, that is, a change from Q_s and Q_w to Q_s^+ and Q_w^- results in an increase in energy slope.

$$Q_s^+ \ Q_w^- \sim S^+ \qquad (1\text{-}21)$$

Figure 1-10 shows that an increase in total bed material load and a decrease in water discharge results in a decrease in depth of flow. Hence:

$$Q_s^+ \ Q_w^- \sim S^+ \ d^- \ . \qquad (1\text{-}22)$$

Equation 1-9 indicates that for an increase in total bed material load and a reduction in water discharge, the width can either increase or decrease.

$$Q_s^+ \ Q_w^- \sim S^+ \ d^- \ W^\pm \qquad (1\text{-}23)$$

To decide upon the direction of variation of depth of flow and energy slope using Eqs. 1-13 and 1-17, the magnitude of the increase and/or decrease in total bed material discharge and water discharge must be known. To decide the direction of change of depth of flow and energy slope in Eqs. 1-13, 1-17 and geomorphic equations derived by other investigators can be used. In applying the geomorphic equations derived by other investigators it must be assumed that the depth of flow, energy slope and width of flow will become equal to channel depth, channel slope, and channel width, or at least it must be assumed that both sets of variables are closely related. Specifically, geomorphic equations relating the channel sinuosity and the width-depth ratio to water and sediment discharges are necessary. Schumm's (1971) Eqs. 4.8, 4.18, 4.5 included in this work as Eqs. 1-24, 1-25, 1-26 were chosen. These equations follow.

$$F = 56 \frac{Q_m^{0.10}}{M^{0.74}} \qquad (1\text{-}24)$$

$$P = 0.94 \, M^{0.25} \qquad (1\text{-}25)$$

$$M = \frac{55}{Q_{ss}} \quad . \qquad (1\text{-}26)$$

In Eqs. 1-24, 1-25 and 1-26, F is the width-depth ratio, Q_m is the mean annual flow, P is the sinuosity, and Q_{ss} is the percentage of total load that is bed material load. Equations 1-24, 1-25 and 1-26 can be transformed into the following functional relationships:

$$P \sim \frac{1}{Q_{ss}} \qquad (1\text{-}27)$$

$$F \sim Q_m \, Q_{ss} \quad . \qquad (1\text{-}28)$$

According to the relationships 1-27 and 1-28, the sinuosity is inversely proportional to the sediment discharge and the width-depth ratio is directly proportional to the water and sediment discharge.

Applying the functional relationships 1-27 to Eq. 1-13 a decrease in channel sinuosity may be expected. A decrease in channel sinuosity straightens the channel causing the channel slope to approach the valley slope, therefore, the channel slope may be expected to increase. The application of the functional relationship 1-28 to Eq. 1-13 indicates that an increase in the width-depth ratio may be expected. An increase in the width-depth ratio will cause the depth of flow in Eq. 1-13 to remain constant or probably to decrease because both F and W increase.

In Eq. 1-17 the application of the functional relationship 1-27 indicates that an increase in channel sinuosity may be expected. This causes the channel slope to become smaller than the valley slope, therefore, the channel slope may be expected to decrease. The functional relationship 1-28 indicates that the width-depth ratio may be expected to decrease if it is applied to Eq. 1-17. Following the same reasoning as in the preceding paragraph, it can be concluded that the depth of the channel will probably remain constant or increase.

Additional equations can be obtained from Figs. 1-1 through 1-6 and Fig. 1-10, for the cases when only one of the independent variables vary. Consider the diversion of flow from one river to another that changes Q_s and Q_w to Q_s and Q_w^+. Using Figs. 1-1 through 1-6 and Fig. 1-10 the following equation results.

$$Q_s \, Q_w^+ \sim S^- \, d^+ \, W^+ \qquad (1\text{-}29)$$

1-17

If clear water is diverted from one river to another, that river from which the water was diverted will experience a change from Q_s and Q_w to Q_s and Q_w^-. To obtain the equation for this case Figs. 1-1 through 1-6 and Fig. 1-10 are utilized yielding

$$Q_s \; Q_w^- \sim S^+ \; d^- \; W^- \; . \tag{1-30}$$

If for any reason the amount of total bed material load is increased while the amount of water discharge is maintained constant, the river conditions will change from Q_s and Q_w before introducing the extra sediment into the river, to Q_s^+ and Q_w afterwards. Utilizing Figs. 1-1 through 1-6 and Fig. 1-10, the following equation is obtained.

$$Q_s^+ \; Q_w \sim S^+ \; d^- \; W^+ \tag{1-31}$$

A dam on a river may decrease the amount of total bed material load downstream, but may not alter the water discharge. For this case, the river condition downstream from the dam may change from Q_s and Q_w before construction to Q_s^- and Q_w afterwards. Utilizing Figs. 1-1 through 1-6 and Fig. 1-10 yields.

$$Q_s^- \; Q_w \sim S^- \; d^+ \; W^- \tag{1-32}$$

The decrease in channel width indicated in the foregoing equation seems to be only possible if the stream transports a significant amount of fine material.

In the development of Eqs. 1-13, 1-17, 1-20, 1-23, 1-29, 1-30, 1-31, and 1-32, the variation of the median size of bed material was not included. To include the effects of variation of the median size of bed material in these equations, it would be necessary to postulate the changes in the characteristics of the bed material discharge, that can occur in the future. Specifically, it needs to be postulated whether the median size of the bed material discharge to be transported in the future will remain constant, or whether it will increase or decrease. The postulate defining the probable future changes in characteristics of the bed material discharge, will in the long term control the variation of the median size of bed material. The inclusion of the bed material size in Eqs. 1-13, 1-17, 1-20, 1-23, 1-29, 1-30, 1-31 and 1-32, will, therefore, be straightforward once the variations in the characteristics of the bed material discharge are assumed or known.

With the information presented one can consider possible long term changes (engineering time) in stage due to increase and/or decrease in total bed material discharge and water discharge.

1.4 APPLICATION OF LONG TERM EQUATIONS TO ESTIMATE STAGE

The set of equations proposed help bridge the gap between the water and sediment discharge equations and the changes in magnitude of the hydraulic variables that occur when changes in the water and sediment discharges of the river take place.

The water surface elevation (stage) for a short reach and a certain recurrence interval discharge can be predicted by routing sediment through the short reach (Santos, 1972). The prediction of stage for a certain recurrence interval discharge involves the following steps.

1. The total discharge of sands is computed using Colby's (1964) relationships for each subreach constituting the short reach under consideration.

2. The equation of continuity for sediment is applied throughout the short reach to determine the bed elevation variations in each subreach for a time interval. The duration of time interval, step of the hydrograph, should be short compared with the total duration of the flood hydrograph.

3. The starting depth of flow for each hydrograph step (d_m) is affected by the bed elevation variation in the hydrograph step (∂Z_m). Using the affected depth of flow $d_m + \partial Z_m$, the flow velocity is computed for each subreach. In addition, the energy slope is computed for each subreach of the short reach studied.

4. Using the depth of flow ($d_m + \partial Z_m$), the flow velocity and the energy slope, the stream power is computed for each subreach.

5. Entering Fig. 1-12 with the values of stream power computed in step (4), a value of the Manning's roughness coefficient (n) is obtained for each subreach.

6. The final depth of flow for the present hydrograph step and each subreach is computed using the Manning's roughness coefficient obtained in step (5) and the energy slope obtained in step (3).

7. The stage for each subreach was computed by adding the bed elevation of each subreach computed in the previous hydrograph step the bed elevation variation and the depth of flow of each subreach computed for the present hydrograph step.

8. The water discharge was increased to that corresponding to the next hydrograph step, and the flow velocity was computed using the depth of flow in step (6). The cycle was repeated by returning to step (1).

The stage predicted for a certain recurrence interval discharge following the outlined procedure will remain a valid estimate only as long as the river conditions reflected in the data used remain the same. If the river conditions are changed by man works, or by climatic or any other change, the stage predicted previously will no longer correspond to the discharge for which it was obtained. Long term changes in river geometry

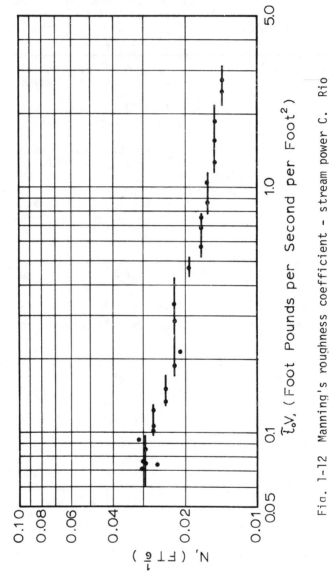

Fig. 1-12 Manning's roughness coefficient - stream power C. Rio Grande near Bernalillo. Median grain diameter 0.29 mm.

produced by water resources development in the watershed, will produce long term changes in the river stage.

Equations 1-13, 1-17, 1-20 and 1-23, can be used in conjunction with the base level concept (Lane, 1955) to predict long term variations in stage due to water resources developments in the watershed. In the following applications of Eqs. 1-13, 1-17, 1-20, 1-23, the energy slope (S) is considered equal to the channel slope.

An increase in land use, or climatic changes can cause a decrease in water discharge and an increase in sediment discharge $(Q_s^+ \, Q_w^-)$. Referring to Fig. 1-13 and utilizing Eq. 1-23 one observes that for a decrease in water discharge and an increase in sediment discharge, the depth of flow (d) will decrease, and the channel gradient (S) will increase. In Fig. 1-13, line CA, indicating the original equilibrium channel gradient will become C A. In this case the depth of flow (d) will decrease counteracting to some degree the increase in bed elevation, resulting from the increase in channel slope. Whether the channel stage increases or decreases then depends on the relative magnitude of the changes in bed elevation and depth of flow. By the same reasoning, it seems likely that increases in bed elevation will be larger than the decrease in depth of flow. Therefore, an increase in stage with time will probably result. The stage corresponding to the original discharge of a certain recurrence interval for which flood protection works were designed will be exceeded jeopardizing the protection works and increasing the flood hazard.

With a diversion of essentially clear water from one river to another the receiving river will experience an increase in water discharge from Q_w to Q_w^+ , and a relative decrease in total bed material load from Q_s to Q_s^- . Referring to Fig. 1-14 and utilizing Eq. 1-21 it can be shown that, for a decrease in sediment discharge and an increase in water discharge $(Q_s^- \, Q_w^+)$, the depth of flow (d) will increase, and the channel gradient (S) will decrease. In Fig. 1-14, line CA, indicating the original channel gradient, will become C'A. In this case the increase in depth of flow (d) counteracts to some degree the increase in bed elevation resulting from the decrease in channel slope. Whether the channel stage increases or decreases depends on the relative magnitude of the changes in bed elevation and depth of flow. Consequently, the stage corresponding to a particular discharge will decrease. In other words, the stage discharge relation will be shifted downward.

Next consider a tributary entering the main river at point C, Fig. 1-13. This will increase the water and sediment discharge from Q_s and Q_w to Q_s^+ and Q_w^+ . Equation 1-13 and the discussion of its application suggests that, for an increase

1-21

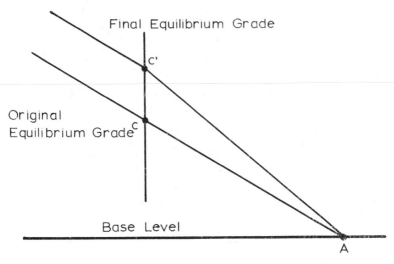

Final Equilibrium Grade

c'

Original
Equilibrium Grade c

Base Level

A

Fig. 1-13 Long term change in channel slope.

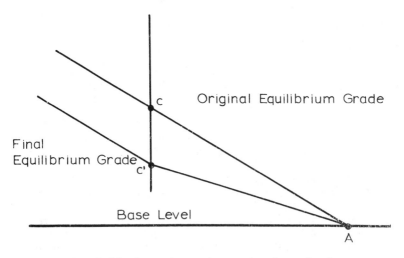

c Original Equilibrium Grade

Final
Equilibrium Grade
c'

Base Level

A

Fig. 1-14 Long term change in channel slope.

in water and sediment discharge $(Q_s^+ \; Q_w^+)$ the depth of flow (d) will probably decrease, and the channel gradient (S) will probably increase. In Fig. 1-13, line CA indicating the original channel gradient will change with time to C'A. The channel stage will probably decrease because the decrease in bed elevation due to the reduction in channel slope will probably exceed the decrease in depth of flow. This increases the probability of surpassing the stage previously established for a particular discharge.

Construction of a dam on a river usually causes a decrease in water and sediment discharge. Referring to Fig. 1-14, and using Eq. 1-17 and the earlier discussion it can be concluded that for a decrease in water and bed material discharge from Q_s and Q_w to Q_s^- and Q_w^-, the depth of flow (d) will probably increase, and the channel gradient (S) will probably decrease. In Fig. 1-14, line CA, indicating the original channel gradient, will become C'A, verifying a decrease in bed elevation throughout the channel with time. Hence, the channel stage will probably decrease, because the decrease in bed elevation due to the reduction in slope will exceed the increase in depth of flow (d). This decreases the probability of reaching the stage originally established for a particular discharge.

The preceding paragraphs indicate long term response of stage to changing flow conditions. The engineer is generally more interested in quantities rather than in directions of variations, therefore, the previous reasoning must be considered only as an initial step in analyzing long term channel response problems. However, this initial step is useful, because it warns of possible future difficulties in designing channel improvement and flood protection works. The prediction of the magnitude of possible errors in flood protection design, because of changes in stage with time, requires the quantification of changes in stage. To quantify these changes it is necessary to be able to quantify future changes in the variables that affect the stage. In this respect, knowledge of the future flow conditions are necessary.

The prediction of future flow conditions must be undertaken based on past data and on the evaluation of the effects of present and planned man-made works. The prediction of future flow conditions represents a problem which is, in its own right, worthy of individual consideration.

Once future flows are assumed, the quantification of future changes in stage can be further refined if one can estimate future changes in other variables, i. e., bed material, temperature, etc. Once the future changes of these variables are assumed, they can be included in the mathematical model outlined and an estimation of changes in stage and channel geometry can be made.

REFERENCES

Blench, T., 1957, Regime Behaviour of Canals and Rivers; Butterworths, London.

Brush, L. M., Jr., 1961, Drainage Basins, Channels, and Flow Characteristics of Selected Stream in Central Pennsylvania; U. S. Geological Survey Professional Paper 282-F, 40 p.

Carlston, C. W., 1965, The Relation of Free Meander Geometry to Stream Discharge and its Geomorphic Implication; American Journal of Science, Vol. 263, pp. 864-885.

Colby, B. R., 1964, Discharge of Sands and Mean-Velocity Relationships in Sand-Bed Streams; U. S. Geological Survey Professional Paper 462-A, 47 p.

Davis, W. M., 1899, The Geographical Cycle; Geographical Journal, Vol. 14, pp. 481-504.

Dury, G. H., 1965, Theoretical Implications of Underfit Streams; U. S. Geological Survey Professional Paper 452-C, 43 p.

Einstein, H. A., 1950, The Bed Load Function for Sediment Transportation in Open Channel Flows; Technical Bulletin No. 1026 of the U. S. Department of Agriculture, September, 71 p.

Graf, W. H., 1971, Hydraulics of Sediment Transport; McGraw-Hill Book Co., New York.

Hack, J. T., 1957, Studies of Longitudinal Stream Profiles in Virginia and Maryland; U. S. Geological Survey Professional Paper 294-B, pp. 45-97.

Lane, E. W., 1955, The Importance of Fluvial Morphology in Hydraulic Engineering; American Society of Civil Engineers Proceedings, Vol. 81, Paper No. 745, July, 17 p.

Leliavsky, S., 1966, An Introduction to Fluvial Hydraulics; Dover Publications, Inc., New York.

Leopold. L. B., Wolman, M. G., and Miller, J. P., 1964, Fluvial Processes in Geomorphology; W. H. Freeman and Co., San Francisco.

Mackin, J. H., 1948, Concept of the Graded River; Bulletin, Geological Society of America, Vol. 59, May 1948, pp. 463-512.

Nordin, C. F., 1964, Aspects of Flow Resistance and Sediment Transport, Rio Grande near Bernalillo, New Mexico; U. S. Geological Survey Water Supply Paper 1498-H, 41 p.

Schumm, S. A., 1960, The Shape of Alluvial Channels in Relation to Sediment Type; U. S. Geological Survey Professional Paper 352-B, pp. 17-30.

Schumm, S. A., 1969, River Metamorphis; American Society of Civil Engineers, Journal of Hydraulic Division, Vol. 95, No. HY1, January.

Schumm, S. A., 1971, Fluvial Geomorphology: The Historical Perspective; River Mechanics, Vol. I, Chapter 4, Edited by H. W. Shen, 30 p.

Shulits, S., and Hill, R. D., 1968, Bed Load Formulas; The Pennsylvania State University.

Santos-Cayado, Julio, 1972, Stage Determination for High Discharges, Ph.D. Dissertation, Colorado State University.

Chapter 2

FLOW OVER ALLUVIAL BED

by

Hsieh W. Shen, Professor of Civil Engineering, Engineering
Research Center, Colorado State University,
Fort Collins, Colorado.

Chapter 2

FLOW OVER ALLUVIAL BED

2.1. INTRODUCTION

When fluid flows over a movable bed, the bed surface is normally being deformed into various configurations. The occurance, description, and definition of alluvial bed forms in both rivers and laboratories have been well presented in Chapter 9 of River Mechanics Volume I. A detail description of an approach to determine the alluvial bed form roughness is also given there. Various physical and mathematical models about alluvial bed forms together with some statistical descriptions on bed forms are presented in Chapter 10 of River Mechanics Volume I.

This chapter is to discuss i) some of the available suggested methods of estimating as well as predicting these resistances, ii) some of the difficulties in analyzing alluvial bed form resistance, and iii) a few recent studies on the statistical properties of bed forms.

2.2 APPROACH TO THE BED FORM RESISTANCE ANALYSIS

When fluid flows over a deformed bed surface with various configurations, it experiences a resistance force to oppose the motion. This resistance is called the drag or resistance. The total drag may be decomposed into skin friction or friction's drag, which equals to the integral of all shearing stresses taken over the surface of the body, and form drag or pressure drag which equals to the integral of all pressure taken over the surface of the body in the direction of motion. The shape, the orientation and the surface roughness of the bed configurations determine to a great extent which part of the total drag is due to pressure and which is due to skin friction. Since the skin friction and the form drag are governed by different sets of laws it is reasonable to decompose the total resistance as follows:

$$\tau_b A_b = \tau_b' A_b + \tau_b'' A_b \qquad (2\text{-}1)$$

or

$$\tau_b = \tau_b' + \tau_b'' \qquad (2\text{-}2)$$

where τ_b is the total shear stress on the bed, A_b is the area of the bed, τ_b' is the skin shear stress on the bed, and τ_b'' is the form resistance stress on the bed. In a steady uniform flow and assuming that the total shear characteristic does not vary in its transverse direction.

$$\tau_b = \gamma R_b S \quad \text{or}$$

$$\gamma R_b S = \gamma R_b' S + \gamma R_b'' S \tag{2-3}$$

where γ is the specific weight of the fluid, R_b is the hydraulic radius attributed to the entire bed, S is the energy slope, R_b' is the hydraulic radius attributed to the skin roughness on the bed and R_b'' is the hydraulic radius attributed to the form roughness on the bed.

One could also divide the energy slope as follows:

$$\gamma R_b S = \gamma R_b S' + \gamma R_b S'' \tag{2-4}$$

where S' is the energy slope attributed to the bed skin roughness and S'' is the energy slope attributed to the bed form roughness.

The summation of the two types of resistance forces to obtain the total drag was verified by experiments (for instance See Goldstein, 1938).

2.3. AVAILABLE ALLUVIAL BED FORM RESISTANCE ANALYSES

Many investigators have attempted to used skin resistance knowledge obtained from plane rigid boundary for the estimation of τ'_b and then to study the variation of τ_b'' with flow conditions.

Einstein - Barbarossa (1952). Einstien and Barbarossa were perhaps the first to seperate the total resistance into skin resistance and form resistance. They presumed that the skin resistance can be estiamted from a universal logarithmic velocity relation in the following form.

$$\frac{U}{\sqrt{\tau_b'/\rho}} = 5.75 \log_{10} \left(12.27 \frac{R_b' \chi}{k_s} \right) \tag{2-5}$$

where U is the average main velocity, ρ is the density of the fluid, k_s is the representative grain roughness and is taken to be d_{65} (the sediment particle size of which 65% is finer), and χ is a correction parameter to adjust for hydraulically smooth, rough, and transition boundaries.

The variation of χ with k_s/S is given in Fig. 2-1 where δ is the viscous sublayer thickness and is expressed as

$$\delta = \frac{11.6 \, \nu}{\sqrt{\tau_b'/\rho}} \tag{2-6}$$

where ν is the kinematic viscosity of the fluid.

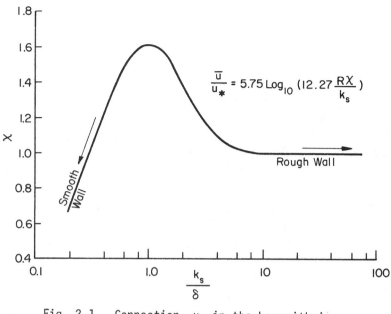

Fig. 2-1. Connection x in the Logarithmic
Friction Formula in Terms of k_s/δ
$\delta = 1.16\nu/\sqrt{\tau_b'/\rho}$ (after Einstein, 1950)

From river as well as flume data, Einstein and Barbarossa
then found the variation of the form resistance with flow
conditions as given in Fig. 2-2. Fig. 2-2 indicates that the
dimensionless form resistance plotted on the ordinate is essentially a function of the dimensionless flow parameter ψ' which,
according to Einstein (1950), governs the sediment transport
rate. See notation section - page 2-27 for the definition of Ψ.
   Shen (1962). He attempted to modify the Einstein and
Barbarossa's method to include the effect of various sediment
sizes and densities. As shown in Fig. 2-3 and Fig. 2-4, he
found that for $Wd_{50}/\nu > 100$ (approximately), $\sqrt{\tau_b'/\rho}$ may be
expressed as a function of ψ' alone and for $Wd_{50}/\nu < 100$,
$\sqrt{\tau_b''/\rho}$ is a function of both ψ' and Wd_{50}/ν, where W is
the full velocity of the average sediment size.
   The data still scattered considerably around the curves
as shown in Fig. 2-3. Shen's major findings can perhaps be
summarized as follows: i) ripple does not occur for sediment
with Wd/ν greater than 100 (approximately) (for sand greater
than 0.6 mm.), ii) for coarse sediment with $Wd/\nu > 100$. The
flow roughness can decrease as flow decreases if bed configuration is changed from dune to flat bed, iii) for fine sediment
with $Wd/\nu < 100$, the form roughness $\sqrt{\tau_b''/\rho}$ always increases as

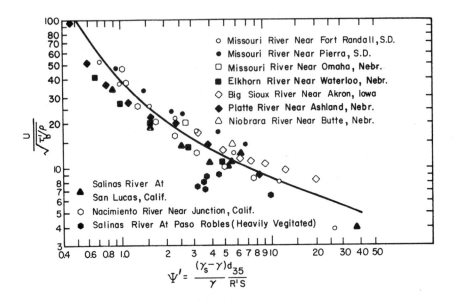

Fig. 2-2. Einstein-Barbarossa Bar Resistance Graph (1952)

flow decreases and iv) the form roughness as calculated by Einstein and Barbarossa's methods is greater for smaller sediment if the ψ's are the same. In other words, finer sediments have a greater tendency to develop larger bed irregularities.

Cunha (1967). He also found from his field data that form roughness behaves differently for coarse and fine sand for $\psi' \nless 5.5$. This result is quite similar to those found by Shen (1962) in laboratory flumes.

Liu and Hwang (1961). Their approach is to use Manning's type equation and try to adjust the exponents of the hydraulic radius and energy slope according to various bed configuration regimes. Since it is difficult to predict the occurance of various bed configuration regime, this approach, although, may have considerable potential, is difficult to apply at the present stage.

Simons and Richardson's (1966) and Haynie and Simon's (1968). Based on extensive data collected from laboratory flumes (8-ft. wide by 150 ft. long and 2 ft. wide by 60 ft. long) and other canal data. They presented three different methods to analyze bed form roughness.

2-4

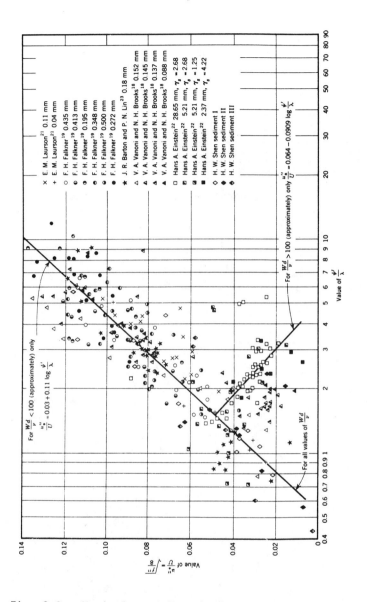

Fig. 2-3. Variation of Form Resistance From Flume Studies

2-5

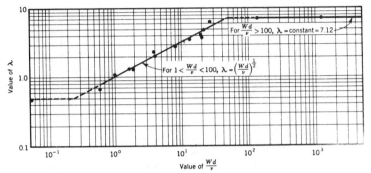

Fig. 2-4. Variation of the Correction Parameter
λ with W d/ν

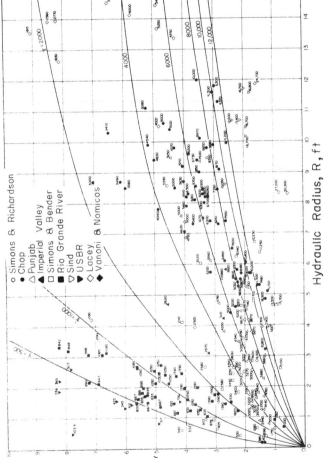

Fig. 2-5. Velocity Correction (after Haynie and Simons, 1968)

Simons and Richardson first based their analysis on Eq. (2-4) and obtained experimentally that

$$\frac{U}{\sqrt{gRS'}} = (7.4 \log \frac{D}{k_s}) C_*$$ (2-5)

where R is the hydraulic radius, D is the average flow depth, k_s is the representative grain roughness and C_* is a correction factor depending on slope, grain size, bed forms, etc. The entire analysis based on the principle that S' , the energy loss due to grain roughness can be estimated from a logarithmic relationship as given by Eg. 2-5 which was deduced from an analysis of laboratory data with flat bed flows. Unfortunately, the variation of C_* is not established and there is no means to apply this method.

Simons and Richardson (1966) presented another method by dividing the flow depth into two parts, D and D' . According to them the depth adjustment, D - D' , takes into consideration the increase in energy dissipation resulting from the form roughness and the possible error in depth measurement resulting from inclusions of the separation zones downstream from ripples and dunes in the total area of flow. Some limited relationships were found among D - D' , D and a string of third variables such as slope, roughness, temperature. A detail description of this method is given in Chapter 9 of River Mechanics Volume II and will not be repeated here.

Haynie and Simons (1968) developed still another method for a velocity correction, as follows. For each flow, the velocity correction, ΔU , is calculated as the difference between the actual velocity and that predicted by Tracey and Lester (1961) friction factor relation for hydraulically smooth rectangular channel. ΔU was found to be a function of the hydraulic radius R and the energy slope as shown in Fig. 2-5.

Garde and Raju (1966). Garde and Raju collected a large amount of data and found that none of the existing proposed methods by Einstein and Barbarossa (1952) and Shen (1962) were particularly agreeable to these data. They proposed

$$\frac{U}{\sqrt{\frac{\gamma_s - \gamma}{\gamma} g \, d_{50}}} = K \left(\frac{R}{d_{50}}\right)^{2/3} \left(S \frac{\gamma}{\gamma_s - \gamma}\right)^{1/2}$$ (2-6)

in which γ_s is the specific weight of the sediment, K is a function of $U/[gR(\gamma_s-\gamma)/\gamma]^{1/2}$ defined in their graphs obtained from laboratory and field data. For sand bed channels, K = 3.2 for ripples and 6.0 for the antidune and transition ranges. Actually the data scattered considerable about these relationships and do not provide convincing support to their relationships.

Raudkivi (1967). Raudkivi also plotted a large body of data
as shown in Fig. 2-6.

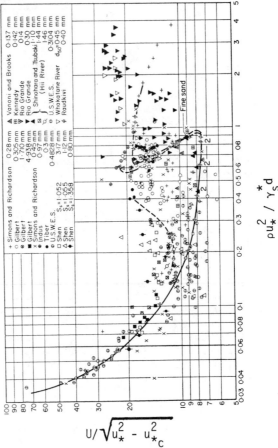

Fig. 2-6.   Resistance in an Alluvial Channel as a
           Function of the Entrainment Function
           (after Raudkivi, 1967)

Vanoni and Hwang (1967). Attempted to determine experimentally the important geometric characteristics of alluvial bed forms for hydraulic form roughness they divided the energy slope into two parts as shown by Eq. 2-4. The skin friction τ' was calculated from an equivalent Darcy-Wesbach f' value as obtained in Moody's diagram for pipe flow. In other words,

$$\tau' = \gamma RS' = \rho \frac{f'U^2}{8} \qquad (2-7)$$

They then found that (as shown in Fig. 2-7)

$$\frac{U}{\sqrt{8\tau''/\rho}} = 3.5 \log \frac{R_b}{eh} - 2.3 \qquad (2-8)$$

where e is the exposure parameter = A_S/A, A_S is the horizontal projection of the lee faces of the bed forms, A is the total area over which A_S is measured, and h is the mean height of dunes.

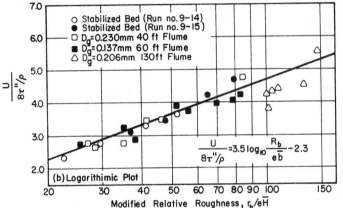

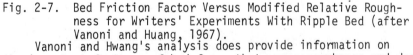

Fig. 2-7. Bed Friction Factor Versus Modified Relative Roughness for Writers' Experiments With Ripple Bed (after Vanoni and Huang, 1967).

Vanoni and Hwang's analysis does provide information on the important features of bed forms that cuase roughness and does not give guides for the prediction of bed form roughness.

Englund (1966, 1967) and Englund and Hansen (1967). Englund started from Eq. (2-4) to estimate the form resistance by Carnot's formula for expansion loss., i.e.

$$S'' \overset{\sim}{=} \alpha \frac{U^2}{2gL} \left(\frac{h}{D}\right)^2 \qquad (2-9)$$

where α is a loss coefficient, h is the dune height, and L is the dune length.

Dividing Eq. 2-4 by $(\gamma_s - \gamma)d$, one obtains

$$\frac{\tau}{(\gamma_s - \gamma)d} = \frac{\tau'}{(\gamma_s - \gamma)d} + \frac{\tau''}{(\gamma_s - \gamma)d} \qquad (2\text{-}10)$$

or

$$\tau_* = \tau_*' + \tau_*'' \qquad (2\text{-}11)$$

The above two equations can serve as definitions for the respective demensionless shear stresses. Englund hypothesized that in two dynamically similar streams: i) the two τ_*' must be the same and ii) the two ratios of τ_*''/τ_* must be the same. From these two similarity principles he concluded that τ_* must be a function of τ_*' alone. The data collected by Guy, Simons and Richardson (1966) seemed to verify his hypothesis as shown in Fig. 2-8. (τ_*' was calculated from a universal velocity distribution similar to Eq. 2-5 with $\chi = 1$).

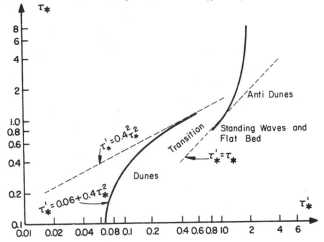

Fig. 2-8. τ_*' vs τ_* (after Englund and Hansen, 1967)

Lovera and Kennedy (1969) and Alam and Kennedy (1969). For sand and water, Lovera and Kennedy analyzed data obtained from field and laboratory alluvial channel flows which are known, or can reasonably be assumed to have produced flat beds and an active state of sediment transport. Their results are given in Fig. 2-9.

From Eq. 2-4 with S' calculated from the above relationship for flat bed, Alam and Kennedy (1969) found that f_b'' is a function of $U/\sqrt{gd_{50}}$ and d_{50}/R_b as shown in Fig. 2-10. The f_b'' is defined as $8R_b gS''/U^2$. This relationship is limited to sand and water also.

Maddock (1969). Maddock found that average flow velocity can be expressed as three different functions of unit flow discharge, energy slope, sediment particle size and sediment fall velocity for three different flow velocity ranges. Unfortunately, these

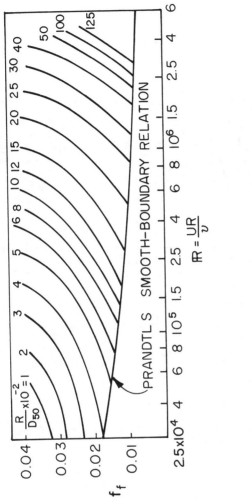

Fig. 2-9. Friction-Factor Predictor For Flat-Bed Flows in Alluvial Channels (The Number By Each Point is $R/d_{50} \times 10^{-2}$) (After Lovera and Kennedy, 1969)

velocity ranges overlap each other and there is no guideline to indicate which relationship one should use.

Mahmood (1971). Mahmood modified Einstein and Barbarossa's (1952) approach by using i) d_{84} instead of d_{65} for representative sediment roughness and ii) a slightly different logarithmic flow velocity distribution and found four curves for four different flow regimes between the dimensionless bed form roughness and ψ (similar to Fig. 2-2 by Einstein and Barbarossa). Since the data still scattered considerably about his curves and the ability to predict the occurence of flow regimes, any improvement over Fig. 2-2 is not significant.

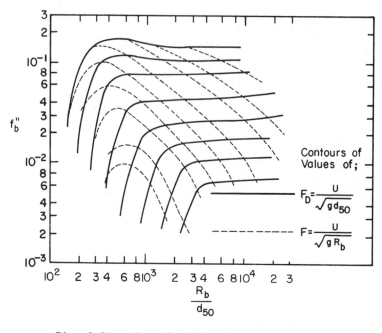

Fig. 2-10. Graphical Predictor for the
Bed-Form Friction Factor (After
Alam and Kennedy, 1969).

Kennedy (1971). Kennedy summarized some of these above mentioned analysis and also stated that three important factors:
water temperature, channel pattern and the effect of sediment
discharge were not included in many analyses.

2.4. DIFFICULTIES IN ALLUVIAL BED FORM RESISTANCE ANALYSIS

As discussed in the previous section, most of the investigators followed the work of Einstein and Barbarossa (1952) to
use either Eq. 2-3 or Eq. 2-4 for their analyses. However,
there are the following several difficulties (or factors to be
considered) in applying these two equations to alluvial bed form
resistance analysis.

Rigid Boundary Versus Movable Boundary. When fluid flows over
a flat rigid boundary, the total resistance contributed by the
boundary to the flow occurs right at the interface between the
flow and the boundary. However, when fluid flows over a flat
movable boundary, the total resistance consists of the resistance
between the fluid and the top moving layer as well as the resistance existed among the various moving sediment layers (moving
at different speeds). It is rather unlikely that the resistance

over rigid boundary and movable boundary could be the same.
Einstein and Bagnold attempted to measure the shear resistance
among the various moving sediment layers in cylinders and,
unfortunately, the results were not conclusive. Lovera and
Kennedy (1969) found that the skin resistance at movable flat
bed is quite different from that of flat rigid boundary as
shown in Fig. 2-9.

Flat Boundary Versus Curved Boundary. As calculated by
Scholz (1951) [See Schlichting (1968)] ΔC_f , the increase in
the coefficient of skin friction, related to the wetted surface,
as against its value for a flat plate at zero indicence C_{f_0}
can be 80% for a two dimensional body and 20% for a axially
symmetrical body for a ℓ'/ℓ of 0.25 as shown in Fig. 2-11.
Of course, when seperation occurs in the downstream end of the
curved boundary, the ΔC_f related to the ℓ length can be
smaller.

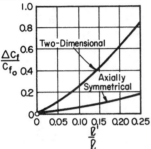
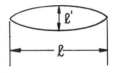

Fig. 2-11. Increase in the Coefficient of Profile Drag Plotted
in Terms of Relative Thickness, as Calculated By
Scholz (1951)

This effect can also be shown by the measurement on shear
stress distribution on a ripple form by Raudkivi (1963), as
shown in Fig. 2-12.

Many studies have been made on the characteristics of flow
over a wavy boundary. The reader is referred to the numerous
articles published in the Journal of Fluid Mechanics. Benjamin's
article (1959) is perhaps an example.

Mutual Interference Of Various Bed Forms. As shown in Fig.
2-13, two peaks can occur quite close to each other and several
ripples can occur on the upstream face of a dune. The mutual
interference of these bed forms could effect both the skin
resistance and the form resistance significantly.

Characteristics of Time Fluctuation of Boundary Shear Stress.
Blinco (1972) has just begun to measure the time fluctuation over
a smooth flat rigid boundary by a hot-film sensor mounted at
the bottom of a smooth flume at the Colorado State University.
A record is shown in Fig. 2-14. The variation of these elements
on a curved boundary probably would be quite different from that
over a smooth flat rigid boundary.

Effect of Suspended Sediment Load. Vanoni (1946), Vanoni and
Nomicos (1960) found that suspended load concentrations of 1.2

2-13

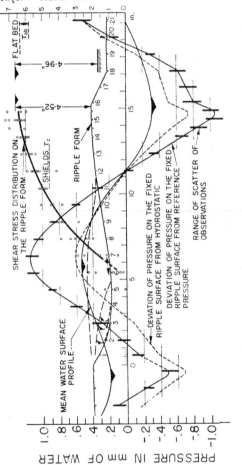

Fig. 2-12. Ripple Formation, Water Surface Profile, and Distribution of Pressure Deviations and Bed Shear Stress (After Raudkivi, 1963)

2-14

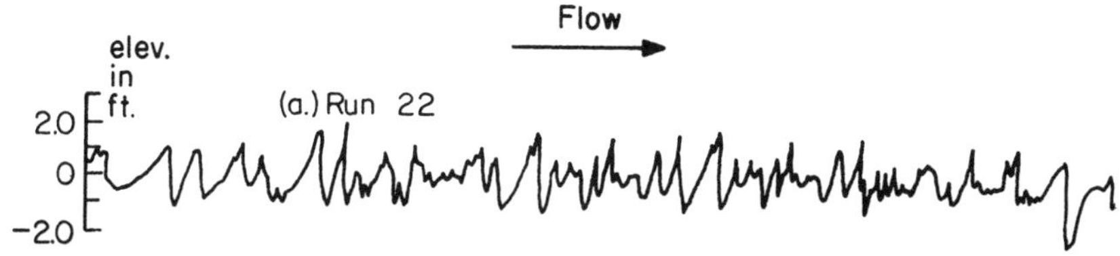

elev. in ft.

(a.) Run 22

Flow

2.0
0
-2.0

(a.) Water Temperature 75°F
Discharge (cfs) 34,300
Mean Velocity(fps) 3.74
Hyd. Mean Rad. (ft) 14.00
Slope$\times 10^4$ 1.350
d_{50} 0.20mm.

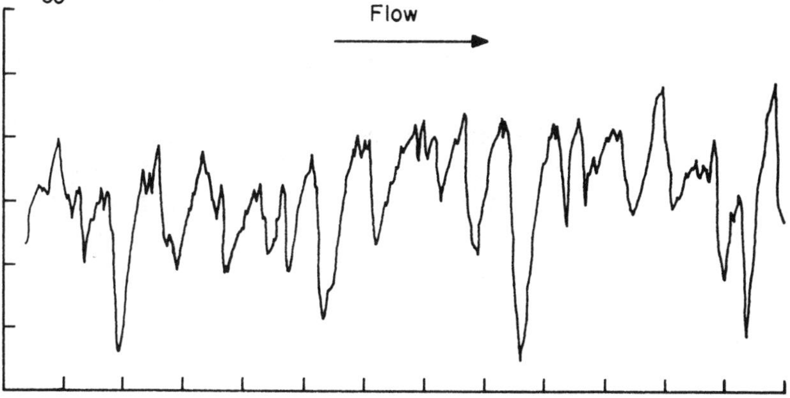

Flow

(b.) C.S.U. 8ft Flume
Mean Velocity(fps) 2.63
Mean Depth of Flow 1.20
Slope $\times 10^3$ 5.3
Water Temperature 61° F
d_{50} =1.1mm.

Vertical Scale 1"=0.2'
Horizontal Scale 1"≃10'

Fig. 2-13.(a) Missouri River Bed Profile (after Annambhotla,1969)
        (b) Flume Bed Profile

grams per liter to 3.3 grams per liter can reduce the Darcy-
Weisbach friction factor for flat beds by up to 18%. Simons,
Richardson, and Haushild (1963) concluded from their experiments
that the resistance to flow and bed material transport decreased
in the lower flow regime and increased in the upper flow regime
when sediment was added to the flow.

The effect of suspended sediment load has not been specifically included in the many resistance formulae although it might
have been taken care of at least partially by the use of some
flow parameters such as ψ . Many cases the presence or the
absence of wash load has not been considered in friction formulae.

Effect of Temperature. Straub, Anderson and Flammer (1958)
found from their laboratory experiments that the energy slope
(or friction resistance) increased by more than 50% when flow
temperature decreased from 86°F to 35°F for a mean flow velocity

2-15

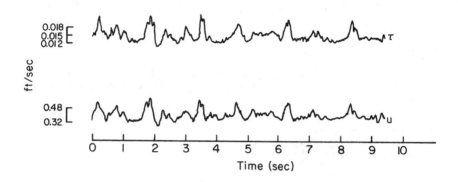

τ, Boundary Shear Stress (lbs/ft^2)

u, Longitudinal Velocity Fluctuation in feet per second at $y_* = 5$

Fig. 2-14a. Velocity and Boundary Shear Stress
Fluctuation With Time (after Blinco, 1972)

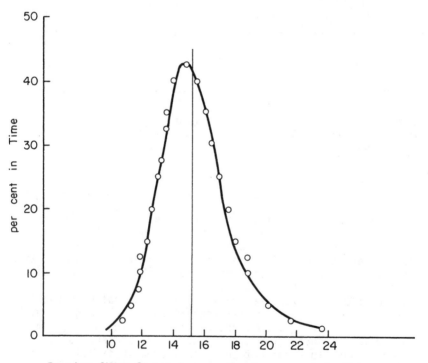

Boundary Sheer Stress in pounds per square inch Histogram
of the Boundary Shear Stress $\overline{\tau} = 0.0153 \# 1 \, in^2, R \sim 1.5 \times 10^4$

Fig. 2-14b. Boundary Shear Stress Fluctuation
With Time (after Blinco, 1972)

of about 2.2 feet per second and a flow depth of about 0.23 feet. Franco (1968) determined from his laboratory experiments that the energy gradient (or friction resistance) increased by about 20% when the flow temperature decreased from $80^\circ F$ to $40^\circ F$ for the same flow depths and flow velocities. Hubbell and Al-Shaikh (1961) presented evidences that increasing temperature could either increase or decrease flow resistances.

Actually, the temperature could effect the flow resistance differently depending on the range of flow conditions that one is in. This was concluded by Taylor (1971) in his experiments that i) in a stream with a rippled bed of fine sand, an increase in water temperature (discharge and depth held constant) may effect either an increase or a reduction in bed roughness and sediment discharge, ii) under certain conditions (unspecified by Taylor), an increase in water temperature alone can accomplish a change in bed form, and iii) in flows where $\sqrt{\tau_b'/\rho}\, d/\nu$ is less than 8, the transitions from ripples to dunes is accomplished at a lower velocity in the warmer water flow.

Growth of Bed Form Limited By Either Flow Depth or Flow Width. This is an extremely important problem and up to now no conclusive evidence has been found. If the development of bed forms should·be limited by the small flow depths and/or narrow flow width, the usefulness of using laboratory experimental data for field application is rather questionable. Much more field data are needed to investigate this. Annambhotla (1969) and Cheong and Shen (1973) have shown from the limited field data (collected by Annambhotla) that some statistical properties of alluvial bed forms in the field are actually quite similar to that obtained from the flume.

Porosity of the Bed. Munoz Goma and Gelhar (1968) have shown that the friction factor for porous pipe is much greater than the rigid boundary. However, for fine sediment this effect probably is still small and can be neglected.

Effect of Three Dimensional Flow. Secondary currents and other variations in the transverse direction may have significant effects on the development on bed configurations. For instance, the development of bed configuration in river bends is quite different from that of a straight reach.

2.5. SOME STATISTICAL PROPERTIES OF ALLUVIAL BED FORMS

The investigation of the statistical properties of alluvial bed forms probably begun in the mid 1960's by the U.S. Geological Surveys Research Unit stationed at the Colorado State University. Since then the more important works are listed as follows: Nordin and Albert (1966), Plate, E.J., (1967), Ashida and Tanaka (1967), O'Loughlin and Squarer (1967), Hino, (1968), Englund (1969), Annambhotla (1969), Nordin (1971), Jain and Kennedy (1971), Taylor (1971), and Cheong and Shen (1973). The above results are briefly summarized in the following sections with the definition sketch given in Fig. 2-15.

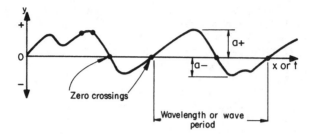

Fig. 2-15.   Definition Sketch of Bed Profile

Bed Elevation Distribution. Nordin and Algert (1966) and
Nordin (1971) concluded from their laboratory studies that the
values of the bed elevation follow an approximate Gaussian distribution.
    Annambhotla (1969) found from his Missouri River data that
the bed elevations follow approximately the normal distribution
both before and after filtering the data. Filtering the data
seems to improve the conformity to the normal distribution.
    Jain and Kennedy (1971) stated that "the Gaussian approxi-
mation (for bed elevation) has some advantages for descriptive
and predictive purposes in that many properties of interest
relate to fair simple parameters, such as the variance and the
moments of the spectrum which are easily calculated. However,
the analogy should not be pushed too far, because the bed elevation clearly is not Gaussian except in a range of about plus and
minus two standard deviations from the mean. In addition, it
still remains to relate the statistical properties of the sand
waves to properties of the flow and the sediment to a physically
meaningful model.---"
    Cheong and Shen (1973) attempted to use a modified Edgeworth
distribution function to fit the histograms of the standardized
bed elevations (zero mean and unit variance) for the filtered
Missouri River Runs (obtained by Annambhotla) and laboratory
runs (obtained by Nordin). The Edgeworth distribution is in
the form of

$$\rho(\eta) \stackrel{\sim}{=} \frac{1}{\sqrt{2\pi}} [1 + \frac{1}{6} k_3 H_{e3}] \exp (- \frac{\eta^2}{2}) \qquad (2-12)$$

where η is the standarized bed elevation, k_3 is the skewness,
and H_{e3} is the Hermite polynomial of η of degree 3. They still
have not found the variation of skewness with flow conditions.
    Wave Number Spectra. Hino (1968) argued from pure dimensional
condiderations that the wave number spectra at high wave numbers
should follow the wave number k to the minus three power and
that the frequency spectra should vary as the minus second power
of the frequency.

Englund (1969) derived a universal dimensionless wave number spectrum from similarity criteria in the form of

$$\frac{2gDS}{U^2} \frac{G(x)}{\nabla} = \psi_* \frac{\nabla kU^2}{2gDS} \qquad (2\text{-}13)$$

where $G(x)$ is in (cycles per foot)$^{-1}$, ψ_* is an arbitrary function, k is the wave number in cycles per foot, and ∇ is the standard deviation of bed elevation $f(x)$.

Nordin (1971) found for his laboratory data that for process $y(x)$ the dimensionless spectra varies with the dimensionless wave number $G'(x) = G(x)g/v^2$, in a minus 3.2 power for values of dimensionless wave numbers $k' = kU^2/g$ greater than 0.03.

Jain and Kennedy (1971) based on results obtained with fine sand (0.2 - 0.35 mm median diameter) and coarse sand (1.1 mm median diameter) to conclude that particle size in this range has little effect on the dimensionless spectra (defined the same as that by Nordin (1971) They also stated that channel width has a direct effect on sand wave spectra. Their dimensionless spectra varies approximately to the negative third power with the dimensionless wave number also.

Taylor (1971) presented data to show that the spectra varies with a minus 3 power with the wave number for dunes. For ripples the slope between the spectra and the wave number is about minus 4.

Cheong and Shen (1973) presented the spectra of the bedforms for narrow and wide laboratory flumes and those from the field are shown for comparison. The spectra for the Missouri River data (private communication with Mr. Liversey of the U.S. Corps of Engineers, Omaha District, and Professor W.W. Sayre of the University of Iowa, Iowa City) were filtered numerically using the filter recommended by Kinsman and suggested for use by Annambhotla (1969). The filter is given by the equations

$$y_i = (1 - \alpha) y_{i-1} + (1 - \frac{\alpha}{2}) (x_i - x_{i-1})$$
$$y_1 = x_1 = 0. \qquad (2\text{-}14)$$

where the x_i's are the untreated input data and the y_i's are the filtered output data. With $\alpha = 0.1$, the above filter attenuates the variance in the spectrum at the low wavenumbers (with an attenuation factor of 0.25 for $k = 3 \times 10^{-3/m}$) while the variances at the higher wave numbers are left unaffected.

The high wave number range of each spectrum in Fig. 2-16 follows approximately the "-3 power" form

$$G_{ff}(k) = f(\phi)k^{-3} \qquad (k_o < \; << \frac{1}{d}) \qquad (2\text{-}15)$$

postulated by Hino (1968). $G_{ff}(k)$ is the spectral density function of the bed elevation f , $f(\phi)$ is a function of the angle of repose ϕ of the sand having a representative diameter

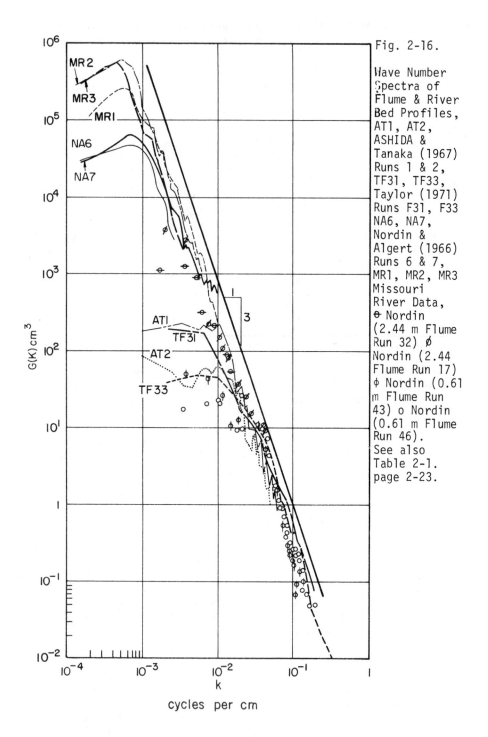

Fig. 2-16.

Wave Number Spectra of Flume & River Bed Profiles, AT1, AT2, ASHIDA & Tanaka (1967) Runs 1 & 2, TF31, TF33, Taylor (1971) Runs F31, F33 NA6, NA7, Nordin & Algert (1966) Runs 6 & 7, MR1, MR2, MR3 Missouri River Data, θ Nordin (2.44 m Flume Run 32) ϕ Nordin (2.44 Flume Run 17) ϕ Nordin (0.61 m Flume Run 43) o Nordin (0.61 m Flume Run 46). See also Table 2-1. page 2-23.

cycles per cm

d , and k is the wave number defined to be the reciprocal of the wavelength. The function $f(\phi)$ may be observed to vary over the approximate range

$$2.5 \times 10^{-4} < f(\phi) < 7.0 \times 10^{-4}$$

for the flume records (except run No. 3 collected by Algert and Nordin (1966) in a narrow flume) and the lower limit is found to be about 1.5 (10^{-4}) for the conveyance channel data. The variability of $f(\phi)$ is not surprising since ϕ may depend not only on the size of the sand, but also its gradation, its angularity, etc. In fact $f(\phi)$ may also well be a fairly weak function of k since ϕ may not be the only significant variable determining the limiting configuration of the sand bed.

To explore the conditions to be satisfied for spectral similarity, two assumptions are made in the ensuing analysis. Firstly, it is assumed that the "-3 power" spectral form exists over the high wave number range for each spectrum and secondly, there exists a similarity condition between the wave number spectra. The second assumption implies that a dimensionless spectrum of a universal form exists. It may be inferred that a parameter, α , which may be related to the hydraulic conditions through some functional form may be used for dimensional scaling. Concerning the second assumption, experimental evidence (Nordin (1971), Jain and Kennedy (1971)) seem to lend some support that there may exist a universal form of the wave number spectrum Let

$$s^2 \, \hat{G}_{ff}(k) = G_{ff}(k) \tag{2-16}$$

and

$$k_u = \alpha k \tag{2-17}$$

where s^2 is the variance of the bed elevations about its mean level, $\hat{G}_{ff}(k)$ is the normalized spectral density function and k_u is a dimensionless wave number defined by Eq. (2-17). Since

$$\hat{G}_{ff}(k)dk = \hat{G}_{ff}(k_u)dk_u \tag{2-18}$$

we have

$$\hat{G}_{ff}(k_u) = \hat{G}_{ff}(k)/\alpha \tag{2-19}$$

The variance of the process explained by the "-3 power" range of the high wave numbers is given by

$$a^2 = \int_{k_o}^{k_\infty} G_{ff}(k)dk \tag{2-20}$$

where k_o , k_∞ are the lower and upper cutoff wave numbers of the "-3 power" range, and

$$a^2 = \int_{k_0}^{k_\infty} f(\phi) \, k^{-3} dk$$

$$= \frac{f(\phi)}{2} \left[\frac{1}{k_0^2} - \frac{1}{k_\infty^2} \right]$$

$$\simeq \frac{f(\phi)}{2k_0^2} \text{ since } k_\infty \gg k_0 \; . \qquad (2\text{-}21)$$

The fraction of the total variance attributed to the "-3 power" range of wave numbers is

$$\frac{a^2}{s^2} = \frac{f(\phi)}{2s^2 k_0^2} \qquad (2\text{-}22)$$

However,

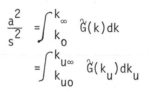

$$\frac{a^2}{s^2} = \int_{k_0}^{k_\infty} \hat{G}(k) dk$$

$$= \int_{k_{uo}}^{k_{u\infty}} \hat{G}(k_u) dk_u$$

$$= \text{constant}$$

by the similarity assumption. Hence, it follows that

$$\frac{s k_0}{\sqrt{f(\phi)}} = \text{constant} \qquad (2\text{-}23)$$

The tabulation below provides the values of the "constant" in Eq. 2-23.

A difficulty lies in estimating k_0 from the wave number spectrum especially where the spectrum is multipeaked and considerable judgement has to be exercised owing to the variability of the spectral estimates. Errors will probably enter into the computation especially when interpolating on log scales and the fitting of the "-3 power" line is to some extent subjective since in some instances, the exponent in the power law vary as $(3 \pm \alpha)$ where α is real and positive and appear to be weakly dependent on k .

From the last column of Table 2-1, it can be readily appreciated that the computed values show some variation. The average value for the Missouri River runs is 1.24 as compared to 1.36 for the laboratory runs. The values are excessively higher for the conveyance channel where the dune heights could possibly be limited by the small flow depths. To provide a meaningful com-

TABLE 2.1. LIST OF AVAILABLE DATA

Source	Run No.	Standard Deviation Bed Elevation s cm	Critical Wave No. k_0 cycles/ cm X 10^2	$f(\ )$ X 10^4	Eq. (2-23) $\dfrac{sk_0}{\sqrt{f(\phi)}}$
Nordin	17	6.28	0.42	2.4	1.59
(1971)	32	4.42	0.58	2.4	1.54
Ashida &	A1	1.60	1.10	2.5	1.11
Tanaka	A2	1.50	1.20	2.8	1.08
(1967)	A3	1.00	1.80	2.7	1.10
Nordin &	1	0.82	1.80	3.0	0.86
Algert	2	1.06	2.00	5.0	0.95
(1966)	3	1.46	1.50	1.2	2.00
	4	3.52	6.60	3.0	1.34
	5	5.34	3.90	3.5	1.11
	6	19.45	0.16	0.8	3.48
	7	22.70	0.13	1.0	2.95
Taylor	F31	1.53	3.00	3.9	2.32
(1971)	F32(High Temp.)	1.84	1.20	3.2	1.23
	F33	1.07	4.00	6.7	1.65
	F34(High Temp.)	1.86	1.30	4.3	1.16
Missouri	MR1	16.90	0.13	2.2	1.48
River	MR2	23.30	.075	4.0	1.14
	MR3	20.5	.059	1.8	1.11

Note: Not all the runs presented by the respective investigators
       are included in this table and not all the runs listed
       in this table are plotted in Fig. 2-16. The purpose of
       Fig. 2-16 is to illustrate the typical behavior of the
       spectra of the different runs and those runs not plotted
       are not materially different from those shown. It is
       difficult to show all the runs in a single chart.

parison, the same filtering technique should be applied to all
the data. Until this is done, the results of the above attempt
to ascertain the possibility of the similarity between the stochastic components of alluvial bedforms in the laboratory and
in the field cannot be conclusive.
    It is informative to determine the line spectrum for a
periodic function constructed of triangles of length L and
side slopes m_1 (upstream) and $-m_2$ (downstream). The line
spectrum of a periodic function is given by

$$G(n) = \frac{a_n^2 + b_n^2}{4} \quad , \quad n=0 \ , \ \pm 1 \ , \ \pm 2 \qquad (2\text{-}24)$$

where a_n and b_n are the Fourier coefficients of the periodic
function $f(x)$,

$$a_n = \frac{2}{L} \int_0^L f(x)\cos\left(\frac{2\pi nx}{L}\right) dx \qquad (2\text{-}24)$$

and

$$b_n = \frac{2}{L} \int_0^L f(x)\sin\left(\frac{2\pi nx}{L}\right) dx \qquad (2\text{-}25)$$

It can be shown that

$$a_n = \frac{\sin(nka)}{n}(m_1+m_2)\frac{a}{\pi} - \frac{2m_2}{k} + \frac{\cos(nka)}{\pi n^2 k}(m_1+m_2)$$

$$- \frac{1}{\pi n^2 k}\left[m_1 + (-1)^n m_2\right]$$

$$a_0 = \frac{am_1}{3} \qquad \text{for } n=1,2,\ldots$$

and

$$b_n = \frac{\sin(nka)}{\pi n^2 k}(m_1+m_2) + \frac{\cos(nka)}{nk}\left[2m_2 - \frac{ka(m_1+m_2)}{\pi}\right] \quad \text{for } n=1,2,\ldots$$

where $k = \frac{2\pi}{L}$ and $a = \frac{m_2}{m_1+m_2} L$

Distance Between Two Zero Crossings (Wave Length). Ashida and Tanaka (1971) concluded from their experiments that the wave lengths follow a Rayleigh distribution. Annambhotla (1969) found from both laboratory runs and river data that the wave lengths follow an exponential distribution.

Nordin (1971) stated that the distribution of the distances between two zero crossings are approximately exponential.

From a research in progress at the Colorado State University, Cheong proved from theoretical consideration and experimental evidence that the distances between two zero crossings can not be distributed exponentially if the bed elevation follows a Gaussian distribution. According to his preliminary analysis, the wave length can be either Rayleigh or Gamma distributed with shape parameter between about 2 and 4.

Wave Height (a^+ and a^- in Fig. 2-13). The wave heights a^+, a^- are defined by Nordin (1971) as the respective maximum and minimum bed elevations between two successive zero crossings. In addition, $a^+ > 0$, and $a^- < 0$. Nordin found from laboratory data that a^+ are distributed exponentially and a^- are distributed according to a Gaussian distribution.

Annambhotla (1969) found that both a^+ and a^- distributed exponentially.

Ashida and Tanaka (1967) stated that the wave lengths (although not clearly defined) follow the Rayleigh distribution.

Stochastic Model. Nordin and Algert (1966) used a second order Markovian Model and then was criticized by Plate (1967)

2-24

because Plate can not see how a development of the sediment wave at a point in space can depend only on the characteristics of two points on the same, or a neighboring sediment wave.

Ashida and Tanaka concluded from their analysis that a Markov-second order linear process is approximately applicable to the sand waves in the regime of dunes and standing waves. On the other hand, the sand dunes in the regime of ripples and transition are composed from one or more dominant wave lengths superimposed on a second order Markov process. In this case, a higher order Markov process may be applicable.

Statistical Properties of Alluvial Bed Forms and Flow Conditions. There is an urgent need to relate the various statistical properties of alluvial bed forms and flow conditions to make all previous studies more meaningful. Annambhotla (1969) made an attempt and the result was not conclusive.

2.6. CONCLUDING REMARKS

It is evident from the discussion presented in this chapter that the alluvial bed resistance problem is by no means solved. The problem is not only due to the diffuculty of predicting form roughness but also the difficulty of using the correct skin roughness. Research results presented in this chapter should serve as useful guides to analyze the resistance of alluvial bed forms for a particular situation. Experienced engineers and researchers probably can derive a reasonable figure for design based on available information, although much more research effort should be conducted in this area.

One immediate problem that is facing us today is the limited flow depth and flow width used in conducting laboratory studies. How much and under what conditions can laboratory results be applied to field conditions where the ultimate test must lie? More data from the rivers where flow conditions are two dimensional uniform and steady, would certainly keep to answer the above question. The investiation on the statiscal properties of alluvial bed profiles offers a promising future. It is especially attractive for the investigation on the similarities and differences between laboratory bed forms where flow depths are limited and river bed forms where bed forms are not normally limited by flow depth and width.

2.7. NOTATION

A	Area
A_b	Area of the bed
A_s	Horizontal projection of the lee faces of the bed form
a	Variance of the process as defined by Eq. 2-19
a_n	Fourier coefficients
a^+	Maximum dune height between an upcrossing and the next downcrossing
a^-	Maximum trough height between a downcrossing and the next upcrossing

b_n	Fourier coefficients
C_{fo}	Coefficient of skin friction for flat plate
ΔC_f	Increase of coefficient of skin friction due to change of body form
$C*$	Correction factor
D	Flow Depth
D'	Flow Depth corresponding to smooth bed
d, d_{50}	Sediment size or mean sediment size
$d_{55}, d_{65},$ d_{85}	Sediment sizes of which 35%, 65% and 85% are finer respectively
e	A_s/A
f'	Darcy Weisbach fricition factor for skin roughness
$G(x)$	Dimensionless spectra
$G'(x)$	Dimensionless spectra
$G_{ff}(k)$	Spectra density function of bed elevation
$G_{ff}(k)$	Normalized spectral density function
g	Universal gravitational constant
h	Mean dune height
He_3	Hermite polynomial degree 3
K	Correction factor
k	Wave number in cycles per foot
k'	Dimensionless wave number
k_s	Representative grain roughness
k_o	Lower cutoff wave number
k_∞	Upper cutoff wave number
k_3	Skewness
k_u	Dimensionless wave number
L, ℓ	Dune length
ℓ'	Body height
m_1	Upstream slope of dunes
m_2	The downstream slope of dunes
R	Hydraulic radius
R_b	Hydraulic radius of the bed
R_b'	Hydraulic radius attributed to the bed skin roughness
R_b''	Hydraulic radius attributed to the bed form roughness
s	Energy slope
s'	Energy slope attributed to the bed skin roughness
s''	Energy slope attributed to the bed rough roughness
S^2	Variance of the bed elevation
U	Mean flow velocity
ΔU	Corrected flow velocity = actual flow velocity - flow velocity for smooth bed
W	Fall velocity of the mean sediment
x	Main flow direction
y	Bed elevation in vertical direction
α	Filter parameter
α_*	Loss coefficient due to expansion of flow area
γ	Specific weight of the fluid
γ_s	Specific weight of the sediment
δ	Viscous sublayer = $11.6\nu \sqrt{\tau'/\rho}$
η	Standarized bed elevation

ν	Vinematic viscosity of the fluid
ρ	Density of the fluid
∇	Standarized bed elevation $y(x)$
τ	Shear stress
τ_b	Shear stress in the bed
$\tau_b{}',\tau'$	Skin shear stress in the bed
$\tau_b{}'',\tau''$	Form shear stress in the bed
$\tau_*{}'\ \tau_*{}''$	Dimensionless shear stress as defined by Eq. (2-10) and Eq. (2-11)
ϕ	Angle repose
χ	Correction parameter to adjust for the characteristic of hydraulic boundary
ψ	Dimensionless flow parameter $= \dfrac{\gamma_s - \gamma}{\gamma}\ \dfrac{d_{35}}{R_b{}'S}$

REFERENCES

Alam, A.M.Z., and Kennedy, F.J., 1969, Friction factors for Flow in Sand Bed Channels; Journal of the Hydraulics Div. ASCE, Vol. 95, No. HY6, Proc. Paper 6900, pp. 1973- 1992 November.

Annambhotla, V.S.S., 1969, Statistical Properties of Bed Forms in Alluvial Channels in Relation to Flow Resistance; Ph.D. Thesis, The University of Iowa, Iowa City, Iowa.

Ashida, K. & Tanaka, Y., 1967, A Statistical Study of Sand Waves; Proc. XII Congrees, International Association Hydraulic Research Vol. 2, pp. 103-110.

Benjamin, T. Brooke, 1959, Shearing Flow over a Wavy Boundary; Journal of Fluid Mechanics, Vol. 6, Part 2, pp. 161-205.

Blinco, P., 1972, Research in Progress at the Colorado State University.

Cheong, H.F. and Shen, H.W., 1973, Spectral Properties of Alluvial Bed Forms in Rivers and Flumes; International Symposium on River Mechanics, Asian Institute of Technology, January.

Cunha, Veiga da L., 1967, About the Roughness in Alluvial Channels with Comparatively Coarse Bed Material; Proceedings Twelfth Congress of the International Association for Hydraulic Research, Vol. 1, Paper No. A10, Colorado State University

Einstein, H.W., 1950, The Bed Load Function for Sediment Transportation in Open Channel Flows; USDA Soil Conservation Service Technical Bulletin No. 1026, September and also appeared in Sedimentation edited and published by H.W. Shen, P.O. Box 606, Fort Collins, Colorado 1972.

Einstein, H.W. and Barbarossa, N.L., 1952, River Channel Roughness; Transactions, ASCE, Vol. 117, Paper No. 2528, pp1121-1132.

Engelund, F., 1966, Hydraulic Resistance of Alluvial Streams; Journal of the Hydraulics Division, ASCE, Vol. 92, No. HY2, Proc. Paper 4739, pp. 315-326, March.

Engelund, F., 1967, closure to Hydraulic Resistance of Alluvial Streams; Journal of the Hydraulics Division, ASCE, Vol. 93, No. HY4, pp. 287-296, July.

Engelund, F., and Hansen, E.A., 1967, Monograph on Sediment Transport in Alluvial Streams; Teknisk Forlag, Copenhagen.

Engelund, F.A.,1969, On the Possibility of Formulating a Universal Spectrum for Dunes; Basic Research Prog. Report 18 p.1-4 Hyd. Lab. Technical University of Denmark, Copenhagen.

Franco, John J., 1968, Effects of Water Temperature on Bed
    Load Movement; Journal of the Waterways and Harbors Division,
    ASCE Vol. 94, No. WW3, Proc. Paper 6083, pp. 343-352,
    August.

Garde, R.H. and Raju, K.G.R., 1966, Resistance Relationships
    for Alluvial Channel Flow; Journal of the Hydraulics Div.
    ASCE, Vol. 92, No. HY4, Proc. Paper 4869, pp. 77-100,
    July.

Guy, H.P., Simons, D.B. and Richardson, E.V., 1966, Summary
    of Alluvial Channel Data from Flume Experiments; U.S.
    Geological Survey Professional Paper 462-I.

Goldstein, S., 1938, Modern Developments in Fluid Dynamics;
    Oxford University Press, Vol. II, pp. 409-410.

Haynie, R.B., and Simons, D.B., 1968, Design of Stable Channels
    in Alluvial Materials; Journal of the Hydraulics Division
    ASCE, Vol. 94, No. HY6, Proc. Paper 6217, pp. 1399-1420
    November.

Hino, Mikio, 1968, Equilibrium Range Spectra of Sand Waves
    Formed by Flowing Water; Journal of Fluid Mechanics,
    V. 34, pt. 3, p. 565-573.

Hubbell, D.W., and Al-Shaikh Ali, K.S., 1961, Qualitative
    Effects of Temperature on Flow Phenomena in Alluvial
    Channels; U.S. Geological Sruvey Professional Paper 424-D
    pp. d-21-D-23.

Jain, S.C., & Kennedy, J.F., 1971, The Growth of Sand Waves;
    International Symposium on Stochastic Hydraulics, Pittsburgh,
    May 31-June 2.

Kennedy, J., 1971, Sediment Transportation Mechanics: F. Hy-
    draulic Relations for Alluvial Streams; Task Committee
    for Preparation of the Sedimentation Manual, Committee
    on Sedimentation of the Hyd. Div., Journal of the
    Hydraulics Division, ASCE, Vol. 97, HY1, Proc. Paper
    7786, January.

Liu, H.K. and Hwang, S.Y., 1961, Discharge Formula for Straight
    Alluvial Channels; Transactions, ASCE, Vol. 126, Part 1
    Paper No. 3276, pp. 1787-1822.

Lovera, F. and Kennedy, J.F., 1969, Friction Factors for Flat-
    Bed Flows in Sand Channels; Journal of the Hydraulics
    Division, ASCE, Vol. 95, No. HY4, Proc. Paper 6678, July.

Maddock, T. Jr., 1969, The Behavior of Straight Open Channels
    with Movable Beds; U.S. Geological Survey Professional
    Paper 662-A.

Mahmood, K., 1971, Flow in Sand-Bed Channels; Water Management
    Technical Report No. 11, Colorado State University, Fort
    Collins.

Munoz, Goma, R.J. and Gelahar, L.W., 1968, Turbulent Pipe Flow with Rough and Porous Walls; Hydrodynamic Laboratory Report No. 109, Department of Civil Engineering, Mass. Inst. of Technology.

Nordin, C.F., Jr., and Algert, J.H., 1966, Spectral Analysis of Sand Waves; Journal of the Hydraulics Division, ASCE Vol. 92, HY5, Proc. Paper 4910, pp. 95-114, September.

Nordin, C.F., Jr., 1971, Statistical Properties of Dune Profiles; U.S. Geological Survey, Prof. Paper 562-F.

O'Laughlin, E.M. and Squares, D., 1967, Areal Variations of Bed Form Characteristics in Meandering Streams; Proc. XII, Int. Assoc. Hyd. Research Congress, Fort Collins, Colo. Vol. 2, p. 118-127.

Plate, E., 1967, Discussion of Spectral Analysis of Sand Waves; by C.F. Nordin Jr. and J.H. Algert, ASCE. Proc. J. of Hyd. Division, Vol. 93, HY4, p310-316.

Raudkivi, A.J., 1963, Study of Sediment Ripple Formation, J. of the Hydraulics Division, ASCE, Vol. 89, No. HY6, Proc. Paper 3692, pp. 15-33, November.

Raudkivi, A.J., 1967, Loose Boundary Hydraulics; Pergamon Press.

Schlichting, H., 1968, Boundary Layer Theory, Translated by J. Kestin, McGraw Hill, Sixth Edition, p. 718.

Scholz, N., 1951, Uber Eine Rationelle Berechnung des Stromungs widerstandes Schlanker Korper mit beliebig rauher oberflache; Jb. Schiff bautechn, Ges. 45, 244-259.

Shen, H.W., 1962, Development of Bed Roughness in Alluvial Channels; Journal of the Hydraulics Division, ASCE, Vol. 88, No. HY3, Proc. Paper 3113, May.

Simons, D.B., Richardson, E.V. and Haushild, W.H., 1963, Some Effects of Fine Sediment on Flow Phenomena; U.S. Geological Survey Water-Supply Paper 1498-G.

Simons, D.B., and Richardson, E.V., 1966, Resistance to Flow in Alluvial Channels, U.S. Geological Survey Professional Paper 422-J.

Squarer, D., 1968, An Analysis of Relationship Between Flow Conditions and Statistical Measures of Bed Configurations in Straight and Curved Alluvial Channels; Ph.D Thesis, The University of Iowa, Iowa City, Iowa.

Straub, L.G., Anderson, A.G., and Flammer, G.H., 1958, Experiments on the Influence of Temperature on the Sediment Load; M.R.D. Sediment Series No. 10, U.S. Army Engineer Division Missouri River, Corps of Engineers, Omaha, Nebraska.

Taylor, B.D., 1971, Temperature Effects in Alluvial Streams; Rept. No. KH-R-27, W.M. Keck Laboratory of Hydraulics and Water Resources, California Institute of Technology, Pasadena, California.

Tracy, H.J. and Lester, C.M., 1961, Resistance Coefficients and Velocity Distribution in a Smooth Rectangular Channel; U.S. Geological Survey Water-Supply Paper 1592-A.

Vanoni, V.A., 1946, Transportation of Suspended Sediment; Transactions, ASCE, Vol. III, Paper No. 2267, pp. 67-102.

Vanoni, V.A., and Nomicos, G.N., 1960, Resistance Properties of Sediment-Laden Streams; Transactions, ASCE, Vol. 125, Part 1, Paper No. 3055, pp. 1140-1175.

Vanoni, V.A., and Hwang, L.S., 1967, Relation Between Bed Forms and Friction in Streams; Journal of the Hydraulics Division ASCE, Vol. 93, No. HY3, Proc. Paper 5242, pp. 121-144, May.

Chapter 3

Flow Resistance Over Short Simulated Vegetation and
Various Tall Simulated Vegetation Groupings on Flow
Resistance and Sediment Yield

by

Hsieh W. Shen, Professor of Civil Engineering, Engineering
Research Center, Colorado State University,
Fort Collins, Colorado.

Chapter 3

FLOW RESISTANCE OVER SHORT SIMULATED VEGETATION AND
VARIOUS TALL SIMULATED VEGETATION GROUPINGS ON FLOW
RESISTANCE AND SEDIMENT YIELD

3.1. INTRODUCTION

The effect of vegetation on flow resistance has been discussed in various books dealing with watershed management, for
instance see Colman(1953), and forest management, for instance
see Molchanov (1963). From a hydraulic engineer's view point
the effect of vegetation on flow retardation can be divided into three parts: i) tall vegetation, such as trees, on the
order of flow depths, ii) short vegetation, such as grasses,
on the order of normal boundary roughness, and iii) vegetation
in the order of 20 to 80 percent flow depth. In this chapter
the main efforts are to present some knowledge on flow resistance over short simulated vegetation and the effect of various
tall simulated vegetation groupings on flow resistance and
sediment yields. These should be useful in watershed management
as well as overbank flows at which large amount of vegetation
is encountered.

The effects of vegetation on sediment yield in watersheds
are numerous, for instance, tall vegetation - a forest could:
i) intercept solar radiation and affect soil temperature, ii)
diminish wind speed and decrease evaporation, iii) induce
rainfall, and iv) reduce sediment yield. Vegetation is a
rather effective method to reduce sediment yield by: i) protecting soil from direct rainfall impact, ii) retarding flow
rate, iii) reducing soil resistance, and iv) enhancing
infiltration and decreasing surface runoff.

Only the flow resistance over short vegetation and the
effect of reducing sediment yield from watersheds by retarding
flow rates due to flow through tall vegetation on the order of
flow depth are discussed here. The effects óf tree leaves and
branches are ignored in order to simplify the problem.

3.2. FLOW RESISTANCE OVER SIMULATED SHORT VEGETATION

Rigid Roughness Elements. The energy loss, h_L , defined as

$$h_L = f \frac{L}{4R} \frac{U^2}{2g} \qquad (3-1)$$

where h_L is the energy loss in length dimension, L is the
length of reach, f is the Darcy-Weisbach friction coefficient,
U is the mean flow velocity, R is the hydraulic radius and
g is the universal acceleration constant.
For hydraulically smooth boundary

$$\frac{1}{\sqrt{f}} = 2.0 \log_{10} N_R \sqrt{f} - 0.8 \qquad (3-2)$$

and for hydraulically rough boundary

$$\frac{1}{\sqrt{f}} = 2 \log_{10} \frac{2R}{k_s} + 1.14 \qquad (3\text{-}3)$$

where N_R is the Reynolds number of flow and is equal to $4UR/\nu$, and k_s is the representative roughness.

If Chezy coefficient, C, is used

$$\frac{C}{\sqrt{8g}} = \frac{1}{\sqrt{f}} \qquad (3\text{-}4)$$

If Manning's n is used,

$$\frac{1.49}{\sqrt{8g}} \frac{R^{1/6}}{n} = \frac{1}{\sqrt{f}} \qquad (3\text{-}5)$$

    For large roughness elements, investigators have attempted to define the representative roughness k_s for each roughness pattern.

    As shown in Fig. 3.1, the dimensions of the roughness elements are a, b and c in height above the floor, perpendicular to the flow direction and in the longitudinal flow direction respectively. The lateral spacing between two roughness elements (center to center) is t and the longitudinal spacing between two successive roughness elements (center to center) is ℓ.

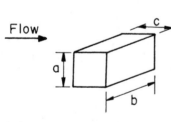

(a) Element, Size, Elevation View

(b) Distribution Spacing, Top View

Fig. 3-1. Roughness Elements Definition Sketch

    Sayre and Albertson (1961) results are shown in Fig. 3.2 where y_n is the normal flow depth. With a particular choice

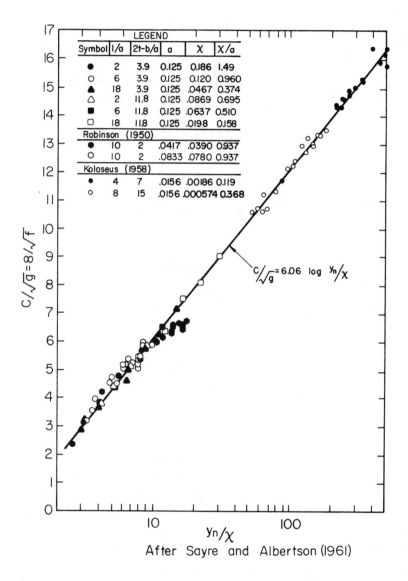

Fig. 3-2. Variation of Resistance Function With Relative Roughness y_n/x

of X value, they were able to combine all data into one curve. The unfortunate part is the lack of knowledge on this variation of X values.

Based on Iwasa's (1954) stability criterion and the data collected by Koloseus and Davidian (1966). Rouse (1965) determined the relationship as shown in Fig. 3.3, where F*, is the Froude number of the flow and is equal to $U/\sqrt{gvco\theta}$ for a rectangular channel, y is the depth of flow measured normal to the channel flow, θ is the angle of inclination of the channel, λ is the areal roughness concentration, a is the roughness height, R is the hydraulic radius, and F_s is the limiting value of $F*$ for stable flow and is equal to

$$F_s = \frac{1}{\sqrt{(0.5 + 1.30f^{1/2} - 0.78f)^2 - 0.78f(1 + 0.78f)}} \qquad (3-6)$$

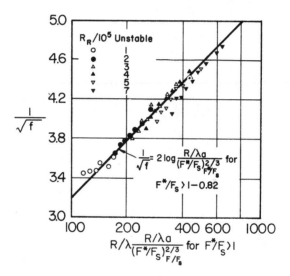

Fig. 3-3. Superposition of Data From Koloseus and Davidian (1966) (after Rouse, 1965)

When flow is classified as unstable, free-surface perturbations of infinitesimal size, having the characteristics of shallow water waves are supposed to become larger as they travel downstream and give rise to what termed "roll waves" this phenomenon can take place in either turbulent flow or initially laminar flow. If this flow is stable, waves are supposed to be damped out.

Rouse (1965) also concluded that the concentration of roughness elements is as essential as their size in determining surface resistance, an optimium concentration of 15% to 25%,

3-4

depending upon element shape and arrangement, yields a maximum roughness effect.

Koloseus and Davidian (1966) based their study on the Nikuradse's (1933) tests on sand-grain roughness pipes, i.e., for wide channel

$$\frac{1}{\sqrt{f}} = 2 \log \left(\frac{4y_n}{k_s} 3.06\right) \tag{3-7}$$

They calculated the value of k_s for each run and adjusted the value of m so that all curves between k_s/ma and λ^* will fall on a common line for $\lambda^* < 0.8$, as shown in Fig. 3.4. λ^* is defined as a roughness concentration factor and represents the ratio to the sum of projected areas of roughness elements normal to mean direction of fluid movement to the total flow area.

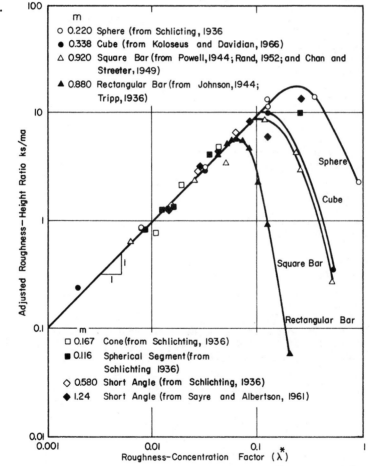

Fig. 3-4. Interference Effects of Roughness Elements as Concentration Increases. (after Koloseus and Davidian, 1966)

3-5

Koloseus and Davidian (1966) then compared their empirical m values with the individual drag coefficient as shown in Table 3-1.

Table 3-1. Correspondence between changes in m and C_D for similar geometric variations after Koloseus and Davidian (1966)

	m	C_D	
Variation of c/a			
Long bar............................			Cyliner - axis parallel to flow.
Johnson - c/2a = 2..	0.880	0.85	Length/diameter = 2
Powell, Chu and			
Streeter, Rand = 0.5	.920	1.02	Length/diameter = 0.5
Variation of b/a			
Square bar c/a....................			Rectangular plate c/a = 0
Koloseus &			
Dividian - b/2a=0.5	.338	1.17	b/2a = 0.5
Powell, Chu and			
Streeter, Rand -			
b/2a = 16	.920	1.42	b/2a = 16
Rectangular plate -			
c/a = 0..........................			Rectangular plate - c/a = 0
Schlichting b/2a=1.33	.580	1.16	b/2a = 1.33
Sayre &			
Albertson -b/2a=2	1.23	1.17	b/2a = 2
Axisymmetric bodies:			
Spheres...........................			
Schlichting........	.220	.220	Spheres
Cubes............................			Rectangular plate c/a = 0
Koloseus &			
Davidian..........	.338	1.17	b/2a = 0.5

In a recent study conducted by the writer at the Colorado State University (co -investigator Li, Ruh-ming), for roughness in staggered pattern (because this usually gives the greatest resistance) it is assumed that (note that $U/U_* = \sqrt{8/f}$),

$$\frac{U}{U_*} = \beta_0 + \beta_1 \ln \left(\frac{y_n}{a}\right) + \beta_2 \ln \left(\frac{t}{b}\right) + \beta_3 \ln \left(\frac{\ell}{b}\right)$$

$$+ \beta_4 \ln \left(\frac{c}{b}\right) + \beta_5 \ln \left(\frac{a}{b}\right) + \ln \varepsilon \qquad (3-8)$$

Table 3-2 gives a summary of the data used in the multi-variate regression analysis.

Table 3.2. Summary of Roughness Geometry of Data Used in
Analysis

Investigators	Roughness Size (inches)			Spacings (inches)		Roughness Concentration
	a	b	c	ℓ	t	ab/tℓ
Robinson &	1/2	2	1/2	5.5	1.5	0.121
Albertson	1	4	1	11	3	0.121
(1952)						
	1.5	6	0.05	3.05	11.85	0.249
	1.5	6	0.05	9.05	11.85	0.084
Sayre	1.5	6	0.05	27.05	11.85	0.028
& Albertson	1.5	6	0.05	3.05	23.7	0.125
(1961)	1.5	6	0.05	9.05	23.7	0.042
	1.5	6	0.05	27.05	23.7	0.014
	3/16	3/16	3/16	3	3	0.004
	3/16	3/16	3/16	1.5	1.5	0.016
Koloseus &	3/16	3/16	3/16	3/4	3/4	0.063
Davidian	3/16	3/16	3/16	3/4	3/4	0.063
(1966)	3/16	3/16	3/16	3/8	3/8	0.250
	3/4	3/4	3/4	2	4	0.070
	3/4	3/4	3/4	1.5	3	0.125
	3/4	3/4	3/4	1	2	0.281
Waterways	3/4	3/4	3/4	2	1	0.281
Experiment	1/2	1/2	1/2	1.25	2.5	0.080
Station, U.S.	3/8	3/8	3/8	6	12	0.002
Army Corps of	3/8	3/8	3/8	1	2	0.070
Engineers	3/8	3/8	3/8	2	1	0.070
(1953)	3/8	3/8	3/8	2	2	0.035
	3/4	3/8	3/8	6	12	0.004
	3/4	3/8	3/8	1	2	0.141
	3/4	3/8	3/8	0.5	1	0.563

Notes: 1) Total percent of floor area occupied by roughness
0.002-0.563
2) t/b between 0.75 to 32, ℓ/c between 1.3 to 541,
a/b between 0.008 to 1
3) y_n/a between 1.4 to 51.5

The procedure of "all possible regressions" is used to
find the most significant regression equation. The highest
multiple correlation coefficient within each possible set of
combinations of independent variables in a regression equation
is summarized in Table 3.3.

Table 3.3 indicates that the successive addition of the
variables c/b and a/b when y_n/a , t/b and ℓ/b are al-

ready in the regression equation will remove very little of the unexplained variance. This is clearly shown by the very slight increase in R* from set 3 to sets 4 and 5. The criterion for deciding the significant terms in the regression equation can be obtained by successive partial F-test as follows:

    i) Partial F-test to test the significance of adding a/b into the equation already with y_n/a , t/b , ℓ/b and c/b (β_0 , β_1 , β_2 , β_3 , β_4 , and β_5 refer to y_n/a , t/b , ℓ/b , c/b and a/b respectively)

    ii) Similarly for c/b

$$F = \frac{\text{MS due to } \hat{\beta}_4 \; \hat{\beta}_0, \; \hat{\beta}_1 \; , \; \hat{\beta}_2 \; , \; \hat{\beta}_3}{\text{MS Residual}} = 4.512$$

$$< F(1,323,0.975)$$

Thus, the addition of c/b is again not worthwhile for test size 0.025.

    iii) Similarly for ℓ/b

$$F = \frac{\text{MS due to } \hat{\beta}_3 \; \hat{\beta}_0 \; , \; \hat{\beta}_1 \; , \; \hat{\beta}_2 \; ,}{\text{MS Residual}} = 74.083$$

$$> F(1,324,0.975)$$

Therefore the addition of ℓ/b is worthwhile for test size $\overline{\alpha} = 0.025$.

Table 3.3. Examination of "All Possible Regressions"

Set	Variables in Equation With Highest Multiple Correlation Coefficient Within Each Set	Multiple Correlation Coefficient R*
1. One independent variable	$U/U_* = \text{function}(y_n/a)$	0.532
2. Two independent variables	$U/U_* = \text{function}(y_n/a$, $t/b)$	0.940
3. Three independent variables	$U/U_* = \text{function}(y_n/a$, t/b , $\ell/b)$	0.946
4. Four independent variables	$U/U_* = \text{function}(y_n/a$, t/b , ℓ/b , $c/b)$	0.946
5. Five independent variables	$U/U_* = \text{function}(y_n/a$, t/b , ℓ/b , c/b , $a/b)$	0.946

The regression result of the multiple regression model of Eq. (3.8) is (multiple correlation coefficient 0.945, standard error of estimate 1.269)

$$\frac{U}{U_*} = -0.0229 + 2.917 \ln \left(\frac{y_n}{a}\right) + 1.871 \ln \left(\frac{t}{b}\right) + 1.229 \ln \left(\frac{\ell}{b}\right)$$

$$(3-9)$$

Let Ω denote a dimensionless parameter to describe roughness geometry and let $\textcircled{H} = y_n/a$, the relative roughness height. Then, Eq. (3-9) can be expressed as

$$\sqrt{\frac{8}{f}} = \frac{U}{U_*} = 2.917 \ln \left(\frac{H}{\Omega}\right) \qquad (3-10)$$

Compare Eqs. (3-9) and (3-10) and one can obtain the roughness geometry descriptor Ω as

$$\Omega = 1.008 \left(\frac{t}{b}\right)^{-0.641} \left(\frac{\ell}{b}\right)^{-0.421} \qquad (3-11)$$

All data are plotted in Fig. 3-5 with U/U_* vs $\textcircled{H}/\Omega$. One must remember that in a regression curve such as that presented by Eq. (3-10) is, at best, applicable only to the flow and roughness conditions within the range of experimental data of which it is derived.

From the regression analysis, y_n/a , t/b and ℓ/b appear to exert strong influence on the development of the friction factor. The roughness dimension c has an insignificant effect for $\ell/c > 1.3$ (in that case $t/b = 2.67$) . Conceivably, when ℓ/c and t/b reach some lower limits then below these limits the friction factor will decrease with a further decrease in c and b . Ultimately, when $c = 1/2\ell$ and $t=b$ the boundary becomes smooth.

Flexible Roughness Element. Shen and Li hoped that Eqs. (3-9), (3-10), and (3-11) can be applied to flexible roughness such as vegetation. The only reliable data (known to us) is by Kouwens (1970) and these data points are plotted on Fig. 3-6.

For flexible roughness, $\textcircled{H}$ is taken to be y_n/h and Ω is defined by Eq. (3-11) (h is the roughness height after bending). Data points indicate that for $h/a < 0.5$, the flow resistance seems to be lower than the corresponding rigid resistance value for the same flow condition. This is reasonable because the concentration of the bending roughness elements should decrease the friction, i.e., ultimately, when the density of the roughness element increases to equal the floor area, the boundary could become smooth, as discussed previously. For $h/a > 0.5$, the flow resistance is higher than the corresponding rigid resistance value for the same flow condition. This may be due to the vibration of flexible roughness. An estimation of correction factors incorporated into Eq. (3-10) with the form $U/U_* = 2.917 \ln (\textcircled{H}/a\Omega)$ are determined as shown in Fig. 3-6. More data on the development of the friction factor for flexible roughness is needed for further analysis.

3-9

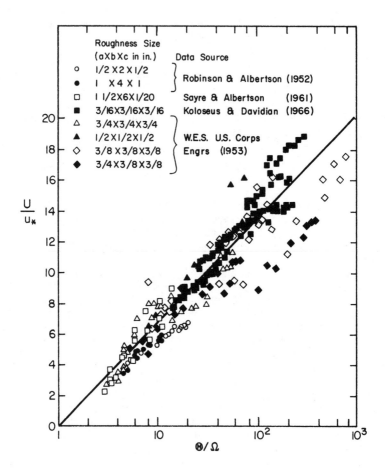

Fig. 3-5. $\frac{U}{U^*}$ vs $\frac{H}{\Omega}$ for Rigid Roughness Elements

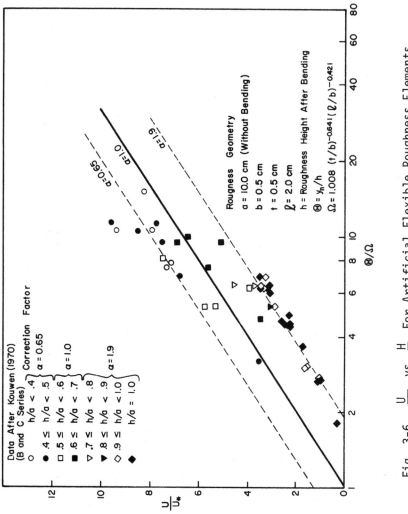

Fig. 3-6. $\dfrac{U}{U_*}$ vs $\dfrac{H}{\Omega}$ For Artificial Flexible Roughness Elements

3.3. FLOW RESISTANCE THROUGH SIMULATED TALL VEGETATION

<u>Single Cylinder (Simulated Tall Vegetation) in Open Channel Flow.</u>
   <u>Flow Field Descriptions.</u> The flow structure is rather complex around a single cylinder inserted in an open channel flow. As described by Roper, Schnieder and Shen (1967) and in Chapter 23, River Mechanics Vol. II the dominant feature of the flow near a cylinder is a large scale eddy structure or the system of vortices, which develop about the cylinder. Depending on the type of cylinder and free stream conditions, the eddy structure can be composed of any, all, or none of the following three basic systems: the horseshoe-vortex system, the wake-vortex system, and/or the trailing-vortex system. The vortex systems are an integral part of the flow structure and strongly affect the vertical component of the velocity in the neighborhood of the cylinder. The vortex filaments, transverse to the flow in a two-dimensional undisturbed velocity field, are concentrated by the presence of a cylinder to form the horseshoe-vortex system. The mechanism by which the concentration is accomplished is the pressure field induced by the cylinder. If the pressure field is sufficiently strong, it causes a three-dimensional separation of the boundary layer which, in turn, rolls up ahead of the cylinder to form the horseshoe-vortex system. The cylinder serves as a focusing or concentrating device for the vorticity already present in the undisturbed stream. The ends of the vortex filaments, composing the horseshoe-vortex, stretch downstream toward infinity, increasing the rotational velocities in the vortex core in accordance with the kinematic laws of vortex behavior. Clearly, the geometry of the cylinder is important in determining the strength of the horseshoe vortex. The horseshoe-vortex is shed periodically.
   The vorticity concentrated in the wake-vortex system is generated by the cylinder itself, contrary to the case of the horseshoe-vortex. The wake-vortex system is formed by the rolling up of the unstable shear layers generated at the surface of the cylinder. The shear layers are detached from either side of the cylinder at the separation line. At low Reynolds number (3 to $5 < \bar{R} < 40$ to 50), these vortices are stable and form a standing system downstream close to the cylinder. For Reynolds numbers of practical interest, however, the system is unstable, and the vortices are shed alternately from the cylinder and are converted downstream. The strength of the vortices in the wake system varies greatly depending on cylinder shape and fluid velocity. The regularity of shedding ranges from the very stable Von Karman vortex stress (80 to $90 < \bar{R} < 150$ to 300) to a practically chaotic state in the transcritical range $[(3.5 \times 10^6 < \bar{R})$, Roshko (1961)].
   The wake-vortex system is related to the so-called upflow which has been observed by Posey (1949), Masch and Moore (1963), Roper (1965 and 1967), and others.

The trailing-vortex system usually occurs only on completely submerged cylinders and is similar to that which occurs at the tips of finite lifting surfaces in finite wing theory. It is composed of one or more discrete vortices attached to the top of the cylinder and extending downstream. These vortices form when finite pressure differences exist between two surfaces meeting at a corner, such as at the top of the cylinder.

Roper (1965 and 1967) gave a more detailed description of these vortex systems and many of the remarks stated in the past few paragraphs were his.

At the request of the writer, Hung (1968) made detail velocity and pressure distribution measurement near a circular cylinder in an open channel. The width of channel was 4 feet, the depth of flow was 0.64 feet, the cylinder was 1.7 inches in diameter and the average flow velocity was 1.29 feet per second in the upstream approached section.

The pressure coefficient C_p is defined as follows:

$$C_p = \frac{p - p_y}{\frac{1}{2} \rho U_y^2} \tag{3-12}$$

where p is the local measured pressure, p_y is the upstream undisturbed flow static pressure at y, ρ is the fluid density, U_y is the upstream undisturbed flow velocity at level y and y is the reference elevation above channel bottom.

The C_p measurements as a function of the elevation and relative cylinder location are shown in Fig. 3.7.

Petryk (1969a) observed under the same flow conditions as Hung (1968) that the secondary flow along the front and back of the cylinder is downward, and at the back of the cylinder the pressure is higher near the surface than near the bottom.

The downward secondary flow along the front of the cylinder is attributed to the nonuniform approach velocity. The downward circulation pattern at the back of the cylinder disagrees with previous investigations where a two-dimensional object was placed in a nonuniform flow field.

In shear flows, it has generally been reported that the secondary flow in the near wake region of a cylinder is in the direction of increasing velocity head. This phenomena has been argued from the fact that generally as the approach velocity to the cylinder increases, the pressure at the back of the cylinder decreases. It follows that the secondary flow should be in the direction of decreasing pressure, or in the direction increasing velocity head. All wind tunnel investigations report this circulation pattern [see Baines (1965) and Roper (1967)]. Dalton and Masch (1968) also found that the secondary flow was in the direction of increasing velocity head. They placed a cylinder in a water tunnel with a linear velocity profile, and demonstrated that this secondary flow pattern was applicable to flow without free surface effects. Masch and Moore (1963)

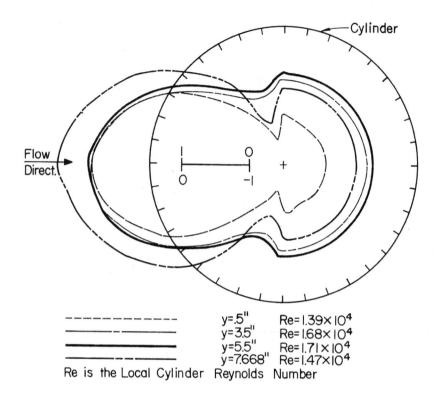

― ― ― ― ― ―	y=.5″	Re= 1.39×10⁴
―――――――	y=3.5″	Re= 1.68×10⁴
▬▬▬▬▬▬	y=5.5″	Re= 1.71×10⁴
―――――――	y=7.668″	Re=1.47×10⁴

Re is the Local Cylinder Reynolds Number

Fig. 3-7. Pressure Coefficient C_p .

and Roper (1965) reported the same secondary flow pattern downstream of a cylinder in an open channel flow with a nonuniform
velocity profile.

The observed downward circulation at the back of the
cylinder under the flow conditions given in the beginning of
this section may be explained by Petryk (1969a): i) the free
surface effects, and ii) the vortex shedding pattern at
the back of the cylinder. The vortices are shed irregularly
and their strength is relatively low. The flow in the separated
region circulates quiescently.

The pressure throughout the separated region is expected
to be approximately hydrostatic because of the relatively low
flow velocities in that region. The reentrainment velocity is
expected to be higher near the surface than near the bottom
because of the higher approach velocity near the surface. The
higher reentrainment velocity, impinging on the rear portion
of the cylinder, appears to be enough to cause a pressure
gradient downward. It follows that, with a downward pressure
gradient, the secondary flow is also downward.

3-14

At lower velocities the vortex shedding pattern changes
and the secondary flow is directed upward. The separated region
swings from side to side as the strong vortices are shed alternately from the cylinder. With the strong shedding of the
vortices, the separation points on the cylinder and the rear
stagnation point vibrates with the vortex shedding frequency.
A very good description of this separation phenomena is given
by Mattingly (1962). A sketch showing a strong vortex in the
upper half of the separated region is shown in Fig. 3-8. The
upper vortex is shedded and then a strong vortex in the lower
half is formed, it is shed, and so on.

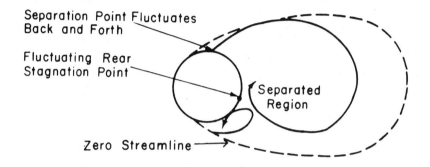

Fig. 3-8. Separation and Oscillation Behind Cylinder (top view)
           (after Petryk, 1969a)

Under these latter flow conditions, the higher velocity
near the surface forms stronger vortices which are produced
immediately behind the cylinder. Therefore, it follows that
the pressure behind the cylinder will decrease with increasing
distance from the floor in a fully developed channel flow. In
this case, the free surface appears to have little effect and
the secondary flow is upward.

Drag Coefficient. The drag coefficient of a cylinder in
two-dimensional cross flow varies significantly as the Reynolds
number (average flow velocity x cylinder diameter/fluid
viscosity) increases from 5×10^6 . The drag coefficient is
dependent on the regime of flow around the cylinder, and the
Reynolds number at which these different regimes of flow occur.

One can define three regimes of flow for a cylinder at
high Reynolds number. Each type of flow may be defined by the
separation characteristics of the cylinder boundary layer. The
subcritical flow occurs when the boundary layer separates
laminarly between 72° and 90° to form a relative wide wake
(all angular readings are with respect to the forward stagnation
point, unless specified otherwise). The critical flow occurs
when the boundary layer separates laminarly, quickly becomes
turbulent and reattaches to the cylinder to separate again at
about 135°. This separation phenomena is generally referred

3-15

to as a "laminar separation bubble." The supercritical region
occurs when the boundary layer Reynolds number is high enough
for transition to turbulence to occur before any separation
takes place; the turbulent boundary layer separates at about
110°. The drag coefficient generally decreases as the angle
of separation increases.

The coefficient of drag in an idealized two-dimensional
flow is about 1.2 for a cylinder Reynolds number range of 8 x
10^3 to 2 x 10^5, as reported in standard texts such as
Schlichting (1968). At higher Reynolds numbers the coefficient
of drag drops as one approaches the cylinder Reynolds number
of 2 x 10^5.

The flow around a vertical cylinder in open channel flow
has many characteristics which could significantly change the
drag from the well known idealized two-dimensional flow
conditions. Petryk (1969a) summarized and discussed the
following four kinds of effects on drag in open channel flow:
i) The Effects of Open Channel Turbulence: Bearman (1968),
and Sevik (1966) placed a cylinder in two-dimensional flow
downstream of a turbulence grid and studied the effects of
turbulence characteristics in the transition Reynolds number.
They found that turbulence tends to cause turbulent transition
in the separated cylinder boundary layer sooner than in a
corresponding idealized two-dimensional flow case. The transition Reynolds numbers were in the order of 5 to 6 x 10^4 with
increased turbulence fluctuations from the value of 2 to 3 x
10^5. Below this transition Reynolds number the effects of
turbulence on cylinder drag are negligible. ii) Free Surface
Effects: "Wave drag" is a common term used to describe the
free surface effects on drag magnitude for cylinder Froude
numbers less than or equal to about one, i.e., before aeration
occurs. Hsieh (1964) attributed wave drag to explain the
increase of drag coefficient over that in a two-dimensional
flow. Actually Hsieh's experimental results could also be
partially due to the blockage effects as discussed later.
Issacs (1965) showed that the effect of the free surface on
drag is small and that the wave drag is actually negative for
deep flows where the water depth cylinder diameter ratio is
greater than about four. iii) The Effect of a Non-Uniform
Velocity Profile: Dalton and Masch (1968) studied experimentally
the variation of drag coefficient with the height of a cylinder
which was placed in a flow with linear velocity profile. They
found that the drag coefficient varied from 0.8 to 2.4 for a
typical run and the corresponding drag coefficient for a cylinder in a two-dimensional flow is about 1.2. Petryk (1969b)
pointed out that if the drag coefficient was based on the
averaged integrated flow velocities across the cylinder and
with the blockage effect eliminated, the deviation from the
two dimensional case would be negligible. iv) The Effect of
Blockage: Allen and Vincenti (1944) considered the wall
interference in a dimensional flow wind tunnel. Petryk (1969a)
gave a detailed analysis of how blockage effect may be estimated.

Hung (1968) found the variations of the drag coefficient C_d, with y as shown in Fig. 3-9 where (x is the main flow direction).

$$C_d = \frac{\text{pressure drag force at } y \text{ in x-direction}}{\frac{1}{2} \rho U_y^2 \, d} \qquad (3\text{-}13)$$

and d is the cylinder diameter.

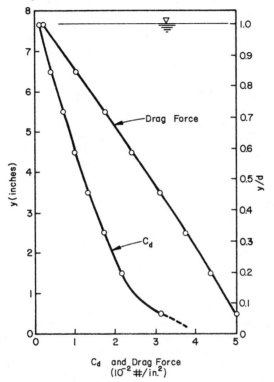

Fig. 3-9. Variation of Drag Force and Drag Coefficient

Petryk (1969a) concluded from the results obtained by Hsieh (1964), Isaacs (1965) and Petryk (1969a) that i) at low F* values, the effect of blockage is smaller than at higher F* values for subcritical channel flow for values of $F_d \lesssim 1$. ii) the wave drag is positive in subcritical channel flow for shallow depths (where the depth-to-diameter ratio is less than or equal to about four). The maximum value of wave drag occurs for cylinder Froude numbers between .5 and .9 at channel Froude numbers greater than or equal to .5. Hsieh's data shows how the wave drag increased as the depth-to-diameter ratio decreased from four to two. This is in agreement with the Petryk (1969a) data in Fig. 3-10; the effect of wave drag becomes more important as one moves along the dotted lines of decreasing depth-to-diameter ratio.

iii) The effect of wave drag is very small for a depth-to-diameter ratio greater than or equal to about four for cylinder Froude numbers less than or equal to about one, as found by Isaacs. Hsieh's results which show large values of C_d , larger than 1.2, at D/d equal to four are due to blockage effects. iv) From ii) and iii), it follows that the mechanics of flow near the surface are significantly influenced by the channel floor at shallow depths. v) The high drag coefficient values of 1.5 to 2.0 given in Fig. 3-10 are mostly due to wave drag at these shallow depths, and partly a consequence of the free surface effects due to blockage. Two-dimensional blockage corrections, according to Allen and Vincenti (1944) would reduce these high drag coefficients by less than or equal to about eight percent. vi) The experimental data indicates that for $F_d \overset{<}{\sim} 1$, the increase in drag coefficient due to wave drag may be as high as about 60% above the two-dimensional value of 1.2, when the depth-to-diameter ratio is less than about four.

In summary, from the experimental results of Hsieh, Isaacs, Dalton and Masch, and Fig. 3-10, it is concluded that if there is no aeration behind the cylinder $(F_d \overset{<}{\sim} 1)$ the best estimate of the drag coefficient is the two-dimensional value of 1.2, if the flow conditions are outside of the wave drag region, as shown in Fig. 3-10.

Wake Spread and Wake Decay. Eskinaze (1959) found that in a two-dimensional uniform flow with zero pressure gradient, the velocity defect is a Gaussian distribution i.e.

$$\frac{U_1}{U_{max}} = e^{-0.69} (\frac{z}{b_{1/2}})^{1/2} \qquad (3\text{-}14)$$

where U_1 is the velocity defect in the wake region, U_{max} is the maximum defect velocity at the center of the wake averaged over the depth of flow, $b_{1/2}$ is one-half of wake width where $U_1 = (U_{max})^{1/2}$, and z is the transverse direction.

Hung (1968) measured transverse velocity distribution in the wake of cylinder at x/d = 8.5, 9.5, 18.5, and 27.5 and found that Eq. 3-14 agreed well with his measurements, as shown in Fig. 3-11 for x/d = 8.5, when x is the longitudinal flow direction and d is the cylinder diameter.

From the limited experimental results Petryk (1969a) gave approximately the same spread and decay rate of a wake as measured by Eskinazi (1959) i.e., (for convenience Petryk replaced Eq. 3-14)by the following Eq. (3-15)).

$$u_1 = \frac{u_{max}}{2} \left[1 + \cos \left(\frac{\pi z}{2b_{1/2}} \right) \right] \qquad (3\text{-}15)$$

$$\frac{u_{max}}{U} = -.90 \left(\frac{x}{C_d d} \right)^{-.7} \qquad (3\text{-}16)$$

3-18

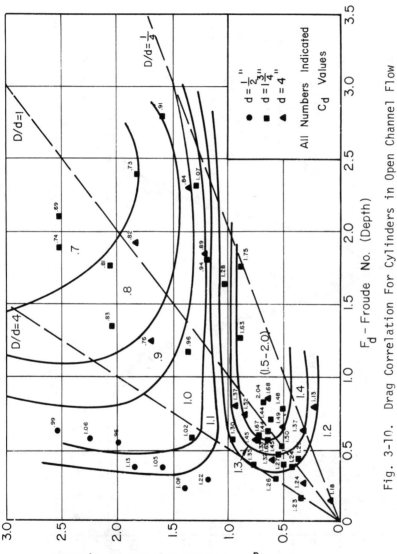

Fig. 3-10. Drag Correlation For Cylinders in Open Channel Flow

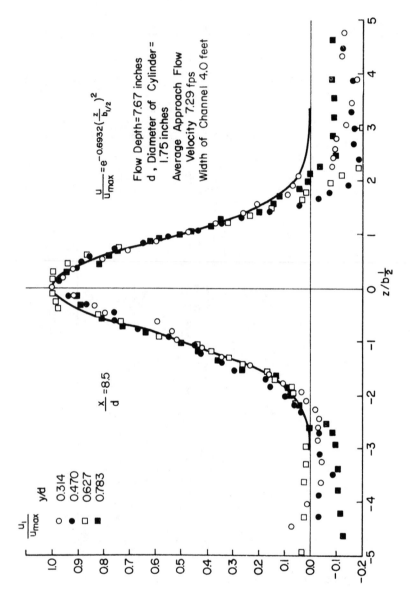

$$\frac{u}{u_{max}} = e^{-0.6932\left(\frac{z}{b_{1/2}}\right)^2}$$

Flow Depth=7.67 inches
d , Diameter of Cylinder =
1.75 inches
Average Approach Flow
Velocity 7.29 fps
Width of Channel 4.0 feet

$\frac{x}{d} = 8.5$

$\frac{u_1}{u_{max}}$	y/d
○	0.314
●	0.470
□	0.627
■	0.783

$z/b\frac{1}{2}$

Fig. 3-11. Shape of Open Channel Wake

$$\frac{2b_{1/2}}{C_d d} = .48 \left(\frac{x}{C_d d} \right)^{.59} \tag{3-17}$$

where x and z are longitudinal, and transverse directions respectively, and U is the mean flow velocity based on channel flow area.

Wakes decay and spread much faster in open channels than in the idealized two-dimensional case. Petryk (1969a) presented a useful and reasonable method to estimate the effect of slope on wakes in open channel flow. He reasoned that the effect of slope is to reduce the velocity defect u_{max}, while its effect of the wake width $b_{1/2}$ is small. This result follows when one compares the physics of flow for a wake developing in fully developed channel flow with a turbulent wake developing in a non-turbulent negative pressure gradient flow field. Hill, et. al., (1963) found that the velocity defect u_{max} will decay more rapidly with x in a negative pressure gradient wake than in a corresponding zero pressure gradient wake, and the wake width $b_{1/2}$ will spread less rapidly with x than in a corresponding zero pressure gradient wake. Petryk (1969a) argued that the effect of slope on u_{max} in an open channel is qualitatively the same as for a wake produced in a negative pressure gradient flow. Although the effect of slope on the rate of spread of a wake ($b_{1/2}$ vs x) is not qualitatively the same, the effect of slope is still assumed to be negligible in this analysis.

If the change in displacement thickness varies with downstream distance according to relationships developed by Hill, et. al. (1963) Petryk (1969a) found that u_{max} will vary according to

$$\frac{u_{max}}{U} = - .9 \, \frac{x}{C_d d}^{-.7} \, \frac{1}{1 + \dfrac{gxS}{\dfrac{U^2}{2}}}^{3/2} \tag{3-18}$$

where g is the gravitational acceleration and S is the channel bottom slope. The variation of $b_{1/2}$ is as given in Eq. 3-17. Equations 3-15, 3-17 and 3-18 completely describe the mean velocity distribution for a wake in open channel flow. Yano's (1966) basic wake equations in zero pressure gradient, are:

$$\frac{u_{max}}{U} = -.83 \, \frac{x}{C_d d}^{-.5} \tag{3-19}$$

$$\frac{2b_{1/2}}{C_d d} = -.57 \, \frac{x}{C_d d}^{.5} \tag{3-20}$$

3-21

If Yano's equations are used in open channel flow, then relation corresponding to Eq. 3-17 and Eq. 3-18 are Eq. 3-20 and

$$\frac{u_{max}}{U_o} = -.83 \left(\frac{x}{C_d d}\right)^{-.5} \frac{1}{1 + \frac{gxS}{\frac{U^2}{2}}} \qquad (3-21)$$

3.4. INDIVIDUAL CYLINDER DRAG IN AN OPEN CHANNEL WITH A MULTI-CYLINDER DISTRIBUTION

Two Dimensional Cases: (these are partially reviewed by A.T. Roper at the request of the writer). A good deal of testing has been carried out for multi-cylinder arrangements in conjection with tube banks in heat exchanges. An interesting flow visualization study of such arrangements is presented by Wallis (1939) [they also are reproduced in Knudsen and Katz (1958)].

In qualitative tests investigators generally consider the total effect of an entire array of cylinders on the flow. The total effect is then presented in terms of a modified friction factor expression. This expression contains factors describing the array such as the numbers of cylinders, the size, the spacing, orientation, etc. A wealth of such information was presented by Kays and London (1954), Bergelow, et.al. (1950), Chilton and Genereaux (1933), Gunter and Shaw (1945), Grimson (1937) and Jakob (1938). The results of most of these tests were summarized and discussed by Knudsen and Katz (1958).

Very little detail work seems to have been done on the detail interference of the individual cylinder flow fields in multi-cylinder arrangements. Some early aeronautical work was done on the influence of cylindrical struts in close proximity. Some of these results are available in Hoerner (1958) and Biermann and Herrnstein (1933). These results will be discussed in the section on lateral and longitudinal interference. Yano (1966) suggested a method for obtaining multi-cylinder wake behavior through superposition of momentum defect fluxes which is also discussed later.

One analytical solution for wake behavior behind a row of cylinders in a uniform flow exists. This solution was due to Gran Olsson (1936) and will be discussed in the next section. The solution was also discussed by Schlichting (1960) (pp. 604-605).

Wake Behind a Row of Cylinders in a Uniform Flow. Consider such a configuration with pitch t as shown in Fig. 3-12. This case was investigated both experimentally and theoretically by Gran Olsson (1936). At a certain downstream location, the width of the wake of a given cylinder will equal the pitch t . It is assumed that the Olsson approximations are valid and that the applicable form of the governing equation is

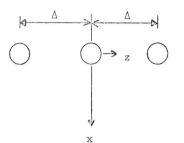

Fig. 2-12. Cylinder
Definition
Sketch

$$-U \frac{\partial u_1}{\partial x} = \frac{1}{\rho} \frac{\partial \tau}{\partial z} \qquad (3-22)$$

where U is the upstream undisturbed flow velocity, u_1 the velocity defect, ρ the fluid density and τ the shear stress. The mixing length hypothesis was used to determine the form of τ .

In fully developed flow the periodic dependence of u_1 upon z is assumed to be of the form,

$$u_1 = U A \left(\frac{x}{z}\right)^{-1} \cos (2\pi z/t) \qquad (3-23)$$

A is a free constant which Schlichting (1960) determined to be

$$A = (t/\ell') 8 \pi^3 \qquad (3-24)$$

where ℓ' is the mixing length. The magnitude of ℓ is dependent upon t/d (Gran Olsson obtained $\ell'/t = 0.103$ for $t/d = 8$). Gran Olsson found the above solution to be valid for $x/t > 4$.

Longitudinal and Lateral Interference. There are two distinct interference mechanisms at work in this problem. One is due to the effects of longitudinal, the other due to lateral interference. Some cases must, of course, be considered a combination of both.

Longitudinal Interference. The behavior of the flow in the cavity is very dependent upon conditions in the first few diameters downstream of the base [Roshko (1961) and Mattingly (1962)]. Roskho (1954) investigated the effect of splitter plate interference and found that the conditions return to their undisturbed levels when nose of the plate moves more than approximately 2.5 diameters downstream from the first cylinder. The conclusion was that the major interference effects occur in the first 2.5 diamters downstream due to modification of the pressure depression. This conclusion was substantiated by Hoerner (1958) who showed that the major interference effect on C_d caused by placing a second cylinder in the wake of the first occurs in the

3-23

first 2.5 diameters downstream. The effect on both cylinders was favorable in this range (i.e., drag reduced on both).

The drag on the second cylinder is greatly reduced partially due to the result of decreased wake dynamic pressure. A second effect is the increased turbulence level of the flow approaching the second cylinder. This increased turbulence level can delay separation and effectively push the second cylinder from the subcritical regime (separation before 90°) into the lower drag critical or supercritical regime (separation beyond 90°).

The dynamic pressure effect can be expected to be negligible for $x/d > 600$ (this number was arrived at somewhat arbitrarily from Eskinazi's data on the decrease of the peak defect to 1/10 its maximum value at 5.1 diameters). The effect of turbulence decays much more rapidly and is probably negligible by 100 diameters.

Lateral Interference. The behavior of a pair of cylinders with various lateral spacings was investigated by Hoerner (1958). When the spacing between the cylinder sides was zero they presented a more bluff object to the flow than a single cylinder of their combined diameter, and, hence, a slightly higher drag coefficient. The wake vortex structure is that of a single body. As the lateral distance is increased beyond the point the behavior continues to be that of a combined system until the spacing between centerlines is 2d . The behavior is apparent in the rising portion of the Strouhal frequency curve up to t/d = 1 (i.e., centerline distances of 2d). Beyond this point there is a rapid drop in the shedding frequency as the system is altered from a combined system to two single systems. For larger separations the behavior is that expected of two independent systems.

For close spacings the flow visualization photos by Wallis (1938) [see also Knudsen and Katz (1958)] appear to indicate a coupling of adjacent wakes. For all cases the wake growth appears to be reduced from the no interference case, This could be a result of the favorable pressure gradient induced by a distortion of the external velocity field discussed in section (x). While the variation may not be of the x^n variety, other variations could produce the same gross behavior.

The distortion of the flow field in closely spaced cylinders produces regions of increased velocity between the cylinders. For spacings close enough to produce favorable pressure gradients equivalent to $n > + 1/3$, the wake width would be expected to decrease with x (that is collapse rather than flow). This behavior appears to be substantiated by Schlichting's description (1960), (p. 605) of Von Bohl's experiments on bar spacings in wind tunnels. Von Bohl found that for large solidarity ratios (i.e., ratio of total bar area to total cross-sectional area) that the regions of high velocity (jets) close in on one another. This would appear to be a case of wake collapse.

Lateral and Longitudinal Interference. Bierman and Herrnstein (1933) took drag measurements on two cylinders at different spacings in a wind tunnel. The cylinders were arranged

in-line and then crosswise with respect to the flow direction.
The drag force on each cylinder was measured at different spacing
ratios for different cylinder sizes. The cylinder Reynolds
number was greater than or equal to about 7×10^4 .

Apelt and Isaacs (1968) measured the total drag force on
two cylinders spaced at 1-5/8, 2, 3 and 4 diameters at different
angular positions. The experimental work was carried out in a
laboratory flume at a cylinder Reynolds number of about 1.2×10^4 .

Yano (1966) used wake superposition concept to predict mean
velocity profiles downstream of multi-cylinder distributions.
Superposition refers to the method by which the effects of the
upstream wake producing objects are added to predict the final
downstream flow field. Linear superposition refers to adding
linearly the effects of two or more wake producing bodies.

Laird, et. al. (1959), studied the effect of a similar
sized cylinder placed upstream at different radial angles. Their
cylinder Reynolds numbers were mostly in the subcritical to
critical regime of flow. The scatter of data for different
runs at similar flow conditions was fairly large. As a result,
they could only reach qualititive conclusions that the presence
of a neighboring cylinder caused a reduction in the mean drag
force, and a large increase in the fluctuating lift and drag
forces, and that the spacing was important in these effects.

Yano (1966) suggested a method for obtaining multi-cylinder
wake behavior through superposition of momentum defect fluxes,
i.e.,

$$u^2_{total} = u_1{}^2 + u_2{}^2 + u_3{}^2 + \ldots \qquad (3\text{-}25)$$

Yano obtained his justification of this form from a
discussion of the characteristics of the turbulent kinetic energy.

From Reichardt's (1943) theory of turbulence, Petryk (1969a)
argued that linear superposition of velocity defects was
permissible, or

$$u_{total} = u_1 + u_2 + u_3 \ldots \qquad (3\text{-}26)$$

The Effect of Various Tall Vegetation Groupings On Flow
Retardation and Sediment Yield. Based on the analysis and
experimental evidence of Petryk (1969a) Li, Ruh-Ming and the
writer have recommended the following approach to estimate the
effect of various tall vegetation groupings on flow retardation.
(See also Shen, 1972).

Basically the model predicts the drag on each cylinder if
certain conditions are met, and the following data are given:
i) the size and distribution of cylinders, ii) the discharge,
iii) the bottom slope and the width of the channel, iv) the
local coefficient of drag of the cylinders in the channel, and
v) the depth of flow.

Assumptions are necessary for a closed form solution to
the problem. The cylinders are assumed to be distributed in

such a manner than uniform flow in the channel exists. The slope in the channel should be uniform. Each wake decays independently of the downstream or upstream distribution of cylinders; this assumption allows one to use the superposition of wakes concept to calculate the approach velocity to each cylinder. Once the approach velocity is known then the cylinder drag is calculated according to a normal drag force equation if the local drag coefficient C_d is known.

This section describes how superposition may be used to predict the velocity profile across the channel and to predict the drag force on each cylinder. From now on, superposition will be used as a general term, unless otherwise specified. It may refer to either Yano's method or to Petryk's method.

The following analysis starts with flow characteristics behind a single cylinder, and then proceeds to a multi-cylinder arrangement.

Single Cylinder. The flow approaching the cylinder is assumed to be fully developed open channel flow. Experimental drag measurements verify that the two-dimensional value of 1.2 is a satisfactory value for the local drag coefficient if: i) the wave drag is small, ii) no aeration takes place behind the cylinder, and iii) the cylinder Reynolds number is low enough where the cylinder is well in the subcritical regime of flow, but greater than or equal to about 8×10^3. The velocity distribution in the wake of the cylinder is described by (see Fig. 3-13),

$$\overline{U}(x,z) = U_\infty(x) + u_1(x,z) \qquad (3-27)$$

where $u_1(x,z)$ is the defect velocity (at point (x,z) and can be solved from Eqs. 3-15, 3-17, 3-18, or Eqs. 3-15, 3-20, and 3-21, depending on whether Petryk's or Yano's method is used. $\overline{U}(x,z)$ is the resultant mean velocity at point (x,z) and $U_\infty(x)$ is regarded as the reference free stream velocity at distance x from the cylinder; $U_\infty(x)$ can be derived as follows:

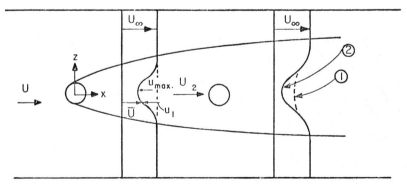

Fig. 3-13. Velocity Profile in Wakes

From Continuity eqaution

$$Q = U \, WD = D \int_W \overline{U}(x,z) \, dz$$

$$= D \int_W [U_\infty(x) + u_1(x,z)] dz$$

$$= D \, U_\infty(x) \, W + D \int_W u_1(x,z) dz$$

and will then result in

$$U_\infty(x) = U - \frac{1}{W} \int_W u_1(x,z) dz \qquad (3\text{-}18)$$

where D is the depth of flow, W is the width of the channel and U is the mean velocity based on the flow area. From Eqs. 3-27 and 3-28 one can compute the velocity distribution in the wake.

Multiple Cylinders Distributed in a Given Pattern.
A. Petryk's (1969a) Method (Linear Superposition of Velocity Defect).

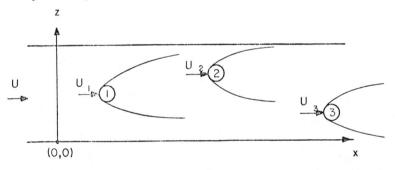

Fig. 3-14. Multiple Cylinder Wake

Referring to Fig. 3-14 the corrdinates of ith cylinder are expressed as (x_i, z_i) and the approach velocity of the first cylinder is taken to be $U_1 = U$ (the upstream undisturbed flow velocity).

The cylinder diameter is assumed to be small enough to be considered as a point in comparison with the whole channel width, and the approach velocity U_2 for the second cylinder can be evaluated according to the single cylinder wake solution, or

$$U_2 = \overline{U}(x_2, z_2)$$

3-27

$$= U_\infty(x_2) + u_1[(x_2-x_1),(z_2-z_1)] \quad (3-29)$$

where

$$U_\infty(x_2) = U - \frac{1}{W} \int_W u_1[(x_2-x_1),(z-z_1)]dz \quad (3-30)$$

Now, consider the third cylinder, the velocity defect at point (x_3,z_3) can be expressed from Eq. 3-25 to be

$$u(x_3,z_3) = u_1[(x_3-x_1),(z_3-z_1)] + u_2[(x_3-x_2),(z_3-z_2)]$$

then

$$U_3 = \bar{U}(x_3,z_3)$$

$$= U_\infty(x_3) + u(x_3,z_3)$$

$$= U_\infty(x_3) + u_1[(x_3-x_1),(z_3-z_1)] + u_2[(x_3-x_2),(z_3-z_2)] \quad (3-31)$$

and

$$U_\infty(x_3) = U - \frac{1}{W}\int_W u(x_3,z)\ dz$$

$$= U - \frac{1}{W}\int_W u_1[(x_3-x_1),(z-z_1)]dz$$

$$- \frac{1}{W}\int_W u_2[(x_3-x_2),(z-z_2)]dz \quad (3-32)$$

where u_1 is the velocity defect due to the first cylinder and u_2 is that due to the second. With known U_1 and U_2, one can solve U_3 by Eqs. 3-31 and 3-32.

Similarly, for the nth cylinder

$$U_n = U_\infty(x_n) + \sum_{i=1}^{m} u_i[(x_n-x_i),(z_n-z_i)] \quad (3-33)$$

$$U_\infty(x_n) = U - \frac{1}{W}\sum_{i=1}^{m}\int_W u_i[(x_n-x_i),(z-z_i)]dz \quad (3-34)$$

where m is the number of cylinders which have had influence on the nth cylinder and where $x_i < x_n$ and $u_{imax}/U_i \geq 0.02$. It is arbitrarily assumed that when $u_{imax}/U_i \leq 0.02$ the wake effect due to the ith cylinder has been completely dissipated.

When the wake spreads to the edge of the channel, the wake is constricted by the wall, the integration limits in Eq. 3-24 should not be greater than the width of the flume.

B. Yano's (1966) Method. To use linear superposition of momentum defects (Eq. 3-26) instead of velocity defects on (Eq. 3-25), one can follow the similar procedures for establishing Petryk's method and obtain

$$U_n = U_\infty(x_n) - \sqrt{\sum_{i=1}^{m} u_i^2 [(x_n - x_i), (z_n - z_i)]} \qquad (3-35)$$

$$U_\infty(x_n) = U + \frac{1}{W} \int_W \sqrt{\sum_{i=1}^{m} u_i^2 [(x_n - x_i), (z - z_i)]} \, dz \qquad (3-36)$$

From the above analysis, the model predicts the velocity at any point in the channel. That is, the approach velocity to every cylinder is known. The drag on each cylinder is also known from

$$F_i = \frac{1}{2} C_d \, \rho U_i^2 d_i D \qquad (3-37)$$

where F_i is the drag force on the ith cylinder, C_d is the local drag coefficient or the drag coefficient on an individual cylinder without any influence from other cylinders, ρ is the density of water, d_i is the diameter of the ith cylinder.

The local drag coefficient, C_d, which is based on the approach velocity to the cylinder, was assumed to be constant at 1.2. The mean drag coefficient is defined as

$$\overline{C_{d_i}} = \frac{F_i}{\frac{1}{2} \rho U^2 d_i D} = \frac{\frac{1}{2} C_d \rho U_i^2 d_i D}{\frac{1}{2} \rho U^2 d_i D}$$

$$\overline{C_{d_i}} = \frac{U_i^2}{U^2} C_d . \qquad (3-38)$$

Discussions. According to Petryk (1969a), his method and Yano's method are quite comparable. Since Petryk's method is easier to apply, therefore, Petryk's method is adopted for the following analysis.

A. Comparison of Mathematical Models (Petryk's Method) with Petryk's Experimental Results.

Petryk (1969a) performed an extensive experimental study, measured the drag by "drag balance" as described by Petryk and Shen (1971) and Petryk (1969a). Petryk tested 21 different cylinder patterns of parallel, staggered and random distribution, for the following ranges of flow conditions; i) 2.25 < D < 11.5 inches, ii) 0.75 < U < 3.37 ft/sec, and iii) cylinder diameters of two inches and 4-1/2 inches. A total of 113 sets of data were obtained and a more detailed description of the testing conditions is given by Petryk (1969a).

3-29

The agreement between the computed mean drag coefficients and the measured mean drag coefficient is generally satisfactory for Petryk's method (Fig. 3-15 shows the comparison for Petryk's method). The deviations are generally within $\pm$ 30%.

The experimental $\overline{C}_d$ decreased with the increase of the average velocity U_o. Figure 3-16 shows the relationship between the computed mean drag coefficient and the average velocity for selected runs.

B. Limitations of Mathematical Models as Stated by Petryk (1969a)

The mathematical model, in its present form, is applicable to flow situations where the following limitations apply: i) the flow in the channel is uniform. ii) the spacing between cylinders is at least six diameters in the downstream direction or three diameters in the crosswise direction, iii) the flow around each cylinder is such that free surface effects are small, i.e., outside of the wave drag region, and outside of the region where aeration affects the drag coefficients.

It should be noted that the model was verified experimentally for only subcritical cylinder Reynolds numbers. However, this probably can also be valid for critical and supercritical Reynolds numbers if the proper local drag coefficient is known or can be estimated. The mathematical model does not consider the important free stream turbulence effects on wake characteristics. If there is a large scale and high intensity turbulence created by the upstream cylinder, the computed superposition solution would likely yield poor agreement with actual cases.

C. Local Drag Coefficient of a Single Cylinder in a Group of Cylinders.

As discussed before, the best estimate of the drag coefficient for an individual cylinder is the two-dimensional value of 1.2 provided that i) no aeration exists behind the cylinder, ii) there is no blockage effect, and iii) it is a subcritical flow range. However, this local drag coefficient C_d could be different for a single cylinder in a multiple cylinder arrangement.

In Petryk's (1969a) experiment, F_i, ρ, d_i and D are all known for all runs and it is found that the minimum optimization function, F occurs at $C_d \approx 1.1$ where

$$F = \sum_{i=1}^{n} (\overline{C}_{d_i} - \hat{C}_{d_i})^2 \qquad (3-39)$$

and

$$\hat{C}_{d_i} = \frac{F_i}{\frac{1}{2} U^2 d_i D} \qquad (3-40)$$

and $\overline{C}_{d_i}$ is the computed mean drag coefficient by Eq. 3-38 and

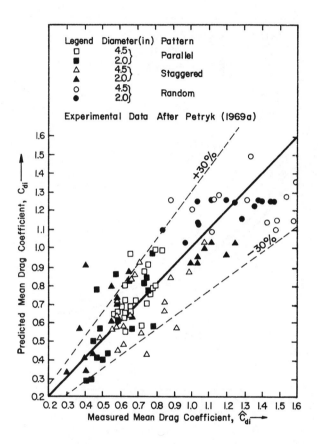

Fig. 3-15. Comparison of Predicted Mean Drag Coefficients (Petryk's Method) With Measured Mean Drag Coefficient.

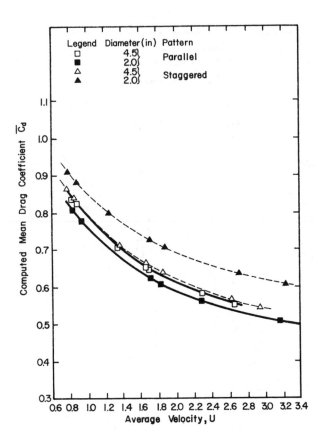

Fig. 3-16. Relation Between Computed Mean Drag Coefficient and Average Velocity For Selected Runs.

$\hat{C}_{d_i}$ is the measured mean drag coefficient computed by Eq. 3-40 with measured drag force F_i .

The conclusion is to use C_d = 1.2 for the local drag coefficient in the model since there is no strong evidence to prove otherwise.

D. Effect of Cylinder Patterns and Spacings on the Mean Drag Coefficient.

There are two basic regular patterns: parallel and staggered and the effects of these two cylinder patterns at different spacings on drag coefficients were studied. Fig. 3-17 shows that the mean drag coefficients are increased with increasing spacing for parallel patterns, but, the trend is reversed for staggered patterns for a particular flow condition. It should be stressed here that if the transverse spacing is very large the trend for staggered pattern may not be the same as shown in Fig. 3-17.

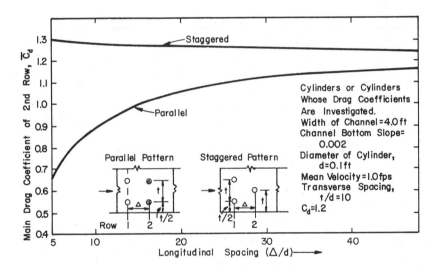

Fig. 3-17. Example of Relation Between Spacings and Mean Drag Coefficient.

E. The Variation of Drag Coefficient for a Single Row of Cylinders.

Figure 3-18 shows a single row of cylinders with coordinates of ith cylinder being (x_i, z_i) and $z_1 = z_2 = z_3$ ... $= z_n = 0$.

The approaching velocity for the first cylinder is the average velocity U , i.e.,

$$U_1 = U$$

From Eq. 3-29 the approaching velocity for the second cylinder is

$$U_2 = U_\infty(x_2 + u_i(x_2-x_1,0)).$$ (3-41)

From Eq. 3-30

$$U_\infty(x_2) = U - \frac{1}{W} \int_W u_i(x_2-x_1,z)dz$$ (3-42)

in which (according to Eq. 3-15)

$$\int_W u_1(x_2-x_1,z)dz = \int_W \frac{1}{2} u_1(x_2-x_1,0)[1 + \cos \frac{\pi z}{2b_{1/2}(x_2-x_1)}]dz$$

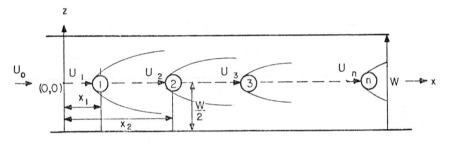

Fig. 3-18. A Single Row of Cylinders

For $2b_{1/2}(x_2-x_1) \leq W/2$

$$\int_W u_1(x_2-x_1,z)dz = \int_{-2b_{1/2}(x_2-x_1)}^{2b_{1/2}(x_2-x_1)} \frac{1}{2} u_1(x_2-x_1,0)$$

$$[1 + \cos \frac{\pi z}{2b_{1/2}(x_2-x_1)}]dz$$

$$= 2 u_1(x_2-x_1,0) b_{1/2}(x_2-x_1).$$ (3-43)

For $2b_{1/2}(x_2-x_1) > W/2$, the wake spreads to the wall and is constricted; then

$$\int_W u_1(x_2-x_1,z)dz = \int_{-W/2}^{W/2} \frac{1}{2} u_1(x_2-x_1,0)[1 + \cos \frac{\pi z}{2b_{1/2}(x_2-x_1)}]dz$$

$$= \frac{W}{2} u_1(x_2-x_1,0) \left[1 + \frac{4b_{1/2}(x_2-x_1)}{\pi W} \sin \right.$$

$$\left. \frac{\pi W}{4b_{1/2}(x_2-x_1)})\right] \quad (3\text{-}44)$$

From Eqs. 3-41, 3-42, 3-43, and 3-44 for $2b_{1/2}(x_2-x_1) \leq W/2$

$$U_2 = U + u_1(x_2-x_1,0) \left[1 - \frac{2}{W} b_{1/2}(x_2-x_1)\right] \quad (3\text{-}45)$$

and, for $2b_{1/2}(x_2-x_1) > W/2$,

$$U_2 = U + u_1(x_2-x_1,0) \left[\frac{1}{2} - \frac{4b_{1/2}(x_2-x_1)}{\pi W} \sin \left(\frac{\pi W}{4b_{1/2}(x_2-x_1)}\right)\right]$$

$$(3\text{-}46)$$

Similarly for the nth cylinder

$$U_n = U + \sum_{i=1}^{n-1} u_i(x_n-x_i,0) B_i(x_n-x_i) \quad (3\text{-}47)$$

where

$$u_i(x_n-x_i,0) = u_i\text{max}(x_n-x_i)$$

$$= -0.9 \left(\frac{x_n-x_i}{C_d d}\right)^{-0.7} \left(\frac{1}{1 + \dfrac{gS(x_n-x_i)}{\dfrac{U_i^2}{2}}}\right)^{3/2} U_i$$

$$(3\text{-}48)$$

$$B_i(x_n-x_i) = 1 - 2/W\, b_{1/2}(x_n-x_i); \quad \text{for } 2b_{1/2}(x_n-x_i) \leq W/2$$

$$(3\text{-}49)$$

$$B_i(x_n-x_i) = \frac{1}{2} - \frac{4b_{1/2}(x_n-x_i)}{\pi W} \sin \left(\frac{\pi W}{4b_{1/2}(x_n-x_i)}\right)$$

$$\text{for } 2b_{1/2}(x_n-x_i) > W/2 \quad (3\text{-}50)$$

$$b_{1/2}(x_n-x_i) = 0.24 (x_n-x_i)^{0.59} (C_d d)^{0.41} \quad (3\text{-}51)$$

The mean drag coefficient based on U of the nth cylinder is

$$\overline{C}_{d_n} = \frac{U_n^2}{U^2} C_d . \quad (3\text{-}52)$$

3-35

From Eq. 3-48, one can see that the magnitude of the velocity defect u_i increases with increasing approach velocity which, in turn, increases with increasing average velocity. From Eq. 3-47 this will result in the decrease in the approach velocity of the next cylinder and, therefore, the mean drag coefficient is decreased with increasing average flow velocity.

A flow condition with a channel width of 4.0 ft., a channel bottom slope of 0.002, a cylinder diameter of 0.1, a mean velocity of 1.0 ft/sec and a drag coefficient for a single cylinder of 1.2 was selected to illustrate this effect. Figure 3-19 shows that the mean drag coefficient becomes approximately constant for larger distances. These asymptotic mean drag coefficients are increased with increasing cylinder spacing and these asymptotic values are generally reached at approximately 200 diameters from the first cylinder.

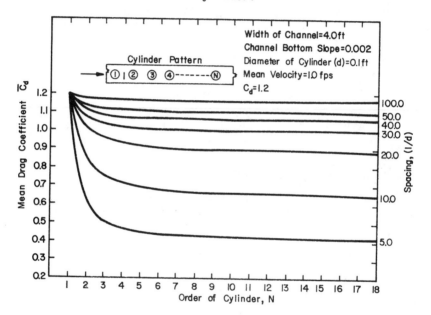

Fig. 3-19.   Example of Mean Drag Coefficient Distribution in Open Channel Flow

F.   Variation of Drag Coefficients in a Multiple Row of Cylinders (with longitudinal spacings equal to the transverse spacings) in Parallel and in Staggered Patterns.

The asymptotic mean drag coefficient of a staggered type distribution is generally greater than that of a parallel type distribution (as shown in Fig. 3-20). The asymptotic mean drag coefficient for a parallel and staggered type distribution with different cylinder spacings for a selected flow condition is shown in Fig. 3-21.

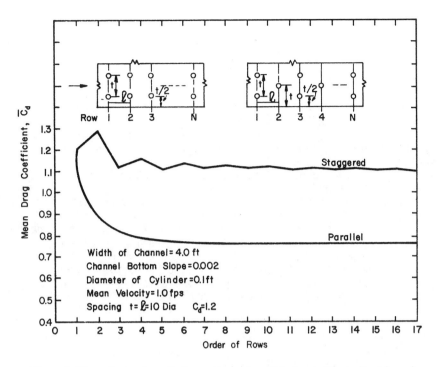

Fig. 3-20.   Example of Mean Drag Coefficient Distribution in
             Open Channel Flow for Different Cylinder Patterns.

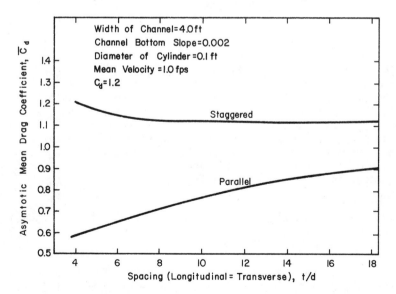

Fig. 3-21.   Example of Relation Between Spacings and Asympotic
             Mean Drag Coefficient.

Application on Flow Retardation and Sediment Yield.
A. Assumptions Made in This Analysis
   i)   The flows are steady and uniform
   ii) The linear superposition of the velocity defect,
as suggested by Petryk is valid.
   iii) The turbulent velocity distribution for a
completely rough boundary is valid to calculate the boundary
shear stress on the bed surface.
   iv) The form resistance is assumed to be entirely
due to vegetation and the bed form resistances on the bed
surface are negligible.
   v)   The boundary shear stress is uniformly distributed
over the entire bed.
   It must be stressed here that the following analysis is
mainly for the comparison of the relative effect of sediment
yields by various combinations of tall vegetation and it is not
to be used for an accurate prediction of sediment yields.
Although assumptions iii) and v) as listed above may not be
exactly true in actual cases, they should be reliable enough
to give a qualitative comparison for the effect of various
patterns of tall vegetation on sediment yields as described
below.
B. Calculation Procedure
   Referring to Fig. 3-22

$$(WL \ D - \frac{1}{4} N \ D \ \pi \ d^2) \ \gamma \ S$$

$$= (WL - \frac{1}{4} N \ \pi \ d^2) \ \tau + \frac{1}{2} \rho \ U^2 \ D \ d \ \Sigma \ \overline{C_{d_i}}$$

$$(3-53)$$

where τ is the average boundary shear stress on the bed, W
is the width of the plot, L is the length of the plot, D
is the depth of the flow, N is the total number of vegetations,
d is the diameter of the vegetations (assume that the diameters
are equal), γ is the specific weight of the water, S is the
bottom slope of the plot, ρ is the density of the water, U
is the average velocity based on the flow area and $\Sigma \ \overline{C_{d_i}}$ is
the sum of the mean drag coefficient.
   According to assumption iii)

$$\sqrt{\frac{8}{f}} = \frac{U}{\sqrt{\frac{\tau}{\rho}}} = 2.5 \ \ln \ (\frac{D}{d_{65}}) + 6.0 \qquad (3-54)$$

where d_{65} is the size of the sediment on the bed of which 65%
is finer, and f is the Darcy-Weisbach friction coefficient.
   Combining Eqs. 3-53 and 3-54, one obtains

$$(\text{WL } D - \frac{1}{4} N D \pi d^2) \gamma S_0$$

$$= (\text{WL} - \frac{1}{4} N \pi d^2) \frac{\rho \, (\frac{Q}{WD})^2}{[2.5 \, \ell n \, (\frac{D}{d_{65}}) + 6.0]^2}$$

$$+ \frac{1}{2} \rho \, (\frac{Q}{WD})^2 \, D \, d \, \Sigma \, \overline{C_{d_i}} \, . \tag{3-55}$$

The solution to the above equation is obtained by trial-and-error with an assumed value of the flow depth D. $\Sigma \, \overline{C_{d_i}}$ is obtained from Petryk's method as given before.

One can use one of the many currently available sediment transport equations to estimate the effect of various vegetation patterns on sediment yield with bed shear stress as calculated from Eq. 3-54 for the value of D as calculated from Eq. 3-55.

C. Examples

The following examples have been worked out to investigate the effect of various vegetation patterns on sediment yield for given flow conditions.

Example I (with the restriction of certain patch-cut groupings.

As shown in Fig. 3-22, group A consists of basically parallel patterns and group B consists of basically staggered patterns.

The following Table (Table 3-4) gives the computation results of the various patterns consisted of the same basic group.

Table 3-4. Summary of Computation Results

---

i) Vegetation distributed in parallel pattern and square basic group

Diameter of vegetation: $d = 0.5$ ft.

Width of plot: $W = 40.0$ ft.

Length of plot: $L = 40.0$ ft.

Bottom slope of plot: $S = 0.002$

Median grain size: $d_{65} = 0.003$ ft.

Water discharge: $Q = 208$ cfs

Critical tractive force: $\tau_c = 0.0185$ lb/ft^2 ($\tau_c = 0.06$

Sediment discharge $Q_s = \dfrac{10(\tau - \tau_c) \, Q \, S \, \gamma}{(\gamma_s - \gamma) \, d_{65}}$ $\qquad \dfrac{(\gamma_s - \gamma) d_{65}}{}$

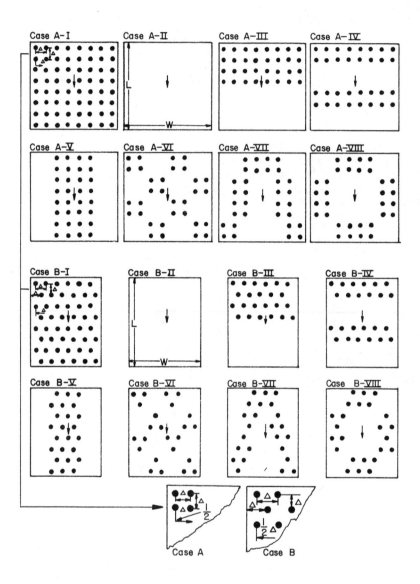

Fig. 3-22. Example I. (Patch cut groupings).

Table 3-4. Summary of Computation Results (Continued)

Case	Number of Vegeta-tions N	Flow depth (ft) D	Average Velocity Based on Flow Area (ft/sec) U	Average Boundary Shear Stress (lb/ft^2) τ	Sediment Trans-port Rate (lb/sec) Q_s	Relative Sediment Trans-port Rate Q_s/Q_{sm}
A-I	64	2.11	2.468	0.0235	4.225	0.047
A-II	0	1.00	5.208	0.1248	89.447	1.000
A-III	32	1.64	3.176	0.0413	19.144	0.214
A-IV	32	1.70	3.064	0.0381	16.469	0.184
A-V	32	1.54	3.382	0.0475	24.378	0.273
A-VI	32	1.71	3.046	0.0376	16.053	0.179
A-VII	32	1.63	3.195	0.0418	19.621	0.219
A-VIII	32	1.69	3.082	0.0386	16.894	0.189

NOTE: Q_{sm} is the maximum sediment transport rate (when there is no vegetation)

ii) Vegetation distributed in staggered pattern and triangular basic group
Diameter of vegetation: d = 0.5 ft.
Width of plot: W = 32.5 ft.
Length of plot: L = 40.0 ft.
Bottom slope of plot: S = 0.003
Median grain size: d_{65} = 0.003 ft.
Water discharge: Q = 169 cfs
Critical tractive force: τ_c = 0.0185 lb/ft^2 (τ_c = 0.06

Sediment Discharge $Q_s = \dfrac{10(\tau-\tau_c)Q\,S\,\gamma}{(\gamma_s-\gamma)\,d_{65}}$ $\qquad \dfrac{(\gamma_s-\gamma)\,d_{65}}{}$

Case	Number of Vegeta-tions N	Flow depth (ft) D	Average Velocity Based on Flow Area (ft/sec) U	Average Boundary Shear Stress (lb/ft^2) τ	Sediment Trans-port Rate (lb/sec) Q_s	Relative Sediment Trans-port Rate Q_s/Q_{sm}
B-I	48	2.36	2.207	0.0184	0.0	0.0
B-II	0	1.00	5.208	0.1248	72.676	1.000
B-III	24	1.77	2.942	0.0348	11.141	0.153
B-IV	24	1.80	2.893	0.0335	10.265	0.141
B-V	24	1.69	3.082	0.0386	13.726	0.189
B-VI	24	1.81	2.877	0.0331	9.984	0.137
B-VII	24	1.76	2.959	0.0353	11.443	0.15
B-VIII	24	1.80	2.893	0.0335	10.265	0.141

From Table 3-4 it may be concluded that: i) the various patterns or groupings of tall vegetations have a rather significant effect on the retardation of flow rates; ii) for the same number of tall vegetations or trees, the staggered grouping (Case VI) is the most effect pattern and Case III is the second best pattern in reducing sediment yields; iii) the staggered grouping (Case VI) is recommended for planting tall vegetation; and iv) the staggered grouping (Case VI) is not economical for the harvest of tall vegetation, in this case, some variation of Case III should perhaps be considered.

Example-II (Without the Restriction of Patch-Cut Grouping)

The most effective patterns for the harvest of 1/4, 1/2, 3/4, 7/8 tall vegetations are given in Fig. 3-23 and their effect in sediment yields are given in the following table (Table 3-5). Flow conditions are the same as Case A-I, Example I (Table 3-4).

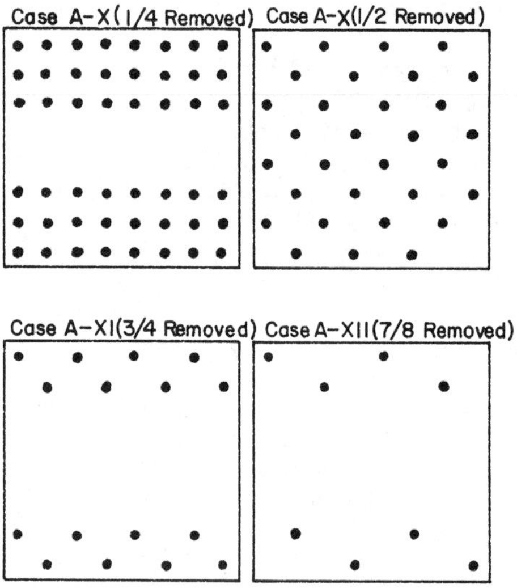

Fig. 3-23. Example II (Most Effective Groupings).

Table 3-5.   Summary of the Most Effective Pattern for Different
Number of Harvesting

Case	Number of Vegeta- tions N	Degree of Harvest- ing	Flow Depth (ft) D	Velocity Based on Flow Area (ft/sec) U	Average Boundary Shear Stress (lb/ft^2) τ	Sediment Transport Rate (lb/sec) Q_s	Relative Sediment Transport Rate Q_s/Q_{sm}
A-I	64	0	2.11	2.468	0.0235	4.225	0.047
A-IX	48	1/4	1.94	2.685	0.0284	8.298	0.093
A-X	32	1/2	1.75	2.976	0.0357	14.463	0.162
A-XI	16	3/4	1.44	3.617	0.0552	30.842	0.345
A-XII	8	7/8	1.23	4.234	0.0785	50.461	0.564
A-II	0	1	1.00	5.208	0.1248	89.447	1.000

NOTE;   Degree of harvesting $= \dfrac{\text{Number of Vegetation Harvested}}{\text{Total Number of Vegetation Before Harvesting}}$

From this example one may conclude that the degrees of harvesting have a rather significant effect on the retardation of flow.
Figure 3-24 shows the exponential trend of the relationship
between relative sediment transport rate and degree of harvesting for the various best effective vegetation grouping as
described in Table 3-5.   It must be stressed here that the
grouping pattern in this example may not be economical.   More
feasible patterns are already introduced in Example-I.

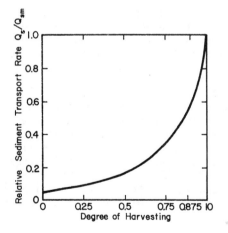

Fig. 3-24.   Example of Relationship Between Sediment Yields
and Degree of Harvesting for Various Best
Effective Pattern Flow Conditions Given in
Table 2.

Example-III. The variations of average boundary Shear
Stress τ with i) flow discharge Q ,
ii) plot bottom slope S , iii) size
of sediment d_{65} , and iv) diameter of
vegetation d .

The vegetation distribution of Case A-X as shown in Fig.
3-23 is used to examine the variations of τ with Q , S ,
d_{65} , and d . The results are shown in Fig. 3-25. From Fig.
3-25 one may draw the following conclusions. i) the average
boundary shear stress is not sensitive to the variation of
discharge and sediment size. However, it is much more sensitive
to the plot bottom slope and diameter of vegetation. ii) the
average boundary shear stress increases with increasing discharge, plot bottom slope and sediment size but decreases with
increasing diameter of vegetation (therefore, one may expect
that vegetation will have much more effect on sediment yield
as trees growing larger).

<u>Conclusions.</u>

A. The different patterns or groupings of tall vegetations
have a significant effect on retardation of flow rates and
sediment yields.

B. The retardation of flow rate due to tall vegetations,
whose heights are of the same order of magnitude as flow depth,
can be estimated from the present method if the spacing between
the vegetations is at least six diameters in the downstream direction and three diameters in the transverse direction. The
Reynolds number based on the vegetation diameter should be
less than 2×10^5 , although there is no evidence to indicate
that this method will not be applicable for other range of
Reynolds numbers.

C. Tall vegetations grouped into staggered patterns, are
much more effective in reducing flow rate than any other pattern
for the same number of tall vegetations. Thus if the main aim
of planting tall vegetations is for reducing flow rates and
sediment yield, these tall vegetations should be planted in
staggered patterns.

D. Since it is difficult to harvest tall vegetation to
make a staggered pattern, the next best thing is to harvest
tall vegetation in rows which are perpendicular to flow direction.

E. The average boundary shear stress on the bed is much
more sensitive to its change of plot bottom slope and the size
of vegetation than the variation of flow discharge and sediment
size. The retardation of boundary shear stress on the bed will
increase significantly as trees grow larger. All these effects
can be estimated quantitatively by a method presented here.

3.5. NOTATIONS

a   Height of roughness element above the floor

b   Width of roughness element perpendicular to the flow
direction

$b_{1/2}$ One-half of wake width where $u_1 = u_{max}/2$

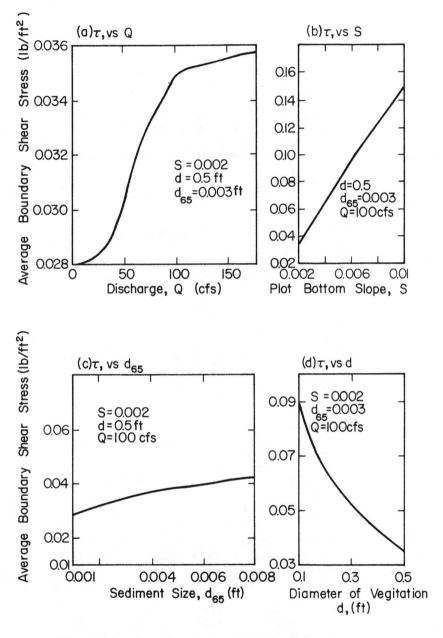

Fig. 3-25. Example of Partial Relationships of
τ , Q , S , d_{65} , and d (Case A-X).

3-45

$B(\ )$	Some function
c	Thickness of roughness element longitudinal to the flow direction
C	Chezy resistance coefficient
$\overline{C}_d$	Local coefficient of drag based on U_{oi}
$\hat{\overline{C}}_d$	Mean coefficient of drag based on U_o
$\hat{C}_{di}$	Measured mean drag coefficient based on the measured drag force
C_{dp}	Pressure coefficient defined by Eq. 3-12
d	Diameter of cylinder or vegetation
d_i	Diameter of ith cylinder
d_{65}	Size of the sediment on the bed of which 65% is finer
D	Depth of flow
f	Darcy-Weisbach friction coefficient
f^*	limiting Froude number
F	Optimization function
F_d	Froude number based on cylinder size
F_i	Drag force on ith cylinder
F_s	limiting Froude number F^*
F^*	Froude number based on depth of flow
g	Gravitational constant
h	Roughness element after bending
h_L	Energy loss in reach L
k_s	Representative roughness
L	Length of reach
ℓ	Longitudinal spacing between two successive
ℓ'	Turbulent mixing length
m	Adjusting factor or number of internal cylinders or vegetations
n	Manning's friction coefficient of number of cylinders involved
N	Total number of cylinders or vegetation
N_R	Reynolds number of flow
p	Local measured pressure
p_y	Static pressure for upstream undisturbed flow at y
Q	Water discharge
Q_s	Sediment discharge
R	Hydraulic Radius
$\overline{R}$	Cylinder Reynolds number based on Mean flow velocity
R_e	Local cylinder Reynolds number based on local flow velocity at level y
S	Bottom slope of channel or plot
t	Transverse spacings between two successive cylinders
u_i	Defect velocity in a wake due to ith cylinder
u_y	Upstream undisturbed flow velocity at y
u_{max}	Maximum defect velocity at the center of the wake, averaged over the depth of flow

u_*	Shear velocity
u_{total}	Total velocity defect due to upstream cylinders, averaged over depth of flow
U	Mean velocity of flow based on the channel flow area
U_i	The average approach velocity to the ith cylinder
U_y	The upstream undisturbed flow velocity at level y
$U_\infty(x)$	Reference free stream velocity at x from which the velocity defects are subtracted to obtain the actual velocity
$\overline{U}(x,z)$	Resultant point mean velocity at point (x,z) which is averaged over the depth of flow
W	Width of flume or plot
x	Longitudinal direction respective to flow
y	Vertical direction respective to the channel bottom
y_n	Depth of flow measured normal to the channel flow
z	Transverse direction respective to flow
α	Correction factor
$\overline{\alpha}$	Test size in hypothesis testing
β_i	Regression coefficient in regression equation
γ, γ_s	Specific weight of the fluid and solid respectively
H	Relative roughness height
σ	Inclination of channel
λ	Areal roughness concentration
$\lambda*$	Roughness concentration factor and represents the ratio of the sum of projected areas of roughness elements normal to mean flow direction to the total flow area
ν	Kinematic viscosity of water
ρ	Density of water
τ	Average boundary shear stress on bed
τ_c	Critical shear stress to move the sediment
Ω	Roughness geometry descriptor
θ	Angle of inclination of the channel

REFERENCES

Allen, H.J., and W.G. Vincenti, 1944, Wall interference in a two-dimensional flow wind tunnel with consideration of the effect of compressibility; NACA Report 782.

Apelt, C.J., and Isaacs, L.T. 1968, Bridge piers-hydrodynamic force coefficients; Journal of the Hydraulics Division, ASCE, Vol. 94, No. HY1, January, pp. 17-30.

Baines, W.D., 1965, Effect of velocity distribution on wind loads and flow patterns on buildings; Wind Effects on buildings and structures; Vol. 1, Her Majesty's Stationary Office, London, England, pp. 197-224.

Bearman, P.W., 1968, The flow around a circular cylinder in the critical Reynold's number regime, NPL-Aero 1257, also see STAR No. N69-13290.

Bergelow, O.P., Brown, G.A., Hull, H.L., and Sullivan, F.W., 1950, Trans. ASME 72, 881.

Bierman D., and Herrnstein, W.H., Jr., 1933, Interference between struts in various combinations, NACA Report No. 468.

Chu, Hsien, and Streeter, V.L., 1949, Fluid flow and heat transfer in artificially roughened pipes; Final rept., Proj. 4918, Illinois Inst. Technology, Chicago, p. 62.

Chilton, T.H., and Genereaus, R.P., 1933, Trans. AICLE 29, 161.

Colman, E.A., 1953, Vegetation and watershed management; Ronald Press

Dalton, C., and Masch, F.D., 1968, Influence of secondary flow on drag forces; Journal of Engineering Mechanics Division, ASCE, Vol. 94, No. EM5, Proc. Paper 6193, October.

Eskinazi, S., 1959, Mixing of wakes in a turbulent shear flow; NASA TN-D-83.

Gran Olsson, R., 1936, Geschurndigkeits - and Temperaturverteilung hinter einum Gitter bei turbulenter Strumung. S. fur; Angew Math. Mech 16, pp. 257-274.

Grimson, E.D., 1937, Trans. ASME 59, 583.

Gunter, A.Y., and Shaw, W.A., 1945, Trans. ASME 67, p. 643.

Hill, P.G., Schaub, U.W., and Senoo, Y., 1963, Turbulent wakes in pressure gradients; Journal of Applied Mechanics, Vol. 30, pp. 518-524.

Hoerner, S.F., 1958, Fluid dynamic drag; published by author.

Hsieh, T., 1964, Resistance of cylinder piers in open-channel flow; Journal of the Hydraulics Division, ASCE, Vol. 90, pp. 161-173.

Hung, C.S., 1968, A preliminary study on the res stance of cylinders in open channel flow; unpublished report, Colorado State University (study made at the request of H.W. Shen).

Isaacs, L.T., 1965, Hydrodynamic forces on surface piercing circular cylinders and flat plates; Thesis presented to University of Queensland at St. Lucia, Brisbane, Australia, in partial fulfillment of the requirements for the degree of Master of Science in Engineering.

Iwasa, Y., 1954, The criterion for instability of steady uniform flows in open channels; Memoir, Faculty of Engineering, Kyoto University, Vol. 16, No. VI.

Jakob, M., 1938, Trans. ASME 60, 381.

Johnson, J.W., 1944, Rectangular artificial roughness in open channels; Am. Geophys. Union Trans., pt. 6, p. 906-912.

Kays, W.M., London, A.L., Lo, R.K., 1954, Trans. ASME 76, 387.

Koloseus, H.J., 1958, The effect of Free-Surface instability on channel resistance; Ph.D. Thesis, The University of Iowa, Iowa City, Iowa.

Koloseus, H.J., and Davidian, J., 1966, Free surface instability corrections and roughness-concentration effects on flow over hydrodynamically rough surfaces; Laboratory studies in open channel flows, U.S. Geological Survey Water-Supply Paper 1592-C,D, U.S. Government printing office, Washington, D.C.

Knudsen, J.G., and Katz, D.L., 1958, Fluid dynamics and heat transfer, McGraw-Hill Co.

Kouwen, N., 1970, Flow retardance in vegetated open channels, Thesis presented to the Faculty of Graduate Studies of the University of Waterloo in partial fulfillment of the requirements for the degree of Docotr of Philosophy in Civil Engineering.

Laird, A.D.K., Johnson, C.S., and Walders, R.W., 1959, Water forces on accelerated cylinders, Journal of Waterways and Harbors Division, ASCE, Vol. 85, March, pp. 99-119.

Masch, F.D., and Moore, W.L., 1963, Drag forces in velocity gradient flow; ASCE, Vol. 128, Part 1, pp. 48-64.

Mattingly, G.E., 1962, An experimental study of the three-dimensionality of the flow around a circular cylinder, Institute of Fluid Dynamics and Applied Mathematics, University of Maryland, Tech. Note BN-295.

Molchanov, A.A., 1963, The hydrological role of forest; Israel program for Scientific Translations, Jeruseleum.

Nikuradse, J., 1933, Stromgsgesetze in rauhen Rohren: VDI-Forschungsheft 361. [Translation, NACA Tech. Memo. 1292, November 1950.]

Petryk, S., 1969a, Drag on cylinders in open channel flow; Dissertation presented at Colorado State University, Fort Collins, Colorado, in partial fulfillment of the requirements for the degree of Doctor of Philosophy.

Petryk,S., 1969b, Discussion of Dalton and Masch's paper; Journal of Engineering Mechanics Division, ASCE, Vol. 95, No. EM5, October, pp. 1288-1289.

Petryk, S., and Shen, H.W., 1971, Direct measurement of shear stress in a flume; Journal of the Hydraulics Division, ASCE, Vol. 97, HY6, Tech. Notes, June.

Rouse, H., 1965, Critical Analysis of open-channel resistance; Proc. Paper 4387, J. of Hyd. Div., Vol. 91, No. HY4, ASCE, July.

Sayre, W.W., and Albertson, M.L., 1961, Roughness spacing in rigid open channels; Journal of the Hydraulics Division, ASCE, Vol. 87, No. HY3, May, pp. 121-150.

Schlichting, Hermann, 1936, Experimentelle Untersuchungen zum Rauhigkeit's problem: Ingenieur-Archiv., v. 7, no. 1, p. 1-34. [Translation, NACA Tech. Memo. 823, April 1937].

Schlichting, H., 1960, Boundary layer theory; McGraw-Hill Co., 4th Edition, pp. 590-604.

Schlichting, H., 1968, Boundary layer theory; McGraw Hill Co., 6th edition.

Schwind, Richard G., 1962, The three-dimensional boundary layer near a strut; Gas Turbine Laboratory Report No. 67, Massachusetts Institute of Technology, May.

Sevik, M., 1966, Effect of turbulence on vortex shedding from circular cylinders; Meeting on Ground Wind Load Problems in Relation to Launch Vehicles, NASA Langley Research Center, June, pp. 22.1-22.19.

Shen, H.W., 1972, Sedimentation and contaminant criteria for watershed planning and management; Completion Report No. 31, Environmental Resources Center, Colorado State University, June, Chapter 2.

Tripp, William, 1936, Friction losses in an artificially roughened rectangular channel; Jour. Aeronaut. Sci., v. 4 P. 10-11.

Wallis, R.P., 1939, Photographic study of fluid flow between banks of tubes, Engineering 148, October 13, pp. 423-425.

Waterways Experiment Station, 1953, Roughness standards for hydraulic models report No. 4 study of finite boundary roughness in rectangular flumes, U.S. Army Corps of Engineers, Vicksburg, Mississippi, Tech. Memorandum No. 2-364.

Yano, M., 1966, Turbulent diffusion in a simulated vegetative cover; Dissertation presented at Colorado State University, Fort Collins, Colorado, in partial fulfillment of the requirements for the degree of Doctor of Philosophy.

Chapter 4

THE RHEIN STUDY

by

Hans A. Einstein, Emeritus Professor, University of California,
Berkeley, California.

Chapter 4

THE RHEIN STUDY

4.1. INTRODUCTION

The Rhein above the Lake of Constance is not a particularly
large or otherwise important stream, and its problems are very
similar to those of many other mountain streams. I have chosen
it as the subject of this lecture, because of the study connected with the solution of the problem, rather than the problem
itself. In contrast to most of the studies connected with
sediment transport in this country since the Second World War
which are mostly concerned with large streams carrying sand as
bed load, the Rhein is a mountain stream with a gravel bed and
it carries this gravel as bed load. Such streams were very
actively studied between the two World Wars in all countries
along the Alps, but this particular study stands out by the
thoroughness with which all possible aspects of the problem
were covered. This thoroughness was not so much predicated by
the particularly great importance of the object (there are many
other streams of similar character that may have much greater
economic significance) but it was rather the conviction of
one man who felt that such a study was long overdue which should
be able to test the rules, methods and equations by which such
streams could be described and their behavior predicted. This
man was Professor E. Meyer-Peter.

An excellent engineer, Meyer-Peter was long convinced that
problems of this sort could be solved only with the help of a
hydraulic laboratory. For years he tried to convince the
direction of the Swiss Federal Institute of Technology in Zurich
(ETH) that the school was the proper place for such a national
laboratory and finally succeeded. In 1930 it was opened and in
the following year the writer joined the staff and was soon
chosen to organize a general study on the transport of sediment,
with particular emphasis on conditions as they existed in the
particular reach of the Rhein River. Very little was known at
that time about the quantitative description of sediment motion
except that there were about 20 odd formulas in the literature
for the prediction of bed-load motion, that Froude's law of
similarity applied to the flow and that some light weight
materials such as soft coal produced workable models for the
study of sediment carrying streams. Meyer-Peter decided already
long before the laboratory was built, that similarity and the
application of sediment-transport laws to rivers could be
established in a dependable form only if materials and flows
could be duplicated in the laboratory in close to full size.
He incorporated in the basic design of the laboratory a flume
with a 2.0 x 2.0 m cross section and a 50 m usable channel
length (which was much later extended to twice that length).
He hoped that by comparison of the results obtained in this
large flume with those of about five times smaller dimensions

4-1

it should be possible to establish once and for all the various
conditions of similarity governing sediment motion. This was
to some degree achieved, and permitted the derivation of the
rules governing the flow and sediment motion in mountain streams
such as the Rhein.

4.2. THE FLUME EXPERIMENTS

Before the large-scale flume experiments were conducted it
was attempted to foresee the necessary ranges of the variables
by comparison with the results of previous experiments conducted
in the various laboratories of Europe and America. Using the
formulas derived there and the Froude similarity law the predi-
cations varied so much from one source to another that this
approach was soon abandoned. It was decided instead to use a
more or less uniform sediment of an average sieve diameter of
28.65 mm and to test this material through for water depths of
0.34 to 1.10 m and transportation rates from 0.01 to 2.6 kg/m/
sec. This is the weight of sediment transported per meter of
width and per second with the weight measured under water. It
was expected that this range of transport rates is sufficient
to cover all conditions naturally occurring in the river. For
the results see Meyer-Peter (1934), Muller (1943) and Johnson
(1943). The small scale experiments were conducted with sediment
of 5.21 mm mean sieve diameter for water depths between 6 and
24 cm and rates of transport between 0.002 and 0.274 kg/m/sec.
All sediments of these two series had a specific gravity of
2.65 - 2.70. In addition a series each was conducted for soft
coal (s = 1.25) and baryt (s = 4.22) of the same size. For
results see Meyer-Peter (1934), Muller (1943), and Johnson (1943).
It was attempted to describe by the results of these flume
experiments a relationship between the rates of sediment transport and the corresponding flow conditions after equilibrium
has been reached in each case. Equilibrium was herefore
defined as the condition under which all along the flume the
time average rate of sediment motion was the same. This could
unfortunately not been checked. The condition for equilibrium
was therefore reduced to the condition that the average rate
at which sediment was deposited at the downstream end of the
flume had to be the same as that at which sediment was fed to
the flume at the upper end. This condition was usually rather
easily satisfied, but it was unfortunately observed that the
flow condition along the flume was not uniform, particularly at
the larger depths. Near the point of the sediment supply at the
upper end of the flume the bed was usually low, from there it
was rising in the downward direction to culminate in a hump up
to one third to the flume length down and from there it would
drop slowly towards the downstream end of the flume, sometimes
going through some more fluctuations. It may be understood that
this description refers to the time-average profile and has
nothing to do with the travelling bars and waves of the bed.
The water surface underwent an opposite set of changes, but

usually of smaller magnitude. The water depth undergoes strong changes along such a profile, and with it the average water velocity. As the water surface slope in some cases was much different from the bed slope, both seemed to be unfit to describe the flow condition individually. It was thus attempted to calculate point by point the energy level of the flow and it was found to everybody's astonishment, that the points laid with the accuracy of the determination on straight lines defining accurately an energy slope.

There was still some question as to the reliability of this slope. After some discussions it was decided that this entire difficulty with the profiles was probably just an entrance effect of the flume and that in effect the flume was too short for the water depths used. But at the time the length could not be changed and the large water depths were essential for the study. It was thus decided, that the entrance effect must depend on the particular velocity distribution at the entrance of the flume and possibly on the strength and distribution of the turbulence there. Both could be changed drastically by introducing appropriate screens at the upper end of the flume. The screen consisted of five vertical bars, wide at the bottom and gradually narrowing towards the water surface. By running the identical flows and sediment rates at the same water depth with and without screen an entirely different set of profiles were obtained for the bed and the water surface, but the energy slope changed only by about 1% which was within the accuracy of the calculation and of the measurements. It was decided, therefore, that the description of the bedload equation to be derived from the measurements should include only those parameters which were significant in the entrance sections, too, i.e. the sediment size, the sediment rate, the discharge of the flow and the energy slope, The resulting relationship is today known in the literature as the Meyer-Peter formula, in honor of the man who mastminded the entire study of the Rhein.

But the entrance effect of the flumes was not the only difficulty experienced at the analysis of the flume experiments. It was soon found that the Froude similarity appeared to hold not only for the flow, but also for the sediment motion (the sediments used were sufficiently large to preclude any suspension to occur!) except that some significant, more or less systematic deviations occurred between the various water depths. The significant influence of the energy slope indicates the importance of the energy dissipation in the sediment-transportation process. It was suspected, therefore, that the energy dissipation process somehow influences the transport process. It appeared somewhat inconsistent in that case, that the description of the friction should be based on the hydraulic radius as the characteristic length, while the sediment transport should depend on the water depth, as most tractive-force formulas are formulated. It appeared much more consistent to express the tractive force in terms of the hydraulic radius, too. This gave an occasion to study the entire concept of the hydraulic radius somewhat more basically. The result was a paper (Einstein, 1934) in which the physical concept of the hydraulic radius was analyzed. It was argued that the entire flow may be divided into units, whereby each unit consists of a unit frictional surface area and of a section of the flow volume adjacent to it, such that the two represent a unit from the point of view of energy dissipation. It is assumed that one can somehow divide the entire flow volume into units such that no momentum is transmitted from one unit to the next. In general this is impossible since all waves are transmitted in this way. But in a steady uniform flow it is thinkable that all the components of the weight of the fluid in direction of the flow are transmitted to a corrssponding unit of the frictional wall only, and that the turbulence created there is then diffused out into the fluid unit. In a homogeneous flow such as in a straight pipe of circular cross section all such double units are alike. The same friction equation with the same values of all the parameters for the double unit are the same as for the entire section. The hydraulic radius is thus the ratio between the volume unit and the frictional surface unit. If the latter is chosen to have the magnitude equal to unity, the hydraulic radius may be interpreted as the corresponding volume unit.

Most useful is the application of this thought to sections in which not all the frictional boundaries have the same character. For instance in a normal flume with a sediment bottom the frictional characteristics of the bed are basically different from those of the side walls. The first assumption that in such a section also double units can be established to describe the friction condition, and the second assumption, that those double units may be calculated exactly as if they were double units of a section consisting only of equal double units proved to give good results. On the basis of these assumptions one can predict the friction factor for a section in which various parts of the perimeter have different friction factors. While the original paper used exclusively the Manning equation, the same method is applicable to any combination of friction equations for the various parts of the section as follows:

$$f_m \ (v_m, \ S_m, \ k_m, \ R_m) = 0 \qquad (4-1)$$

the friction equation applicable to the m-th part of the section and p_m its perimenter then (Eq. 4-1) can be rewritten in the form:

$$f'_m \ (v_m, \ S_m, \ k_m) = R_m \qquad (4-2)$$

where v_m is the average velocity, S_m the energy slope, k_m the friction factor and R_m the hydraulic radius, all for the part m of the section. The part of the cross-sectional area pertaining to m is $A_m = p_m R_m$. From this one may conclude that the total corss-sectional area of the section

$$A = \Sigma \ A_m = \Sigma \ (p_m \cdot f'_m) = p \cdot f' \ (v, \ S, \ k) \qquad (4-3)$$

4-4

with the values without subscript referring to the entire
section as a unit. Since all units of the section reach from
the wall with zero velocity to the point of maximum velocity
it is reasonable to set $v = v_m$. Also the energy slope is
equal for all parts of the section, or $S = S_m$. This equation
(4-3) can be used to determine for a given section the representative friction factor k if the individual friction factors
k_m, their extents p_m, the slope S and the average velocity
v are known. If the same friction equation is used for all
parts m and for the entire section, v and S may drop out.

4.3. THE BEDLOAD FORMULA

The meyer-Peter formula was first published for gravel only
in dimensional form. (1934). In this form it applies only to
coarse sediment of specific gravity 2.65 to 2.70. Its constants
are correct in metric units only, but since that was the general
method of expression in Switzerland, this form was the simplest
possible for practical use by engineers. It had the form of
eq. (4-4).

$$S \cdot q^{2/3}/d = a + b \cdot g^{2/3}/d \qquad (4-4)$$

Herein are S the energy slope, q the flow discharge per
unit of width and time, d the grain diameter, g the
sediment rate per unit of width and time and a and b some
constants. The two constants were found to remain the same as
long as the density of the sediment remains the same and none
of the grains go into suspension. For the finer grain sizes of
Gilbert (1914) for instance, the gravel constants do not apply.
Figure 4-1 shows the results of the ETH gravel experiments as
$S \cdot q^{2/3}/d$ against $g^{2/3}/d$ and it may readily be seen that for
most points the straight line relationship of Eq. (4-4) is
quite satisfactory. Systematic deviations occur only at the
very low sediment rates. Significant transport will occur
at flows considerably below the zero-intersection point of the
straight line of Eq. (4-4). This indicates that Eq. (4-4)
cannot be used, for instance, for the design of riprap.
Equation (4-4) is dimensional, but can always be made
dimensionally correct by giving the constants a and b the
proper dimensions. The three terms of the equation can individually be made dimensionless by proper introduction of the
constant gravitational acceleration G, the specific gravity
s of the sediment, and the specific weight γ of the fluid,
if q and g are measured in weight per unit of width and
time.
With the help of the experiments that use coal and baryt
as sediment a correction can be introduced for the terms of
the equation for sediment densities different from that of
quartz. This was done in the form

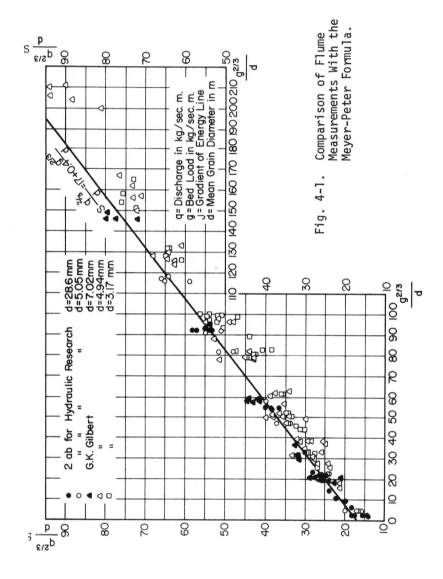

Fig. 4-1.   Comparison of Flume Measurements With the Meyer-Peter Formula.

$$\frac{S \cdot q^{2/3}}{d \cdot G^{1/3} \gamma^{2/3}} = 0.0446 \ (s-1)^{10/9} + 0.336 \left[\frac{g^{2/3}(s-1)^{1/3}}{G^{1/3} d \ \gamma^{2/3}} \right] (4-5)$$

in which G is the acceleration of gravity and γ the specific weight of water. To my knowledge this exact form was never published. The two brackets contain dimensionless combinations which may be calculated in any consistent set of units. This form of the equation is particularly useful in application to the transport of light weight materials in models. Meyer-Peter indicated later that the first term of Eq. (4-5) must be corrected by excluding the part of the energy dissipation which is attributed to the presence of bars (bar resistance), but this consideration was not important in the Rhein River with its rather coarse sediment.

4.4. RIVER OBSERVATIONS

The valley bottom through which the particular reach of the Rhein flows is shown in the map of Fig. 4-2. It has been heavily developed agriculturally over the centuries and local interests have built dikes in order to reduce the flood danger. Under natural conditions most of the coarse sediment was deposited upstream and only the fine sediment components reached the lower part of the valley, close to the lake. The alluvial deposits in the valley bottom contain heavy layers of peat, reducing greatly the stability of the ground as a foundation for flood protection works. All developments were greatly hampered by the fact that the river in this reach makes the boundary between Austria and Switzerland, forcing all decisions and designs to be developed by an international commission which to a great part consisted of non-technical members. Many decisions were rather politically motivated and usually long delayed by uncertainty and formalities.

The more of the upstream river reaches were contained by dikes, the farther downstream did the heavy sediment progress and at the time of this study, the deposition of gravel had advanced in the study reach to a degree that the capacity of the channel was considerably below the design capacity in spite of the two large cut-offs which had been built in the first quarter of the century. For the extent of the deposits see Fig. (4-3) cross sections in the upper cut-off. It was one of the main aims of this study to find a feasible solution which would permit to reverse this development. A channel section was to be found which increased significantly the carrying capacity of the river with the available slopes. Hopefully, the river should clean out its bed or at least be able to transport the naturally supplied sediment after the channel has been dredged to the proposed depth.

For this purpose a large number of measurements and observations were made in the prototype. Repeated cross sections and longitudinal profiles were established, discharges and the

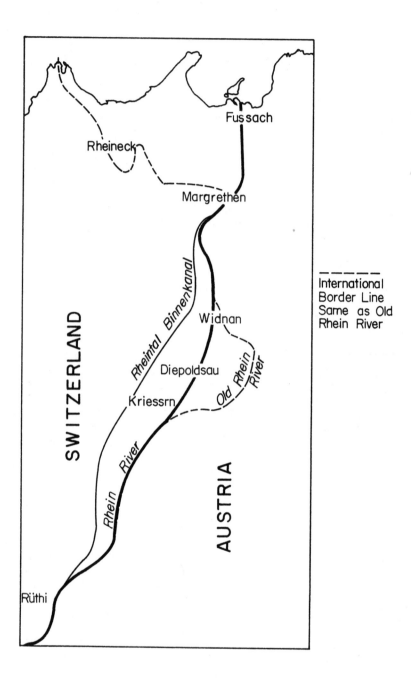

International
Border Line
Same as Old
Rhein River

Fig. 4-2. Map of the Rhein Valley Above
the Lake Constance

4-8

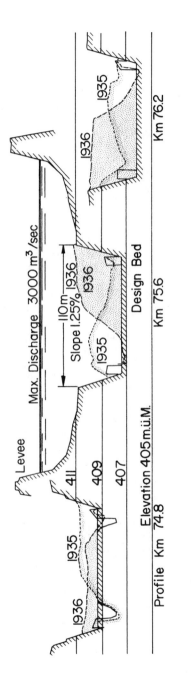

Fig. 4-3. Characteristic Cross Sections Showing the Degree of Aggradation

4-9

corresponding water surfaces recorded, which are the normal
observations describing the shape and flows in a natural river.
But that was not sufficient to solve the problem at hand; considerable amounts of information were required in connection with
the sediment characteristics in the reach. The composition of
the bed was described by taking large samples of the material
(about one m^3 each) from exposed bars and by sieving them in
the field. But also the transport rates were directly measured.
The suspended load was determined by means of sampler, home
built for the purpose, which collected the sample through a
brass tube into the innertube of a football. This sampler
permitted sampling to within about 20 cm from the bed. But the
bed-load was measured, too, with a bed-load trap as it had been
developed and used by Ehrenberger (1931). This trap as seen
in Fig. 4-4 is a metal frame covered by screen of about 5 mm
openings, with the front side open to let water and sediment
enter freely. The sediment is deposited inside while the water
escapes through the screen. The sediment load was sampled from
one of the bridges which was fortunately located at one of the
few permanent bars where the sediment load was not influenced by
the passage of large bars. Figure 4-5 shows that the sediment
transport follows a well defined function of the discharge from
which the annual transport can be derived by integration. Most
interesting is the fact that the composition of the bars is
almost identical to that of the transport. This indicates that
the bed-load transport can be equated with the movement of the
exposed bars while the sediment in the scour holes may be different, but seems to contribute only a small part of the transport. Both the suspended load and the bed-load were integrated
over the measurements of the year 1936 and it was found that
the suspended load including the grain sizes below 5 mm amounted
to 5,000,000 tons (metric) or about 98% of the total while the
bed-load including the sizes above 5 mm amounted to only 91,000
tons or about 2%. But since it is the 2% which are responsible
for the build-up of the bed, it is the bed-load which was
studied most intensely. Very interesting is the fact that the
measurements show a definite lack of grain sizes between 0.6
and 3 mm. The larger sizes and the smaller sizes are much
heavier represented. The question was raised if these sizes
are actually lacking or if their lack is just the expression
of a systematic mistake of the sampling procedure. If these
sizes are heavily concentrated near the bed their representation
in the suspended samples would be significantly reduced since
the bottom 20 cm are not sampled. In the bed-load they are not
represented since they can leave the sampler with the water
through the screen. However it was not worth while to study
this question more in detail because these sizes are not important in the build-up of the bed. More important was the
question of the efficiency of the bed-load sampler which
directly affects the rate at which bed material is moving.

Fig. 4-4. Models 1:2.5, 1:5 and 1:10 of the Bed-Load Sampler

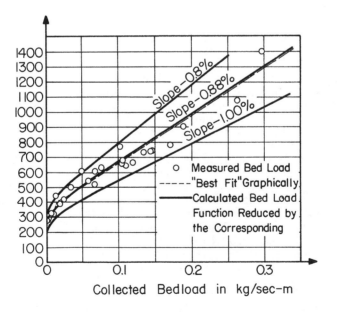

Fig. 4-5. Measured River Bed-Load Rates Plotted
Against The Discharge

4 -11

4.5. CALIBRATION OF THE BED-LOAD SAMPLER (EINSTEIN, 1937)

Any sampler must be calibrated for useful application, but this is particularly important for bed-load samplers, which interfere greatly with the local flow conditions due to their bulky design. This fact was well known to their designers and users and they developed a method by which such a "calibration" could be performed in the field. The results of such a "calibration" is given in Fig. 4-6. The left major part of this figure shows in chronologic order the results of a continuous series of measurements at the same point of the river. The sampling duration of each measurement is changed cyclically from 60 sec to 40 sec, 20 sec, 10 sec, 5 sec and starting again with 60 sec etc. The results are plotted in kg/m/sec and are therefore directly comparable. All samples with the same collection time are then connected by a curve and averaged. The averages are plotted in the right hand part of the graph as a function of the sampling time. The rates decrease very distinctly from the small to the large sampling times and previous users (Muhlhofer, 1933) had concluded that this decrease was to be attributed to the gradual filling of the sampler which caused an increasing resistance to the flow and to the motion of the approaching particles. This explanation lead to the conclusion that the actual transport should be obtained by extrapolating the curve to zero sampling time, in the case of the given calibration somewhat above 0.50 kg/m/sec.

This explanation appeared to be somewhat artificial in view of the fact that the total amount of sediment collected in the sampler in each individual operation was only a very small percentage of the sampler volume and could hardly have such a strong influence on the approaching flow. It was decided, therefore, to duplicate the calibration in the large sediment flume of the hydraulic laboratory in Zurich, where the extension of the sediment-transport experiments were in progress using sediment mixtures. A model of the sampler (see Fig. 4-4) was built and used there in exactly the same manner as the large one was used in the river. To everybody's astonishment the sample time had no influence in the laboratory. Something had to be basically different in the river to cause this curve, to develop. The change of scale had been taken in account in every respect. The sampler was also raised and lowered by a vertical cable and held in place in the direction of the flow by a sloping cable. But there was a difference. The horizontal cable was in the laboratory anchored against a solid plank while it was anchored at the river to a long horizontal cable spanning the stream. In the laboratory it was anchored rigidly while the support in the prototype was elastic. In order to test the influence of this elasticity a spring was introduced between the plank and the cable in the flume. The result was as expected: the efficiency dropped with the sampling time and it was the long duration efficiency which equalled that without spring. In order to eliminate the bad effect of the elasticity of the

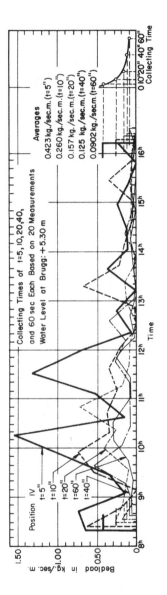

Fig. 4-6. Continuous Sampling in One Point for the Construction of "Calibration" Curve

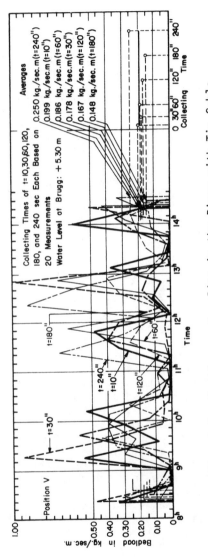

Fig. 4-7. Continuous Sampling in the River with Tie Cable

4-13

cross-river cable in the prototype, it was pulled downstream towards the bridge by means of an additional cable which prevented all major horizontal motions of the cross cable. (See Fig. 4-7.)

Observation in the laboratory of the elastic support showed that the sampler on its way down through the high-velocity part of the vertical is pulled downstream and the elastic support is more extended than corresponds to the lower velocities near the bed. The sampler approaches the bed moving upstream and literally shovels bed material into its opening. This process has no connection to the sediment transport in the stream and must be prevented.

With the shoveling prevented the efficiency of the sampler was somewhat dependent on the grain size of the sediment and on the sediment rate, but it was decided to apply to the river measurements and average value of 45%. As the sampler is used in one point of a steadily flowing stream for a considerable number of times the individual samples vary strongly in size and range from zero to many times the size of the average sample due to the passing of sand or gravel waves. The size distribution of the samples is fully random and their distribution and frequency can be described by probability considerations.

4.6. THE MODEL EXPERIMENTS FOR THE DESIGN OF THE RIVER CROSS SECTION. (MEYER-PETER, 1937)

The flume experiments with the gravel and the corresponding smaller sizes of sediment proved the fact that at least for these materials the Froude similarity does not only apply to the flow parameters but that the sediment transport follows the same rules. The use of the model study for the design of an alluvial channel of this kind is possible, therefore, and the rules of similarity are known. For practical reasons such as space, cost and necessary time it was necessary to reduce the model 1:100 with respect to the prototype. With such a reduction the sediment sizes would become an average of 0.28 mm in the model and experience proved that for such small sizes the Froude similarity does not apply any more to the transport equations. Also a time scale of 1:10 becomes prohibitive for experiments in which many years of flow sequence must be duplicated.

It was already well known at that time that with the use of lighter sediment materials both of these drawbacks can be avoided, particularly crushed soft coal was often used in those years. The combination of soft coal (s = 1.25) and the scale reduction of 1:100 had been used successfully before. It was thus decided to apply this combination again but it was still necessary to determine the distortion of the grain size and of the time scale. The grain size was chosen such that the sediment began to move at corresponding flow rates (Einstien and Muller, 1939). This could be determined by calculation on the basis of the flume experiments.

More difficult was the determination of the sediment time-
scale. First it was decided to use in the model a sediment mixture which was similar to that in the river bed, but reduced in
size according to the above mentioned similarity calculation.
Then such a bed was filled into the river model and the transport rates determined for equilibrium at various discharges.
Hereby it was observed that the bar pattern of the bed developed
differently at each flow, but at none of the flows it duplicated
the bar patterns of the prototype. That was not very promising,
but there was still the hope that a sequence of flows as they
occur in the river in an average year may behave differently.
This was actually the case. Not only developed an entirely
different bed pattern but this pattern would change with the
time scale applied to the hydrograph. At the time scale 1:360
(one day in the prototype = 4 minutes in the model) gave a bar
pattern very similar to that in the river. From the point of
view of the practicality of the model study this was very
acceptable as one year could be reproduced in less than 6 hours
as not all days of the year had flows sufficiently high to move
the sediment. It is most interesting that at this time scale
corresponding volumes of sediment were moved in corresponding
times. (Einstein and Muller, 1939).

The river had already at that time a double cross section
consisting of a lower center channel and shallower over-bank
areas on both sides. The model studies showed convincingly
that the existing bed width of 90 m of the center channel is
not the best solution, but that a narrower center channel of
70 m bed width had a considerably higher sediment capacity,
particularly if the secondary bank between center channel and
overbank is developed into an overflow levee. Because of the
political difficulties it was not possible to make these
changes soon. It was thus decided to continuously dredge a
part of the natural sediment load from the river in an upstream
section. Today, after continuing dredging (the gravel is
commercially used) and the proposed narrowing of the center
channel the river appears to be in equilibrium at a sufficiently
low position of the bed to guarantee the necessary flow capacity.

4.7. CALCULATION OF THE SEDIMENT LOAD IN THE RIVER (MULLER,
1937)

Particularly for design purposes it is always much easier
to make some calculations rather than to be forced to determine
the behavior of each proposed solution by a model study. It
was for this reason that attempts were made to find methods by
which at least some of the results of the model study could be
predicted. The flume experiments had established the laws for
the unit width of the sediment transport. It is important to
realize that formulae such as the Meyer-Peter equation predict
only the total amount of the transport but not its composition.
It is always assumed that the composition of the transport is the
same as that of the bed. It has already been mentioned that at

least the composition of the bars in the river was very similar
to that of the measured transport. The low part of the bed
between bars is usually coarser than the bars. The composition
of the transport on a flat bed may not be the same as that of
the bed. There a calculation method may be required which
determines the rates for the individual grain sizes separately.

The question arose, how the bed-load equation which has
been derived for two-dimensional conditions, can be applied to
a river channel with strongly developed three-dimensional bars.
An attempt of calculating simply with an average water depth
failed. The measured sediment rates could not be duplicated.
The next try was rather successful. It was based on the
assumption that due to the non-linearity of the relationships
the mean alone was not sufficient to describe the transport.
The deviations from the mean were introduced in the form of a
cross section which represented the frequency curve of the
various depths. This curve was obtained by integrating over
a river reach the areas with constant depth and by assessing
parts of the channel width proportional to those areas to the
individual depths. This section is then divided into vertical
strips which are calculated as independent sections. The
result for the individual strips is meaningless since the
deepest sections contribute the strongest transport while in
reality the deep scour holes have no transport at all. The
total transport through the section comes out rather accurately
as may be seen in Fig. 4-5 in which the heavy curve gives the
values calculated in this fashion while the rings give the
measured points corrected according to the calibration. This
method was used to compare various solutions, but can be applied
only if the statistical distribution of the water depths is
known.

4.8. SUMMARY

1. The reach of the Rhein River described here is a
mountain stream with a gravel bed of 28 mm average grain size.
The channel is improved but was at the time of the study steadily
aggrading. This should be checked and possibly reversed.

2. A set of flume experiment in two scales, one close to
prototype scale, the other about 5 times smaller (in linear
scale) led to the Meyer-Peter formula for bed-load transport.
This formula satisfied the Froude similarity between different sizes of sediment.

3. A rule was derived according to which the shear stress
could be divided among different parts of the perimeter with
different roughness.

4. Systematic river measurements of the geometry, the flow
conditions and of the sediment transport were carefully coordinated with the studies in the laboratory.

5. The grain-size composition of the bed-load transport
appears to be almost identical to that of the large gravel bars.

6. The calibration of the bed-load sampler proved the suspension of the sampler to be very important for the quality of the results.

7. The model study of the river channel led to the establishment of similarity rules for the transport of distorted bed material.

8. A stronger concentration of the medium discharges in the main center channel increased the transporting capacity of the river considerably.

9. For the calculation of the bed-load transport in a channel with strongly developed alternate bars of considerable height the assumption of an evenly distributed shear stress over the bed is insufficient; the variation of the shear stress must be introduced, for instance as a variation of the water depth.

10. The figures are reproduced from the papers quoted as references.

REFERENCES

Ehrenberger, R., 1931, Direkte Geschiebemessungen an der Donau
bei Wien und deren bisherige Ergebnisse; Die Wasserwirtschaft, Wien, Heft 34.

Einstein, H.A., 1934, Der hydraulische oder Profil-Radius;
Schweizerische Bauzeitung, Vol. 103, Nr. 8, 24 Febr.

Einstein, H.A., 1937, Die Internationale Rheinregulierung von
der Illmundung bis zum Bodensee. - IV Die Eichung des
im Rhein verwendeten Geschiebefangers; Schweizerische
Bauzeitung, Vol. 110, Nr. 12-15.

Einstien, H.A., und Muller, R., 1939, Ueber die Aehnlichkeit
bei flussbaulichen Modellversuchen; Schweizer Archiv fur
angewandte Wissenschaft und Technik, Heft Nr 8, Vogt-
Schild A.G., Solothurn.

Gilbert, G.K., 1914, Transportation of debris by running water;
U.S. Geol. Survey, Professional Paper Nr. 86.

Johnson, J.W., 1943, Laboratory Investigations on Bed-Load
Transportation and Bed Roughness; U.S. Dept. of Agriculture,
SCS-TP-50, March.

Meyer-Peter, E., Favre, H., and Einstein, H.A., 1934, Neuere
Versuchsresultate uber den Geschiebetrieb; Schweizerische
Bauzeitung, Vol. 103, Nr. 13, 31 March.

Meyer-Peter, E., Hock, E., und Muller, R. 1937, Die Internation-
ale Rheinregulierung von der Illmundung bis zum Bodensee.
- Beitrag der Versuchsanstalt fur Wasserbau an der E.T.H.
Zurich zur Losung des Problems; Schweizerische Bauzeitung,
Vol. 109, Nr. 16-18.

Muhlhofer, L., 1933, Schwebestoff - und Geschiebemessungen am
Inn bei Kirchbichl; Wasserkraft und Wasserwirtschaft, 4
Heft, 28. Jahrgang, 16 Febr.

Muller, R., 1937, Die Internationale Rheinregulierung von der
Illmundung bis zum Bodensee. - V. Ueberprufung des
Geschiebegesetzes und der Berechnungsmethode der Versuch-
sanstalt fur Wasserbau an der E.T.H. mit Hilfe der Direkten
Geschiebemessungen am Rhein. Schweizerische Bauzeitung
Vol. 110, Nr. 12-15.

Muller, R., 1943, Theoretische Grundlagen der Fluss-und Wild-
bachverbauungen; Mitteilunger der Versuchsanstalt fur
Wasserbau an der E.T.H. Zurich, Nr.4, Verlag AG Gebruder
Leemann & Co.

Chapter 5

REGIME PROBLEMS OF RIVERS FORMED IN SEDIMENT

By

T. Blench, Emeritus Professor of Civil Engineering,
University of Alberta,
Edmonton, Alberta

Chapter 5

REGIME PROBLEMS OF RIVERS FORMED IN SEDIMENT

5.1 INTRODUCTION

1. This chapter is an extended but relatively non-
technical background for two informal illustrated lectures.
Its topic is the quantitative relations that have been found
to exist in rivers, canals and laboratory flumes where, starting from an imagined arbitrary state, the imposition of an
average-steady flow of water and sediment has resulted in the
development of an average-steady channel whose boundary has
formed itself, at least partially, from the sediment in the
flow. The practical objectives are:-
    i. To provide, by graphs and formulas obtained from
observations, a means for estimating quantitatively the changes
that will develop in the breadth, depth, slope and meander
sizes of rivers after human interference with their regimes
(states).
    ii. To demonstrate and discuss, step by step, appli-
cations of the graphs and formulas to a hypothetical practical
situation important to conservationists in all disciplines.
    iii. To provide two special dimensionless graphs,
derived by coordinating and condensing depth and slope data
from the whole observed ranges in rivers, canals and laboratory flumes. They locate (a) present zones of information and
(b) the zones of variables in which different modes of transport occur. This information, confined to the second half
of the chapter, is for persons interested in the factual base
of the science -- which is necessarily inductive -- or in
specialised river engineering.
    2. The presentation is for a mixed audience of ecolo-
gists, engineers, geographers, geologists and hydrologists,
each assumed to have knowledge of basic mathematics and physics
at elementary university level, plus specialised knowledge of
a topic relevant to the fight to arrest and reverse the damage
that man has inflicted ignorantly on his environment in the
blind rush to create material "wealth". All require information on the sequence of changes that may occur in rivers
after they have been altered for Water Resources Projects or
other purposes. The reasons are that (a) both the intended
and actual behaviour of a river and its surroundings after it
has been manipulated for such purposes may be catastrophic
ecologically, economically or socially and (b) few engineering
schools give effective instruction in the relevant aspects of
river science.
    3. Given the graphs and a general appreciation of river
behaviour, objections to a project can be made on the grounds
that, according to the evidence of the behaviour of actual
rivers as recorded on those graphs, the river will not remain
as designed but will adjust itself to attain a certain fairly

predictable state whose consequences to the environment can be assessed by ecologists. Such objections can be refuted only on the grounds that interpretation of the graphs was incorrect, so should compel reference to experts in river regime. If the objections are overruled, though valid, they will remain on record along with the evidence of the graphs to ensure that responsibility for error will fall eventually in the proper place so that action will be taken to prevent a repetition.

4. In detail the whole topic is enormously diffuse and its science has to be inductive (22). Luckily most of the diffusion arises from "failing to see the channel for the theories" -- to parody the saying about the forest and the trees -- and appreciation of the broad facts of channel self-formation is automatic once they have been charted. So the presentation is rather like an Atlas of Channel Self-Formation which requires a relatively simple introduction and some annotations and descriptions -- not a treatise on surveying -- to make it rapidly useful to travellers who are fully competent to undertake journeys into the world of river regime. The "exploration, survey and mapping" side receives attention elsewhere (5, 9, 31, 32) and after paragraph 44. The observed facts are from (a) rivers, (b) irrigation canals and (c) laboratory flumes, and have been coordinated only recently. The difficulties that have delayed coordination include that (i) several factors are at work concurrently, (ii) some factors are not measureable usefully or at all, (iii) the motion is only average-steady, (iv) there are visibly different phases of bed movement (with dunes of different shapes and even directions of progression, or no dunes at all), (v) some of the sediment may pass in suspension and not be found on the bed while, at the same time, some rolls along the bed and some spends its time hopping off the bed (saltating) even as far as the free surface, (vi) experts disagree on classification of these different fractions of the moving sediment, (vii) rivers meander, and (viii) no single source of information covers the whole range of different behaviours.

5.2 BASICS OF RIVERS FORMED IN SEDIMENT

5. Salient features and terms. Most rivers form their channels in sediment deposited by themselves or by previous rivers. Only such channels will be considered in this chapter. Normally they transport a variety of sediment sizes and shapes while in flood, when formative action is vigorous. On long term the origin of the sediment is catchment erosion and the depository is a delta in a lake or sea. The finer sediments tend to deposit on the flood plains while the coarsest are found in the deep bed during floods; in general material sizes tend to decrease as elevation increases from deep bed to top of flood plain. The modes of motion in a bed are various (paragraph 4). At a section the quantity per second

of the finer sediment which is not found on the bed during a particular flow, so is practically washed through the channel, will be called the wash load or suspended load and can be measured with fair accuracy in the field. Some writers include saltating material (paragraph 4(v)) in suspended load (12). Suspended load is responsible for rapidly growing deltas. The common term bed-load implies, in a vague way, the load of sediment having sizes found on the bed. It may be reported as "measured" when only the parameters (slope, etc.) in one of the widely contradictory formulas of the subject (12) have been measured. Genuine measurement may be by traps laid on the bed (catching progressively less as they fill) or by samplers held above the bed where there has to be suspended load also. It is difficult to visualise what is caught over or on a duned bed, and the use of traps on gravel beds in flood is prohibitively expensive except in small streams. The writer recommends that figures quoted for bed-load should be taken as orders of magnitude and should never be used for research unless the user knows exactly how they were obtained. However, the term bed-load remains in use because bed-material size and load are major factors in determining depth and slope; like the distribution of roughnesses in pipe hydraulics it must be kept in mind despite the difficulty of attaching a figure to it. At one time and section different parts of a bed may have different sizes of sediment and may show different bed-forms (for example, dunes and no dunes); and the bed at one section will change its composition with time. Sand beds, however, are much less variable than gravel ones since sand, being the final product of natural elutriation, has a remarkably steady constitution. Rivers meander unless cut into relatively inerodible material; that is they develop migrating sinuosities that can be classified according to simple shapes and modes of progression (5, Chapter 2); if they do not progress the river does not meander but is tortuous. Within a meander pattern short reaches of relative straightness, with two definite banks, can usually be found. These are the reaches where observations for deducing self-formation formulas can be made; the deviations of river behaviour, as a whole, can then be related to the ideal behaviour of its straights. Braided streams, with multiple and rapidly changing channels, are not suitable for analysis. Definite banks, at about the angle of repose of their materials, do not partake of the peculiar formations of bed movement, for their circumstances are different and they may even be cohesive; they can be eroded and redeposited and have to resist the shearing and plucking action of the flow, and the pull of gravity, by forces of internal friction and cohesion.

6. River Equilibrium and Regime. If man leaves a river alone it may not change its average behaviour, or regime, appreciably for centuries, except in the deltaic region where changes may be too slow for the ordinary observer to notice over a couple of decades. This steadiness of regime gives the

wrong impression that rivers are rigid, so will not change
after engineering operations that alter breadth, depth, slope,
meander pattern and constitution of the water-sediment complex
(or just complex) as we shall call the combined water-sediment
mixture in future. In fact there is a close parallel between
rivers and the water-deposited fine-grained cliffs notorious
for slides after human activities put a load on them, alter
their moisture content, or dig away their toes. The cliffs
can stand for ages with the gravity force on the moist soil
in equilibrium with resistance to sliding but must displace,
sometimes dramatically though often by slow creep, as soon as
the balance of forces is upset. The rivers retain their
average regime, or state, because there is equilibrium between
gravity acting through the complex against resistance to
transportation and to disintegration of sides. As with the
cliffs reaction to a disturbance will produce a readjustment
more or less slowly but sometimes dramatically fast (10);
normally reaction will be obvious within a few years. A river
in equilibrium over a period is said to be "in regime" for
that period (5, paragraph 4.4). When changing from one
equilibrium to another it is changing its regime.
    7. The basic principle of regime. It is convenient now to
state the fact of equilibrium behaviour as a principle:-
        "In the absence of constraints, an average steady flow
        of water with an average steady flow of sediment will
        tend to produce, from an arbitrary state, a river of
        average steady behaviour (state, or regime)".
As a corollary, if anyone interfers with the water sediment
complex's quantity or nature, or alters dimensions, the river
must react by adjusting itself, slowly but surely, to a new
regime consistent with the new circumstances.
    8. Specific Gages as Regime Change Indicators. A powerful
method of demonstrating such adjustment is to plot, for some
specified discharge, the river gages of successive years
before and after an interference. Figure 5-1 is such a
"specific gage record" at a gaging station just downstream of
a barrage on a major Indian river (5, paragraph 4.5); as the
site was important, specific gages were recorded for several
levels of discharge and for rising and falling stages. It
shows that entrapment of sediment by the barrage was reflected
immediately by a drop of downstream specific gage, followed
by recovery as the trapped sediment filled and spilled from
the available storage; eventual recovery was to gages higher
than existed previously, since the river downstream of the
barrage suffered (i) reduced discharge due to abstraction of
water by canals and (ii) increased intensity of bed-load
because of sediment exclusion from canals.
    9. Obtaining graphs and formulas for equilibrium. Accord-
ing to the principle of paragraph 7 a logical direct way to
obtain regime relations from the observed equilibrium
dimensions of channels (according to the objective of paragraph 1(i)) is to observe measures of the equilibrium values

of: (i) - (ii) meander length and belt width, (iii) - (v) breadth, depth and slope, (vi)- (vii) bed form height and length, and plot them separately against, or correlate them with: (a) water discharge and properties, (b) sediment discharge and properties. Disregarding, till paragraph 10, the removeable difficulty that equilibrium values of river quantities are mostly undefineable time-means, the fact remains that the required plots have to ignore, in general, item (b) and the seldom-recorded viscosity of the water, which is the only relevant property in item (a). Three major reasons are: the bed and suspended load have different effects; the properties of each class of load are mainly unmeasureable and too numerous for practical correlations; the bed-load cannot be measured as a routine in canals or rivers. So there are two main restrictions on useful plotting. First, plots for canals and rivers must be (directly or indirectly) against water discharge Q alone. Second, because of this, the data for any one plot must be chosen so that the unmeasureables, namely sediment discharge and properties and water property, are as invariable as practical and unassociated with discharge. It is to be expected that plots from different groups of such data, with the same ranges of variables, will then have the same shapes but will occupy different positions on a single sheet of paper; that is, they will correspond to one functional form with different coefficients. The coefficients will represent, in some way, the effect of the unmeasureables. (Note to engineers. Compare with the derivation of a rigid boundary flow formula, for example Manning's. It was obtained virtually by plots of V against R and S in groups where the surface roughness in each looked the same. The discovery was that $AV = R^{2/3} S^{1/2}$ where A was fixed when "roughness" was fixed; so A was taken as the measure of roughness in the metric system and n = A/1.49 was used in the ft-sec. system to agree. If S is replaced by gS it is obvious that an arbitrary multiple of A could be regarded as the sixth root of a "roughness height" corresponding to some standard texture). Flume data, by their nature, cannot be grouped in the preceding manner; but they have an advantage of useable values of bed-load charge, despite use of unstandardised bed-materials and some disagreement on definition of bed-load (9, Conclusions). A dimensionless method of coordinating them with canal and river data is presented after paragraph 44 and shows that, unfortunately, they cannot be extrapolated.

10. The use of averages. (Note. The terms average or mean will be used in the general statistical sense" .. a more or less typical value of the variable, used to characterize the location of the distribution as a whole. It is in some sense a central value of the distribution ..." (24). If the law of distribution were known then an "equivalent uniform value" (5, paragraph 4.12) could be calculated; an average is a substitute that is hoped to approximate this perfect value). Continuing from paragraph 9, the difficulty of deciding the

time-mean discharge to use as an equilibrium value in plots
of river data is avoided by analysing groups whose individuals have, in addition to the properties already specified,
as nearly the same hydrograph shape as possible. Practically,
such a group will usually be within a selected river system,
as in the pioneering data collection and analysis of Ref. 27.
In such a group every individual time-mean discharge will be
about the same fraction of the unknown equivalent-uniform one,
so the shape of the data plot should be an approximation to
the shape that would be shown by steady flow conditions within
the same range of variables; the position of the plot will
depend on the joint effect of the various unmeasureables including hydrograph shape. Ref. 27 verifies this by plotting
breadth and depth against various levels of discharge (10%,
20% ....excedance) in each of several groups believed to be
fairly homogeneous. This explains why an engineer can talk
of a river's discharge, breadth, depth, etc., as if they were
steady; the average figures he has subconsciously in mind are
just as good for ordinary purposes as any other person's and,
in the terminology of paragraph 11, are his personal fractions
of dominant values.

   11. <u>Dominant (formative or equilibrium) discharge</u>. The
popular term "dominant discharge" expresses an intuition that
there is an equivalent-uniform discharge (paragraph 10) which
can be related to an equivalent-uniform quantity (for example,
channel breadth) or quantities by exactly the same functional
relations as exist between the counterparts in perfectly
steady flow. Obviously there must be different dominant discharges for different quantities in any one river. For
example, the dominant discharge for breadth in a straight
incised reach of a river whose suspended load is incompetent
to rebuild eroded banks is likely to be close to record flood
value. On the other hand the dominant discharge for slope
has been argued to be the discharge which, running for a long
time, would move the sediment actually carried by the river
in that time. Presumably this discharge would have to fall
rather centrally between the highest flow that does not displace the bed on the one hand, and high flood on the other;
also, its water sediment complex would have to correspond
roughly with that of the real river at that discharge; and
the tortuosity of the river would have to be retained. There
are some philosophical difficulties in the matter, such as an
intermediate discharge being unable to move the large gravel
moved by a very high flood, but the general idea seems
reasonable enough. The writer likes to use the term "dominant
discharge" because, like "the average man", it expresses a
common broad concept without pedantry. This average man
shares the schizophrenic tendencies of dominant discharge by
being different for weight, income, I.Q., etc.

   12. <u>Formulas and measures</u>. All ensuing formulas are,
deliberately, in terms of integral or simple fractional
indices. This acceptance of physicists' belief that natural

basic laws can be reduced to "simple" mathematical expressions
seems to have been introduced into mobile-bed hydraulics by
Gerald Lacey (25, 26). To exemplify, the formula

$$b = cQ^{1/2} \qquad (5-5)$$

from paragraph 19 states the tentative belief that the proper
measure of b , in a system in regime, varies as the square
root of the proper measure of Q if all factors other than
Q are held constant. The factual evidence for the belief is
a host of observations on canals and rivers by all sorts of
observers, under all sorts of circumstances and using various
measures of b (surface breadth, wetted perimeter, breadth
at half depth, etc.) and various time-mean discharges. The
initial evidence was from canals where the measure of b was
wetted perimeter and of Q was the full supply discharge
(which fluctuated a little in practice); the index was exceedingly close to 0.5. Canal data continue to support the finding. River data provide indices differing appreciably but,
on an average, giving no good reason for changing the index
from 1/2 to an adjacent "simple" one. In addition the formula
can be derived from others based on observation, and can be
rationalised in terms of common dynamically acceptable parameters although it cannot be deduced a priori (any more than
anything else in mobile boundary hydraulics can). Finally, it
is efficient in applications using the various measures in
common use (which is reasonable, since the various measures
of b are roughly in proportion to each other over considerable practical ranges of application).

5.3 SIMPLE REGIME RELATIONS, WITH APPLICATIONS

   13. Preliminary. This section starts with a composite
statement of the simple relations indicated, by observations,
to exist between proper equilibrium measures of meander length
M_L , meander breadth (between outside tangents to bends) M_B,
channel breadth b, depth d, and slope S on the one hand
and discharge Q on the other; in these relations the natures
of the water-sediment complex and the self-adjusting sides are
assumed fixed. Thereafter the solution of a hypothetical
ecologically important problem will be developed, step by step,
along with outline discussions of the relations. For a detailed exposition relevant to this presentation attention is in-
vited to Refs. 5,7,8,9,13. Familiarity with BASICS (paragraphs
5 to 12) is assumed.
   14. The Q Formulas. To fix ideas in terms of a prototype
case imagine a long straight horizontal channel. Into it a
steady water-sediment complex, whose steady water discharge is
Q , is run under arrangements ensuring that a non-cohesive bed
will form out of the complex and that sides may either erode
or receive deposit from the complex; further, gentle maintenance is performed to prevent irregularities of the sides and

the development of meandering. Then, in due course, the
channel will acquire equilibrium values of b, d and S
depending on Q, on various properties of the complex, on
the properties of the sides if they erode and, of course, on
the body force, g, of gravity. If the experiment is repeated
with other values of Q while the various properties remain
unaltered then b, d, S will be functions of Q only. If
new experiments are done permitting meandering to develop
fully (years might be needed) then M_L, M_B would also appear
as functions of Q only, b and d would apply only to
straight portions so would be unaltered, and S over the whole
length would acquire a dependence on the degree and type of
meandering which would depend on previous properties and
possibly a new one of the bank material. If further experiments were performed with fluctuating but average-steady Q
then we shall assume, tentatively, according to paragraphs 10,
11, that the same functional forms of relations would apply
in terms of suitable specific averages but the coefficients
would depend on the nature of the particular average used.

    15. The writer accepts, tentatively, that the evidence
from rivers, canals and laboratory flumes indicates the
following functional relationships with Q :-

    i. River and canals. b varies as the 1/2 power of Q.

    ii. Duned sand-bed canals and rivers. d, S vary
respectively as the 1/3 and minus 1/6 powers of Q .

    iii. Small and medium sized gravel rivers, and small
laboratory flumes in which 90% of bed-material median sizes
are between 0.2 and 2 mm. d, S vary respectively as the
2/5 and minus 2/5 powers of Q . (Information on presence or
absence of dunes is poor, but they were absent in the rivers
and probably in many flumes).

    iv. All rivers. M_L and M_B vary as the 1/2 power of
Q .

    v. Intermediate cases. The index of Q is not constant.
Fortunately the data in terms of which engineering problems
for rivers are posed cannot be specified exactly, so most
problems can be solved from the starting assumption that the
change from a formula with one fixed index to the corresponding one with another is discontinous; in any case flume and
river data are not good enough to define a transition well.

    16. The obvious reason for change of indices is that
moving beds may be flat or covered with dunes of various forms.
The relationship of changes of formula to bed-forms is clear
in Figs. 5-8, 9 which will be discussed later. The straight
lines on their right are for duned sand-bed canals with small
bed-loads and can be extrapolated to the largest similar
rivers; the straights on the left are for case iii with small
bed-loads; the curves in the middle are all from laboratory
flumes; the dashed interior curves roughly define the zones of
different bed-forms.

17. Meander Formulas. Inglis (21) discovered the
formulas:-

$$M_L \propto Q^{1/2} \tag{5-1}$$

$$M_B \propto Q^{1/2} \tag{5-2}$$

from rivers in the alluvial plains of India and used them to
define his idea of "dominant discharge" (paragraph 11). Good
confirmation continues to date. Ackers (1) has added model
confirmation and discussed theoretically. The coefficient in
Eq. (5-1) does not seem to depend on meander pattern, but the
ratio M_B/M_L varies from about 0.5 to 1.5 according to whether
the fully developed pattern is sinusoidal or serpentine.
18. Geologists have been relating meander dimensions
to incised channel breadth since the beginning of the century.
Figure 5-2, adapted from Fig. 45, Ref. 28, deliberately fits
a line:-

$$M_L = 10b \tag{5-3}$$

to discharges from models up to several thousand cfs. Perhaps
the best confirmations of such a relation along with:-

$$M_B \propto b \tag{5-4}$$

for a given pattern are that no model-maker has adopted
geometric dissimilarity in plan and nobody has found how to
estimate the size of a river from a scale-less tracing of its
profile from an airphoto. Equations (5-3,4) are algebraically
consistent with Eqs. (5-1, 2,5).
19. Breadth Formula. For channels which have formed both
sides and bed in alluvium the formula is:-

$$b = cQ^{1/2} \tag{5-5}$$

where Q is a measure of average discharge and c is constant
for channels whose sides and bed retain the same properties
for channels of all discharges. It was discovered, from sand-
bed irrigation canals systems, in the 1920's by Gerald Lacey
(25). It was rediscovered, with the index 1/2 as an average,
for rivers in a wide range of physiographic settings by
Leopold and Maddock (27); Figure 5-3 shows fitting curves to
their data for eight different river systems of which one was
artifical, namely an irrigation system of canals in Madras.
The inconsistent curve probably concerns a system whose downstream channels passed through bad-lands or one whose upstream
channels were in relatively inerodible soil. Evidence to date
gives no reason to change the index 1/2.
20. The coefficient c may be regarded as a measure of
the ratio of the action that keeps the bed in equilibrium to

the action that keeps the sides in equilibrium. In specialised work (5, Chapter 7) the equation is written as:-

$$b = (F_b Q/F_s)^{1/2} \qquad (5-6)$$

where F_b is called the <u>bed-factor</u> and F_s is called the
<u>side factor</u>.

21. Practical engineering problems involving the meander
and breadth relations concern the initial span in bridge
design (30) and the shifts that a river will try to impose on
deep zones (required for intakes, docks, etc.) after a change
in dominant discharge or sediment load.

22. <u>A Worked Problem (Part 1)</u>. The following worked
problem, concocted from real happenings, illustrates how to
estimate final regime (after an interference) from the
formulas or curves presented so far, and use of commonsense
and experience to visualise possible damages to the environment during the years before final regime is attained. In
Fig. 5-6 the stream B joins a large river at E . An
adjacent stream A is assumed, for simplicity, to have
exactly the same water sediment complex and flood plain
characteristics as B . B meanders in a lightly cultivated
flood plain; its incised channel hits the valley walls at
long intervals in places that move gradually during the normal
course of meandering; some ranch houses are perched on top
of the steep valley walls; high floods deposit light loads of
generally beneficial fine sand, silt and clay over the flood
plain; the stream bed is of coarse sand. Planners decide, for
increasing irrigation along the main river, to divert water
from river A along a cut DC, length 10 miles, into river
B at C which is 15 miles upstream of E . Suppose, for
simple calculation and to dramatise matters, that their action
is tantamount to doubling the dominant discharge, Q, of
river reach CE and that they proceed with their plan after
persuading the farmers that, as the river will soon settle
down to the change, there is no point in objecting.

23. For final regime Eq. (5-5) states that doubling Q
with no change in c will multiply b by $\sqrt{2}$, so the river
will finish with 41% more breadth than originally. If A had
a different complex from B's, then c in river B would be
altered and the change in breadth would not be 41%; an expert
could estimate the difference. (Of course, since the scales
are logarithmic, Fig. 5-3 could be used instead of the equation
by entering it at any Q on any line of slope 1/2 and then
proceeding to 2Q on the same line if c were fixed).
Equations (5-1,2) state that meander dimensions would increase
by 41% also. No further information can be obtained from
equations.

24. The picture of events during the decades that may
be required for the river to attain its new regime is not
difficult to outline. The doubled flow, running in a channel

that nature made for the undoubled value, will cause, during
the new enhanced floods, relatively violent bank and bed
erosion and unprecedently high flood levels. Obviously meander
activity, with its associated cutoffs, will be more pronounced so that farmers will have more frequent nuisance from
pieces of land changing from one bank of the river to the
other, farm buildings having to be moved back from eroding
banks, more frequent crumbling of valley walls where they are
hit by the stream, and, of course, plain losses of land by the
stream getting wider. They are likely to find that high floods
dump coarse bed sand on arable land and cause reduced crop
yields. Direct losses from depth and extent of flooding will
be enhanced. Eventually, after several decades the river will
have reached its final enlarged state, flood levels will be
back to a little below normal and the activity of the new
river will be about the same as for the old; but a strip of
land whose area is 0.41 times original channel breadth times
length along the winding river will have vanished, a ranch
house may have slid to the bottom of a cliff, and there may be
bitter memories of a lawsuit lost because the defendants
pleaded "Act of God" and there was no trained technical man
to present their case.

25. <u>Depth formula; dunes.</u> For duned sand-bed canals
(paragraph 19) with cohesive erodible sides Lacey (25) found
a depth relation of the form:-

$$d = c'Q^{1/3} \tag{5-7}$$

However, this was deduced from his fundamental discovery that,
regardless of breadth:-

"The Froude Number in terms of regime depth, namely
$V/\sqrt{gd}$, is fixed when the nature of the water-sediment
complex is fixed."

Naturally this discovery led to using the Froude Number (from
which g was dropped as an arithmetic nuisance) as a <u>bed-
factor</u> measuring, in some way, the joint effect of various
factors in the water-sediment complex on the depth of the bed
below water level. In turn, the use of a bed-factor caused
thought about the factors contained in it and called for a
couple of standard definitions and symbols. So, for information, paragraphs 26-29 will deal with these matters with
minimum technicality and show how Eq. (5-7) is deduced.

26. First, because of the practical need for different
definitions of the measure, b, of breadth, b, d will
always be defined together so that bd = A = cross-sectional
area of flow. Then V, the mean velocity of flow, is
Q/A = Q/bd so that the discharge intensity q can always be
defined as $q \equiv Q/b = Vd$. These definitions allow a common
symbolism, defer definitions of "proper" measures till there
are enough facts for the purpose and do not hamper the search
for the functional forms that express the physical laws behind phenomena (paragraph 12).

27. Second, define a bed-factor, F_b, as g times the square of the Froude Number in terms of depth, so that:-

$$F_b \equiv V^2/d \equiv q^2/d^3 \qquad (5\text{-}8)$$

Also, to give a neat dimensionless way of visualising bed-load (paragraph 5) define bed-load charge, C, as:-

$$C = (\text{bed-load})/(\text{weight discharge of water}) \qquad (5\text{-}9)$$

(The writer expresses C in parts per hundred thousand; thus C = 3 means that practically three thousandths of the total weight flow of complex is bed-load material). Also, allocate the letter D to mean the median diameter by weight of the bed-load material. (Then the weight of particles larger than D equals the weight of particles smaller than D).
     28. Finally, we can summarise popular views on the bed-factor symbolically to:-

$$F_b = \text{fn}(C, D, \text{etc.} \ldots) \qquad (5\text{-}10)$$

where "fn" means "some function of". The "etc" includes shape and shape distribution of bed-load material and suspended material, suspended load charge, density and density distribution of solid materials, viscosity and g . Strictly b/d should be included, but analysis by Cooper (16) of special observations by Garnett Williams, shows that there is observable effect only when b/d is less than 2 which is below the range of practical interest. The term C is made explicit because engineers think in terms of it, wish they could measure it in the field, and make guesses at its magnitude in terms of widely discordant formulas obtained from flumes that may operate in the wrong phase of behaviour (12). The term D is accurately measureable in sands but can be vague in gravels (5, paragraphs 10.42, 43) when different materials appear on the bed at different stages of flow. In special circumstances suspended load and viscosity can be important but detailed information is scarce.
     29. Equation (5-7) can be deduced from the definition of the bed-factor and from Eq. (5-5) as follows. Rewrite Eq. (5-8) as:-

$$d = q^{2/3}/F_b^{1/3} \qquad (5\text{-}8a)$$

Then, because:-

$$b = cQ^{1/2} \qquad (5\text{-}5)$$

if sides are adjustable, it follows that:-

$$q \equiv Q/b = c^{-1}Q^{1/2} \qquad (5\text{-}11)$$

Inserting this value of q in Eq. (5-8a) yields:-

$$d = Q^{1/3}/(c^2 F_b)^{1/3} \qquad (5\text{-}12)$$

which has the form of Eq. (5-7) but displays the nature of
the coefficient.

30. <u>Depth formula; gravel beds, no dunes.</u> In engineering
practice channels without dunes are normally those with
gravel beds and, usually, small bed-load charges. In Fig.
5-8 the band at the left, with slope minus 1/2, encloses data,
mainly from Kellerhals and Lane (23), believed to owe most of
its breadth to random scatter. Its mean line has a formula
of the type:-

$$F_{bo} \propto (D/d)^{1/2} \qquad (5\text{-}13)$$

where F_{bo} is the value of F_b when C is very small, and
is called the <u>zero bed-factor.</u> (The mathematical definition
of F_{bo} as a limit for C tending to zero is no better than
the practical one since there is no clear-cut cessation of
bed-motion in a real gravel). Equation (5-13) shows that,
when there are no dunes, the bed-factor as defined by Eq.
(5-8) no longer depends on the nature of the water-sediment
complex alone. (When there are dunes, in sand or gravel, F_{bo}
can be taken from Fig. 5-4.) However, Eq. (5-12) is still
correct algebraically, and insertion of F_{bo} from Eq. (5-13)
into it in place of F_b gives:-

$$d \propto Q^{2/5}/(c^2 D)^{1/5} \qquad (5\text{-}14)$$

in accordance with paragraph 15 (iii). (If the index in
Eq. (5-13) should be really 2/3, as flume data might suggest,
then the indices 2/5 and 1/5 in Eq. (5-14) become 0.43 and
0.29.)

31. The index 2/5 in Eq. (5-14) is exactly that
recommended, as a mean, by Leopold and Maddock (paragraph 19
and Fig. 5-3) from their observations of river systems. In
that early work bed forms and bed material sizes were not
recorded, but there were both sand and gravel beds. So the
exact agreement of indices must be regarded as fortuitous.
There is further support from rigid boundary hydraulics and
from laboratory flume experiments for an index close to 2/5.
(<u>Note to engineers.</u> The form of Eq. (5-13) is given by solving the Meyer-Peter (or Shields) shear stress relation with
Lacey's amendment of the Manning equation's index of R from
2/3 to 3/4. If the Prandtl logarithmic formula is used instead of Lacey's, remembering that it does not fit rigid
boundary facts when extrapolated and that Prandtl warned it
was not rigorous (9, page 1885), then a flat curve replaces

the straight line of Eq. (5-13) on double-log paper without
any obviously better fit to data).

32. _Application in river engineering_. The main use of the
formulas in river engineering is in estimating scoured depths
at river works. For this purpose coefficients, based on
standard cases, have to be applied to the depths estimated for
straight flow, (5, paragraph 11.39).

33. _A Worked Problem (Part 2)_. Continuing from paragraph
22, the depth formula can indicate roughly whether bed scour
would be violent in the early stages when discharge has been
doubled but breadth has not had time to increase. Here we
can neglect the reduction of discharge in the incised channel
by flood plain spill, as a first approximation, and assume
that q for a high flood was doubled. Then by Eq. (5-8a) for
fixed F_b, d would tend to increase $2^{2/3}$ = 1.6 times, so
long as b did not change. Near E the large river would
hold water level to normal so that the extra 60% of depth
would be taken by bed scour. Further upstream water level for
the doubled discharge would be greater than for the original
discharge so that potential drop in bed would be less. The
calculation is good enough to give credibility to farmers'
statements that the interference with the river bed caused unprecedented quantities of bed material to be whipped into
suspension and dumped on their land.

34. _Slope formula; dunes_. For duned sand-bed canals
(paragraph 19) with cohesive erodible sides Lacey (7,26) found
a slope relation of the form

$$S = c''Q^{-1/6} \qquad (5-15)$$

where c'' depends on the natures of the water sediment complex
and the sides. This relation is deduced from a more fundamental one:-

$$d^{1/2}S = \text{constant} \qquad (5-16)$$

in a system with a fixed water sediment complex and fixed
erodible side nature. His d was hydraulic radius. There
have been secondary refinements since, that do not alter Eq.
(5-15).

35. A basic difficulty with all slope formulas for any
kind of mobile boundary is that slope has to depend on bed
and side "roughnesses" which are generally different in genesis
and operation. There is no satisfactory way of separating the
effects of these two parts of the boundary. If the matter is
dealt with by pure data plotting, to avoid necessarily dubious
theory, then at least one more independent variable, b/d,
must be added to the three that were required for dealing with
depth. A second basic difficulty is that river meandering has
a major effect on slope. So a fourth and fifth independent
variables are important in rivers.

36. As there is no obvious end to arguments that must arise about the best formulas, in the absence of adequate data and theory, the writer presents, without argument, Fig. 5-5 which is based on the following slightly adjusted Lacey formula that has proved useful for sand-bed rivers:-

$$S \propto kF_{bo}^{11/12}.f'''(C)b^{-1/6}Q^{-1/12} \qquad (5-17)$$

Note that if the value of b from Eq. (5-5) is inserted there is agreement with Eq. (5-15). Specialised information is in Chapters 7, 8, 11, Ref. 5 and in Ref. 9.

37. In this formula the peculiar indices are due to algebraic combination of formulas with simple indices so do not denote complexity. The factor k is a practical meander correction coefficient to allow for the extra energy dissipation required by tortuosity. For a straight channel its value is 1.0. For fully developed meandering the writer takes it as 2.0, as an "order of magnitude" figure based on general canal and river experience. Recently Ackers (2,3) has conducted valuable model experiments which suggest that 2.0 is high. The field studies of Leopold and Wolman (28) suggest that 2.0 is possible. Ignoring k can produce enormous errors in some engineering applications. $f'''(C)$ is a function of bed-load charge for which a very rough graph is available (5, Fig. 7-2). It tends to 1.0 as C tends to zero; $f'''(C) = 2.0$ indicates charge of the order of 10 parts per hundred thousand which is believed to be a high figure for most rivers; $f'''(C) = 4.0$ represents charge of the order of 100, which is enormous for dominant conditions. The occurrence of b, explicitly, arises from b/d being included in one of the foundation formulas.

38. To graph the formula for easy use it is rewritten as:-

$$Z \equiv (Sb^{1/6}/F_{bo}^{11/12}) \propto k.f'''(C).Q^{-1/12} \qquad (5-17a)$$

and the coefficient is taken from canal observations at a water temperature of 20 degrees Centigrade. Z may be regarded as a composite slope with a simplifying objective analogous to that of specific speed in turbine work. The lines on the graph, Fig. 5-5, have slope = minus 1/12, so are for fixed values of $k.f'''(C)$. The bottom line has $k = 1$, $f'''(C) = 1.0$, so $kf'''(C) = 1.0$ is for straight canals with very small C. The middle line is for $k.f'''(C) = 2.0$ so can represent canals with small load that have been neglected for decades till they have developed mature meandering, or straight canals with considerable load, or rivers with intermediate meandering and intermediate load. The top line is for $k.f'''(C) = 4.0$ so represents rivers with considerable loads and fully developed meandering, or a straight diversion channel with enormous load and no meandering (see paragraph 42), or intermediate conditions. A point plotted on the Figure from river measurements at

dominant discharge shows, by its vertical position within the
band, the combined meandering and load characteristics; this
makes the chart valuable for classifying rivers. Because of
the very flat slope of the band even a very badly estimated
dominant discharge will still make little difference to the
vertical position of a plotted point within the band. (A
comparable Figure for gravel rivers would have a steep band
so would not be so useful).

39. Slope formula; gravel bed; no dunes. River data are
of little help in producing a formula for this case. Leopold
and Wolman (28, Fig. 46), have produced a graph of S against
Q for a large range of rivers in different systems, mainly
gravel, and recorded the sediment properties and whether the
channels were braided, meandering or relatively straight.
Their routine fitting line to the widely scattered points
showed variation of slope according to the minus 0.44 power
of discharge but there was no intention to propose a meaningful formula. The writer prefers to deduce a power from the
band on the left of Fig. 5-9, which is the counterpart of the
band on the left of Fig. 5-8 and is for small C and no
meandering. It gives:-

$$S \propto D^{6/5}Q^{-2/5} \qquad (5\text{-}18)$$

by combining Eq. (5-24) with Eq. (5-8a); in general the coefficient would have to contain a function of charge and a
meander correction coefficient. The formula is so sensitive
to errors in dominant discharge and in measuring D that the
writer does not rely on it in design; it has special uses in
conjunction with other more reliable information. Recent
scientific field observations and analyses of sand and gravel
river data detailed by Bray (13) throw considerable light on
this and other formulas; formulas are compared statisically.

40. A Worked Problem (Part 3). Continuing from paragraph
33, consider the change in slope of CE from its original
undisturbed state and of the diversion channel DC from its
designed and constructed state. As CE's discharge was
doubled and its ultimate breadth has been found to be $\sqrt{2}$
times the original, and no ultimate change will be imposed on
F_{bo}, C and k, Eq. (5-17a) makes S proportional to
$b^{-1/6}Q^{-1/12}$. So the ultimate S will be $2^{-1/6}$ = about 7/8
times the original. To get a sense of proportion assume that
the original slope of CE was 2 feet per mile and of DC was
6 feet per mile so that CE had 30 feet drop and DC had
60 feet drop. It follows that, ultimately, the river at
dominant conditions at C will be 30/8 = about 4 feet lower
than originally.

41. For DC no calculation is necessary. It has the
discharge of the original CE, the same water-sediment
complex and the same type of flood plain. Therefore it must

acquire the original meandering, dimensions and slope of CE.
That is, it will have, ultimately, a slope of 2 feet per mile
and, possibly, a winding length of about 15 miles. Then its
drop will be 30 feet instead of 60 and its tail, being the
head of CE, will be 4 feet lower than originally. This
makes its head 34 feet lower than constructed. Its head
regulator will certainly require a lot of remodelling during
the decades that are required for such a drastic change in
regime.

42. Figure 5-5 gives a quick way of visualising the
enormity of expecting DC to remain permanent. Suppose that
the point for original CE was on the middle-line of the band
in Fig. 5-5. The designer makes DC, presumably of about the
same b as CE, with 3 times the slope of CE. So his Z
value is 3 times that for CE and the designed state point
for it is therefore at a height of log 3 above the state
point for CE. That is, it is appreciably above the band, so
corresponds to abnormally large load whereas CE, with its
statepoint in the middle of the band, is a quite ordinary
stream. The abnormality of load is actually very large because DC has been made straight. In fact, whereas $k.f'''(C)$
for CE is 2.0 and that channel meanders so that k is close
to 2.0 and C must therefore be of the order of 1, $k.f'''(C)$
for DC is 6.0 and k is 1.0 so that $f'''(C)$ is 6.0, which
corresponds to C of the order of a few hundred -- an
enormous value. As the huge charge cannot come from river A
it has to be picked up from the bed of DC -- so erosion will
be intense.

43. If the soil in CD is of the same nature as the
bed-load from A, CE will suffer badly from the misdesign.
The enormous quantities of sediment picked up from the bed of
DC will enter CE and might even dump an alluvial fan. As
they advance, the head reach of CE will steepen and diking
will be required to stop flooding. The details over the years
are difficult to work out, but there is no doubt that CE is
going to suffer aggradation seriously while it tries to dispose
of the great quantities of material that are torn out of DC.
Moreover the material will be more than corresponds to bed
erosion for, as DC degrades 34 feet at its head, side slopes
will fall into it. CE is not the only part of river B that
will feel the effects of DC. As C rises the river B upstream of it will rise and, therefore, suffer deposition and
flooding on its own flood plain. If the soil along CD is
cohesive, then the slope of CE may not increase and might
even decrease since there will be no added bed-load and suspension reduces apparent roughness.

44. The straight diversion example here is a special
case of straightening meandering rivers for various worthy
causes, such as avoiding the need for a bridge, or eliminating
the need for rip-rapping a highway or railway, or "improving"
navigation or, sometimes, under a vague impression that making
a river look tidy is good for it. Often these acts do not

come to public notice because a channel hits bedrock after a
little erosion so that action ceases, or there is no human
habitation or cultivation to suffer, or the sufferers are
compensated, or remedies are applied (such as constructing
falls in DC so as to break it into reaches running at natural
slopes). Generally, however, they are likely to cost society
more dollars, sometimes many more, than proper initial
planning and design. From an environmental viewpoint they are
all potentially dangerous; for example they can destroy
aquatic life by changing streams from clean to muddy, kill
vegetation by dropping the water table, flood lands and deposit
sediment on them, and destroy land when the banks fall in.

5.4 GENERALISED GRAPHS FOR d AND S

45. <u>Preliminary</u>. The object of this section is to demonstrate graphically, for understanding and design, the implications of all data available for the depth and slope of
channels in regime. This can be achieved in general by a set
of charts, each for its own sediment size, for dimensionless
depth and slope. However, as world data are of limited range,
Figs. 5-8, 9 suffice for the present; similar figures for
larger and smaller bed-materials will be added when research
expands. The steps toward graphing observed facts are exactly
the commonsense ones employed for the classic "friction-factor
plot" (or Stanton Diagram) for the flow data of rigid circular
pipes. They are, (i) a simple adequate verbal "statement of
case" is made, (ii) it is then written symbolically as an
equation between the variables that the statement has shown to
be interdependent, (iii) the number of variables is reduced to
the minimum by arranging them into <u>numerics</u> (dimensionless
groups), (iv) data are plotted to the number and kind of coordinates that (iii) shows to be mandatory. The difference
from the pipe case is that the plot for dimensionless d has
to be four dimensional and for S has to be six dimensional
unless some temporary subterfuges are adopted. (We do not
consider, here, special experiments and observations where all
but a couple of variables remain constant so that special precision can be obtained in portions of the plot).

46. Figures 5-8 and 9 draw attention to (i) inadequacies
of data,(ii) controversies due to ignoring different phases of
flow, (iii) the zones in which existing formulas are reasonably
useable. They can be used instead of formulas, if desired,
but good formulas have an advantage of standardising fits to
different zones and may be very simple in use. The long time
required to implement the preceding commonsense type of
analysis was consumed in (a) gaining enough field and laboratory
experience for use with an adequate statement of case, (b)
developing computer technology, (c) collecting and compiling
data from scattered sources, (d) learning the practical uses
of dimensionless algebra (6). Nevertheless the functional
equations to use, and various dimensionless manipulations,

were known to experts a couple of decades ago (Refs. 4, 31).

47. The prototype case adopted for statement here is worded to describe a classic set of flume experiments with which the behaviour of real rivers can be put into correspondence by the concept of dominant discharge and by making practical allowances for aberrations. It is:-

"A steady volumetric discharge Q of Newtonian fluid with kinematic viscosity ν and mass density ρ is diverted into a long horizontal rectangular flume of breadth b, whose sides behave as if hydraulically smooth. A granular material of fixed constitution is added to this discharge at a fixed rate, or "charge", C units of weight discharge per unit of fluid weight discharge. The granular material is selected with a constitution such that, when it has formed a bed, it will all move in the rolling and/or saltating manner recognized as bed-movement. Its median size is D and the mass density of every particle is ρ_s; shapes and the distribution of sizes and shapes are susceptible to definition by a host of non-dimensional factors represented by X .... . The motion takes place in the earth's field of body-force, g .

"When, and only when, all the above factors have been imposed the channel will form a granular bed and adjust itself to have a unique space-mean depth d, and a unique energy degradation rate of gS per unit mass per unit length along the flow (corresponding to a surface slope S).

"There will be, also a definite mean flow velocity V and, under many circumstances, bed waves of mean wavelength and amplitude λ, α ."

48. The preceding verbal statement can be symbolized as four ten-dimensional equations (counting X .... as one composite variable, "texture"):-

$$d, gS, \lambda, \alpha = \text{fns}(V, \nu, \rho, b, C, D, \rho_s, X...., g) \qquad (5\text{-}19a,b,c,d)$$

or in various algebraically equivalent forms. Here "fn" means only "some function of", so there is no need to use suffices with it for d, gS, etc. The four equations can then be reduced to four seven-dimensional equations in numerics. Many equivalent different-looking sets of four can be derived but all they do is provide different coordinates to which the physical statements inherent in Eqs. 5-19 can be plotted. Experts should know them all since some are better than others for suggesting physical meanings and for giving useful formulas. We shall use:-

$$\frac{V^2}{gd}, S, \frac{\lambda}{D}, \frac{\alpha}{D} = \text{fn}(\sqrt[3]{\nu g} \frac{D}{\nu}, C, \frac{d}{D}, \frac{b}{d}, s, X...) \qquad (5\text{-}20a,b)$$

and ignore the bed-wave formulas. The Reynolds Number $\sqrt[3]{\nu g}\,\dfrac{D}{\nu}$ is called the "Vig Number" from "viscosity-gravity"; s stands for ρ_s/ρ.

49. Reduction for plotting. For practical plotting, Eq. (5-20a) for the dimensionless depth, V^2/gd can be simplified. Of its last three terms, b/d has been demonstrated to be ineffective if less than 2.0, and s is practically constant. The multitude of factors X... which represent a general property that may be called "texture" is omitted because of unmeasureability, the hope that it does not often matter too much, and the facts that natural duned river-bed sand has an exceedingly steady size distribution (5, Fig. 3.4), flume material is usually quite uniform, and river-bed gravels during high flows are of fairly steady size distribution. However, the variability of X should always be considered as a cause of scatter in plotted data. The simplest reasonably acceptable plotting formula is, therefore, the four-dimensional:-

$$V^2/gd \;=\; fn(\sqrt[3]{\nu g}.D/\nu,\ C,\ d/D) \qquad\qquad (5\text{-}21)$$

50. Visualising the four-dimensional plot. The general mental picture of Eq. (5-21) is a set of surfaces. For example, V^2/gd is measured along a vertical (z) axis in Fig. 5-7, d/D is measured along a horizontal (x) axis in the plane of the paper, and C is measured along a horizontal (y) axis running perpendicularly into the paper. When the data for a small range of D are plotted to these axes they define a surface, such as shown, for the range's mean value of Vig Number with which the surface should be labelled. By splitting extensive data into small D ranges a set of surfaces can be drawn each marked with its own Vig Number. At least for small C , the combined data of rivers, canals and flumes indicate that the equi-Vig surfaces tend to co-incidence at small d/D and acquire generating lines parallel to the d/D axis at large d/D. So the appearance of the set of surfaces might be likened to that of the turbulent part of a pipe-friction diagram that had acquired an extra dimension.

51. The four-dimensional picture must be expected to have several merging geometries - each with its own formula - corresponding with the visibly different bed-forms and perhaps, as in the pipe friction-factor diagram, with invisible phases of flow. The bed-form zone boundaries can be estimated from distinctive marking of data points for different bed-forms. On the approximately-constant (paragraphs 54, 55) Vig Number surface of Fig. 5-7, zones for ripples, dunes and plane bed have been approximated by this method.

52. For ordinary use and for numerical applications a set of actual Vig Number surfaces, each as depicted in perspective in Fig. 5-7, is not practical, so each surface has

5-20

to be represented by contours on a sheet of paper labelled
with its own fourth parameter. Fig. 5-8 shows the single Vig
Number surface of Fig. 5-7 by means of contours of C to coordinates of V^2/gd, d/D; it is for a Vig Number averaging
the material sizes in a major collection of world flume data
by Cooper and Peterson (15) but has a bias at its right-hand
end (paragraph 55). (Actually the C curves of Fig. 5-8 were
prepared first from the data and used to draw Fig. 5-7.)

53. Composite plot of V^2/gd data (Fig. 5-8). World information on V^2/gd is from rivers, canals and laboratory
flumes and, as indicated in paragraph 15 et seq, is far from
accurate or exhaustive. In fact, were it plotted on several
Vig Number sheets with the co-ordinates of Fig. 5-8 most would
be practically empty. Accordingly, canal and river data, for
which there are no measures of C, are packed into Fig. 5-8
along with world flume data whose range and dispersion of D
do not justify splitting into sub-groups of different Vig
Numbers.

54. It is convenient to start discussing Fig. 5-8 using
the flume data shown by the C curves since they are four-
dimensional and link the three-dimensional data of gravel
rivers, which have small d/D and are believed independent of
Vig Number, with the three-dimensional ones of duned sand-bed
canals, which have large d/D and are independent of it but
dependent on Vig Number. The flume data suffer from the
limitation that 90% of median bed-material sizes fall between
the tight limits of 0.2 and 2.0 mm. Further, even were they
free from defects, their total number of about 3,000 would
hardly suffice to define exact C curves and the four zones
of geometrically different bed-forms (marked plane bed, ripples,
dunes and upper flow regime in Fig. 5-8) in a surface for one
Vig Number. In fact they suffer two important defects. The
first is that bed-materials were neither standard nor, in
general, natural; this makes the definition of D dubious and
makes different experimental runs with one-material likely to
have varying indeterminate parts of bed-load and suspended
load (9). The second is the irreparable statistical one that
there was strong accidental negative association between d/D
and Vig Number (14, Fig. C-11), so that the flume data, by
themselves, cannot separate the influences of these two factors.
The separation can be achieved, roughly, because of auxiliary
information from the left-hand zone of Fig. 5-8 where it seems
likely that the effect of Vig Number vanishes, and from the
zone of duned canals to the right where the effect of d/D has
vanished. The wild discordance among competitive theoretical
flume-tested formulas for bed-load and the doubts about their
field applicability (12) should be viewed in terms of the preceding situation and the fact that the flume domain of d/D
and D is smaller than and outside of the domain of most
irrigation canals and rivers (Fig. 5-3, Ref. 17).

55. Clearly, refined methods of fitting C contours to data are not justified and could conceal the true nature of available facts. Cooper (14) fitted the curves of Fig. 5-8 by eye, trying not to be influenced by theory; the disordances of curve shapes advertise the nature of the data. Because useable bed-form information is not recorded by many observers bed-form zone lines were drawn from observations of Gilbert, Lieu and Simons and Richardson, as explained in Ref. 14. For detailed study the data of 26 sub-collections by different observers, plotted according to Fig. 5-8 without the C lines, have now been made readily available (17, Figs. 5-7a-z). They demonstrate why the data must be analysed as a whole and with full consideration of the indications from rivers and canals outside of their range (17, Figs. 3, 8). It is important to remember that the statistical defect of negative association between d/D and Vig Number (paragraph 54) causes the surface of Fig. 5-7, and therefore the C curves of Fig. 5-8, to be for a Vig Number decreasing in the direction of the d/D axis instead of for a truly constant Vig Number. The effect of this should not be noticeable towards the left of Figs. 5-7,8 because, even where V^2/d depends entirely on Vig Number to the exclusion of d/D, it is believed to vary as the fourth root of Vig Number when D is greater than 1 mm, and as about its square root when D is about 0.25 mm.

56. <u>The duned sand-bed canal data</u> of Lacey and subsequent observers (paragraphs 19, 25) fall within the length of the two firm horizontals marked "Regime Theory", but most D values were between 0.15 and 0.4 mm. The line locations are from the part of Fig. 5-4 which is from the canal data and, conventionally, takes F_{bo} as the value of F_b obtained from them since (i) there are negligible authenticated cases of F_b having been discovered smaller for a specified D, and (ii) C is unmeasureable as a routine. The term "duned" is used here in its popular sense of "covered with unsymmetric undulations". Canal engineers were not interested in bed-forms so did not classify them; the dunes were probably mainly the rather three-dimensional ones classified in North America as "ripples".

57. No attempt has been made to reconcile the horizontal line for a particular Vig Number with the lines of small C for flumes. It would fail because (i) F_{bo} cannot be a definite quantity since the cessation of bed-movement is indefinite (paragraph 30), (ii) F_{bo} of Fig. 5-4 is really the F_b of certain canals of small but unknown C, (iii) F_{bo} is influenced by suspended load which was large during the river flood season in those canals and nil in flumes. Anyway there is no means of extrapolating the crude C curves for decreasing Vig Number (paragraph 55) beyond their own zone.

A proper way to examine the effect of C in canals would be
to establish a large-scale research station on a by-pass canal
in a major system where ranges of variables would be practical
and the control of variables scientific. Rough methods of
dealing with C are in Chapter 7 and paragraph 11.28 of Ref.5.
    58. The chained horizontal marked 50 mm is from the
part of Fig. 5-4 which rests on passable verifications from
river problems and on the conjecture (21, paragraph 3.24),
that F_{bo} varies as the square root of particle settlement
velocity for all materials in the proper phase of bed movement.
It terminates to the right where river size would be remarkably
large.
    59. The unduned gravel river beds, with small C, of
Kellerhals and Lane (paragraph 30) are fitted with the band
of slope minus 1/2 on the left of Fig. 5-8, for reasons given
in paragraph 31. Pending better field-scale data the writer
uses the fitting line:-

$$V^2/d \;=\; 48(D/d)^{1/2} \qquad\qquad (5\text{-}22)$$

equivalent to the useful design formula:-

$$d \;=\; 0.21q^{4/5}D^{-1/5} \qquad\qquad (5\text{-}23)$$

in which 0.21 is $48^{-2/5}$. The coefficient 48 was adopted, after
several adjustments, to suit river scour problems. (Note to
engineers. It corresponds roughly to a Shield's coefficient
of 0.02). An obvious cause of the band's large breadth is
subjectively estimated dominant discharges. Possibly the
variety of stone shapes in rivers, and the ways in which the
stones adjust in paved beds associated with small C, is
another major cause (18). Fortunately 15% error in the coefficient makes only 6% error in 0.21. Reasons for disregarding the slope of the small-C lines in the d/D range of the
band include scarcity of points, discordance with adjacent
lines for larger C, and unreality of flume gravels. (Curi-
ously, if the index of Manning's equation is retained in
the Note to paragraph 31 the small-C line slope is predicted
closely as 5/8; but that equation is for channels where C
increases with Q.) Obviously all data are unsatisfactory. A
recent major controlled collection and analysis of gravel
river data (13) improves the situation but confirms that
scientific research in large-scale field stations is needed to
deal reliably with real and large river gravels (paragraph 57).
    60. Transition from gravel rivers to sand canals; small
C; paragraph 15.v. There are no data competent to indicate
how V^2/gd would change in an experiment where, at small C
and fixed Vig Number, d/D changed progressively from 2 to
2×10^4 . The writer visualises that, starting from the extreme
left on the line of Eq. (5-22), plotted points would run along

it to some position depending on the Vig Number and then start
to head off to the proper Vig Number horizontal on the right.
There is some flimsy evidence that the approach to the horizontal would not be monotonic so, for D = 1 mm and 50 mm,
imagined dotted alternative transitions are marked on Fig.
5-8. Only large-scale field research can settle the matter
(paragraph 57). Meanwhile(paragraph 15.v.) practical calculations can assume infinitely short transitions.

61. <u>Supercritical flow, gravel, small C</u>. Information on
super-critical flow, with small C, in gravel streams is
practically nil, so nothing is shown on Fig. 5-8. Large-scale
field station research is needed.

62. <u>Composite plot of S data</u>. Fig. 5-9 is the counterpart of Fig. 5-8 and requires discussion only of the effect
of the fifth dimension, b/d, in Eq. (5-20b). The difficulty
is that bed and sides are of different natures and affect S
differently; even in rigid flumes without sediment the distribution of shear stress and its mean value are different over
sides and bed (20). The presence of b/d in Eq. (5-20b)
merely takes note of the problem; the true function that the
equation represents is likely to contain b/d in a complex
manner, so there is little chance of finding it from present
data. Laboratory flume workers have crude methods for estimating either the part of S, or the part of d, due to
the bed, so that they can replace the actual channel by a
hypothetical sideless one for analysis. In Canal practice
King's Equation (5, paragraphs 6.8, 7.6, 7.22) contains a
factor $(b/d)^{1/4}$ which obviously cannot apply indefinitely
outside of his range of derivation; King's b is surface
breadth. The original Lacey equation used d = hydraulic
radius and had no shape correction. Fig. 5-9 uses King's
equation, from which Fig. 5-5 is derived, to plot the two
canal lines on the right for b/d = 10. Their slope is
minus 3/8. Had Lacey's original equation been used the slope
would have been minus 1/2 but then d would be hydraulic
radius and, from a design viewpoint, the results would be only
a little different. The flume data lines have no correction,
although b/d varied considerably; Garnett Williams' observations (16) show that the correction should be considerable
for b/d < 5 and comparable with King's. The gravel river
zone has no correction either, but b/d was generally rather
large. The writer fits the gravel band tentatively with a
small-C line:-

$$S = 0.042(D/d) \qquad (5-24)$$

for practical work with rivers.

63. <u>Uses of Figs. 5-8, 9</u>. The unextrapolated dimensionless
plots of actual data, or lines fitting them, are analogous to
unextrapolated plots of pipe flow data on the classic friction
factor diagram (5, Fig. 4.2). (Nonrigorous theoretical curves

5-24

extrapolated beyond the data, as in the Moody Diagram, are not considered or recommended here.) They:-

(a) Demonstrate the existence of the different phases of flow requiring different formulas.

(b) Locate the more obvious phases approximately in ordinary coordinates.

(c) Locate them further in approximate curved zones not readily expressible in terms of the ordinary coordinates.

(d) Warn against misapplication of formulas.

(e) Draw permanent attention to the gaps and lack of precision in essential information.

(f) Permit design in terms of facts.

(g) Provide frames of reference on which to record one's own observations and information.

Item (f) requires use of a river meander coefficient (paragraph 37) in Fig. 5-9, so Fig. 5-5 is probably superior for rivers with duned beds. Item (g) is the most important to the practical user because, (i) even were the curves of the Figures perfect, they would be perfect only for one set of the variables of paragraph 49 that have been omitted from initial practical analysis, and because (ii) organised experience is the basis of expertness.

5.5 NOTATIONS

b	a breadth
c	a coefficient
C	bed-load charge defined in paragraph 27
d	a depth
D	a mean particle size, usually the median by weight
f	a particular function of
fn	any function of
F_b	the bed-factor defined in paragraph 27
F_{bo}	the "zero bed-factor" defined in paragraph 30
F_s	the side factor, limiting side deposition and erosion
g	body force due to gravity
k	a coefficient related to meandering
M_b	meander belt width
M_L	meander length
q	discharge intensity
Q	discharge of water in volume per unit time
S	slope along the flow
V	mean velocity over a section
x	an index
X	a set of numerics measuring sediment characteristics other than D .
Z	a modified slope
ν	kinematic viscosity

REFERENCES

1. Ackers, P. and Charlton, F.G., The geometry of small meandering streams: Proc. Instn. of Civil Engineers, Paper 7328S, Supplement XII, 1970.

2. Ackers, P., and Charlton, F.G., The slope and resistance of small meandering streams: Proc. Instn. of Civil Engineers, Paper 7362S, Supplement XV, 1970.

3. Ackers, P., and Charlton, F.G., Dimensional analysis of alluvial channels with special reference to meander length: Journal of Hydraulic Research, Vol. 8, 1970-3, pp. 287-317 and Vol. 9, 1971-2, pp. 267-279.

4. Blench, T., Regime behaviour of canals and rivers: Butterworths, London, 1957.

5. Blench, T., Mobile-Bed Fluviology: 2nd Ed., University of Alberta Press, 1969.

6. Blench, T., Dimensional analysis and dynamical similarity: University of Alberta Bookstore, 1969.

7. Blench, T., Regime theory design of canals with sand beds: Journal of the Irrigation and Drainage Div., ASCE, Vol. 96, No. IR2, Proc. Paper 7381, June 1970, pp. 205-213.

8. Blench, T., Mobile bed hydraulics: Journal of Hydraulic Research, Vol. 8, 1970, No. 2.

9. Blench, T., Coordination in mobile-bed hydraulics: Journal of the Hydraulics Div., ASCE, Vol. 95, No. HY6, Proc. Paper 6884, Nov. 1969, pp. 1871-1898. Closure in Vol. 97, No. HY2, Proc. Paper 1364, Feb. 1971.

10. Blench, T., Morphometric Changes: Chapter in "River Ecology and Man". Oglesby, Ray T., Carlson, Clarence A., and McCann, James A., Academic Press, 1972, pp. 287-308.

11. Blench, T., Discussion of Sediment transportation mechanics, F. Hydraulic relations for alluvial streams: Journal of the Hydraulics Div., ASCE, Vol. 97, No. HY11, Proc. Paper 8483, Nov. 1971, pp. 1908-1913.

12. Blench, T., Discussion of Sediment transportation mechanics, H. Sediment transport formulas: Journal of the Hydraulics Div., ASCE, Vol. 98, No. HY1, Proc. Paper 8620, Jan. 1972, pp. 284-289.

13. Bray, D.I., Generalised regime type analysis of Alberta rivers: Ph.D. Thesis, University of Alberta, 1972.

14. Cooper, R.H., A study of bed material transport based on the analysis of flume experiments: Ph.D. Thesis, University of Alberta, 1970.

15. Cooper, R.H. and Peterson, A.W., A review of data from sediment transport experiments: Report No. HY-1969-ST2, Dept. of Civil Engineering, University of Alberta, and U.S. Dept. of Commerce Clearing House Accession Number PB-190233, 1970.

16. Cooper, R.H., Dimensional Analysis of U.S.G.S., Prof. Paper 562-H, by Garnett P. Williams, 1970: U. of Alberta, Hydraulics Lab Note 650-01-04.

17. Cooper, R.H., Peterson, A.W. and Blench, T., A critical review of sediment transport experiments: Journal of the Hydraulics Div. ASCE, Vol. 98, No. HY5, Proc. Paper 8873, May, 1972, pp. 827-843.

18. Galay, V.J., Some hydraulic characteristics of coarse-bed rivers: Ph.D. Thesis, University of Alberta, 1971.

19. Guy, H.P., Simons, D.B. and Richardson, E.V., Summary of alluvial channel data from flume experiments: U.S.G.S. Professional Paper 462-I, 1966.

20. Hollingshead, A.B., Boundary shear stress distribution in open channel flow: Ph.D. Thesis, University of Alberta, 1972.

21. Inglis, C.C. Sir, The behaviour and control of rivers and canals: Research Publication No. 13, Central Board of Irrigation, Simla, India, 1949.

22. I.U.T.A.M., Report on the I.U.T.A.M. Symposium on the flow of fluid-solid mixtures: Journal of Fluid Mechs. (1969), Vol. 39, part 2, pp. 375-405.

23. Kellerhals, Rolf, Stable channels with gravel-paved beds: Journal of the Waterways and Harbours Div., ASCE, Vol. 93, No. WW1, Proc. Paper 5091, Feb. 1967, pp. 63-84.

24. Kenney, J.F. and Keeping, E.S., Mathematics of Statistics: van Nostrand, 3rd Edit. 1954.

25. Lacey, Gerald, Stable channels in alluvium: Proc. Instn. of Civil Engineers, 229. 1929-30.

26. Lacey, Gerald, Uniform flow in alluvial rivers and canals: Proc. Instn. of Civil Engineers, 237, 1933-34.

27. Leopold, L.B. and Maddock, T., Jr., The hydraulic geometry of stream channels and some physiographic implications: U.S.G.S. Prof. Paper 252, 1953.

28. Leopold, Luna B., and Wolman, Gordon, M., River channel patterns, braided, meandering and straight: U.S.G.S. Prof. Paper 282-B, 1957.

29. Leopold, Luna B., and Langbein, W.B., River meanders: Scientific American, June 1966, pp. 60-69.

30. Roads and Transportation Assocn. of Canada. Guide to bridge hydraulics: (Editor, C.R. Neill). 875 Carling Avenue, Ottawa, Canada.

31. Simons, D.B., Richardson, E.V. and Albertson, M.L., Flume studies using medium sand (0.45 mm): U.S.G.S. Water Supply Paper 1498-A, 1961, pp. A-7-19.

32. Simons, D.B. and Richardson, E.V., Resistance to flow in alluvial channels: U.S.G.S. Professional Paper 422-J. 1966.

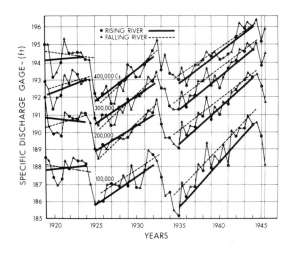

Fig. 5-1. Test for regime change. (Ack. Ref. 21).

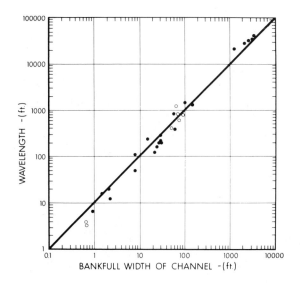

Fig. 5-2. M_L varies as b. (Adapted, Ref. 28).

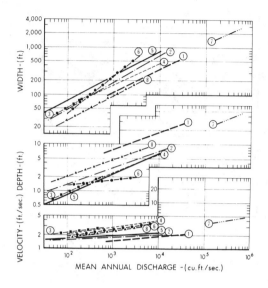

Fig. 5-3. b,d against Q . (Ack. Ref. 27).

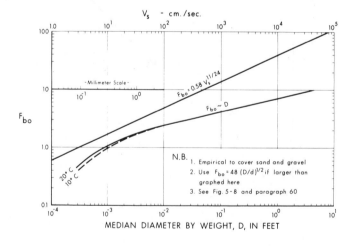

Fig. 5-4. F_{bo} against D for duned bed.
(Adapted, Refs. 5,8,9).

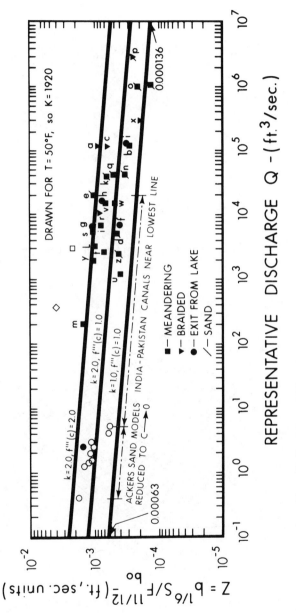

Fig. 5-5. Specific slope, duned bed. (Adapted, Refs. 5,8,9).

5-31

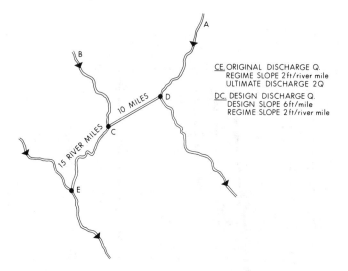

Fig. 5-6. Diagram for worked problem.

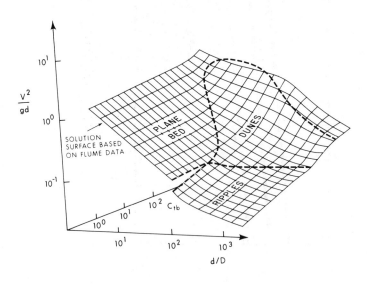

Fig. 5-7. Smoothing surface for flume data.
(Ack. Ref. 14).

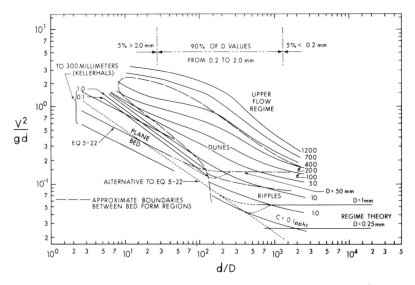

Fig. 5-8. Coordinated smoothed depth data of canals,
flumes and rivers. (Adapted, Refs. 11,14).

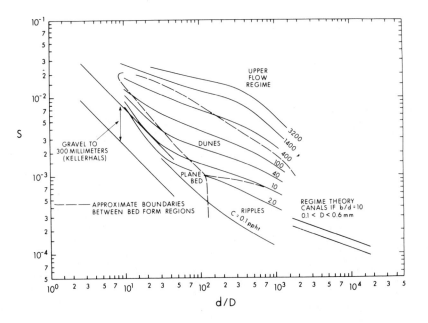

Fig. 5-9. Coordinated smoothed slope data of canals,
flumes and rivers. (Adapted, Refs. 11,14).

Chapter 6

NATURAL MIXING PROCESSES IN RIVERS

W.W. Sayre, Professor and Research Engineer, Institute of
Hydraulic Research, University of Iowa, Iowa
City, Iowa

Chapter 6

NATURAL MIXING PROCESSES IN RIVERS

6.1 INTRODUCTION

Natural mixing due to turbulent and convective transfer
play an important role in river ecology. Starting with the
fundamental three-dimensional conservation equation, and proceeding on to more tractable mathematical models of longitudinal dispersion, and transverse and vertical mixing, this
chapter reviews the current state-of-the-art for predicting
mixing in rivers. Particular emphasis is given to the early
stages of the mixing processes, before pollutants become uniformly distributed over the flow cross section and to mixing
in sinuous channels. Examples are presented, which show how
the principle of superposition, together with concentration
distributions resulting from idealized initial source conditions, can be used to predict concentration distributions
resulting from more complex situations, where sources are
distributed in space and/or time. Although many aspects of
mixing in rivers are not yet fully understood, the progress
achieved in the last fifteen years is encouraging.
Nature has endowed the land masses of this planet with
a network of streams, lakes and rivers that serves many essential functions in supporting terrestrial and aquatic life.
Traditionally, one of these functions has been to serve as a
waste disposal and treatment system. Largely as a result of
increasing pressures due to expanding population and industrial
activities, innumerable situations have arisen where the capacity of its remarkable system has been overtaxed to the point
where other essential functions of the surface water resource
have been severely impaired, if not eliminated. Certainly in
the heavily populated and industrialized regions we have long
since passed the point where "dilution is the solution to
pollution."
If dilution is not the answer, one may legitimately question the importance of continued research on natural mixing
processes in rivers. There is, of course, always the possibility of an accidental release such as occurred with the
chemical thiodane, which killed an estimated 40 million fish
along a 185 mile reach of the Rhine River in June, 1969. In
situations like this the results of many years of field, laboratory, and analytical research on longitudinal dispersion
can be used to predict at what time, and for how long, downstream water intakes should be shut down. A less obvious and
dramatic reason for studying mixing processes in rivers, although in the long run probably a more important one, is the
fundamental role that these processes play in the ecology of
aquatic systems.
A parcel of water as it moves along in a flowing stream
carries with it the properties and substances that collectively

constitute the water quality. Some of the substances may be undergoing degradation or conversion to other chemical and physical forms due to various chemical, biological and physical processes. The rates at which these processes occur are apt to be sensitive to transient states of the parcel of water such as temperature, dissolved oxygen concentration, biochemical oxygen demand, and the concentrations of various other constituents. Turbulence and secondary currents are continually at work mixing each parcel of water with its neighbors, smoothing out any differences in the water quality which exist within the stream cross section. However, this is sometimes a slow process, particularly in large rivers. For example it has been well documented by Mackay (1970), from measurements of sodium and chloride concentrations, temperatures, and turbidity, that 300 miles downstream from their confluence, the waters from the Liard and Mackenzie Rivers in Canada's Northwest Territory are still not completely mixed. This distance corresponds to a flow through time of nearly three days.

The assumption often made in environmental studies, that properties of the water do not vary within a stream cross section or along the stream axis, is clearly not always valid. If the water environment is to be managed soundly, the overall mixing and transport processes must be thoroughly understood.

6.2 MATHEMATICAL MODELS OF THE MIXING PROCESS

All mathematical representations of the mixing process are based either directly or indirectly on the principle of the conservation of some scalar quantity such as a mass of marked fluid particles, dissolved substance, suspended particles, or heat, that is transported and dispersed by the flowing water. The mathematical model is essentially a bookkeeping operation for describing the space-time distribution of the dispersing substance as a function of flow and channel properties. Distribution functions which do this are closely related to probability density functions. For example, if a large number of identical fluid particles are released at a point (x', y', z', t') in space and time, the problem of finding the concentration of these particles at some point (x, y, z, t) further downstream at a later time, is exactly the same as finding the probability that a single particle will go from (x', y', z') to (x, y, z) in the time $t - t'$.

Except for a few remarks in the next section, the discussion herein is limited to a binary system consisting of a conservative substance that is dispersing in river water under conditions of steady, or at most, slowly varying river flow. A conservative substance is defined here as one which undergoes no process other than dilution. Processes such as decay, chemical reactions, transformation to a different form, and production or removal by sources or sinks are not considered. It is furthermore specified that the fluid properties of the

conservative substance are identical to those of the ambient
river water.
General Convective-Diffusion Equation. To derive the general
convection-diffusion equation, let us apply the conservation
of mass principle to the mass of dispersing substance

$$M = \rho \int_{V} C \, dV$$

contained in an arbitrary control volume, as shown in Fig. 6-1,
that is fixed in a velocity field defined by the vector $\vec{u}$,

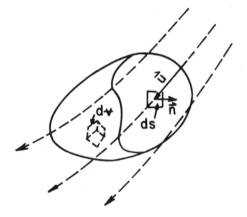

Fig. 6-1. Arbitrary control volume.

where ρ = mass density of dispersing substance, and C = its
concentration by weight. The rate of change of mass in the
control volume is

$$\rho \frac{d}{dt} \int_{\mathcal{V}} C \, d\mathcal{V} = \rho \int_{\mathcal{V}} \frac{\partial C}{\partial t} \, d\mathcal{V}$$

which in turn is equal to

$$-\rho \int_{S} C \, \vec{u} \cdot \vec{n} \, ds + \rho \int_{S} \varepsilon_m \, \nabla C \cdot \vec{n} \, ds,$$

| rate of change of mass in c.v. due to convection across surface of c.v. | rate of change of mass in c.v. due to molecular diffusion across surface of c.v. |

where $\vec{n}$ = unit normal vector directed outward from surface of control volume, and ε_m = molecular diffusion coefficient. Transforming the surface integrals to volume integrals by means of the divergence theorem

$$\int_{S} C \, \vec{u} \cdot \vec{n} \, ds = \int_{\mathcal{V}} \nabla \cdot (C \, \vec{u}) \, d\mathcal{V}$$

$$\int_{S} \varepsilon_m \, \nabla C \cdot \vec{n} \, ds = \int_{\mathcal{V}} \varepsilon_m \, \nabla^2 C \, d\mathcal{V} \quad,$$

and collecting the terms within the volume integrals, we get

$$\int_{\mathcal{V}} \left[\frac{\partial C}{\partial t} + \nabla \cdot C \vec{u} - \varepsilon_m \, \nabla^2 C \right] d\mathcal{V} = 0 \quad.$$

Since this relationship is true for a control volume of any shape or size, the quantity within the volume integral must be equal to zero, whence

$$\frac{\partial C}{\partial t} + \nabla \cdot C \, \vec{u} = \varepsilon_m \nabla^2 C \quad. \tag{6-1}$$

For incompressible flows where $\nabla \cdot \vec{u} = 0$, Eq. (6-1) is usually written

$$\frac{\partial C}{\partial t} + \vec{u} \cdot \nabla C = \varepsilon_m \nabla^2 C \quad. \tag{6-1a}$$

For turbulent flows, it is customary to resolve the instantaneous concentration and velocity into sums of time averaged and fluctuating components

6-4

$$C = \bar{C} + c'$$

$$u_i = \bar{u}_i + u_i'$$

where the subscript i denotes the i'th coordinate direction. and employ the Reynolds averaging procedure. The averaging period is sufficiently long to permit the averages of c' and u_i' to converge to zero, but not so long as to significantly damp the variation of $\bar{C}$ with respect to time. Also in turbulent flows, the contribution of molecular diffusion to the mixing process is usually negligible, so that it is customary to discard the molecular diffusion term. Equation (6-1) for turbulent flows then becomes, in Cartesian tensor form,

$$\frac{\partial \bar{C}}{\partial t} + \bar{u}_i \frac{\partial \bar{C}}{\partial x_i} = - \frac{\partial}{\partial x_i} \ \overline{c'u_i'} \ . \qquad (6-2)$$

By analogy with the Boussinesq eddy viscosity concept, the concentration-velocity covariance is usually represented as a gradient-type transfer term

$$\overline{c'u_i'} = -\varepsilon_{ij} \frac{\partial \bar{C}}{\partial x_j} \qquad (6-3)$$

where ε_{ij} is a turbulent mixing tensor. If the principal axes of ε_{ij} are aligned with the axes of the coordinate system, $\varepsilon_{ij} = 0$ for $i \neq j$. In a wide channel, alignment of these axes may be assumed throughout most of the flow cross section. In the vicinity of sloping banks this assumption is not true. In view of the approximate nature of Eq. (6-3), Fischer (1970b) the considerable complications that would be introduced by taking the off-diagonal ($i \neq j$) terms of ε_{ij} into consideration do not seem warranted. Consequently it will be assumed herein that

$$\overline{c'u_i'} = -\varepsilon_i \frac{\partial \bar{C}}{\partial x_i} \qquad (6-3a)$$

where ε_i is a scalar quantity, interpreted as a local coefficient for the turbulent transfer of mass in the i'th direction. In keeping with this interpretation, the summation convention does not apply to the right hand side of Eq. (6-3a). The main limitation on Eq. (6-3) or Eq. (6-3a) is that it does not apply until the dispersing substance is spread over a region that is larger than the size of the turbulent eddies, Corrsin (1964). In turbulent open channel flow, the size of the eddies is limited by the depth.

Substitution of Eq. (6-3a) into Eq. (6-2), expansion to conventional rectangular Cartesian notation, and dropping the averaging bars, results in the usual form of the general convection-diffusion equation for a conservative substance in a turbulent open-channel flow

$$\frac{\partial C}{\partial t} + u \frac{\partial C}{\partial x} + v \frac{\partial C}{\partial y} + w \frac{\partial C}{\partial z} = \frac{\partial}{\partial x}\left(\varepsilon_x \frac{\partial C}{\partial x}\right) + \frac{\partial}{\partial y}\left(\varepsilon_y \frac{\partial C}{\partial y}\right) + \frac{\partial}{\partial z}\left(\varepsilon_z \frac{\partial C}{\partial z}\right).$$

(6-4)

In this equation $C(x,y,z,t)$ = concentration by weight of dispersing substance, x,y,z = distance coordinates in longitudinal,
vertical and transverse directions, respectively; t = time;
u,v,w = time-averaged local velocity of flow in x,y and z
directions respectively; and ε_x, ε_y, ε_z = coefficients for
local turbulent mass transfer in the x,y and z directions
respectively. The group of terms containing u, v, and w, on
the left side of the equation, are called the convective
transport terms, and the group of terms on the right, contain-
ing ε_x, ε_y and ε_z, are called turbulent transfer or diffusion
terms. Mixing due to the convective terms is generally called
dispersion, and mixing due to the turbulent transfer terms, by
analogy with molecular diffusion, is generally called turbulent
diffusion, or just diffusion.

For a conservative substance there can be no transport of
the substance across either the wetted perimeter or the water
surface by either convection or diffusion. Stated mathematically, these conditions are

$$v\, C\, \frac{\partial y}{\partial n} = 0, \; w\, C\, \frac{\partial z}{\partial n} = 0 \qquad\qquad (6\text{-}5)$$

and

$$\varepsilon_y\, \frac{\partial C}{\partial y}\, \frac{\partial y}{\partial n} = 0, \quad \varepsilon_z\, \frac{\partial C}{\partial z}\, \frac{\partial z}{\partial n} = 0 \qquad\qquad (6\text{-}6)$$

where $\partial/\partial n$ denotes differentiation with respect to an outward
directed normal at the bounding surface.

If the dispersing substance is non-conservative, so that
there is either production or removal due to chemical reactions,
change of state, or transfer across the boundaries an appropriate source or sink term $S(x,y,z,t,C)$ must be added to Eq.
(6-4) and/or incorporated into the boundary conditions. Depending on the nature of the phenomenon, $S(x,y,z,t,C)$ can assume
a variety of functional forms, all of which represent a rate of
addition or removal of the dispersing substance at the point
in space and time for which the equation is written. If the
dispersing substance is subject to decay, the solution
$C(x,y,z,t)$ can simply be multiplied by an appropriate decay
factor such as $e^{-\alpha(t-t')}$. If the physical properties of the
dispersing substance differ from those of the ambient water,
the form of Eq. (6-4) does not change; however, it must be

recalled that the velocities u, v, w and the diffusion co-
efficients ε_x, ε_y, ε_z represent the motion of the dispersing
substance, which is no longer necessarily the same as that of
the transporting fluid. Dissolved oxygen, biochemical oxygen
demand, and heat are common examples of non-conservative
quantities; radionuclides represent a decaying substance; and
suspended sediment and materials that are adsorbed thereon are
examples of substances with different transport properties.

Solving Eq. (6-4) for a natural river situation, whether
by analytical or numerical methods, would be an extremely
formidable task, even if none of the complicating factors
mentioned in the preceding paragraph were present, as they
usually are, and the values of u, v, w, and ε_x, ε_y, ε_z at
every point in the river were known, which they never are. It
is only recently that significant headway has been made for
the idealized and relatively simple case of uniform, two-
dimensional flows which are approximately only in laboratory
flumes, for example, Yotsukura and Fiering (1964), Fischer
(1966), Sayre(1968a), Jobson and Sayre (1970b), Atesman (1970).

Simplified Models and Some Available Solutions. Insofar as
applications to natural rivers are concerned, the usual approach has been to simplify Eq. (6-4), either by assumptions
or averaging procedures, to forms which are amenable to solution but still retain the essential features of whatever aspect
of the mixing process is under investigation. The remainder
of this chapter deals with some of the more promising
approaches.

I. Fickian Equations. In this approach, which was the
earliest and is still the most common, a complete analogy with
molecular diffusion and/or heat conduction is assumed. The
transfer coefficients ε_x, ε_y, ε_z are assumed to be constants
and are replaced by the mixing coefficients K_x, K_y and K_z.
The local longitudinal velocity u is replaced by the cross-
sectional average velocity $\bar{U}$ which is also assumed to be constant. It is furthermore assumed that any effects due to the
variation of u within the cross section can be absorbed into
K_x, and that any effects due to the secondary flow velocities
v and w can be absorbed into K_y and K_z. With these
assumptions Eq. (6-4) becomes

$$\frac{\partial C}{\partial t} + \bar{U} \frac{\partial C}{\partial x} = K_x \frac{\partial^2 C}{\partial x^2} + K_y \frac{\partial^2 C}{\partial y^2} + K_z \frac{\partial^2 C}{\partial z^2} \quad . \qquad (6\text{-}7)$$

The convection term $\bar{U} \partial C/\partial x$ means that mixing is occurring in
a frame of reference that is moving at the velocity $\bar{U}$ in the
x direction. Equation (6-7) is a special form of the well
known heat conduction equation. Solutions of this type of
equation for a great variety of initial and boundary conditions
have been published, for example, by Crank (1956), and Carslaw
and Jaeger (1959).

The solution of Eq. (6-7) for the case of an instantaneous point source, consisting of a slug of conservative substance of weight W, is

$$C(x,y,z,t) = \frac{W}{\gamma} f_X(x;t) \, f_Y(y;t) \, f_Z(z;t) \qquad (6-8)$$

where

$$f_X(x;t) = \frac{1}{2\sqrt{\pi K_x t}} \, e^{-\frac{(x-\bar{U}t)^2}{4K_x t}} \qquad (6-8a)$$

$$f_Y(y;t) = \frac{1}{2\sqrt{\pi K_y t}} \, e^{-\frac{y^2}{4K_y t}} \qquad (6-8b)$$

$$f_Z(z;t) = \frac{1}{2\sqrt{\pi K_z t}} \, e^{-\frac{z^2}{4K_z t}} \qquad (6-8c)$$

and γ = specific weight of water. The functions $f_X(x;t)$, $f_Y(y;t)$, $f_Z(z;t)$ are all probability density functions of the normal probability law with respective means $\bar{x} = \bar{U}t$, $\bar{y} = \bar{z} = 0$, and variances $\sigma_x^2 = 2K_x t$, $\sigma_y^2 = 2K_y t$, $\sigma_z^2 = 2K_z t$. The solution for the instantaneous point source is particularly useful because it can readily be extended to give solutions for sources that are distributed in space and/or time by the method of superposition which will be discussed and applied later in the chapter.

As the dispersing substance is transported along the channel it gradually becomes evenly mixed over the channel cross section so that $f_Y(y;t) \rightarrow \frac{1}{d}$ and $f_Z(z;t) \rightarrow \frac{1}{B}$, where d = depth of flow, and B = width of channel.

The two cases of greatest practical importance are longitudinal dispersion from an instantaneous plane source that is uniformly distributed over the flow cross section, and the steady state case of transverse mixing from a continuous point source. In the former case $\partial C/\partial y$ and $\partial C/\partial z$ both equal zero because of the uniform distribution over the cross section, so that Eq. (6-7) reduces to

$$\frac{\partial C}{\partial t} + \bar{U} \frac{\partial C}{\partial x} = K_x \frac{\partial^2 C}{\partial x^2} \qquad (6-9)$$

for which the solution is

6-8

$$C(x,t) = \frac{W}{A\gamma} \frac{1}{2\sqrt{\pi K_x t}} e^{-\frac{(x-\overline{U}t)^2}{4K_x t}} \qquad (6\text{-}10)$$

where A = cross-sectional area of the channel. The concentration distribution $C(x,t)$ in Eq. (6-10) is related to the normal probability density function $f_X(x;t)$ in Eq. (6-8a) by the proportionality factor $W/A\gamma$, which is equal to the area under the longitudinal concentration distribution curve for a particular value of t. If the concentration is represented as a function of t for a particular value of x, the area under the curve is $W/\gamma Q$ where $Q = \overline{U}A$ is the flow discharge.

In the steady state case of transverse mixing from a continuous point source, let it first be assumed that the channel is much wider than it is deep, so that mixing over the depth of flow occurs relatively rapidly. Then Eq. (6-7) reduces to

$$\overline{U} \frac{\partial C}{\partial x} = K_x \frac{\partial^2 C}{\partial x^2} + K_z \frac{\partial^2 C}{\partial z^2} \qquad (6\text{-}11)$$

for which the solution is

$$C(z,x) = \frac{q_e C_e}{2\pi d \sqrt{K_x K_z}} e^{\frac{\overline{U}x}{2K_x}} K_0 \left[\frac{\overline{U}}{2K_x} \sqrt{x^2 + \frac{K_x}{K_z} z^2} \right] \qquad (6\text{-}12)$$

where q_e = volumetric discharge rate of effluent, C_e = concentration of effluent, and $K_0[\ ]$ = modified Bessel function of the second kind, of order zero. Values of $K_0[\ ]$ are tabulated in mathematical reference books such as Korn and Korn (1961). For

$$\left(\frac{K_x}{K_z}\right) \frac{z^2}{x^2} \ll 1 \text{ , and } x \gg \frac{2K_x}{\overline{U}} \text{ ,}$$

the influence of longitudinal dispersion becomes negligible and Eq. (6-12) converges to

$$C(z,x) = \frac{q_e C_e}{\overline{U}d} \frac{1}{2\sqrt{\pi K_z x/\overline{U}}} e^{-\frac{z^2 \overline{U}}{4K_z x}} \qquad (6\text{-}13)$$

which is the solution of Eq. (6-11) if the longitudinal dispersion term is neglected.

6-9

In a channel of finite width, Eqs. (6-12) and (6-13) apply only in the region extending downstream from the section where $f_\gamma(y;t) \approx \frac{1}{d}$ to the section where a significant amount of the dispersing substance encounters one bank or the other. This situation can be handled by the reflection or image source technique in which the portion of the calculated transverse distribution falling beyond the bank is folded back inside the bank and added to the portion falling inside the channel. The solution for the general case, in which the source is displaced a lateral distance ζ from the origin which is taken at the center of the channel is

$$C(z,x) = C(z-\zeta,x) + \sum_{n=1}^{\infty} \left\{ C(nB - \zeta + (-1)^n z,x) \right.$$

$$\left. + C(-nB - \zeta + (-1)^n z,x) \right\} \tag{6-14}$$

where $-B/2 \leq z \leq B/2$, and n = number of reflection cycles. The terms in the right hand side of the equation are calculated from Eqs. (6-12) or (6-13). There is no significant contribution to $C(z,x)$ from terms with $n > 4$ or 5. The maximum distance required for $C(z,x)$ to become almost uniformly distributed across the channel (C_{min}/C_{max} = 0.98), which occurs when the source is located at one bank, is

$$x = 0.5 \ \bar{U} \ B^2/K_z \ . \tag{6-15}$$

The minimum distance, which occurs when the source is located in the center of the channel, is one-fourth as great. If y and d are substituted for z and B, Eqs. (6-14) and (6-15) can be applied to cases of vertical mixing.

Comparison between solutions of the Fickian equations and experimental observations in channels that are fairly straight and uniform tend to show reasonably good agreement for the transverse and vertical mixing processes except very close to the source, and for the longitudinal dispersion process after x and t become very large. In earlier stages of the longitudinal dispersion process, experimental observations typically indicate a longitudinal concentration distribution that is negatively skewed (weighted in the downstream direction with a tail extending in the upstream direction), whereas Eq. (6-10) always predicts a symmetrical, bell-shaped longitudinal distribution. If the channel is meandering and/or highly irregular the Fickian equations do not represent the transverse and vertical mixing process very well, evidently because they are incapable of faithfully representing the convective transport due to the secondary flow velocities v and w which are apt to be quite important in such cases. However, the Fickian equations work about as well for the longitudinal dispersion process in

meandering and irregular channels as they do in straight uniform channels. All in all, it is fortuitous that the Fickian
equations provide as good a kinematic description of the mixing
process as they do, considering that the principal physical
mechanisms responsible for the mixing have been all but ignored.
Additional details and references concerning the derivation and
application of the Fickian equations are given by Sayre and
Chang (1968).

    II. Diffusion by Continuous Movements. Until now nothing
has been said about how the mixing coefficients K_x, K_y, and
K_z are related to flow and turbulence properties. The first
successful endeavor in this regard was Taylor's (1921) theory
of diffusion by continuous movements which relates the rate of
turbulent diffusion to Lagrangian turbulence properties.
Lagrangian turbulence properties are based on the statistical
histories of the motion of discrete fluid particles as opposed
to Eulerian turbulence properties, which are based on the
statistical histories of instantaneous velocities measured at
fixed points.

    In its simplest form, the theory of diffusion by continu-
ous movements describes the spreading, in one dimension, of a
group of particles in a turbulence field which is spatially
homogeneous and stationary in time. The main result is the
equation

$$\sigma_i^2(t) = 2 \overline{u_i'^2} \int_0^t \int_0^{t'} R_{u_i'}(\tau) \, d\tau \, dt' \qquad (6\text{-}16)$$

which after integration by parts becomes

$$\sigma_i^2(t) = 2 \overline{u_i'^2} \int_0^t (t-\tau) R_{u_i'}(\tau) \, d\tau \ . \qquad (6\text{-}16a)$$

In Eqs. (6-16) and (6-16a) $\sigma_i^2(t)$ = variance of distribution
of particles in the i'th direction at time t, u_i' = instantaneous velocity of a particle relative to the mean velocity
$\overline{u_i'^2}$ = Lagrangian turbulence intensity where the averaging is
done over an ensemble of particles, and

$$R_{u_i'}(\tau) = \frac{\overline{u_i'(t) \, u_i'(t-\tau)}}{\overline{u_i'^2}} \qquad (6\text{-}17)$$

is the Lagrangian correlation coefficient.

In general, $\sigma_i^2(t)$ depends on the functional form of $R_{u_i'}(\tau)$ which, like all Lagrangian turbulence properties, is difficult to determine and is usually not known. Even so, Eqs. (6-16) and (6-16a) are useful for the limiting cases of (1) very small diffusion times for which $R_{u_i'} \approx 1$ so that

$$\sigma_i^2(t) \approx \overline{u_i'^2} \; t^2 \qquad (6\text{-}18)$$

and (2) large diffusion times for which $R_{u_i'}(\tau) \to 0$ in which case

$$\sigma_i^2(t) \approx 2 \overline{u_i'^2} \; t \underbrace{\int_0^\infty R_{u_i'}(\tau)d\tau}_{L_{t_i}} - 2 \overline{u_i'^2} \int_0^\infty \tau R_{u_i'}(\tau)d\tau \qquad (6\text{-}19)$$

where L_{t_i} = Lagrangian integral time scale of turbulence. In a stationary homogeneous turbulence field the second term on the right of Eq. (6-19) is a constant, so that as t becomes very large

$$\sigma_i^2(t) \approx 2 \underbrace{\overline{u_i'^2} \; L_{t_i}}_{\varepsilon_i \text{ or } K_i} \; t \; . \qquad (6\text{-}20)$$

Comparing Eq. (6-20) with the variances σ_x^2, σ_y^2, and σ_z^2 for Eqs. (6-8a) - (6-8c), the product $\overline{u_i'^2} \; L_{t_i}$ emerges as a coefficient of turbulent diffusion, giving physical meaning to the mixing coefficients K_x, K_y, and K_z for cases where turbulence is the principal mixing mechanism. An additional link between the theory of diffusion by continuous movements and the Fickian theory is provided by the extended form of the Central Limit Theorem according to which the distribution of the sum of n random variables tends toward a normal distribution as n increases, even though there is some correlation between successive random variables (spatial displacements due to turbulent impulses).

An important difference between the theory of diffusion by continuous movements and the approximate Fickian theory is that the former predicts an initial mixing period during which the diffusion coefficient

$$\varepsilon_i = \frac{1}{2} \frac{d\sigma_i^2}{dt} = \overline{u_i'^2} \int_0^t R_{u_i'}(\tau)d\tau \qquad (6\text{-}21)$$

is dependent on time and $R_{u_i'}(\tau)$, whereas in the latter theory the diffusion coefficient is constant throughout.

Because the theory of diffusion by continuous movements applies only to a homogeneous turbulence field, it appears at first glance to be not at all applicable to turbulent shear flows, wherein the statistical properties of the turbulence vary with the distance from the boundary. However, Orlob (1961) has shown that planes which are parallel to the bed in wide rectangular channels with uniform flow, for example the water surface, can indeed satisfy the criteria for a homogeneous turbulence field. Therefore, the theory of diffusion by continuous movements is sometimes applicable to the spreading of floating material by turbulent eddies. More importantly, Batchelor and Townsend (1956) pointed out that uniform flows in a confined channel constitute axially homogeneous turbulence fields which satisfy the requirements of the theory of diffusion by continuous movements for the case of longitudinal dispersion. This is because the instantaneous velocity of a fluid particle that is free to wonder all over the cross section, is a stationary random function of time, even though it varies with position in the cross section also. Sayre (1968a) interpreted longitudinal dispersion results predicted by the convection-diffusion equation in terms of the theory of diffusion by continuous movements and found them compatible in all important respects.

III. The Mixing Coefficients. The vertical mixing coefficient K_y is commonly evaluated by assuming that the turbulent transfer of mass and momentum are equivalent (Reynolds' analogy), and that the shear stress $\tau_{xy} = -\rho \overline{u'v'}$ as linearly distributed, ranging from a value of zero at the water surface to $\tau_0 = \gamma \, d \, S_e$ at the channel bed, whence

$$\varepsilon_y \approx \frac{-\overline{u'v'}}{\frac{du}{dy}} \approx \frac{\frac{\tau_0}{\rho}(1-\frac{y}{d})}{\frac{du}{dy}} \quad . \qquad (6\text{-}22)$$

In the above relationships ρ = mass density of water, $\overline{u'v'}$ = covariance of longitudinal and vertical turbulent velocity fluctuations, γ = specific weight of water, and S_e = energy gradient. The bed shear stress and the fluid mass density are usually combined into the parameter $U_* = \sqrt{\tau_0/\rho}$ known as the shear velocity. In an open channel flow with a logarithmic velocity distribution

$$\frac{du}{dy} = \frac{U_*}{\kappa y} \quad .$$

Incorporating this expression with $\kappa = 0.4$ into Eq. (6-21) and averaging over the depth gives

$$K_y = \frac{1}{d} \int_0^d \epsilon_y dy \approx 0.07 \, d \, U_* \ . \qquad (6-23)$$

Equations (6-22) and (6-23) have been verified in laboratory flumes by Kalinske and Pien (1944), Al-Saffar (1964), and Jobson and Sayre (1970a) and have also provided much of the basis for the theory of suspended sediment transport in rivers, Task Committee on Preparation of Sedimentation Manual (1963).

No acceptable theory for predicting the value of the transverse mixing coefficient K_z has been developed as yet. However, numerous experiments in straight channels, ranging from small laboratory flumes to medium sized irrigation canals have indicated that

$$K_z = \alpha \, d \, U_* \ , \qquad (6-24)$$

where the proportionality coefficient $\alpha = K_z/dU_*$ varies between about 0.1 and 0.2, tending to increase with increasing width-to-depth ratio (Okoye, 1970). In large natural streams values of α ranging from 0.6 in the Missouri River, Yotsukura, Fischer and Sayre (1970), to about 2 in the Mackenzie River [author's analysis of data reported by Mackay (1970)] have been found. This range corresponds approximately to the range of α values indicated by Chang's (1971) experiments in sinuous laboratory flumes at the Iowa Institute of Hydraulic Research. Evidently the large α values observed in natural streams is traceable to the influence of secondary flow, rather than to a scale effect.

The longitudinal dispersion coefficient is much larger than either the vertical or transverse mixing coefficient. Values of K_x/dU_* ranging from about 5 for laboratory flumes, Sayre and Chang (1968), to about 5,000 for the Missouri River, Yotsukura, Fischer, and Sayre (1970), have been reported. Further discussion of K_x is deferred until the next section.

Empirical evaluation of the mixing coefficients from observed concentration distribution data is essentially a curve fitting process. Methods that are based on the amount of mixing which occurs along a reach wherein the cloud or plume is observed at two or more cross sections are preferred. Among the preferred methods are: (1) the method of moments, Sayre and Chang (1968), Fischer (1966), according to which

$$K_x = \frac{\overline{U}^3}{2} \frac{d\sigma_t^2}{dx} \qquad (6-25)$$

wherein σ_t^2 = variance of concentration versus time curve observed at a cross section, and

$$K_z = \frac{\bar{U}}{2} \frac{d\sigma_z^2}{dx} \; ; \qquad (6\text{-}26)$$

(2) simulation methods which involve the trial and error substitution of the appropriate mixing coefficient into the numerical or analytical solution of the appropriate governing equation. The routing procedure, Fischer (1966), and the transverse mixing model used by Yotsukura, Fischer, and Sayre (1970) for the Missouri River, both of which are alluded to in later sections, are examples of simulation methods.

IV. Longitudinal Dispersion Process. The following description of the longitudinal dispersion process is based mainly on the work of Fischer (1966, 1967, 1968, 1969), who in turn, extended concepts that were first advanced by Taylor (1954), Aris (1956), and Elder (1959) and made them applicable to natural streams. The main hypothesis is that longitudinal dispersion is predominantly due to the combined mechanisms of mixing over the flow cross section, and the variation of longitudinal velocity within the flow cross section which gives rise to differential convection. Following an initial stage which is dominated by convection, it is further hypothesized that a condition of quasi-equilibrium between the mixing and convection mechanisms becomes established wherein longitudinal dispersion proceeds in accordance with Eq. (6-9), the one-dimensional Fickian equation. The two stages, called respectively the convection period and the Taylor period, are illustrated in Fig. 6-2.

Only the bare outlines of the theory are presented here. Assuming that the structure of the flow and the geometrical properties of the channel are longitudinally homogeneous, Eq. (6-4), the three-dimensional general convection-diffusion equation, reduces to

$$\frac{\partial \bar{C}}{\partial t} + \bar{U} \frac{\partial \bar{C}}{\partial x} = - \frac{\partial}{\partial x} \overline{u'c'} + \varepsilon_x \frac{\partial^2 \bar{C}}{\partial x^2} \qquad (6\text{-}27)$$

when averaged over the flow cross section. The overbars represent cross-sectional averaging and $u' = u - \bar{U}$ and $c' = C - \bar{C}$ are respectively the local deviations from the average velocity and concentration. If, by analogy with turbulent diffusion, it is assumed that

$$\overline{u'c'} = - K_c \frac{\partial \bar{C}}{\partial x} \qquad (6\text{-}28)$$

where K_c is interpreted as a gradient-type diffusion

put in the form of Eq. (6-9), the Fickian equation, in which

$$K_x = K_c + \bar{\varepsilon}_x \; . \qquad (6\text{-}29)$$

6-15

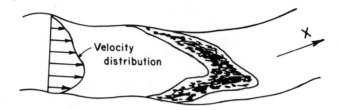

Velocity
distribution

Convective period

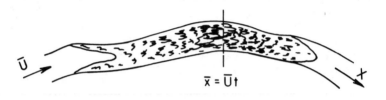

$\bar{U}$

$\bar{x} = \bar{U}t$

Taylor period

Fig. 6-2. Schematic illustration of the stages of the
longitudinal dispersion process.

It has been demonstrated both analytically and experimentally
that $K_c \gg \varepsilon_x$, so that for practical purposes $K_x \approx K_c$.
Subtraction of Eq. (6-27) from Eq. (6-4), together with
the assumption that

$$\frac{\partial c'}{\partial t} + \bar{U} \frac{\partial c'}{\partial x} + \frac{\partial}{\partial x} (u'c' - \overline{u'c'}) \to 0$$

with increasing t , yields the steady state equation

$$u' \frac{\partial \bar{C}}{\partial x} = \frac{\partial}{\partial y} \left(\varepsilon_y \frac{\partial c'}{\partial y} \right) + \frac{\partial}{\partial z} \left(\varepsilon_z \frac{\partial c'}{\partial z} \right) - v \frac{\partial c'}{\partial y} - w \frac{\partial c'}{\partial z} \quad (6\text{-}30)$$

which in principle can be solved to obtain a steady-state
concentration profile

$$\frac{c'}{\frac{\partial \overline{C}}{\partial x}} = f(y,z) \qquad (6\text{-}31)$$

and, using Eq. (6-28), the longitudinal dispersion coefficient

$$K_x = - \overline{u' \; f(y,z)} \; . \qquad (6\text{-}32)$$

Theoretical justification for most of the assumptions made up to this point was provided by Aris (1956) who transformed Eq. (6-4), after leaving off the secondary flow terms, into a simpler set of equations that describe the behavior of the moments of the longitudinal concentration distribution. Aris analyzed the behavior of the moments and proved rigorously that the longitudinal dispersion process converges asymptotically to a Fickian type diffusion process in essentially the same manner and with exactly the same results that Taylor had predicted by intuition and physical reasoning.

Fischer (1966, 1967) went on to hypothesize that in most natural streams the longitudinal dispersion process is dominated by velocity variation and turbulent mass transfer in the transverse direction and that the essential features of the process are retained if Eq. (6-30) is written in the simplified form

$$q' \frac{\partial \overline{C}}{\partial x} = \frac{\partial}{\partial x} \left[K_z \; d(z) \frac{\partial c'}{\partial z} \right] \qquad (6\text{-}33)$$

wherein q' and $K_z \; d(z)$ are respectively the depth-integrated values of u' and ε_z , and it is assumed that the variation of c' and ε_z with respect to y is negligible. Fischer then integrated Eq. (6-33) to obtain the steady-state profile

$$c'(z) = \frac{\partial \overline{C}}{\partial x} \int_0^z \frac{1}{K_z \; d(z)} \int_0^z q' \; dz \; dz + c'(0) \qquad (6\text{-}34)$$

and after multiplying by q' , as in Eq. (6-32), integrated again to obtain the longitudinal dispersion coefficient

$$K_x = - \frac{1}{A} \int_0^B q' \int_0^z \frac{1}{K_z \; d(z)} \int_0^z q' \; dz \; dz \; dz \; . \qquad (6\text{-}35)$$

He also reasoned that

$$K_x \propto \frac{\overline{u'^2} \; L^2}{K_z} \qquad (6\text{-}36)$$

6-17

wherein L is a characteristic transverse length defined somewhat arbitrarily as the distance from the thread of maximum velocity to the most distant bank.

Using velocity and cross-sectional geometry measurements, Fischer (1967, 1968) has numerically integrated Eq. (6-35), predicting values of K_x for several natural streams that agree reasonably well with experimentally determined values. Equation (6-35) is the best currently available method for predicting K_x in natural rivers. Equation (6-36) illustrates more clearly the functional relationship of K_x to bulk flow and channel properties.

Equations (6-34) and (6-35) are applicable only after the dispersion process has passed through the convective period and entered the Taylor period. Fischer concluded from field and laboratory experiments that the Taylor period begins at

$$t \approx 0.4 \, L^2/K_z \qquad (6-37)$$

which corresponds to a distance downstream from the source of

$$x \approx 0.4 \, L^2 \, \overline{U}/K_z \, . \qquad (6-37a)$$

This result was confirmed by Sayre (1968b), from numerical solutions of Aris' moment equations, for point as well as plane source initial distributions.

The Taylor-Elder-Fischer theory gives no direct information on the longitudinal concentration distribution other than that it changes in accordance with Eq. (6-9) once the process has entered the Taylor period, in which case it must ultimately converge to a normal distribution. The skewed form, typically assumed by the distribution during the convective period, may not die out until long after the process has entered the Taylor period. In order to predict the longitudinal distribution in the convective period or the early stages of the Taylor period it is necessary to solve Eq. (6-4) or appropriately simplified forms thereof. Numerical solutions of somewhat simplified two-dimensional forms of Eq. (6-4) by Fischer (1966), and of the Aris moment equations by Sayre (1968a), have provided useful information about the early stages of the process.

Harleman (1966) has shown that for the condition of steady flow in a channel of variable cross section, Eq. (6-9) should be written

$$\frac{\partial C}{\partial x} + \overline{U} \, \frac{\partial C}{\partial x} = \frac{1}{A} \, \frac{\partial}{\partial x} \left(A K_x \, \frac{\partial C}{\partial x} \right) \qquad (6-38)$$

where $\overline{U}$ and A are functions of x, but $\overline{U}A = Q =$ const. The form of the solution will of course depend on the particular nature of the channel geometry.

Fischer (1969) has approached the problem of predicting K_x in a channel of varying cross sectional geometry, wherein the transverse velocity distribution varies from section to section, in the following manner. The channel is divided into 20 stream tubes of constant and equal discharge. The change of concentration in a stream tube segment is related to the longitudinal convective transport in and the transverse exchange between stream tubes by means of a finite difference equation that is based on Eq. (6-4). Assuming that $\frac{\partial \overline{C}}{\partial x}$ = const, this equation can be solved for c' in each stream tube of a cross section that is moving downstream at the mean flow velocity. Equation (6-28) is then used to evaluate K_x for this cross section, the required values of u' having been determined previously by measurement at selected cross sections and by interpolation between.

Hays, Krenkel and Schnelle (1966) proposed a mathematical description of longitudinal dispersion for use in streams with stagnant zones due, for example, to bank irregularities. Such zones tend to trap some of the dispersing material and then release it slowly back into the main stream, causing long tails on the concentration distribution curves. The channel is resolved into a main stream, and a dead or stagnant zone, for which the respective equations are

$$\frac{\partial C_a}{\partial t} + \overline{U} \frac{\partial C_a}{\partial x} = K_x \frac{\partial^2 C_a}{\partial x^2} - \frac{KP}{A_a} (C_a - C_d) \qquad (6\text{-}39)$$

and

$$\frac{\partial C_d}{\partial t} = \frac{KP}{A_d} (C_a - C_d) \qquad (6\text{-}40)$$

in which the subscripts a and d denote main stream and dead zone respectively, K = coefficient for mass transfer between main stream and dead zone, and P = length of interface between the two zones in any cross section. The two equations which are coupled by the mass transfer terms, can be solved simultaneously for C_a and C_d. Concentration distributions obtained by solving Eq. (6-39) and (6-40) resemble those observed in many rivers; however, quantitative information on how the transfer coefficient K and the dead zone geometry are related to bulk flow and channel properties is still very scarce.

Fukuoka (1971) investigated the longitudinal dispersion process in a 10-inch wide sinuous laboratory channel made up of a series of uniform bends, separated by short straight reaches, in alternating directions. Viewing the tracer cloud as a whole, the longitudinal dispersion process was found to behave like a one-dimensional diffusion process, as in a uniform straight channel. The dispersion coefficient K_x

was found to be larger, and the duration of the initial
convective period to be shorter, than in an equivalent straight
channel. From the perspective of a single cross section, however, the dispersion process was found to be longitudinally
periodic with a period of one bend length. The convective
dispersion coefficient

$$K_c = \bar{u} \frac{\overline{u'c'}}{\frac{\partial \bar{c}}{\partial t}} \, ,$$

determined from measured velocity and concentration distributions, attains a maximum value at about the middle of each
bend and a minimum value at about the middle of the straight
reach between bends. Effects of sinuosity on the mixing and
dispersion process are discussed further in the next section.

The mathematical modelling of dispersion processes in
estuaries is still in an early stage of evolution. However,
some promising starts have been made. Holley, Harleman, and
Fischer (1970) have shown that the ratio, T' , of the period
of tidal oscillation to the time scale for cross-sectional
mixing can have an important influence on K_x . For $T' \geq 1$,
K_x for an oscillating flow is equal to K_x for a steady flow
with the same time-averaged bulk flow characteristics. For
$T' < 1$, the time-averaged value of K_x for an oscillating flow
is reduced in approximate proportion to the square of T' .
Carter and Okubo (1972) have devised a method for relating K_x
to the geometry of the system and the attenuation of the peak
concentration. Fischer (1970a) has put together a two-
dimensional numerical model which simulates both the tidal
hydraulics and the transport and dispersion of pollutants in
the longitudinal and transverse directions. Because of geometrical and other complexities that are typical of estuaries,
numerical approaches are more promising than analytical
approaches for predictive purposes. However, the latter are
conceptually useful.

V. Transverse Mixing. Transverse mixing in rivers has
not been investigated as much as longitudinal dispersion. As
indicated in the section on the Fickian equations, either
Eq. (6-12) or Eq. (6-13) with K_z evaluated by Eq. (6-24) predict the transverse concentration distribution resulting from
a continuous point source quite well provided that the channel
is reasonably straight and uniform, and the velocity is reasonably constant across the width of the channel. However, in
most natural rivers this ideal combination of conditions does
not exist and the Fickian equations cannot be expected to provide anything more than a crude representation of the overall
transverse mixing rate.

In order to predict transverse concentration distributions
in rivers more accurately, factors such as the variation in
depth and velocity across and along the channel, variation of

width, and secondary flow have to be taken into account. A
simulation procedure similar to that employed by Yotsukura,
Fischer, and Sayre (1970) to predict transverse mixing in a
six mile reach of the Missouri River near Blair, Nebraska is
described briefly below. Using velocity distribution and
cross-sectional geometry data obtained at several cross sections
along the reach, the stream channel is divided transversely
into 20 stream tubes of constant and equal discharge. Average
velocities and cross-sectional dimensions are assigned at
specified intervals along each stream tube by linear interpolation between measurement cross sections. The steady-state form
of Eq. (6-4), when combined with the continuity equation for
incompressible flow and integrated over the cross-sectional
area of the j'th stream tube can be reduced to

$$
q \frac{\partial C_j}{\partial x} = \left\{ -[d \; \overline{w'c'}^d]_{z,x} + [d \; \overline{\epsilon}_z^d \; \frac{\partial \overline{C}^d}{\partial z}]_{z,x} \right\}_{z_{j-1}}^{z_j} \qquad (6-41)
$$

where q = discharge in stream tube, the overbars followed by
the superscript d represent averaging over the depth of flow
at z,x and the primed quantities deviations from this average,
and z_j denotes the boundary between the j + 1'st and j'th
stream tube. If the dispersing substance is fairly well distributed over the depth of flow and it is assumed by analogy
with Eq. (6-28) that the secondary flow convection term can be
represented as a convective diffusion term according to the
equation

$$
\overline{w'c'}^d = - \epsilon_c \frac{\partial \overline{C}^d}{\partial z} \qquad (6-42)
$$

then the two terms on the right hand side of Eq. (6-41) can
be combined into a single gradient-type diffusion term with
the overall transverse mass transfer coefficient $K_z = \epsilon_c + \overline{\epsilon}_z^d$.
Equation (6-41) can then be put into a finite difference form
like

$$
C_{i+1,j} = C_{i,j} + \frac{\Delta x}{q} \left[\left(\frac{d \; K_z}{\Delta z} \right)_{i,j} (C_{i,j+1} - C_{i,j}) \right.
$$

$$
\left. - \left(\frac{d \; K_z}{\Delta z} \right)_{i,j-1} (C_{i,j} - C_{i,j-1}) \right] \qquad (6-43)
$$

where i represents the number of longitudinal distance
steps of length Δx downstream from the source, d and K_z
are evaluated at the boundary between neighboring stream tubes,
and Δz is the distance between centroids of neighboring

6-21

stream tubes. The boundary condition corresponding to the requirement of no transfer across the banks is that no exchange is permitted across the outer boundaries of the outermost stream tubes.

Equation (6-43) was solved numerically for the Missouri River conditions with Δx = 200 ft. and K_z = 0.6 dU_* . A comparison between predicted and observed transverse concentration distributions for two cross sections is shown in Fig. 6-3. The agreement between predicted and observed distributions in Chang's (1971) experiments in 10-inch and 6-ft. wide sinuous rectangular flumes at the Iowa Institute of Hydraulic Research was comparable.

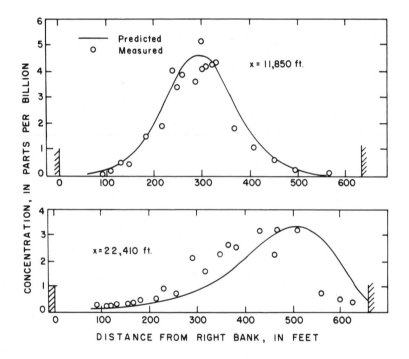

Fig. 6-3. Comparison between predicted and measured transverse concentration distributions, Missouri River, near Blair, Nebraska.

Holley, Siemons and Abraham (1972) followed a somewhat similar approach, when they incorporated transverse variations of depth, turbulent mass transfer coefficients, and longitudinal and transverse velocities into the depth-averaged convection-diffusion equation. However, instead of dividing the channel up into stream tubes and considering the transfer between stream tubes, as in Eq. (6-41), they related the transverse mixing coefficient to the second moment of the transverse distribution of tracer flux, $\overline{duC}$, rather than concentration.

Chang's (1971) results for a sinuous channel indicate that Eq. (6-43) sometimes breaks down, particularly near the inner bank, where the mixing phenomenon is strongly three dimensional. Also, negative values of the transverse convective mass transfer coefficient ε_c may occur near the beginning of bends, where the bend-generated helical secondary flow reverses direction. The negative value indicates convection of tracer away from a region of lower depth-averaged concentration into a region of higher depth-averaged concentration, which violates the concept of a gradient type diffusion process.

The transverse mixing and longitudinal dispersion processes in sinuous channels are very complicated and difficult to represent mathematically, mainly because the structure of the helical secondary flow undergoes cycles of growth, decay, and reversal as the flow proceeds from bend to bend. This is reflected in some typical experimental results of Chang (1971) and Fukuoka (1971), all for the same flow condition, that are shown in Figs. 6-4, 6-5, and 6-6. Figure 6-4 shows the bend geometry and transverse profiles of depth-averaged velocities at various sections along the channel. The flow distribution pattern is consistent with the classical concept of helical secondary flow in curved channels of rectangular cross section. However, it differs considerably from the pattern found in typical natural channels where the thread of maximum velocity tends to be displaced toward the outside of the bend. Figure 6-5 shows the transverse distribution of depth-averaged concentration for the case of a continuous point source located at the right side of the channel at section 8C. Note the profile at section 9B where the position of the peak has migrated away from the right side toward the center. This has to be due to convective transport by the secondary flow because gradient-type diffusion is incapable of producing that kind of bodily displacement. Figure 6-6 shows the variation of three selected parameters with respect to longitudinal position in the bend. The mean square velocity deviation

$$\frac{\overline{u'^2}}{\overline{U}^2} = \frac{1}{A \, \overline{U}^2} \int_A (u - \overline{U})^2 \, dA \qquad (6-44)$$

(equal to $\beta-1$ where β is the more familiar coefficient for non-uniform velocity distribution) varies periodically, reaching a maximum value at section D near the beginning of a bend and a minimum value at section B. Yen (1967) has shown in a channel of similar geometry that the intensity of helical motion, $|\overline{w}^d|/\overline{U}$, where $\overline{w}^d$ is the depth-averaged local transverse velocity near the centerline, is about one half a

6-23

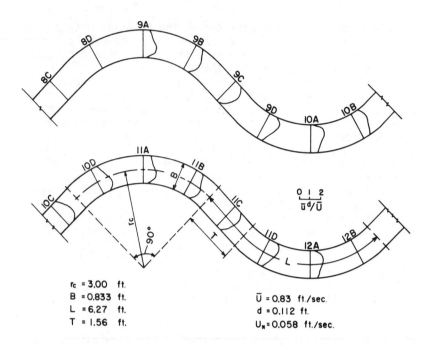

$r_c = 3.00$ ft.
$B = 0.833$ ft.
$L = 6.27$ ft.
$T = 1.56$ ft.

$\bar{U} = 0.83$ ft./sec.
$d = 0.112$ ft.
$U_* = 0.058$ ft./sec.

Fig. 6-4. Plan geometry of sinuous channel and transverse
distributions of normalized depth-averaged velocity
$\overline{u}^d/\overline{U}$.

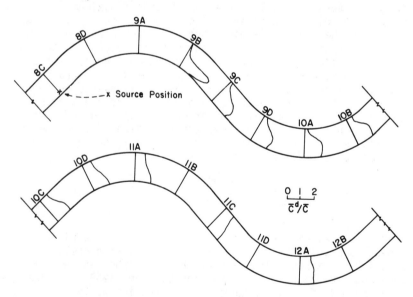

Fig. 6-5. Transverse distributions of normalized depth-averaged
concentrations $\overline{C}^d/\overline{C}$ in a sinuous channel.

6-24

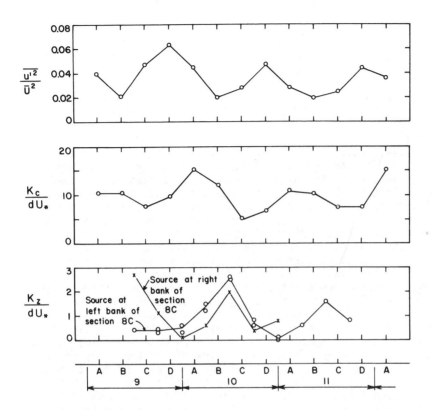

Fig. 6.6. Variation of selected parameters with respect to
longitudinal position in a sinuous channel.

bend length out of phase with $\overline{u'^2}/\overline{U}^2$. The secondary flow
reverses direction shortly upstream of section D. The con-
vective longitudinal dispersion coefficient K_c lags $\overline{u'^2}/\overline{U}^2$
by about one quarter of a bend length. The overall transverse
mixing coefficient K_z is about one half a bend length out of
phase with K_c . The values of K_z shown in Fig. 6-6 are not
strictly local values; they are assumed to be constant across
the channel, and are the values that give the best fit when
routing the transverse concentration distributions from one
section to the next using the simulation method based on Eq.
(6-43). At section 9B, before the plume has spread across
the channel, there is a strong dependence of K_z on the transverse position of the plume, and hence on the position of the
source.

In one set of experiments in the 6-foot-wide sinuous
channel, Chang (1971) obtained measurements of the transverse
velocity component w . Combining this data with his concentration distribution data, he used Eq. (6-42) to evaluate ε_c,
the transverse convective dispersion coefficient. The

6-25

width-averaged values of ε_c , when compared with the K_z values determined by the simulation method based on Eq. (6-43), were found to follow the same general periodic pattern but to be about 0.3 - 1.0 dU_* smaller in magnitude. Although the difference seems somewhat large to attribute to turbulent diffusion alone, the result on the whole supports the assumption that $\overline{w'c'}d$ can be reasonably well approximated by $\varepsilon_c \frac{\partial c^d}{\partial z}$.

Using Rozovskii's (1957) radial velocity distribution function for the central portion of a wide stream rounding a long bend, where the driving centrifugal forces are assumed to be in equilibrium with the pressure forces and turbulent shear stresses, Fischer (1969) has derived an equation analagous to Eq. (6-35) for predicting ε_c . Comparisons between predictions and experimental data obtained around a 180° arc of a circular laboratory flume are mildly encouraging. It is doubtful, however, that river bends are in general either sufficiently long or regular for the required equilibrium conditions to become established. In meandering channels, the secondary flow pattern is mostly in a state of transition. Chang (1971) attempted a similar analysis, but used measured radial velocities instead of Rozovskii's function. Predicted values of ε_c compared fairly well with observed values based on Eq. (6-42) when the secondary flow was in the decay phase of its cycle, but very poorly in the reversal and growth phases.

VI. Vertical Mixing. Provided that secondary flow is not a significant contributing factor, the prediction of vertical mixing in rivers is apt to involve fewer difficulties than the prediction of transverse mixing. For example, considering the case of a continuous point source, the longitudinal and transverse dimensions of the zone required to obtain complete mixing over the depth are much less than the dimensions required for mixing across the width because the depth is ordinarily so much smaller than the width. Because of the relatively small size of the mixing zone, flow conditions are likely to be more nearly uniform over its length and breadth. Furthermore, vertical distributions of flow velocity and the turbulent mass transfer coefficient are generally much more predictable than transverse distributions.

Assuming the existence of uniform flow along and across the mixing zone, and neglecting longitudinal turbulent mass transfer and any vertical components of secondary flow, the steady state form of Eq. (6-4), after integration across the width of the mixing zone, b , is

$$u \frac{\partial}{\partial x} \int_0^b C \, dz = \frac{\partial}{\partial y} \left[\varepsilon_y \frac{\partial}{\partial y} \int_0^b C \, dz \right] \qquad (6-45)$$

with the boundary condition

$$\varepsilon_y \frac{\partial C}{\partial y} = 0$$

at $y = 0$ and $y = d$. Some numerical solutions of Eq. (6-45) obtained by Jobson and Sayre (1970b) for the case of a continuous source at the water surface, a nearly logarithmic velocity distribution, and ε_y distributed approximately according to Eq. (6-22) are shown in Fig. 6-7. The data shown on Fig. 6-7 are from flume experiments. Profiles representing solutions to the Fickian equation, that is Eq. (6-45) with $u = \overline{U} = $ const. and $\varepsilon_y = K_y = $ const. are shown for comparison. The comparison gives some idea of the amount of error introduced by using the simpler Fickian equation. Actually, the initial source distribution used in predicting the profiles from the numerical solution of Eq. (6-45) was modified somewhat, because Eq. (6-45) predicts too rapid vertical mixing in the immediate vicinity of the source. Without this modification the predicted profiles would agree more closely with one another. The length of the mixing zone required to achieve a nearly uniform vertical concentration distribution according to either solution is

$$x = 0.5 \ \overline{U}d^2/\overline{\varepsilon}_y \ . \tag{6-46}$$

Equation (6-46) corresponds to Eq. (6-15) for transverse mixing.

6.3 APPLICATION OF SUPERPOSITION PRINCIPLE

Throughout the literature on mixing processes in rivers, attention is nearly always focused on concentration distributions resulting from idealized sources, most often an instantaneous point or plane source, or a continuous point source. This is not only because the idealized sources are more convenient from an experimental and analytical viewpoint, but also because distributions resulting from an idealized source can, by means of superposition, be used to predict concentration distributions resulting from more complex source conditions. In particular, the distributions resulting from instantaneous point sources can be considered as the basic building blocks for constructing concentration distributions that result from any known or assumed spatial or temporal source distribution. The mathematical basis for superposition is the convolution integral, which expresses the output distribution as the convolution of the idealized source response function and the actual source or input distribution. The most general mathematical statement, for the case where the source is distributed in three-dimensional space and time, is

$$C_0(x,y,z,t) = \int_0^t \int_{-\infty}^{\infty} \int_0^B \int_0^d f_R(x-x', y-y', z-z', t-t')$$

$$C_I(x', y', z', t') \, dy' \, dz' \, dx' \, dt' \quad . \quad (6\text{-}47)$$

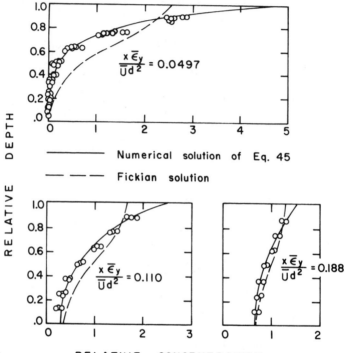

Fig. 6-7. Comparison between predicted and measured vertical
concentration distributions in a large laboratory
flume.

In Eq. (6-47), C_0 = the output distribution, f_R = the normalized concentration distribution function corresponding to the solution of Eq. (6-4) for the case of an instantaneous point source located at x', y', z' at time t' , and C_I = the input source distribution. In normal applications, one-, or at most, two-dimensional forms of Eq. (6-47) are employed. The two applications described below serve to illustrate the method.

The Routing Problem. Suppose, for example, that a substantial quantity of radioactive material has been accidentally

6-28

discharged into a river in an arbitrary and unspecified manner. In order to assess the danger to communities further downstream, the concentration of radioactivity as a function of time is monitored, as the slug of contaminated water flows by, at some cross section, specified by the longitudinal coordinate x', downstream from the point of release. Suppose furthermore, that values of the longitudinal dispersion coefficient K_x and the mean stream velocity $\bar{U}$, appropriate for the reach of river downstream and the present flow conditions, have been determined previously. With the information at hand, it is now desired to predict the concentration as a function of time at a section specified by the longitudinal coordinate x, many miles downstream from x', where a city is located. An approximate solution to this problem, using the superposition principle, is given by

$$C_0(t,x) = \int_0^t f_R(t-t'; x-x') \, C_I(t', x') \, dt' \; , \quad (6\text{-}48)$$

where $C_I(t', x')$ = the concentration versus time relationship observed at x', and $f_R(t-t'; x-x')$ = the normalized concentration versus time relationship for an instantaneous plane source obtained by dividing the Fickian solution, Eq. (6-10), by the area under the concentration versus time curve, $W/\gamma Q$, and replacing t and x by $t-t'$ and $x-x'$ respectively. The time $t-t'$ represents the time taken by an arbitrary radioactive particle in traveling from x' to x. The integration in Eq. (6-48) is usually done numerically.

Figure 6-8 compares a concentration versus time curve that was routed by means of Eq. (6-48) from Decatur, Iowa, 75 miles down the Missouri River to Omaha, Nebraska, with the concentration versus time curve that was actually observed at Omaha. The difference between the routed and observed curves is typical of the one-dimensional routing procedure in which the Fickian equation is used. Sayre (1968b) showed that this results from the fact that even in the Taylor period, the Fickian equation predicts too rapid an approach to symmetry, rather than from any basic defect in the superposition principle.

Fischer (1966) has used the routing procedure extensively as a means for testing estimated values of K_x. Yotsukura (1968) has discussed application of the superposition principle to routing problems from a more general viewpoint.

The Mixing of Two Rivers. Consider a stretch of river downstream from the confluence of River A and River B. Suppose that the quality of water in the two rivers is different and that the problem is to predict the distribution of the relative proportions of water from River A and River B in the channel downstream. Let the origin $(x = 0, z = 0)$ be located in the center of the channel a short distance downstream from the confluence so that both streams are contained in the same

6-29

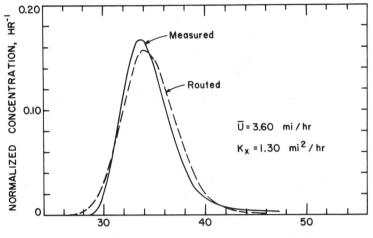

Fig. 6-8. Comparison between routed and measured concentration versus time curves, Missouri River at Omaha, Neb.

channel and there is a sharp demarcation between the water from the two streams. Suppose that the flow from River A occupies a fraction P of the total river width at the origin, starting from the left bank. Assume that the flow is uniformly distributed across the channel so that P also represents the fraction of the total river discharge originating in River A, i.e. $P = Q_A/(Q_A + Q_B)$. Let the variable ζ represent the displacement from the origin in the z direction at $x = 0$. Considering the water from River A as the tracer, the input transverse concentration distribution at $x = 0$ is given by

$$C_I(\zeta,0) = 1 \qquad -B/2 \leq \zeta \leq B(P - \tfrac{1}{2})$$

$$= 0 \qquad B(P - \tfrac{1}{2}) \leq \zeta \leq B/2$$

The normalized transverse concentration distribution function for the case of a continuous vertical line source, extending over the depth of flow and located at $(x = 0, z = \zeta)$, is $f_R(z - \zeta; x)$. It is determined by Eq. (6-14), the function which incorporates reflection from the banks, together with either Eq. (6-12) or Eq. (6-13). The desired output concentration distribution, given by the convolution integral and representing the proportion of water from River A, is

$$C_0(z,x) = \int_{-B/2}^{B/2} f_R(z-\zeta; x) \, C_I(\zeta,0) \, d\zeta$$

$$= \int_{-B/2}^{B(P-\frac{1}{2})} f_R(z-\zeta; x) \, d\zeta \, . \qquad (6\text{-}49)$$

Introduction of the coordinate transformation $z' = z-\zeta$ simplifies Eq. (6-49) to

$$C_0(z,x) = \int_{z+B(\frac{1}{2}-P)}^{z+B/2} f_R(z'; x) \, dz'$$

$$= F_R(z + B/2; x) - F_R(z + B/2 - PB; x)$$

$$(6\text{-}49a)$$

where $F_R(\ )$ is the cumulative probability distribution function corresponding to the probability density function $f_R(\ )$. If Eq. (6-13), which is proportional to the normal probability density function, is used in Eq. (6-49a), the individual terms in the series representing each of the two $F_R(\ )$ terms can be evaluated from tables for the cumulative normal probability distribution function. This is facilitated by dividing the terms containing z by $\sigma_z = \sqrt{2K_zx/U}$, which converts them to standardized normal variables.

Equation (6-49a) with Eq. (6-13) and $P = \frac{1}{2}$ was used to construct the curve shown in Fig. 6-9 for a source that is uniformly distributed across one half of the channel width. Figure 6-9 illustrates the degree of mixing, represented by the ratio of the minimum concentration to the maximum concentration, as a function of the distance downstream from the source. The other two curves, for the cases of a point source at the centerline and a point source at one bank, are shown for comparison. They were constructed using Eq. (6-14). Minimum and maximum concentrations occur at opposite banks for the two curves corresponding to the asymmetrically positioned source, and at the banks and centerline for the curve corresponding to the point source at the centerline. The fact that the distributed-source curve lies much closer to the curve for the point source at one bank than to the centerline source curve is somewhat surprising. Figure 6-9 was used to estimate the values of K_z, referred to earlier in the paper, from Mackay's (1970) data on the mixing of the Liard and Mackenzie Rivers.

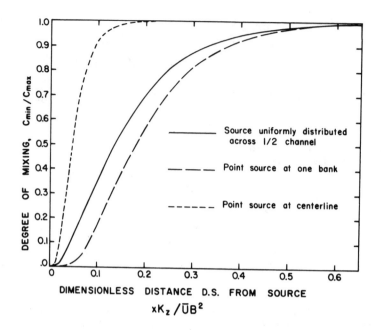

Fig. 6.9. Variation of degree of transverse mixing with distance downstream from source for different source configurations.

6.4 SUMMARY AND CONCLUSIONS

The mechanisms which produce natural mixing in rivers are an important part of the overall transport process for waterborn substances, and therefore of river ecology. For this reason, a thorough understanding of natural mixing processes in rivers is essential to sound management of the water environment.

Starting with the fundamental three-dimensional convection-diffusion equation, and proceeding on to more tractable mathematical models of longitudinal dispersion, and transverse and vertical mixing, current methods for predicting mixing in rivers have been reviewed for the joint purpose of: (1) providing a broad overview and a limited working knowledge for the nonspecialist, and (2) identifying areas of weakness, where additional research is needed, for the specialist.

Accurate and detailed predictions of mixing are now possible for the idealized case of uniform flow in a straight channel of constant cross section wherein the transport properties of the dispersing substance are the same as those of the ambient stream water. In rivers, where conditions of uniform flow in a straight channel of constant cross section are rarely more than roughly approximated, the mixing process is fairly well understood from a qualitative point of view. However, until considerably more quantitative information becomes available concerning the effects of channel curvature and irregularities on transverse mixing, approximate methods for predicting mixing will have to suffice. Because of the wide variety of channel characteristics which exist not only between rivers, but also along the course of any given river, it is probable that detailed predictions for individual reaches will always have to be treated - although within the framework of a common mathematical model - as special cases, with some reliance on field measurements of velocity distributions and mixing coefficients. For less detailed predictions it should be possible, up to a point, to obtain greatly improved functional relationships between the overall transverse mixing coefficient K_z , for example, and bulk flow and channel properties, which take channel curvature and irregularities into account.

Little has been said in this chapter about the mixing process for substances whose transport properties (e.g., density, viscosity, surface tension for fluids, and density and particle size for suspended solids) differ from those of the ambient river water. This is mainly because not much substantive information, applicable to river conditions, is available as yet, except perhaps for materials that behave like sediment in the silt and sand size ranges. Phenomena such as the dispersion of oil slicks and the mixing of heated effluents are only beginning to receive the attention that they deserve.

Finally, there is a need for improved interchange of ideas, insight, and experience among hydraulic engineers, aquatic ecologists and other water environment experts. Only by working together and pooling their resources can they optimize their contributions toward a more complete understanding and better management of the water environment.

6.5 LIST OF SYMBOLS

A	Cross-sectional area of channel.
B	Width of channel.
C	Local concentration, by weight, of dispersing substance.
$\overline{C}$	Average concentration.
c'	Deviation from average concentration.
$C_I(\ )$	Input concentration-distribution in superposition integral.
$C_0(\ )$	Output concentration-distribution from superposition integral.
d	Local depth of flow.
$f_A(a;b)$	Probability density function for random variable A, with respect to a , with parameter b . (A,a,b are arbitrary).

$f_R(\ )$	Response function in superposition integral.
K_c	Convective component of longitudinal dispersion coefficient.
K_x	Overall longitudinal dispersion coefficient.
K_y, K_z	Overall vertical and transverse mixing coefficients.
L_{t_i}	Lagrangian integral time scale for turbulence components in i'th coordinate direction.
q	Discharge in a stream tube.
q'	Depth-integrated value of u'.
$R_{u'_i}(\tau)$	Lagrangian correlation coefficient which correlates the fluctuating component u'_i of the velocity of a fluid particle at the times t and $t + \tau$.
t	Time.
u, v, w	Local velocities in x, y and z directions, respectively.
$\underline{u}', \underline{v}', \underline{w}'$	Deviations from average values of $u, v,$ and w.
$\overline{U}$	Cross-sectional average value of u.
U_*	Shear velocity.
W	Weight of dispersing substance.
x, y, z	Length coordinates in longitudinal, vertical and transverse directions, respectively.
α	Ratio of K_z to $d\,U_*$.
γ	Specific weight of water.
ε_c	Convective component of overall transverse mixing coefficient.
ε_m	Molecular diffusion coefficient.
$\varepsilon_x, \varepsilon_y, \varepsilon_z$	Local turbulent mass transfer coefficients, also called turbulent diffusion coefficients.
ζ	Transverse displacement of a point source from the centerline of the channel.
κ	von Karman turbulence coefficient.
ρ	Mass density of fluid.
$\sigma_x^2, \sigma_y^2, \sigma_z^2$	Variance of concentration distributions in x, y and z directions respectively.
σ_t^2	Variance of concentration distribution with respect to time.
τ_0	Shear stress at bed of channel.
$\overline{}$	Averaging symbol; may denote either a time or a cross-sectional average.
$\overline{}_d$	Denotes averaging over depth of flow.

REFERENCES

Al-Saffar, A.M., 1964, Eddy diffusion and mass transfer in open channel flow; Ph.D. Dissertation, University of California, Berkeley, 138 p.

Aris, R., 1956, On the dispersion of a solute in a fluid flowing through a tube; Royal Soc. (London) Proc., Ser. A, v. 235, p. 67-77.

Atesman, K.M., 1970, The dispersion of matter in turbulent shear flows; Ph.D. Dissertation, Colo. State University, 159 p.

Batchelor, G.K., and Townsend, A.A., 1956, Turbulent diffusion; p. 352-399 in Surveys in Mechanics, ed. by G.K. Batchelor and R.M. Davies, Cambridge University Press, 475 p.

Carslaw, H.S. and Jaeger, J.C., 1959, Conduction of heat in solids; Oxford University Press, London, 2nd Edition, 510 p.

Carter, H.H. and Okubo, A., 1972, Longitudinal dispersion in nonuniform flow; Water Resources Research, v. 8, no. 3, p. 648-660.

Chang, Y.C., 1971, Lateral mixing in meandering channels; Ph.D. Dissertation, The University of Iowa, 195 p.

Corrsin, S., 1964, Theories of turbulent dispersion; p. 27-52 in The Mechanics of Turbulence, CNRS, Gordon and Breach Science Publishers.

Crank, J., 1956, The mathematics of diffusion; Oxford University Press, London, 347 p.

Elder, J.W., 1959, The dispersion of marked fluid in turbulent shear flow; Jour. Fluid Mechanics, v. 5, pt. 4, p. 544-560.

Fischer, H.B., 1966, Longitudinal dispersion in laboratory and natural streams; Calif. Inst. of Technology, Keck Lab, Rept No. KH-R-12, 250 p.

Fischer, H.B., 1967, The mechanics of dispersion in natural streams; Jour. Hydraulics Div., Am. Soc. Civil Engrs., v. 93, no. HY6, Proc. paper 5592, p. 187-216.

Fischer, H.B., 1968, Dispersion predictions in natural streams; Jour. San. Engrg. Div., Am. Soc. Civil Engrs., v. 94, no. SA5, Proc. paper 6169, p. 927-943.

Fischer, H.B., 1969, The effect of bends on dispersion in streams; Water Resources Res., v. 5, no. 2, p. 496-506.

Fischer, H.B., 1970a, A method for predicting pollutant transport in tidal waters; Water Resources Center Contrib. No. 132, Hydraulic Engrg. Lab., University of California, Berkeley, 143 p.

Fischer, H.B., 1970b, Discussion of -- Dispersivity tensor for turbulent uniform channel flow; Jour. Hydraulics Div., Am Soc. Civil Engrs., v. 96, no. HY4, p. 1096-1100.

Fukuoka, Shoji, 1971, Longitudinal dispersion in sinuous channels; Ph.D. Dissertation, The University of Iowa, 139 p.

Harleman, D.R.H., 1966, Pollution in estuaries; Ch. 14 in -- Estuary and coastline hydrodynamics, ed. by A.T. Ippen, McGraw-Hill, p. 630-647.

Hays, J.R., Krenkel, P.A. and Schnelle, K.B., Jr., 1966, Mass transport mechanisms in open-channel flow; Vanderbilt University, San. and Water Res. Engrg., Dept. of Civil Engrg., Technical Rept. No. 8, 138 p.

Holley, E.R., Harleman, D.R.F., and Fischer, H.B., 1970, Dispersion in homogeneous estuary flow; Jour. of the Hydraulics Div., ASCE, v. 96, no. HY8, Proc. paper 7488, p. 1691-1709.

Holley, E.R., Siemons, J., and Abraham, G., 1972, Some aspects of analyzing transverse diffusion in rivers; Jour. of Hydraulics Res., v. 10, no. 1, p. 27-57.

Jobson, H.E. and Sayre, W.W., 1970a, Vertical transfer in open channel flow; Jour. Hydraulics Div., Am. Soc. Civil Engrs., v.96, no. HY3, Proc. paper 7148, p. 703-724.

Jobson, H.E. and Sayre, W.W., 1970b, Predicting concentration profiles in open channels; Jour. of Hydraulics Div., Am. Soc. Civil Engrs., v. 96, no. HY10, Proc. paper 7618, p. 1983-1996.

Kalinske, A.A. and Pien, C.L., 1944, Eddy diffusion; Ind. and Engrg. Chemistry, v. 36, p. 220-223.

Korn, G.A. and Korn, T.M., 1961, Mathematical handbook for scientists and engineers; New York, McGraw-Hill Book Co., 943 p.

Mackay, J.R., 1970, The lateral mixing of the Liard and Mackenzie Rivers downstream from their confluence; Canadian Jour. Earth Sci., v. 7, no. 1, p. 111-124.

Okoye, J.K., 1970, Characteristics of transverse mixing in open-channel flows; Calif. Inst. of Technology, Keck Lab., Rept No. KH-R-23, 269 p.

Orlob, G.T., 1961, Eddy diffusion in homogeneous turbulence; Trans. Am. Soc. Civil Engrs., v. 126, Pt. I, p. 397-438.

Rozovskii, I.L., 1957, Flow of water in bends of open channels; Acad. Sci. Ukrainian SSR (Transl. No. OTS60-51133, Off. Tech. Serv., U.S. Dept. of Comm., Washington, D.C.).

Sayre, W.W., 1968a, Dispersion of mass in open channel flow; Colo. State University, Hydraulics Paper No. 3, 73 p.

Sayre, W.W., 1968b, Discussion of -- The mechanics of dispersion in natural streams; Jour. Hydraulics Div., Am. Soc. Civil Engrs., v. 94, no. HY6, p. 1549-1559.

Sayre, W.W. and Chang, F.M., 1968, A laboratory investigation of open-channel dispersion processes for dissolved suspended, and floating dispersants; U.S. Geo. Survey Prof. Paper 433-E, 71 p.

Task Committee on Preparation of Sedimentation Manual, 1963, Sediment transportation mechanics--suspension of sediment; Jour. Hydraulics Div., Am. Soc. Civil Engrs., v. 89, no. HY5, Proc. paper 3636, p. 45-87.

Taylor, G.I., 1921, Diffusion by continuous movements; Proc. London Math. Soc., Ser. 2, v. 20, p. 196-211.

Taylor, G.I., 1954, The dispersion of matter in turbulent flow through a pipe; Royal Soc. (London) Proc., Ser. A, v. 223, p. 446-468.

Yen, B.C., 1967, Some aspects of flow in meandering channels; Proc. 12th Cong. Int. Assoc. Hydraulic Research, Fort Collins, Colo., v. 1, p. 465-471.

Yotsukura, Nobuhiro, 1968, Discussion of -- Longitudinal mixing in natural streams; Jour. Hydraulics Div., Am. Soc. Civil Engrs., v. 94, no. SA3, p. 568-571.

Yotsukura, Nobuhiro and Fiering, M.B., 1964, Numerical solution to a dispersion equation; Jour. Hydraulics Div., Am. Soc. Civil Engrs., v. 90, no. HY5, Proc. paper 4046, p. 83-104.

Yotsukura, Nobuhiro, Fischer, H.B. and Sayre W.W., 1970, Measurement of mixing characteristics of the Missouri River between Sioux City, Iowa, and Plattsmouth, Nebraska; U.S. Geol. Survey Water Supply Paper 1899-G, 29 p.

Chapter 7

EVALUATION OF THERMAL POLLUTION CONTROL ALTERNATIVES

by

Bruce A. Tichenor, Research Sanitary Engineer, National
Thermal Pollution Research Program, U. S.
Environmental Protection Agency, National
Environmental Research Center, Corvallis,
Oregon.

Chapter 7

EVALUATING THERMAL POLLUTION CONTROL ALTERNATIVES

7.1 INTRODUCTION

During the past few years a great deal of information and misinformation has been presented concerning the discharge of waste heat. The effects of waste heat in the aquatic environment have been widely reported as being detrimental, beneficial, or nil. Terms like thermal enrichment, thermal pollution, and calefaction have been injected into the already burdened environmental vocabulary. Conservationists and power companies have waged both verbal and legal battles over power plant discharges. A large amount of scientific work has been done to answer the questions concerning waste heat discharges, but still the controversy continues.

In the brief introductory remarks that follow, the sources and effects of waste heat discharges will be discussed. This discussion is by no means complete, and is presented only to provide a brief summary.

Sources of Waste Heat. Many types of human activity can change the normal temperature of water. Temperature changes may be a secondary result of altering the environment (for example, through road building or logging, by creating impoundments, or diverting flows for irrigation); or water temperatures may be changed directly by adding heat.

Many industries utilize water for cooling and thereby reject heat to the aquatic environment. About 90 trillion gallons of water is used annually for cooling and condensing purposes by the power and manufacturing industries. This is almost one-half of all the water used in the United States. Power generating facilities alone account for 80 percent of this cooling water usage.

Because the power industry accounts for such a large portion of cooling water usage, projected power requirements offer a good correlation to future waste heat loads. Power generation has increased at a net rate of over 7 percent annually, which means that it has doubled every ten years. This rate of generation is expected to continue for at least as fast as power production. This is because of less power contribution from hydrosources, a limiting efficiency of the conventional light-water-nuclear-fueled plants. Hence, the waste heat load from power plants, on a national basis, will double before 1982 and possibly increase eight-fold by the year 2000.

Two factors which all large, new power plants have in common are the magnitude and low quality of the waste heat load. For example, a modern 1,000 megawatt fossil-fueled plant operating at an efficiency of 40 percent rejects 3.8 billion Btu's per hour through the cooling water and a 1,000 megawatt light-water nuclear power plant discharges about 6.4

7-1

billion Btu's per hour through the cooling water.[1] Massive amounts of cooling water are required to absorb the waste heat rejected in the condenser. Upwards of 1,000 to 2,000 cfs of cooling water are circulated through the large power plants being built today. The cooling water temperature rise is from 15 to 30°F depending on the flow and power plant size. It is this combination of low thermal quality and huge quantities of water which increase the difficulty and cost of treatment or use of the heated effluent. It is important to emphasize the tremendous amounts of cooling water required to operate a single, modern power plant because this factor, by itself, adds to the control problem. Control measures, such as cooling ponds, cooling towers, or dispersion and dilution techniques would be much easier applied to 100 cfs of effluent cooling water, than to the 1,000 or 2,000 cfs which exhaust from today's 1,000 megawatt power plants.

Biological Effects. A summary of the available information on biological effects of waste heat discharges would fill several books. Thus, a detailed discussion in this paper is not practical, instead, the basic biological phenomena will be discussed, but not related to specific species or organisms.

Increasing temperatures can affect the water based ecological system in three, different but not mutually exclusive, ways:

I. Direct Temperature Effects. Organisms can be affected directly by temperature. Excessively high temperatures can kill individual organisms by breaking down essential enzymes. Increasing temperatures can also cause changes in reproductive mechanisms, thus, causing changes in the population. Temperature changes can also cause some subtle effects such as altering growth rate and changing the population of food organisms. High temperature regions in streams have been known to provide a thermal barrier to fish, thus preventing their migration.

II. Effect on Metabolism. As water temperatures increase the metabolic rate and corresponding oxygen requirements of fish and other aquatic organisms also increase. This increased metabolic rate follows vant Hoff's Law which implied that the rate with which respiration and other oxidation processes proceed is approximately doubled or even tripled for every 10°C rise in water temperature. It is also known that as the temperature of a body of water increases, the ability of that water to hold oxygen decreases. These two factors of decreas of available oxygen and an increase of metabolic reaction rate at increased temperatures combine to render a stream less compatible to fish and other aquatic life at high stream temperatures.

III. Synergistic Effects. Synergism can be defined as the simultaneous action of separate agents which, together, have a greater total effect than the sum of their individual effects. In reference to the problem of water temperature, synergistic action refers to the fact that as the water

7-2

temperature increases, the toxicity of poisonous materials is also increased and the suspectibility of the organism within the water to toxic materials may also be increased. Since domestic and industrial waste discharges are quite numerous on our nation's waterways, the synergistic action between water temperature and toxicity is a relatively common occurrence. It has been pointed out that in polluted water fish kills have accompanied a small rise in water temperature which may h ve been relatively harmless in an unpolluted water body where toxic substances were absent. The reverse of this is also true, that is, toxic substances may be of such a concentration as to be unable to cause fish kills without a corresponding higher temperature. Synergistic reactions between water temperature and disease causing bacteria are also important. For example, the myxobacteria Chondrococcus columnaris is one of the most destructive of all fish pathogens. The virulence of this organism increases rapidly at higher temperatures and often has been responsible for extensive and destructive epidemics in both trout hatcheries and natural fish populations.

The three phenomena just discussed makes it obvious that water temperature plays a major role in the ability of any water-based ecological system to maintain optimum characteristics throughout all biological stages. Temperature effects on all organisms in an aquatic community are important because of the interdependence of species. For example, temperatures which are not lethal to fish or shellfish may affect metabolism, reproduction, and growth, as well as reduce important food organisms, thereby inducing a change in the balance of the entire system. Also, temperature effects are different for various age groups of a single species. All natural biological systems are highly complex; hence, it is very difficult and potentially misleading to generalize on the effect temperature changes have on the aquatic biota. This is especially true when discussing the results of field investigations which show no significant effects caused by a thermal discharge. Studies of this nature can only be expected to discover acute short-term effects, while it may be years or even decades before the damage caused by subtle, chronic effects become evident.

Non-Thermal Effects of Cooling Water Systems. Concern about the potential environmental effects of cooling water discharges has focused most of its attention on the biological response to increased temperatures. However, it should be noted that non-thermal effects are also important.

When operating a once-through cooling system, (where the cooling water is merely pumped to the condenser, heated, and discharged back to the source) two non-thermal effects are possible:

1. Mechanical damage can occur as organisms pass through the intake, pump, condenser, and outfall. Both shear and pressure forces can cause such damage.

2. Chemical damage can occur, both for organisms passing through the system and those in the vicinity of the discharge. Chlorination is often used as an antifoulant and excessive residual levels may be toxic. The use of mechanical cleaning devices can alleviate this problem, assuming no anti-foulant treatment is required for the intake and discharge lines.

When a cooling system is operated in a closed-cycle (where the waste heat is removed by a cooling device and the water then recycled back to the condenser), the problem of thermal discharges is solved. However, several potential environmental problems emerge:

1. Discharge of vapor from wet cooling devices may contribute to local fogging.

2. Carry-over or drift of liquid droplets from wet cooling devices may cause problems, especially with saltwater cooling systems.

3. The buildup of dissolved solids in evaporative cooling systems requires discharge of blowdown, which if not controlled could cause chemical pollution.

4. The physical presence and size of cooling devices especially natural draft towers, may be unpleasant to some people and thus be considered aesthetic pollution.

Further discussion of the environmental aspects of closed-cycle cooling systems will be given later in this paper.

This brief introduction has described in general terms the problems associated with thermal discharges, even though detailed information was not provided. However, the purpose of this paper is not to answer all the questions about the pros and cons of thermal discharges. That would be an impossible task at this time. Nevertheless, there are some aspects of the problem for which there is virtually universal agreement:

1. Uncontrolled thermal discharges can cause environmental degradation, thus the term thermal pollution.

2. Thermal discharges can be controlled, such control being both economically and technically feasible.

3. The control of thermal discharges can cause other environmental effects.

These three facts lead to the conclusion that potential thermal discharge sites must be carefully evaluated, and the discharge should be managed so that it causes the least amount of environmental damage due to thermal pollution as well as other effects. In addition, of course, the discharge must conform to regulatory requirements such as water quality standards and permit restrictions.

The purpose of this paper is to discuss the various discharge management techniques which are available, including their technical and economical feasibility. The overall environmental impact of such techniques will also be discussed. The paper will be presented from the standpoint of thermal discharges from steam-electric generating stations, since as mentioned previously they account for the bulk of the waste heat discharged to the nation's waters. However, most of the discussion is valid relative to other types of thermal discharges.

7.2 SITE SELECTION

In evaluating alternative methods of controlling thermal discharges, it should be recognized that the characteristics of the power plant site determine to a large extent which alternatives are feasible. This is especially true if once-through cooling is contemplated, because of the large volumes of cooling water required. It should be recognized, however, that cooling water availability is only one of a myriad of factors that must be considered in selecting an appropriate site.

The process of selecting a site for a thermal power plant is extremely complex; economic, social, technical, legal, and political decisions are all required, and a comprehensive discussion is beyond the scope of both this paper and its author. The purpose of this section is to briefly discuss some of the factors considered in site selection, with emphasis placed on the cooling water supply and factors affecting waste heat disposal.

Various site selection parameters can be segmented as:
A. Location factors
B. Cooling water factors
C. Meteorological factors

A. Location Factors. The primary location factors are:

1. Fuel location. For fossile-fueled plants, the distance from the fuel source is an extremely important site selection criterion. Coal-fired plants must be sited either at the mine mouth or within reasonable coal transport distance via either rail, water, or conveyor. Oil and gas-fired plants are sited either near the source field, near major pipelines, or in close proximity to fuel sources as major determinants of plant sites, although shortening the distance to reprocessing plants does have some economic and environmental benefits.

2. Distance to load center. The transmission of electric power is costly. Direct capital expenditures include the cost of land right-of-way, transmission towers, and power lines, as well as construction costs. Operation and maintenance costs for the transmission facilities are also incurred. In addition, electrical line losses diminish the total power available for consumption. Also, transmission towers and lines are often esthetically unpleasing. All of these factors combine to make it desirable to generate the power as close as possible to the consumer (or load center). While technological advances in transmitting large amounts of power are being made in such areas as DC transmission and cryogenic cables, the distance from the load center will remain an important site selection parameter.

7-5

3. <u>Access to site</u>. The construction of large power stations requires massive amounts of equipment and material. The ease of access to the plant site via rail, water, or major highway is a major factor in construction costs. This is especially true for nuclear power plants using shop fabricated reactor vessels.

4. <u>Land availability</u>. Modern thermal power stations require large land areas for plant sites. The minimum total area for a 1,000 megawatt coal-fired station is about 150-200 acres, including space for coal storage, ash disposal pond, and switch yard. Cooling towers would require an additional 20-40 acres and cooling pond area requirements could run as high as 2,000 acres. Most coal-fired plant sites, exclusive of cooling pond area if required, have land areas of about 500-1,000 acres. Data on nuclear plants now under construction indicate land areas for sites ranging from 517 acres for a 655 megawatt plant to 2,065 acres for a 900 megawatt station. There is no firm guideline for estimating area requirements for plants, however 1,000 acres would be sufficient in the majority of instances.

Since power plants require large land areas, the cost of land is an important parameter in site selection. It is easy to see how a choice urban site could be rejected if land costs were excessive. For example, a 1,000 acre parcel at $20,000 per acre would cost $20 million, which would represent a significant percentage of the overall plant cost. On the other hand, rural land costs are normally less than $1,000 per acre so a 1,000 acre parcel would cost less than $1 million.

While it is obvious that utilities must expend considerable capital in land acquisition costs, it should be recognized that the land purchased is a renewable resource. When the power plant has outlived its usefulness, the utility can sell the land for other uses, often at a higher price than it originally cost. Thus, the purchase of land could be viewed as a long-term investment as well as a necessary capital cost.

The cost of land is also important in evaluating cooling alternatives. As will be discussed in more detail in a later section of this paper, cooling pond sizes and their cost can be varied to minimize the total power plant costs.

Soil conditions are also important in selecting land for a power plant site. As with any large structure, appropriate foundations must be constructed to limit settling. This is especially true for nuclear plants where the integrity of the reactor containment is essential. Special design features are also necessary if the site is in an area with a high potential for earthquakes. Finally, soil permeability is important in selecting a location for ash ponds or cooling ponds. Highly permeable soils might require sealing to prevent excessive seepage. Peripheral collection ditches can also be employed.

5. Land utilization. In the early stages of this country's rapid period of industrial growth, the use of land for generating electric power was usually given priority over other uses. This is exemplified by the vast amounts of land submerged under reservoirs impounded for hydroelectric power. Now, however, there is a more balanced view of land utilization, where all legitimate land uses must be considered in selecting an industrial site. Land management and zoning is now the rule rather than the exception. Therefore, even if a potential power plant site is adequate from the standpoint of its physical attributes, a judgment must be made as to whether the use of the land for power generation is in the best interest of all potential land users. For example, prime agricultural land is being rapidly depleted by suburban growth at a time when an increasing population demands greater food productivity, thus the use of such land for a power plant site may not be desirable. Also, heavy recreational demands are being placed on open spaces due to our increased leisure time. The use of recreational land for power plant sites should, therefore, be carefully assessed. Care should also be taken to insure against siting plants in areas of unique geologic, historic, or scenic value. Even though a plant may not physically destroy a valuable asset, its presence may provide an unacceptable aesthetic intrusion.

In assessing the best use of land, care must be taken not to apply a strictly preservationist point of view (i.e., no site is acceptable). What is needed is a careful balancing of the pros and cons of alternative land uses, along with the recognition that power plants must be built somewhere. It is obvious that a power plant which obliterates the view of a unique scenic vista should be avoided. However, it should also be obvious that a carefully planned and architecturally pleasing structure can be accommodated in a great many locations.

B. Cooling Water. As discussed in the introduction, large thermal power plants require huge amounts of water for cooling purposes. Thus, the availability of cooling water is a prime factor in selecting a plant site. The amount of cooling water required for a specific plant is based upon many factors, including: plant size, thermal efficiency, temperature rise across the condenser, and type of cooling system.

The specific heat of water is 1 BTU/lb $^\circ$F (i.e., for every BTU of heat rejected in the condenser 1 pound of cooling water is raised 1°F). Therefore, in order to determine the total amount of cooling water needed for a particular plant, information on total heat rejected to the cooling water and the cooling water temperature rise is required.

The amount of waste heat absorbed by the cooling water can be determined from a knowledge of the plant's thermal efficiency. The overall thermal efficiency (n_t) of a steam-electric plant is calculated as:

$$\eta_t(\%) = \frac{\text{Electrical Output}}{\text{Thermal Input}} \times 100$$

For one kilowatt-hour:

$$\eta_t(\%) = \frac{3413 \ (\text{BTU/KWH})}{3413 \ (\text{BTU/KWH}) + \text{Waste Heat} \ (\text{BTU/KWH})} \times 100$$

The denominator of the efficiency equation above represents the "heat rate" of a plant, which is defined as the average amount of heat required to produce one kilowatt-hour of electricity. All of the "waste heat" shown in the denominator of the second equation does not enter the cooling water, because of in-plant and stack losses. Plant design and operating data indicate that 15 percent of the thermal input is a reasonable approximation of these losses for fossil-fueled plants; for calculations on a kilowatt hour basis this equals 15 percent of the plant heat rate. Therefore, the following equation applies to fossil fuel plants:

Heat to cooling water (BTU/KWH) = 0.85 x Heat Rate - 3413

The amount of heat rejected to cooling water from nuclear plants may be computed in the same manner, except that heat losses up a stack are not involved. Typical in-plant losses are about 5 percent of the heat rate, so that the resulting equation which applies to nuclear-fueled plants is:

Heat to cooling water (BTU/KWH) = 0.95 x Heat Rate - 3413

As an example of the quantities of waste heat which can be expected in the future, the two types of plants are compared. For a modern fossil-fueled plant at 40 percent efficiency:

$$\text{Heat Rate} = \frac{3413}{\eta_t \div 100} = \frac{3413}{.40} = 8533 \ \text{BTU/HWH}$$

Heat to cooling water = 0.85(8533) - 3413 = 3800 BTU/KWH

For a light water nuclear-fueled plant at 33 percent efficiency:

$$\text{Heat Rate} = \frac{3413}{.33} = 10,342 \ \text{BTU/KWH}$$

Heat to cooling water = 0.95 (10,342) - 3413 = 6400 BTU/KWH

The relationship between plant size, cooling water flow, temperature rise, and waste heat to cooling water can be expressed as:

$$Q = 0.00445 \frac{(WH)(P)}{(\Delta T)(C_p)}$$

where

WH = waste heat to cooling water, BTU/KWH
P = plant size, MWe
ΔT = cooling water temperature rise, ^oF
C_p = specific heat of water = 1 BTU/lb ^oF
Q = cooling water flow, cfs

Figure (15-1) is a graphical representation of this equation. It shows that for equal generating capacity, nuclear plants require considerable greater volumes of cooling water at a given temperature rise than fossil-fueled plants. For example, a 1,000 MWe fossil plant requires 840 cfs of cooling water for a temperature rise of 20°F; a nuclear plant of the same capacity would require 1,430 cfs for an equivalent temperature rise. Another way of stating the same fact is that a nuclear plant will cause a larger temperature increase in a given cooling water flow than a fossil plant of the same size.

The data given in Figure (15-1) indicates the amounts of water circulated through the condenser. For plants with once-through cooling, this is equivalent to the amount of water required at the site, since there is no recycling. For plants operating on a completely closed-cycle system, the cooling water is recycled and only system losses need to be obtained from water at the site. Evaporative cooling towers require make-up water equal to about two to three percent of the circulating water flow. Thus, requirements of a power plant site are 30-50 times greater for plants employing once-through cooling than for plants using the closed-cycle cooling system with wet cooling towers. If a dry cooling system is used, the water requirements of the site are nil. Further information on the various water losses associated with cooling devices will be provided later in this paper.

It is obvious that recycling cooling water in closed-cycle cooling systems is a most effective way of reducing the requirements for water at a power plant site. Another means of accomplishing this objective is the use of power generation equipment which does not require cooling water; gas turbines are much less efficient than steam turbines and even though their use has been increasing rapidly in the past few years, they are used primarily for peaking power. By combining the flexibility and fast start up potential of gas turbines with a proven reliability and efficiency of the steam cycle, cooling water requirements can be reduced and relatively high thermal efficiencies can be obtained.

Manufacturers and consulting engineering companies are now marketing combined cycle power plants. By using the gas turbine exhaust in the steam cycle, combined heat rates

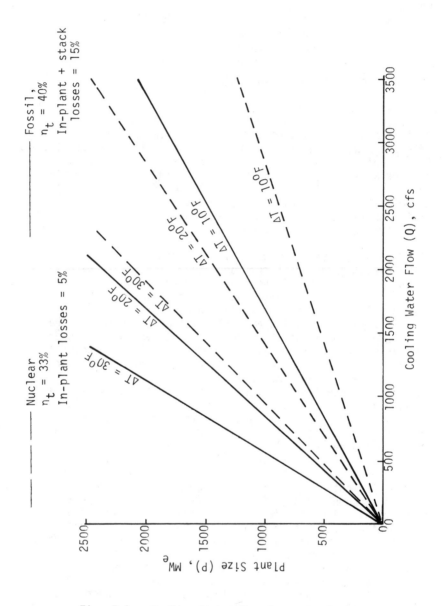

Fig. 7-1. Cooling Water Requirements for
Fossil & Nuclear Power Plants

of 9,000 BTU/KWH are possible. These combined cycle plants are used both for peaking and moderate load demands and range in size from 125 to 250 MWe. Another advantage of the combined cycle plant is the very short construction time relative to large steam plants.

Among the combined cycle units now on the market is Stone and Webster's Fast System which employs dry cooling towers, thus precluding the need for cooling water. Westinghouse's PACE (Power at Combined Efficiencies) plant is operated with conventional cooling techniques, but with 120 MWe out of the 240 MWe capacity from gas turbines, cooling water requirements are reduced substantially. Turbopower and Marine Systems, a subsidiary of United Aircraft Corporation offers a 125 MWe "turbo steam pack" with two 40 MWe gas turbines combined with a 45 MWe steam turbine.

Another factor to consider when assessing the water availability of a power plant site involves the disposal of liquid waste. Several types of liquid wastes can occur in the operation of a thermal power plant:

1. Chemicals (e.g., chlorine) in cooling water discharge
2. Sanitary wastes from on-site personnel and visitors
3. Chemical wastes from boiler water treatment, boiler blowdown, and condensate treatment
4. Ash pond and coal pile drainage effluents (fossil plant)
5. Low level radioactive wastes (nuclear plants)
6. Evaporative cooling device blowdonw

All of these wastes must be discharged in conformance with appropriate regulatory limits, such as water quality standards. Unless limits are placed at the point of discharge (e.g., effluent standards), sufficient water must be available at the site for mixing and dilution of the treated waste streams.

In summary, it has been shown that the availability of large volumes of water at a power plant site may or may not be a major factor in selecting the site. Certainly, if once-through cooling is contemplated large volumes are necessary, but through recycling of the cooling water much less water is needed. Also, combined-cycle plants offer substantial reductions in cooling water requirements.

C. Meteorological Factors. Weather plays an extremely important role in the operation of a thermal power plant. Weather is a predominant factor in determining the power required from the plant. Hot summer days and the associated heavy demand for air conditioning push power plants to their maximum output. Likewise, severe winters increase the demand for space heat, and thus power peaks occur.

Meteorological conditions at the site are important in the design and operation of the plant for several reasons:

1. Dispersion of potential air pollutants. Wind conditions at the site must be carefully assessed to enable prediction of the distribution of material released into the air, such as:

7-11

a. Fly ash, SO_2, and NO_x from fossil fuel plants

b. Low level radioactive gases from nuclear plants

c. Water vapor from cooling towers.

Sites with good ventilation such as an open plain or hill are preferable over sites with enclosed valleys or areas which have atmospheric inversions occurring over most of the annual cycle.

2. Potential for damage due to severe weather. Special design precautions must be used in areas which have a history of severe meteorological events such as floods, tornadoes, or hurricanes. As with any other riverside installation, flood protection must be provided if the plant is in a flood-prone area. While tornadoes are not normally given special design considerations for fossil plants, the containment structures for nuclear plants are designed to withstand tornadic winds. Standard hurricane protection should be provided in appropriate locations. Also, even though natural draft towers can be constructed to withstand winds in excess of 100 mph, their use in hurricane-prone areas is questionable.

3. Cooling system efficiency. The operation of the devices used to dissipate waste heat is primarily a function of the weather. Therefore, an evaluation of their capability requires an accurate set of meteorological data. Significant variations in the climatic factors with respect to season must be accounted for.

The nature of the heat transfer phenomena which a particular cooling device uses to dissipate heat to the atmosphere determines the meteorological data requirements for that device. A compilation of the heat transfer mechanisms and associated meteorological data requirements for alternative heat dissipation methods is given in Table (15-1). More information on how weather affects the operation and design of cooling systems will be provided in a later section of this paper.

7.3 ONCE-THROUGH COOLING

An attribute common to all systems used to reject waste heat from thermal power plants is that this heat is ultimately transferred to the atmosphere. Once-through cooling systems without supplemental (or helper) cooling devices use the adjacent waters of rivers, lakes, estuaries, or oceans to absorb the waste heat before transfer to the atmosphere. Closed-cycle cooling systems use cooling devices, such as ponds, towers, or spray systems, to transfer the waste heat directly to the atmosphere without first affecting any natural water body.

Once-through cooling is the most common type of cooling system used by thermal power plants in the United States. In the past, little concern was given to the thermal pollution potential of such systems. However, control techniques were

TABLE 7-1

METEOROLOGIC DATA REQUIREMENTS FOR
COOLING DEVICES

Cooling Method	Heat Transfer Mechanism	Meteorologic Data Required
Evaporative Cooling Towers	Convection Evaporation	Dry-bulb Temperature Relative Humidity*
Cooling Ponds	Radiation Convection Evaporation	Solar Radiation Dry-bulb Temperature Relative Humidity* Wind Speed Cloud Cover
Spray Cooling Canals	Evaporation Convection	Dry-bulb Temperature Relative Humidity* Wind Speed
Dry Cooling Towers	Convection	Dry-bulb Temperature

*Wet-bulb or dew point temperature can also be used.

used to prevent recirculation of the warm discharge water to
the intake. Also, intakes were designed to optimize the flow
of cold water to the plant. The techniques used include:

A. Skimmer walls, which are placed at the head of the
intake channel. These devices block the flow of warm surface
waters and allow the cool, deep water to enter the plant.

B. Underwater dams, which are placed in the rivers
immediately downstream from the intake channel. These devices
provide a barrier to the cool, deep water, allowing the warm
water to flow downstream and diverting the cool water to the
plant's intake channel.

C. Dishcarge design to prevent recirculation. The most
obvious method is to physically separate the discharge from the
inlet by sufficient distance. When this is not possible, the
outfall can be designed to either rapidly mix the warm discharge
water with the ambient to reduce the temperature difference or
allow the warm discharge water to float on the surface of the
receiving water and use skimmer walls at the intake to prevent
it from entering the plant.

The variety of techniques used in intake discharge design
shows that even when once-through cooling is used, management
of the thermal discharge is practical. As stated previously
such control was normally practiced to maintain high power
plant efficiency by preventing warm water from entering the
intake. The concern for thermal pollution has now provided

new criteria for intake and discharge design. The designer
must now be concerned with preventing adverse thermal effects
and at the same time meet the previous commitment to maximize
plant efficiency. Fortunately, these two goals are compatible,
since reduction in recirculation provide for reductions in
waste heat flow to the aquatic environment.

The goals of the designer in preventing thermal effects
due to cooling water discharges are:

1. To allow a passageway for migrating fish. The
National Technical Advisory Committee (2) recommends that "...
the passageway should contain preferably 75 percent of the
cross-sectional area and/or volume of flow of the stream or
estuary."

2. To minimize the surface area and volume of water
affected by excess temperatures. Normally, biologists are
concerned with excess temperatures of 1 1/2 to 5^{0}F. Rapidly
mixing of the discharge water with the ambient will provide
smaller areas affected by such temperature differences than
will systems designed to inhibit mixing.

3. To prevent entrainment of valuable organisms within
the discharge plume.

4. To reduce the number of valuable organisms which pass
through the plant.

These goals may be attained through a judicious selection
of the location of the intake and discharge structures, as well
as various design alternatives. Once the plant site has been
selected, the designer still has many options available.

Intake structures are normally located at the shoreline
on rivers, but on lakes and oceans may be installed at depth.
As mentioned previously, skimmer walls and underwater dams
can be used to maximize the flow of cool water to the intake
for shoreline locations. Organisms may be prevented from
entering the intake by mechanical blockage with screens and
by reducing the velocity to the intake below one foot per
second. Such measures have proven successful in avoiding the
intake of fish, however, plankton and pelagic eggs are generally
considered to be at the mercy of the currents and thus will be
passed through the plant.

A wide variety of discharge configurations are available,
including low velocity surface discharges, surface jets,
single ports submerged jets, and multiple ports submerged
jets. With each of these configurations, the designer has
the opportunity to affect the mixing process by varying the
discharge area and velocity (thus controlling the discharge
Froude number), the angle of entry, and the number of discharge
ports. Finally, various hydrodynamic conditions, such as
currents, stratification, and ambient turbulence also affect
the mixing process.

A complete discussion of the analytical techniques
available for the design and evaluation of discharge structures
would fill several books and thus will not be attempted here.

Suffice it to say that several good analytical models are available for analyzing the majority of cases discussed above.

A significant step in compiling the present state-of-the art of thermal plume prediction is being made by EPA. Fellow researchers at the National Environmental Research Center in Corvallis, Oregon, have prepared a report entitled "Workbook of Thermal Plume Prediction," Vol. I, Submerged Discharge," (3). Drs. Shirazi and Davis have compiled the most up-to-date methodology and presented graphical solutions in this 229 page report. The report thus enables a non-expert to provide quantitative analyses for complex submerged discharge plume problems without the need for elaborate computer programs. The report is not intended to replace detailed analytical treatment of specific designs, but instead supplements the available technology and puts it within the reach of a broad audience. We, in Corvallis, feel that this is an outstanding example of technology transfer, by compiling sophisticated research results and presenting them in a form useful to the non-researcher. A second volume on surface discharges is now being prepared and is scheduled for publication within a year.

7.4 CLOSED-CYCLE COOLING

When the receiving water is unable to tolerate the thermal and hydraulic insult of once-through cooling, closed-cycle cooling system are necessary. This situation occurs on most rivers and estuaries and may also occur on large water bodies in areas of environmental stress or where the ecosystem is fragile. For example, areas where existing pollution loads have caused ecological changes, further degradation by thermal discharges may be intolerable. Also, locations of unique ecologic importance such as fish spawning areas, shellfish beds, or areas with beneficial aquatic flora may be damaged by the discharge from a once-through cooling system. EPA's policy on thermal discharges has been enunciated by Mr. John R. Quarles, Assistant Administrator for Enforcement and General Counsel. In a May 16, 1972, speech before the Edison Electric Institute's Eighth Biennial Financial Conference (4), he stated that,

> ...each discharge of waste heat to the aquatic environment shall be evaluated on a case-by-case basis. Where our analysis indicates that once-through cooling damages or will damage the environment, EPA will insist on a commitment to off stream cooling as a prerequisite to either continue operations, or to EPA concurrence with company investment plans. In other cases in which we believe that damage will not occur, but in which there is a clear possibility, we shall insist on the establishment of an effective

monitoring system to detect damage before it
becomes serious...

We are putting the power generating industry
on notice of the need for control of thermal
pollution, if any company chooses to ignore
environmental requirements in its planning,
it will be deliberately running the risk of
increasing costs due to backfitting and
possibly of not being permitted to operate
during backfitting.

Thus, EPA's policy calls for a stringent assessment of
once-through cooling plans and in cases of actual damage or
high potential for damage a commitment to closed-cycle cooling.
Fortunately, a wide variety of closed-cycle systems are available for use by the electric power industry, including cooling
ponds, spray cooling systems, wet cooling towers, and dry
cooling towers.

Cooling ponds are the simplest of the devices now in use.
They are merely lakes, which rely on the natural heat exchange
processes of evaporation, radiation, and conduction-convection
to transfer the waste heat to the atmosphere. They can be
quite large, some one to two acres per megawatt of plant
capacity. While considered a waste treatment device, they also
have a potential for recreation (swimming, fishing, boating,
etc.) and aquaculture (e.g., catfish raising in Texas).

Several spray cooling systems are available. Most of
these systems operate by pumping water up through nozzles,
and thus, provide droplets which cool by evaporation as they
fall back to the surface. However, one system employs
spinning discs which propel water droplets into the air. At
the present time, at least two major power plants employ
spray cooling systems and several more have ordered them.

As with spray systems, wet cooling towers rely on
evaporative heat transfer as the primary mechanism for removing
waste heat. However, instead of simply spraying the warm
water into the air, wet towers promote air movement by fans
(mechanical draft) or chimneys (natural draft), and the water
is passed over packing material to either break it into droplets (splash packing) or to allow sheet flow (film flow
packing). The tower can be designed as either a crossflow
device where the air moves horizontally through the falling
water, or counterflow where the air moves upward.

The most common cooling device being used in the power
industry today is the crossflow mechanical draft tower. However, the wet natural draft tower is becoming a popular choice
of power plant cooling. As of November, 1971, a total of 32
power plants have either installed or plan to install natural
draft towers as part of their closed-cycle cooling system.
These plans include a total of 51 natural draft towers (5).

All wet cooling devices use evaporative heat transfer as a major vehicle for waste heat removal; thus, incurring consumptive water lost. Dry cooling towers use only sensible heat transfer and are appropriate in areas of little or no water. There are two types of dry towers:

1. The direct air condenser where the turbine exhaust steam is condensed by the air and no cooling water is employed.

2. Heller type towers where direct spray condensers are used and the cooling water and steam are mixed, with the resultant hot water going through an air heat exchanger, thus, there is no separate cooling water system.

The direct air condenser is limited to power plants of 200 megawatts or less, while the Heller type system is appropriate for larger installations. While several dry tower systems and operating and are under construction in Europe, the only United States experience with dry cooling for power plants is at the Simpson Station in Wyodak, Wyoming. This 20 megawatt unit employs a direct air condenser.

All of the cooling devices discussed are feasible from the standpoint of transferring waste heat, however, one must also assess the potential environmental effects of cooling system, including: fog, consumptive water loss, drift, and blowdown. The location, design, operation, and selection of a cooling device should not proceed without an assessment of these potential environmental side effects.

Local fogging may or may not be affected by cooling devices. Past performance indicates that local fogging will not occur due to closed-cycle cooling systems. However, meteorological conditions of high humidity, low temperature, and high atmospheric stability are conducive to fog formation and locations with conditions such as these should be carefully evaluated prior to actual sight selection.

With the exception of dry cooling towers all of the cooling devices discussed provide some fog potential. Cooling ponds may produce a "steam fog." However, this phenomenon is normally localized over the surface of the pond and does not create local fog problems. Actually, one would not expect the fog conditions over a cooling pond to differ significantly from those over a once-through discharge area of a lake, river, or bay. Cooling towers do produce visible plumes; however, they are not a problem unless they reach the ground and thus cause fog. In fact, only when the fog occurs over inhabited areas would it be considered a problem. Special concern should be directed towards a fog which may cause obstruction of vision on highways or near airports.

Under normal conditions cooling tower plumes rise due to their initial velocity and buoyancy and rarely intersect the ground before they are dissipated. Under some conditions the plumes also have the ability to penetrate through atmospheric inversions. In this respect, natural draft towers are less apt to produce a local fogging condition, and thus may be preferred over mechanical draft units.

All wet cooling devices consume water by evaporation, with the rate of evaporation being a function of the meteorological conditions and waste heat load. In evaluating the data available on evaporative water loss from cooling towers and ponds, two things must be recognized.

1. Evaporation under design summer time conditions is 50 to 150 percent higher than for average annual conditions.
2. Once-through cooling also produces increased evaporation rates.

A study done to evaluate alternative cooling systems for 1,000 megawatt fossil fuel plants near Lake Michigan provides the evaporation data given in the following table (6). Note that cooling ponds experience higher evaporation rates than cooling towers. This is because in addition to the power plant's waste heat load, ponds must also dissipate the thermal input from solar heating.

Evaporation Rates (cfs)

Cooling System	Design Condition	Average Annual
Mechanical Draft Tower	16.1	10.6
Natural Draft Tower	16.1	10.6
Cooling Pond (Flow-through)	37.1	15.2
Spray Cooling System	16.1	10.6
Once-Through Cooling	--	8.2

Cooling tower or spray system drift is the carry over of liquid water droplets from the cooling water flow. These droplets have the same chemical characteristics as the cooling water; thus, if brackish or saltwater is used, the drift could cause problems when deposited on the surrounding landscape. Cooling towers employ drift eliminators to reduce this impact. Past guarantees of manufacturers were limited to 0.2 percent of the circulating water flow, but this value is excessive. The Marley Company recently sold a tower with a guaranteed drift level of 0.002 percent which is a reduction of 100 times below the previously accepted level (7). Measurements of drift at 0.005 percent have been made on operating towers (8).

Evaporative cooling devices require that a small portion of the circulating water be bled from the system to prevent build up of undesirable dissolved material. This liquid stream is called blowdown. In addition to the dissolved material in the original make-up water, blowdown also contains corrosion inhibitors, antifoulants, or biocides added to cooling water. Thus, blowdown is an industrial waste and must be treated as such.

Many of the compounds found in blowdown are toxic and must be controlled. Blowdown can be controlled by: (a) selection of water treatment chemicals, (b) increasing the cycle of concentration through pre-treatment of the make-up water or sidestream filters, or (c) physical and/or chemical treatment of the effluent itself.

7.5 ECONOMICS

The optimum closed-cycle cooling system will provide the smallest increase in power production cost over a basic once-through system. Therefore, rather than minimizing the cost of the cooling system itself, one must minimize the overall economic effect on power generation costs. The designer must not only consider costs of cooling system components, but must also acquire data on total plant cost, fixed charge rates (including interest, amortization, insurance, and taxes), fuel cost, and land costs.

Meteorological data for design conditions must be obtained to assure reliable operation under adverse conditions. Also, weather data representing the full annual cycle must be used to assess the operation of the system under off design conditions and to evaluate annual cost.

All cooling systems perform most effectively at elevated water temperatures. Reduced pumping and fan power, shorter tower packing, and smaller pond surface areas can be achieved by increasing the inlet water temperature to the cooling system. The same temperature increase, however, adversely affects the efficiency of the power plant, since it results in condensing the steam at a higher turbine back pressure, and thus increases the turbine heat rate. An economic optimization, therefore, involves the analysis of these two competing factors for the selection of the condensing steam temperature.

The approach temperature of the cooling device is related directly to the steam condensing temperature and is a primary factor in determining the cost of the cooling system. The smaller the approach, the larger the cooling device's heat exchange surface and consequently its cost. The magnitude of the approach temperature also affects the operation of the power generation system. The smaller the approach, the more efficient the power generation because of the lower sink temperature. This relation between the cooling device and the plant's operating efficiency points to the need to optimize the total plant, and not to consider the cooling device as something which is tacked on as an afterthought. The proper match of the turbine-condenser with the cooling device is as important, perhaps more so, than that the detailed design of the cooling device itself.

The technical literature contains abundant data on cooling system costs, but often times it is difficult to determine what these data really mean. A good way of evaluating such cost data is to determine how much additional cost is incurred over a base plant with once-through cooling. This was done by our research group for power plants near Lake Michigan. For a 1,000 megawatt fossil fuel plant, the additional cost in dollars per kw, mills per kw-hr, and percent busbar increase were computed (6):

Cooling System	Dollars Per Kw	Mills Per Kw-hr	% Busbar Increase
Cooling Pond	2	0.02	<1
Spray System	3	0.06	1
Mechanical Draft Wet Tower	4	0.10	1.5
Natural Draft Wet Tower	7	0.18	3
Mechanical Draft Dry Tower	19	0.58	10
Natural Draft Dry Tower	21	0.53	9

While these cost data are specific for the Lake Michigan area similar cost data are presented in the technical literature (9, 10).

If the economic effect of providing waste heat control is evaluated in terms of cost to the consumer, a true picture of the real cost burden is achieved. It is important to note that busbar cost variation is not the only factor influencing consumer cost. The amount the consumer pays for electric power is substantially higher than the actual production cost. Transmission, maintenance, advertising, etc. all add to the cost which the consumer pays for his electric power. In fact, the production cost may be from 30 to 50 percent of the cost the consumer pays. In most cases, the increase cost to the consumer due to the use of closed-cycle cooling systems is less than 1 percent.

The final point concerning cost is that cooling devices are relatively small factors in the total cost of power production. For example, the cost of natural draft towers in a closed-cycle cooling system in the Lake Michigan area is equivalent to (6):

1. $10 per kilowatt difference in plant capital cost
2. A 1 percent difference in the fixed charge rate
3. A 2 cents per million BTU difference in fuel cost
4. An 80 mile difference in transmission distance

Mr. Quarles, in his May 16, 1972, speech provided the following conclusion with respect to cost (4):

We have now reached a point where we have a clearer picture of the economic consequences of environmental protection. Though precise predictions are still difficult, we can draw two conclusions. One is that environmental protection will not be cheap.

The second is that the costs are not prohibitive. The question, therefore, is not whether America can afford environmental protection, but whether it wants to. On the basis of laws passed by Congress, we must conclude that the environmental requirements now being imposed are desired and can be considered worth the cost by our American Society.

7.6 SUMMARY AND CONCLUSIONS

The methods available to prevent damage due to cooling water discharges include site selection, intake and discharge design, and closed-cycle cooling. Site selection is the first and most important step in providing needed electric power with a minimum of environmental degradation. If adequate water for once-through cooling is available, careful evaluation and design of intake and discharge structures must precede the decision to use a once-through system. In almost all cases, closed-cycle cooling systems are viable alternatives to once-through cooling for thermal power plants. They are definitely feasible from an engineering standpoint, however, they do have environmental side effects which must be assessed and controlled. They cost millions of dollars, but provide only a small increase in consumer costs of power. In short, closed-cycle cooling works, and should be considered a useful tool in our nation's efforts to combat environmental degradation.

REFERENCES

Electrical World, November 15, 1971, page 38.

Electrical World, May 1, 1972, page 106.

Environmental Systems Corp., Development and Demonstration of Low-Level Drift Instrumentation, EPA Water Pollution Control Research Series Report No. 16130GNK 10/71, October 1971.

Oleson, K. A. and R. R. Boyle, "How to Cool Steam-Electric Power Plants," in Cooling Towers, American Institute of Chemical Engineers, New York, 1972.

Quarles, J. R., Jr., "Remarks to Edison Electric Institute's Eighth Biennial Financial Conference," Miami, Florida, May 16, 1972.

Shirazi, M. A. and L. R. Davis, Workbook of Thermal Plume Prediction, Vol. I, Submerged Discharge, National Thermal Pollution Research Program, NERC, Corvallis, EPA, April, 1972. (Preliminary).

USDI, FWPCA, Water Quality Criteria, National Technical Advisory Committee, Washington, D.C., April 1, 1968.

USDI, FWPCA, Industrial Waste Guide on Thermal Pollution, National Thermal Pollution Research Program, PNWL, September, 1968 (Revised).

USDI, FWQA, Feasibility of Alternative Means of Cooling for Thermal Power Plants Near Lake Michigan, National Thermal Pollution Research Program, PNWL and Region V, August 1970.

Woodson, R. D., "Cooling Towers for Large Steam-Electric Generating Station," in Electric Power and Thermal Discharges, Eisenbud and Gleason, Eds., Gordon and Breach Publ, New York, 1970.

Chapter 8

MECHANICS OF HEAT TRANSFER IN NONSTRATIFIED
OPEN-CHANNEL FLOWS

by

Harvey E. Jobson, Research Hydraulic Engineer, U. S.
Geological Survey, Bay St. Louis,
Mississippi

and

Nobuhiro Yotsukura, Research Hydrologist, U. S.
Geological Survey, Arlington,
Virginia

Chapter 8

MECHANICS OF HEAT TRANSFER IN NONSTRATIFIED
OPEN-CHANNEL FLOWS [1]

8.1 INTRODUCTION

The problem of thermal pollution in rivers, lakes, and estuaries has been presented with much fanfare recently. Among various industrial sectors, the power generation sector is the most dominant source of waste heat released into natural water courses. In order to meet the national demand for electric energy which approximately doubles every ten years, the industry is expected not only to keep adding new plants and increasing the size of individual generation units but also to switch substantially from fossil to nuclear fuels in the near future. The industry will thus claim as its cooling water a very significant share of the total national fresh water supply of 440 trillion gallons per year (Parker and Krenkel, 1969). Because this water supply may not be able to satisfy all of the rapidly increasing demands from domestic and industrial users, in the near future it may become necessary to dissipate the bulk of the waste heat from power generations directly into the atmosphere by means of either cooling towers or cooling ponds. Economically, however, natural flowing water will always be the most efficient means of dissipating excess heat provided that use does not conflict seriously with the requirements of other uses such as domestic consumption, recreation, natural conservation, and esthetic enjoyment.

The negative thermal pollution problem, though less publicized than the heating of rivers, exists downstream from reservoirs. As the control of a river basin progresses a series of dams and reservoirs are constructed for the purposes of flood control, supply storage, and recreation. When the cold bottom water is released from such reservoirs, the downstream water temperature is lowered unnaturally. Selective withdrawal of reservoir water is attracting increased attention among engineers and prediction of the effect of these withdrawals on the downstream temperature is important in planning such withdrawals. Of course, prediction of the thermal regime in a reservoir itself has long been a major concern in the western part of the country.

The above mentioned problems for which the ASCE Sanitary Engineering Division compiled an extensive bibliography in 1967 (Gerber, 1967) indicate urgent needs for better understanding of the processes of heat transfer in rivers and other water courses so that these processes can be more accurately modeled. Because changes in river temperatures are brought about by man's activities, actual monitoring of the temperature

---

[1] Publication authorized by the Director of the U.S. Geological Survey.

regime alone provides a very poor basis for planning. Man must be able to predict the changes in water temperature which will result from a planned activity. Such capabilities are the essential components in the planning of individual activities as well as the total river basin development.

The mechanics of heat transfer in natural water systems may be divided into three components, namely, 1) heat exchange at the air-water interface (surface transfer) due to radiation, evaporation, conduction, and advection by the evaporated water, 2) transport of thermal energy within the water (hydraulic transfer) due to convection and diffusion, and 3) transfer occurring at the soil-water interface due to ground water motion and diffusion in solid materials. Up to now each of these components have been modeled almost independently of the others and little effort has been made to integrate them. Thus workers interested in cooling ponds and lake evaporation have been mostly studying the surface-transfer process and have given a minimum of concern to the hydraulic transfer process. On the other hand, those who have been concerned with the design of waste outlets and with the problems of recirculation have paid utmost attention to the hydraulic and densimetric aspects of heat transfer but have shown little interest in surface transfer. Such polarization of interest shows clearly that there are two basic and often alternative methods of heat disposal, namely, dissipation to the atmosphere and/or mixing with cold ambient water. The purpose of this report is to present an approach which attempts to integrate the two transfer mechanisms. It is felt that this approach is the most suitable one for dealing with transient problems in rivers and estuaries. It is also believed that sufficient knowledge concerning each of the transfer processes has been accumulated in recent years in order to undertake such an integration on a sound theoretical basis.

In order to present a relatively concise paper within a given time, two important aspects of the problem must be excluded. The densimetric or stratification effect will not be discussed because it is itself a distinct field wherein the equation of motion must be dealt with in addition to the equation of thermal energy. The heat transfer at the soil-water interface will also be neglected because this component is generally considered to be small and information is rather limited at the present time.

The conservation of thermal energy is the basis of the following development. The three-dimensional problem is formulated by writing the conservation equation in terms of turbulent convection and diffusion and by describing the surface transfer as the boundary condition. The two-dimensional problem is then derived by integrating the above equations with respect to depth. Finally, the one-dimensional problem is developed by another integration, namely that two-dimensional equation with respect to the width. In the derivation of two- and one-dimensional equations, it will be shown that

the surface and hydraulic transfer are combined into one
equation without the necessity of assuming uniformity of water
temperature, which is the basis of conventional derivations.
The nonlinear nature of the equations describing radiation,
evaporation and conduction flux at the air-water interface will
be reviewed and a linearization process which will lead to the
surface exchange coefficient will be presented. The mechanics
of turbulent diffusion and longitudinal dispersion will then
be discussed and the limitations of the derived equations will
be examined on the basis of currently available hydraulic
theories. Further simplification and solution approaches are
discussed separately for the three- and two-dimensional problems and the one dimensional problem, because hydraulic transfer is more important in the two- and three-dimensional problems while the surface transfer is of predominant importance
in the one-dimensional case. Available one-dimensional models
are evaluated in light of the developments contained herein
and a prediction equation for the surface exchange coefficient
is evaluated by use of field data.

8.2 THEORETICAL BACKGROUND

Formulation of Boundary Value Problems in Three-, Two-, and
One-Space Dimensions. The thermal energy stored in a unit
volume of water may be expressed by $C_p \rho T$, where C_p is the
specific heat of water under constant atmospheric pressure, ρ
is the density of water, and T is the temperature of water
measured relative to a reference temperature. Since we will be
dealing only with the influx and outflux of thermal energy for
a given volume of water and not with the absolute thermal
content, the reference temperature is quite arbitrary so long
as it remains constant for the entire description of the pertinent equations. The most common value to be used for the
reference temperature is zero degrees, either Fahrenheit or
Celcius.

The conservation of thermal energy for turbulent flow may
be written in a form similar to the equation describing the
conduction of heat in an anisotropic solid (Carslaw and
Jeager, 1959)

$$\frac{D(C_p \rho T)}{Dt} = \frac{\partial}{\partial x_i} \left\{ \epsilon_i \frac{(C_p T)}{x_i} \right\} , \qquad (8-1)$$

in which t is time, x_i $(i = 1, 2, 3)$ is the space coordinate
in the i-th direction, ϵ_i is the turbulent diffusion coefficient in the i-th coordinate direction: the operator on the
left side is the substantive derivative

$$\frac{D}{Dt} = \frac{\partial}{\partial t} + u_i \frac{\partial}{\partial x_i} , \qquad (8-2)$$

in which u_i is the velocity in the i-th coordinate direction. Equation (8-1) neglects thermal conduction and the dissipation of other energies into thermal energy at the molecular scale, which really should be included in the exact equation of conservation. Such microscopic processes are normally negligible in comparison to those occurring at the macroscopic scales of concern in a turbulent flow. The symbols T , u_i , and ε_i thus designate certain time-averaged values of these quantities which are fluctuating under turbulent conditions. We will not concern ourselves with the turbulent fluctuations of these quantities.

Consider an open channel flow with constant depth where only longitudinal velocity, u , is nonzero finite. The coordinate system will be assumed such that x (longitudinal) and z (transverse) are horizontal and y is vertical, positive downward with y = 0 at the water surface. In most practical cases the values of C_p and ρ are nearly constant, so Eq. (8-1) may be written for an infinitesimal element dxdydz as

$$\frac{\partial T}{\partial t} + u \frac{\partial T}{\partial x} = \frac{\partial}{\partial x} \left(\varepsilon_x \frac{\partial T}{\partial x} \right) + \frac{\partial}{\partial y} \left(\varepsilon_y \frac{\partial T}{\partial y} \right) + \frac{\partial}{\partial z} \left(\varepsilon_z \frac{\partial T}{\partial z} \right) .$$
$$(8-3)$$

It will be assumed that heat transfer with other media takes place only at the water surface, where the thermal flux, H_T , is defined positive when it is transferred from the air into the water. Actually a certain amount of the incoming short wave radiation is not absorbed right at the water surface but transmitted some distance through the water and is absorbed internally. The assumption that all radiation is absorbed at the water surface has little effect on the two- and one-dimensional equations and is convenient. The surface boundary condition is thus

$$\varepsilon_y \frac{\partial T}{\partial y} + \frac{H_T}{C_p \rho} = 0 \quad \text{at} \quad y = 0 . \qquad (8-4)$$

At the solid boundaries, the condition is

$$\varepsilon_n \frac{\partial T}{\partial n} = 0 , \qquad (8-5)$$

in which n designates a normal to the solid boundary. Together with the initial temperature and any source conditions,

Eq. (8-3), (8-4), and (8-5) constitute the classical three-dimensional diffusion problem (Crank, 1956).

The above set of equations may be integrated over the entire depth Y in order to develop a two-dimensional problem as has been shown by Prych (1970, p. 7). First define

$$T = \bar{T} + T' ,$$
$$u = \bar{u} + u' , \text{ and} \qquad \left.\right\} \qquad (8\text{-}6)$$
$$\varepsilon_i = \bar{\varepsilon}_i + \varepsilon_i' \quad (i = 1, 2, 3)$$

where the upper bar indicates the depth-averaged value and the prime designates a local deviation from the average. Obviously the depth averaged values of T' , u' , and ε_i' are all zero by the above definition. Substitute Eq. (8-6) into Eq. (8-3), integrate it term by term with respect to y from 0 to Y, and divide by Y . In this averaging process, Eqs. (8-3), (8-4), and (8-5) are combined into one equation because

$$\int_0^Y \frac{\partial}{\partial y} \left(\varepsilon_y \frac{\partial T}{\partial y}\right) \partial y = \varepsilon_y \frac{\partial T}{\partial y} \Big|_0^Y . \qquad (8\text{-}7)$$

The result for steady uniform rectangular channel flow is

$$\frac{\partial \bar{T}}{\partial t} + \bar{u} \frac{\partial \bar{T}}{\partial x} + \overline{u' \frac{\partial T'}{\partial x}} = \frac{\partial}{\partial x} \left(\bar{\varepsilon}_x \frac{\partial \bar{T}}{\partial x} + \overline{\varepsilon_x' \frac{\partial T'}{\partial x}}\right) +$$

$$\frac{\partial}{\partial z} \left(\bar{\varepsilon}_z \frac{\partial \bar{T}}{\partial z} + \overline{\varepsilon_z' \frac{\partial T'}{\partial z}}\right) + \frac{H_T}{C_p \rho Y} \qquad (8\text{-}8)$$

The diffusive terms involving ε_i' on the right side are smaller than those involving $\bar{\varepsilon}_i$ and may be absorbed into the $\bar{\varepsilon}_i$ terms to make the expression concise. On the other hand, the term, $\overline{u' \frac{\partial T'}{\partial x}}$, designates the transfer of heat by the velocity deviation u' relative to $\bar{u}$ and provides a far greater transfer than that due to $\bar{\varepsilon}_x \frac{\partial \bar{T}}{\partial x}$, on the order of 100 to 1 in a steady uniform flow. Coupled with vertical diffusivity ε_y it causes the effective longitudinal dispersion (Taylor, 1954). Accordingly this transfer will be defined as a diffusive flux in the x direction,

$$- \overline{u'T'} = D_v \frac{\partial \bar{T}}{\partial x} , \qquad (8\text{-}9)$$

where D_v is the longitudinal dispersion coefficient due to the vertical gradient of u. Equation (8-8) is reduced to a form

$$\frac{\partial \overline{T}}{\partial t} + \overline{u} \frac{\partial \overline{T}}{\partial x} = \frac{\partial}{\partial x} \{(D_v + \overline{\varepsilon}_x) \frac{\partial \overline{T}}{\partial x}\} + \frac{\partial}{\partial z} (\overline{\varepsilon}_z \frac{\partial \overline{T}}{\partial z}) + \frac{H_T}{C_p \rho Y} \tag{8-10}$$

Together with the depth-averaged initial and source conditions, Eq. (8-10) describes the two-dimensional problem.

The one-dimensional equation will be derived similarly by integrating Eq. (8-10) over the width, W. Define the cross-sectional average value of the temperature by

$$\langle \overline{T} \rangle = \frac{1}{W} \int_{-\frac{W}{2}}^{\frac{W}{2}} \overline{T} \, dz \tag{8-11}$$

and let $\overline{T}'$ be the local deviation from the cross-sectional average. The bracket and prime signs are similarly defined for the other quantities. It is seen that in the process of substitution and integration of Eq. (8-10), a new transfer term $\langle \overline{u}' \frac{\partial \overline{T}'}{\partial x} \rangle$ comes out from the left side of Eq. (8-10). This term represents the dispersion due to the coupling of the widthwise velocity deviation $\overline{u}'$ with the widthwise diffusivity $\overline{\varepsilon}_z$ in a manner similar to that for the vertical case as discussed by Fischer (1966). Define this component dispersion as

$$- \langle \overline{u}'\overline{T}' \rangle = D_h \frac{\partial \langle \overline{T} \rangle}{\partial x} , \tag{8-12}$$

where D_h is the longitudinal dispersion coefficient due to the transverse gradient of $\overline{u}$. Utilizing Eq. (8-12) and noting the boundary condition that $\overline{\varepsilon}_z \frac{\partial \overline{T}}{\partial z} = 0$ at $z = \pm \frac{W}{2}$, Eq. (8-10) is transformed to

$$\frac{\partial \langle \overline{T} \rangle}{\partial t} + \langle \overline{u} \rangle \frac{\partial \langle \overline{T} \rangle}{\partial x} = \frac{\partial}{\partial x} \{(D_h + \langle D_v \rangle) \frac{\partial \langle \overline{T} \rangle}{\partial x}\} + \frac{1}{C_p \rho} \langle \frac{H_T}{Y} \rangle . \tag{8-13}$$

Equation (8-13) with the cross-sectional-average initial and source conditions defines the one-dimenaional problem. It will be noticed that the diffusive terms involving D_v , $\langle \overline{\varepsilon}_x \rangle$, and $\overline{\varepsilon}_x'$ are all omitted in Eq. (8-13) for the sake of having a concise expression. These contributions can be expressed, if one so desires, as additional coefficients of $\frac{\partial \langle T \rangle}{\partial x}$ in Eq. (8-13) but are normally much smaller than those due to D_h and $\langle D_v \rangle$. In wide open channels, the value of D_h is many times larger than that of $\langle D_v \rangle$ and so the terms may be combined for a satisfactory approximation.

The form of Eqs. (8-3), (8-4), (8-5), (8-10), and (8-13) are very much similar to the classical Fickian diffusion equations with constant or variable coefficients. For all practical purposes, moreover, these equations may not be any simpler or easier to solve than are the classical equations. The difference becomes clear, however, when one examines the difference in the assumptions. In the conventional derivation of two- and one-dimensional diffusion equations, the water temperature, depth, and velocity must be uniform either by approximation or by assuming the existence of such conditions. In the present derivations, no such uniformity is assumed in any of the quantities except depth. The two basic assumptions are that Eq. (8-3) is the correct description of turbulent heat transfer in an elementary body and that Taylor's longitudinal dispersion concept is a satisfactory turbulent transfer theory. As explained in a later section, these assumptions are certainly justified on the basis of experimental evidence obtained in a steady uniform channel flow. Since the approximations in these equations are solely due to the diffusive terms, the limitations of them are determined by the limitation of the diffusive terms. In this connection, it is noted that Eq. (8-3), thus, Eqs. (8-10) and (8-13) can not be applied at source locations in a strict sense.

A discussion of the surface exchange term, H_T, has been deferred to this point. Since this aspect is important and involves nonlinear mechanics, a detailed description of surface-exchange mechanism will be presented in the next section.

The Exchange of Energy Across an Air-Water Interface. The general conservation of thermal energy equation has just been presented. The heat flux at the air-water interface entered this equation as a boundary condition, therefore, a knowledge of this flux is necessary before the equation can be solved. The net flux of radiant energy absorbed from the sun and sky is independent of the water temperature and therefore can be treated as an independent variable which is a function of time and perhaps location. The other processes involved in the total surface exchange are dependent upon the temperature of the water surface and, therefore, analytic expressions relating their dependence on the water temperature are needed. Fortunately such expressions have been reasonably well defined.

In this section the usual expressions describing each of the physical processes involved in the total surface exchange are presented. However each expression will be separated into two components, the first of which is dependent only on the meteorologic variables, which are assumed to be independent of the water temperature, and the second of which depends on the temperature of the temperature of the water surface as well as meteorologic variables. The temperature of the water surface is represented by the symbol ΔT , called the temperature departure. The temperature departure is the difference between the actual water surface temperature, measured on the absolute scale and an arbitrary reference temperature. That is

$$\Delta T = T_{abs} - T_R \tag{8-14}$$

in which T_{abs} is the temperature of the water surface measured on the absolute scale and T_R is the arbitrary reference temperature measured on the absolute scale. If the reference temperature is chosen to be 273.16°K (degrees Kelvin) then the temperature departure, ΔT , is numerically equal to the normal water surface temperature, T , as measured on the Celsius scale. It will be shown that the second component of each expression is proportional to the temperature departure for small departures. If a reference temperature of 273.16°K is selected, the second component is not in general proportional to the first power of the temperature departure and the solution of Eq. (8-3) becomes much more difficult. The constant of proportionality between the second component of the surface exchange and the temperature departure is the kinematic surface exchange coefficient times the specific heat and density of water. A fairly general prediction equation for the surface exchange coefficient is developed and the limitations on the linear approximation are indicated.

The exchange of energy across an air-water interface has been discussed many times. One of the first and perhaps most complete discussions was presented by Anderson (1954, p. 71). The total heat flux, the rate of heat exchange across a unit area of the water surface, can be expressed as

$$H_T = H_N - H_b - H_e - H_h - H_w \tag{8-15}$$

in which
$\quad$ H_T = total heat flux, positive if heat is flowing from the
$\qquad$ air to the water;
$\quad$ H_N = net heat flux caused by the radiation that is
$\qquad$ absorbed from the sun and the sky;
$\quad$ H_b = heat flux caused by the long-wave radiation emitted
$\qquad$ by the water;
$\quad$ H_e = heat flux utilized by evaporation;
$\quad$ H_h = heat flux conducted from the body of water as sensible
$\qquad$ heat; and

H_w = heat flux advected from the system by the evaporated water.

The values of H_T and H_N are positive if the water is gaining thermal energy and the values of H_b , H_e , H_h , and H_w are positive if the water is losing thermal energy.

The net absorbed radiation, H_N , is the sum of the total solar radiation incident to the water surface plus the total incoming long-wave radiation from the atmosphere minus the reflected components of each. This term is completely independent of the water temperature but varies rapidly with time and probably with location.

The incoming solar radiation is short wave radiation which passes directly from the sun to the earth's surface. The flux of short-wave radiation reaching the surface can be easily measured by use of a pyrheliometer, which is an instrument that responds only to short-wave radiation. However its value can also be estimated by use of empirical formulas which depend on astronomical and meteorologic parameters. The astronomical factors such as the solar constant and the altitude of the sun can be allowed for by use of fairly simple calculations (Sutton, 1953, p. 162). However the transparency of the atmosphere, which is a function of the amount of radiation depleted by, (a) absorption by ozone in the upper atmosphere, (b) scattering by dry air, (c) absorption, scattering, and diffuse reflection by suspended particulate matter, and (d) absorption and scattering by water vapor, is much more troublesome. If direct measurements of incoming short-wave radiation are lacking, estimates of its magnitude can be made by using relations between the percentage of possible sunshine or cloud cover to the percentage of possible solar radiation that reaches the ground (List, 1966, Anderson, 1954, p. 71-120). The percentage of the incoming short-wave radiation which is reflected by a water surface is a function of the sun's altitude as well as the type and amount of cloud cover. Anderson (1954, p. 86) has given charts from which the reflectivity of natural water surfaces can be estimated.

The atmospheric, or long-wave radiation is radiation which is emitted by the gases in the atmosphere. Atmospheric radiation does not follow a simple law. It is a function of many variables, notably the distributions of moisture, temperature, ozone, carbon dioxide and perhaps other materials within the atmosphere. For practical purposes it is assumed to depend primarily upon the air temperature, vapor pressure, and the amount and altitude of the cloud cover. It is common to estimate the magnitude of the incoming long-wave radiation by use of an empirical formula such as that given by Koberg (1964, p. 104) or Idso and Jackson (1969). Although improved instruments for the measurement of long-wave radiation are currently available, it is often generally considered more convenient to calculate its magnitude than to measure it. The Lake Hefner studies (Anderson, 1954, p. 98) have shown that the reflectivity of water to long-wave radiation is relatively constant at about 3 percent.

It will be assumed for the purposes of this report that the value of the independent variable, H_N , can be determined as a function of time by some means, either by direct measurement or otherwise.

The long-wave radiation flux emitted by the water surface can be represented using the Stefan-Boltzman law for black body radiation

$$H_b = \varepsilon\sigma \ (T_R + \Delta T)^4 \qquad\qquad (8\text{-}16)$$

in which ε = emissivity of water (0.970) , and σ = Stefan-Boltzman constant for black body radiation (1.171 x 10^{-7} calories centimeter^{-2} day^{-1} degree Kelvin^{-4}) . The temperature departure, ΔT , will be considered to be positive if the water temperature is above the reference temperature. The reference temperature will be chosen very nearly equal to the mean temperature such that the temperature departure will be as small as possible. Expanding Eq. (8-16) about T_R as a Taylor series and retaining only the first two terms

$$H_b = \varepsilon\sigma \ T_R{}^4 + 4\varepsilon\sigma \ T_R{}^3 \ \Delta T \qquad\qquad (8\text{-}17)$$

Equation (8-17) has been shown to be a good approximation to Eq. (8-16) provided that the value of ΔT is less than 20 Celsius degrees (Jobson, 1972). For example if T_R = 293.16°K i.e. 20°C and ΔT is less than ±20 Celsius degrees, the error in Eq. (8-17) is less than 2.5 percent. Therefore to a very good approximation, the back radiation can be assumed to be proportional to the temperature departure when the reference temperature is not too much different from the mean water surface temperature. Equation (8-17) separates the back radiation term into two parts. One part is independent of the water temperature and the other part is linearly dependent on the temperature departure. The second term of Eq. (8-17) is a correction applied to the reference back radiation term, which is represented by the first term of Eq. (8-17). The second term can be either positive or negative depending upon the sign of ΔT . Because actual stream temperatures $(T_R + \Delta T)$ usually fluctuate very little throughout a day or a week, the value of ΔT can remain small.

The rate of evaporation of water, E , is almost invariably estimated by use of a formula of the Dalton type

$$E_v = \psi \ [f \ (T_R - \Delta T) - p_a] \qquad\qquad (8\text{-}18)$$

in which

E_v = rate of evaporation, volume per unit time and area;

ψ = an empirical coefficient or wind function;

$f(T_R + \Delta T)$ = saturation vapor pressure of air evaluated at a temperature equal to that of the water surface; and

p_a = vapor pressure of the air above the water. The height at which p_a is measured is usually equal to that used in determining the wind function.

A considerable amount of information is available from which the wind function for lake evaporation can be estimated (Harbeck, 1962). Unfortunately there is a dearth of information concerning this function for evaporation from rivers.

The saturation vapor pressure of air is a direct function of temperature. The expression used herein is

$$f(T_R + \Delta T) = \exp [54.721 - 6788.6/(T_R + \Delta T) -$$

$$5.0016 \ln(T_R + \Delta T)] \qquad (8\text{-}19)$$

in which $f(\cdot)$ is in millibars; $T_R + \Delta T$ is in degrees Kelvin; and $\ln(T_R + \Delta T)$ is the natural logarithm of $T_R + \Delta T$. Equation (8-19) has the form of the Kirchhoff-Rankine-Dupre formula (Sutton, 1953, p. 4) and its coefficients have been obtained by a least-squares curve fit for temperatures between 0°C and 40°C. The maximum error in Eq. (8-19), for this range, is about 0.015 millibar and occurs at 40°C.

The process of evaporation transfers energy from the water to the atmosphere. This flux of thermal energy can be expressed as

$$H_e = \rho \psi [f(T_R + \Delta T) - p_a] [L_R + s\Delta T] \qquad (8\text{-}20)$$

in which

ρ = water density;

ψ = the empirical wind function;

L_R = latent heat of vaporization of water at the reference temperature;

s = slope of the latent heat of vaporization curve with respect to water temperature (-0.53 calories gram -1 Celsius degree -1).

Expanding the expression for the saturation vapor pressure, Eq. (8-19), about T_R as a Taylor series and retaining only the first two terms, Eq. (8-20) can be expressed as

$$H_e = \rho \psi L_R [f(T_R) - p_a] + \rho \psi \{s[f(T_R) - p_a] + L_R f'(T_R)\}\Delta T \qquad (8\text{-}21)$$

8-11

in which $f'(T_R)$ is the first derivative of $f(T)$ evaluated at T_R. The term involving ΔT to the second power has been shown to be negligible in comparison to the term involving the first power of ΔT (Jobson, 1972). Like Eq. (8-17), Eq. (8-21) separates the energy flux due to evaporation into two parts, one part which is independent of the water temperature and one part which is directly proportional to the temperature departure. Both parts are dependent upon the wind speed and the humidity of the air, so in general both parts will be functions of time. The accuracy of the linearization process used in deriving Eq. (8-21) decreases rapidly with increasing values of ΔT, that is departures from the reference temperature, and varies slightly with the value of the reference temperature. However in general it is a useful approximation for values of temperature departures of less than $\pm 10^{\circ}C$.

The ratio of the thermal energy transferred across a water surface by conduction to that utilized by evaporation has been given by Bowen (1926, p. 785) as

$$\frac{H_h}{H_e} = \beta \left[\frac{(T_R + \Delta T) - T_a}{f(T_R + \Delta T) - p_a} \right] \qquad (8-22)$$

in which T_a = air temperature and $\beta = 0.61\ P/1000$ millibar degrees Celsius -1. The term P is the atmospheric pressure in millibars. Combining Eqs. (8-20) and (8-22), expanding and neglecting the second order term in ΔT, the expression for the heat flux conducted from the water surface is

$$H_h = \beta \rho \psi (T_R - T_a) + \beta \rho \psi [L_R + s(T_R - T_a)] \Delta T \qquad (8-23)$$

The heat flux advected from the system by the evaporated water is usually small, however its value can be computed from

$$H_w = \frac{H_e\ C_p}{(L_R + s\ \Delta T)} \Delta T . \qquad (8-24)$$

Combining Eqs. (8-20) and (8-24), expanding the expression for the saturation vapor pressure as a Taylor series, and retaining only the first two terms

$$H_w = C_p \rho \psi [f(T_R) - p_a] \Delta T + C_p \rho \psi f'(T_R) \Delta T^2 . \qquad (8-25)$$

In general, the entire advection term, H_w, is small and the value of $f'(T_R)$ is much smaller than the value of $f(T_R)$.

Therefore the second term of Eq. (8-25) is ignored and the advected flux is represented by

$$H_w = C_p \, \rho \, \psi \, [f(T_R) - p_a] \, \Delta T \, . \qquad (8-26)$$

The total heat flux across the air-water interface has been given by Eq. (8-15). Expressions for each of the components of this flux have been presented, and each expression contains two terms, one of which depends upon the water temperature and one of which is independent of that temperature. The total flux will now be divided into a part which is independent of the water temperature and one which is proportional to the temperature departure. The part of the total flux which is independent of the water temperature will be called the reference surface exchange term and will be represented by the symbol H_R . Combining Eq. (8-15) with the first terms of Eqs. (8-17), (8-21), and (8-23) the expression for H_R becomes

$$H_R = H_N - \varepsilon \, \sigma \, T_R^{\,4} - \rho \, \psi \, L_R \, \{[f(T_R) - p_a] + \beta \, (T_R - T_a)\}$$
$$(8-27)$$

The total heat flux across the air-water interface is equal to the reference flux, H_R , when the water temperature departure, ΔT , is numerically equal to zero, that is when the water temperature is equal to the reference temperature, T_R . The reference flux is independent of the actual water temperature by definition but it is a function of the assumed value of the reference temparature, the absorbed radiation, the wind speed, the temperature of the air and the humidity of the air. All of these quantities are independent variables, therefore the reference flux term is an independent variable which is a function of time.

The second term of the total heat flux is the part which is dependent upon the water temperature. Provided that the actual water temperature is not too much different than the reference temperature, the second term is directly proportional to the temperature departure, ΔT . The second term represents a correction which must be made to the reference flux term in order to account for a different water temperature. In order to simplify terminology a kinematic surface exchange coefficient, K is defined as the constant of proportionality in the second term divided by the density and specific heat of water. Combining the second terms of Eqs. (8-17), (8-21), and (8-23) with Eq. (8-26) the value of the kinematic surface exchange coefficient becomes

$$K = \frac{4 \, \varepsilon \, \sigma \, T_R^3}{C_p} + \frac{\psi}{C_p} \{s[f(T_R) - p_a] + L_R \, f'(T_R)$$

$$+ \, \beta \, [L_R + s(T_R - T_a)] + C_p \, [f(T_R) - p_a]\} \qquad (8-28)$$

The first term in Eq. (8-28) is the result of a change in heat flux due to back radiation caused by a unit change in the water surface temperature. The first two terms within the brackets are the result of a change in evaporation, the third term is the result of a change in conduction and the final term is a change in the advected flux.

Using the definitive Eqs. (8-27) and (8-28), the total heat flux term can finally be written in a manner which clearly demonstrates its dependence on the temperature departure.

$$H_T = H_R - C_p \, \rho \, K \, \Delta T \qquad (8-29)$$

The accuracy of the linearization procedure which was used to obtain Eq. (8-29) decreases as the value of the temperature departure increases. Therefore it is very desirable to choose the value of the reference temperature so that the value of ΔT remains small.

Even if the exact values of the wind function, ψ , and the constant in Bowen's ratio, β , were known, Eq. (8-29) would still only be an approximation to the total flux H_T , because the various expressions have been linearized in ΔT . The accuracy of the linearization of the processes is a function of many variables including the wind speed, the relative humidity, air temperature, and reference temperature, but the most critical variable is the temperature departure, ΔT . The manner in which the linearization error in Eq. (8-29) increases with increasing magnitudes of the value of ΔT will now be demonstrated so that it is possible to determine how large the actual temperature fluctuations can be before the total surface exchange must be computed using a more complicated formula.

The "exact" value of the total surface exchange can be computed for any assumed set of meteorological conditions by use of Eqs. (8-16), (8-20), (8-22), and (8-24). This "exact" value of the total surface exchange has been computed and the approximate value has been determined from Eqs. (8-27), (8-28) and (8-29) for various assumed meteorologic conditions. The differences in the two exchange rates is the linearization error caused by the use of Eq. (8-29). The variation of the linearization error with the temperature departure and wind function is illustrated for one set of assumed conditions on Fig. 8-1. The assumed values of the meteorologic conditions are given on the figure. A reasonable value of the wind speed which may be associated with the value of the wind function could be determined from

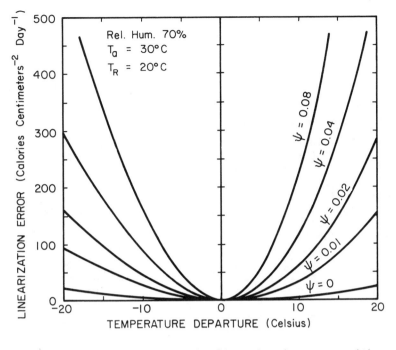

Fig. 8-1   Variation of the linearization error with
the temperature departure and wind function.

$$u_2 = 131\psi \qquad\qquad (8\text{-}30)$$

in which u_2 is the wind speed in miles per hour at a height
of 2 meters and the value of ψ gives the evaporation rate in
centimeters per day when the valuesof the vapor pressures are
in millibars. Eq. (8-30) is the expression suggested by
Harbeck (1962, p. 104) for use when the surface area of the
water is 10 acres. It was found that the linearization error
when expressed in calories per unit area per unit time is
almost independent of the values of air temperature, reference
temperature, and relative humidity. Therefore Fig. 8-1 can be
assumed to be representative of the linearization error for a
wide range of conditions.
      If one knew how large an error was acceptable, Fig. 8-1
could be used to determine the maximum temperature departure
for which Eq. (8-29) could be used. Usually the percentage
error is of more importance, but in order to give the reader
a feel for the magnitude of these values on Fig. 8-1, some
representative calculations will be made. The daily average
value of the clear sky solar-radiation has been given by Koberg
(1964, p. 111). During the month of June at a latitude of 40°N
the value is about 800 cal cm^{-2} day^{-1}. Temperature departures

should remain less than ±5°C if the maximum linearization error is to remain less than 80 cal day^{-1} cm^{-2}. Another way to look at this figure is that if the maximum linearization error is kept below 80 cal cm^{-2} day^{-1} the maximum error in the rate of change of temperature of a body of water 40 cm deep (slightly over a foot) would be 2°C per day.

The linearization error, expressed as a percentage of the true correction of the reference surface exchange term, H_R, is illustrated on Fig. 8-2. This percentage is computed as the error, from Fig. 8-1, divided by the exact value of total surface exchange minus the reference exchange rate. Harbeck (1962, p. 104) estimates that the wind function for lake evaporation can be estimated with a standard error of about 16 percent. It is very unlikely that the wind function which applies to evaporation from rivers can be estimated even this accurately. The linearization error is always less than 16 percent provided that the magnitude of the temperature departure is less than 8°C, Fig. 8-2. It would seem that temperature departures as large as ±8°C could be analyzed with an accuracy that is consistent with the accuracy of the wind function because at high wind velocities the major portion of the correction term results from the evaporation and conduction terms.

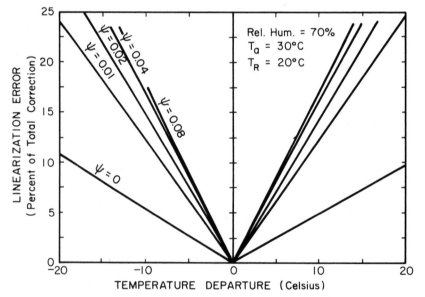

Fig. 8-2 Variation of the linearization error, as a percentage of the total correction, with the temperature departure and wind function.

For temperature departures larger than 8°C a second order equation similar to Eq. (8-29) should be derived and used. This will make the solution of Eq. (8-3) much more difficult.

The next logical question is, what types of problems can be solved by use of Eq. (8-29)? Or alternately, what types of problems exist wherein the maximum temperature swing is less than 16°C? Brown (1969, p. 69) states that diurnal fluctuations of 11°C are not uncommon in exposed streams with summer flows of about 1 cubic foot per second (cfs) (0.0283 cubic meter per second, m^3/sec). Of course the diurnal fluctuations of larger streams is much smaller, for example, the Willamette River, with a mean daily discharge of about 5000 cfs (142 m^3 sec^{-1}), has a diurnal fluctuation in temperature of only about 1°C (Brown, 1969, p. 69). Therefore the variation of temperature throughout a day could be modeled for practically any stream of interest using Eq. (8-29). For longer time periods the temperature swings are greater. Annual temperature variations are of course the greatest. However for many large streams it may be possible to use Eq. (8-29) to model the temperature distribution throughout the entire year. For example Jaske, (1968, p. 6) reports that the annual temperature swing of the Columbia River at Priest Rapids is only 14.8°C. For rivers with larger swings the year could be subdivided into shorter time periods and a different reference temperature could be assumed for each time period such that the maximum temperature swing during any time period was less than 16°C. Therefore it appears that Eq. (8-29) can be very useful and sufficiently accurate to analyze most practical problems.

A Review of the Convective Diffusion Approach to Turbulent Mixing. Since the derivation of the heat transfer equations in the previous sections was presented in a more or less formalistic manner, it is appropriate to review the mechanics of diffusion and dispersion in depth. By doing so, one will be able to evaluate the physical significance of the diffusive terms, which are the major sources of approximation rendered to the otherwise exact equation for conservation of thermal energy. First of all, it is important to realize that the transfer of heat in turbulent flow is considered due entirely to velocities. Thermal conduction at molecular-scale level is negligibly small and slow relative to turbulent velocity transport under most circumstances. It is thus apparent that there is no essential difference between the transfer processes of thermal energy and those of other soluble substances and properties, unless the local variation of thermal energy is so great that it has dynamic effects on the flow itself.

Suppose that the instantaneous longitudinal velocity can be separated, as was done in the previous sections, into the time-average part, u, and a fluctuating part, u_d, by adopting a particular sampling period. The root-mean-square value of u_d may be assumed to be less than 30 percent of u

as in a typical channel flow. The transfer by the average velocity, u , is designated as convection but is not of much interest here because it is just a matter of knowing the velocity variation to calculate such transfer. On the other hand, the transfer by the fluctuating turbulent velocity, u_d , must necessarily be described by some statistical means. This transfer is designated as turbulent diffusion. Note that the above and following discussions on diffusion are equally applicable to fluctuating turbulent velocities in the vertical and transverse directions. In these directions, the time-average velocity may be zero but the root-mean-square value of the fluctuation is finite.

The fundamental approach to turbulent diffusion was laid by Taylor in the paper "Diffusion by Continuous Movements" (1921). He asserted that the correct description of turbulent diffusion must be Lagrangian rather than Eulerian and showed that the Lagrangian time correlation of u_d , the velocity with which the transferred property is moving, is the crux of the problem. In a one-dimensional stationary homogeneous turbulence, the variance of a property distribution initially concentrated at a point is shown to be

$$\frac{1}{2}\frac{d\sigma_v^2}{dt} = \overline{u_d^2} \int_0^t R(\tau)d\tau \qquad (8-31)$$

where $\overline{u_d^2}$ is a mean square of the turbulent velocity and R is the Lagrangian time correlation. If R decreases, often exponentially, to zero as τ increases, $\int_0^\infty R(\tau)d\tau$ defines a Lagrangian time scale L_t . When turbulent transfer is observed as a time much larger than L_t , the total effect is very much similar to that due to purely random diffusion such as molecular diffusion. The right side of Eq. (8-31) is then equal to $\overline{u_d^2} L_t$ and the time rate of increase of σ_v^2 becomes constant. In this manner, the diffusion coefficient may be defined as

$$\varepsilon_x = \frac{1}{2}\frac{d\sigma_v^2}{dt} = \overline{u_d^2} L_t \; . \qquad (8-32)$$

Therefore the formulation of turbulent diffusion coefficient ε_i is valid only for $t >> L_t$ and not at or near a heat source.

In a steady uniform channel flow, the requirement of stationary homogeneous turbulence is satisfied at the free

8-18

surface and in other planes parallel to the free surface if the diffusion is not affected by the side boundaries. Flume experiments by Orlob (1958), Elder (1959), Sayre and Chamberlain (1964), Sayre and Chang (1966), Sullivan (1968), Engelund (1969), Prych (1970) and others show that ε_x , ε_z , on each plane and $\overline{\varepsilon_z}$ are indeed constant and the concentration distribution is Gaussian in the respective directions. Recently, as the techniques of water turbulence measurement improved, some progress is being made toward predicting these coefficients from Eulerian turbulence measurements (McQuivey and Keefer, 1971). Note that, while diffusion tests often represent Lagrangian measurements, turbulence measurements are exclusively Eulerian observations.

The above definition of stationary homogeneous turbulence cannot be applied to the determination of the vertical component, ε_y , because of the shear effect. The measurements of ε_y have always been analyzed in terms of phenomenological theories such as the mixing length hypothesis and the Reynolds analogy between the momentum and heat transfer. Extensive flume studies by Pien (1941), Vanoni (1946), Al-Saffar (1964), Jobson (1968), Chatwin (1971) and others, however, show that the Reynolds analogy is satisfactory despite some shortcomings of the theory (Hinze, 1959) and that the distribution of ε_y can be assessed directly from the knowledge of vertical gradient of longitudinal velocity.

Anisotropy among ε_x , ε_y , and ε_z in a turbulent shear flow is an additional complication. Theoretically, the thermal flux in an anisotropic media may be given by

$$\text{flux}_x = \varepsilon_{xx} \frac{\partial T}{\partial x} + \varepsilon_{xy} \frac{\partial T}{\partial y} + \varepsilon_{xz} \frac{\partial T}{\partial z} , \qquad (8\text{-}33)$$

where ε_{ij} is a second order tensor. It is customary to assume that the coordinate directions x , y , and z constitute the principal axes of the diffusion tensor and that the boundaries are not distorted for the major part of the media (Carslaw and Jager, 1959). The flux is then defined by the gradient in that direction only. Among a few studies devoted to this subject, Dagan (1968) concluded that, under the assumption of Reynolds analogy, there are only two distinct tensor components in an open channel flow; the one tangential to isovels and the other normal to isovels, both being normal to the axial direction.

Summarizing the above discussion, Eulerian transfer terms in Eq. (8-3) are consistent with the Lagrangian description of diffusion in the x and z directions for a steady uniform channel except near the boundaries and at a source. They are satisfactory on an empirical basis in the y direction, for

which no Lagrangian theory is currently available. The approximation by means of Eq. (8-3) is thus satisfactory for most
parts of natural rivers if the flow is steady and uniform.

It is recalled that the above development is based on the
assumption that a proper division of velocity into u and u_d
is possible. When a turbulent flow contains a wide continuous
spectrum of turbulent scales, validity of the diffusion terms
in Eq. (8-3) becomes suspect because a division between u
and u_d may no longer be self-evident. Large estuaries and
embayments often exhibit such turbulence characteristics. The
correct description must still be Lagrangian. One such
description is given by Richardson's "distance neighbor function," in which the diffusion coefficient is proportional to
the four-third power of a time-dependent separation distance.
This concept has been well established in large scale diffusion
tests conducted in oceans (Monin, 1959). It has also been
explained theoretically by Kolmogoroff's similarity theory of
turbulence for a large Reynolds number. Flume studies by Ippen,
Harleman, and Lin (1960) for an idealized estuary verified the
applicability of Kolmogoroff's theory in such a flow. However,
the possibility of obtaining a complete Lagrangian description
of turbulent transfer in a flow with a wide turbulence scale
range is rather remote at the present time. Equation (8-3)
can still be used as a provisional equation, in which the
diffusion coefficients are determined on empirical basis
(Okubo, 1970).

When the two- and one-dimensional equations were derived
from Eq. (8-3), additional diffusive terms, D_v and D_h ,
were introduced in these equations. This is based on Taylor's
theory of longitudinal disperion (1954) and a brief review of
the theory is appropriate. A steady uniform shear flow is
assumed again. Since a shear flow always exhibits vertical and
transverse variations of the longitudinal velocity u , a
substance in a faster velocity region of the cross section
moves downstream faster than that in a slower velocity region.
Because of the vertical and transverse diffusivity, however,
the substance in the faster velocity region also migrates to
the slower velocity region where the concentration is low.
Migration of the substance from the slower velocity region to
the faster velocity region occurs in an analogous manner.
Taylor's theory is based on the recognition that this coupled
action of differential convection and lateral diffusion produces an effective longitudinal dispersion relative to a coordinate which is moving with the cross-sectional average
velocity and is representable by a constant dispersion coefficient just as if it were due to random diffusion. Aris (1956)
provided a rigorous proof that the longitudinal dispersion is
indeed asymptotic to the Gaussian distribution. The theory has
been verified experimentally in model flumes by Elder (1959),
Fischer (1966), Sayre (1968), Sullivan (1968), and many others.

The time required for the establishment of a constant dispersion coefficient is analogous to, but much longer than, the Lagrangian time scale, L_t , mentioned before. This is because transported particles must have adequate time to "sample" all local velocities in the cross section before their motions begin to conform with the one-dimensional stationary homogeneous turbulence of a steady uniform shear flow (Batchelor and Townsend, 1956). Since the particle distribution will be uniform in a cross section at such a time, this time may be called the uniform mixing time. In open channels, the vertical mixing time is expressed by a nondimensional number tU_*/Y . This number has a value on the order of 10 (Chatwin, 1971) when the lower moments of the distribution approach Gaussian values. The transverse mixing time is much longer than the vertical mixing time. Fischer (1967) has proposed the transverse mixing time as $t = \dfrac{L_W^2}{\varepsilon_z}$, where L_W is a characteristic width dimension. If L_W is taken as $W/2$, $\varepsilon_z = 0.2\, YU_*$, and $W = 20Y$, the value of tU_*/Y for transverse mixing is 500, or 50 times longer than the number for vertical mixing. Before the dispersion attains the uniform mixing stage the effective longitudinal dispersion coefficient is transient and smaller than the ultimate constant value.

The importance of the longitudinal diffusivity term in the heat transfer equation depends on flow and source conditions. In a steady river, the transport by longitudinal dispersion is rather small relative to that by the cross-sectional average convection. When a steady heat source is placed in a steady uniform flow, various analytical solutions to the heat transfer equation can be shown to be completely independent of the longitudinal dispersion. When the heat source is instantaneous, on the other hand, the effect of longitudinal dispersion is important. In estuarine flows, the longitudinal dispersion is usually a significant transfer term relative to the cross-sectional average convection because the net transport due to the convection tends to be small over a tidal cycle.

There is a considerable amount of information on the magnitude of diffusion coefficients. An excellent summary of information on ε_x and ε_z is given by Prych (1970). According-ing to this summary and Keefer's recent measurements (1971), the value of ε_x/YU_* ranges from 0.5 to 1.0 in model flumes. Because of the interference by longitudinal dispersion, however, no data on the depth-averaged value of ε_x have been obtained up to the present time. As for the value of ε_z at the water surface, ε_z/YU_* ranges from 0.17 to 0.26 and is closely related to the depth-averaged value, $\overline{\varepsilon_z}/YU_*$, which ranges from 0.11 to 0.23. The value of ε_y may be calculated from the Reynolds analogy as mentioned before. When the logarithmic velocity distribution is assumed, $\bar{\varepsilon}_y/YU_*$ is 0.067. All of the above values of the diffusion coefficients were obtained in rectangular flumes. In natural rivers, the measurements have been mostly concerned with $\bar{\varepsilon}_z$. Studies by Glover (1964) in the Columbia River, Fischer (1967), and Yotsukura and others (1970, 1972) including the Missouri River test indicate that $\bar{\varepsilon}_z/\langle Y \rangle U_*$ varies from 0.23 to 0.70 for straight to moderately meandering rivers. Fischer (1969) proposed that the secondary currents at river bends could drastically increase the value of $\bar{\varepsilon}_z$.

Even though the effects of stratification and currents induced by variations in density are outside the scope of the present report, a remark on Prych's recent study (1970) is worthwhile. He studied the transverse diffusion of thermal energy from a vertical line source. His results show that the total transverse variance consists of the regular variance, σ_v^2 due to turbulence and an excess variance, σ_e^2, due to density currents. At some downstream distance on the order of $x/Y = 2\bar{u}Y/\bar{\varepsilon}_z$, σ_e^2 stopped increasing because of reduction in the density effect. At greater distances downstream, the rate of increase of the total variance was entirely due to that caused by turbulence. The magnitude of $\bar{\varepsilon}_z$ was thus very large near the source but gradually decreased to the constant value determined by the turbulent diffusivity. When a substance is diffused by turbulence alone, on the other hand, the trend of ε_z or D is to increase rapidly to the ultimate constant value at a relatively short distance and stay constant thereafter.

The magnitude of dispersion coefficients will not be discussed here in detail. The coefficient, D_v, due to a vertical gradient can be estimated from Elder's formula (1959) while that induced by transverse velocity gradient, D_h, is given by Fischer's formula (1967). The value of D_v/YU_* is about 6 while that of D_h is much larger than D_v. A measurement in the Missouri River shows that $D_h/\langle Y \rangle U_*$ can be as high as 5,600 (Yotsukura and others, 1970). These dispersion coefficients, especially the ones due to the transverse gradients are for steady uniform channel flows and are not applicable to estuarine conditions. Holley and Harleman (1965) analyzed field and flume studies of longitudinal dispersion

and concluded that the nondimensional coefficient on the order
of 40 is a good value to be used for nonstratified estuaries.

8.3   THE THREE- AND TWO-DIMENSIONAL PROBLEMS

Solution Approaches to the Three- and Two-Dimensional Problems. In Section 8.2, a set of differential equations were
derived from considerations of the conservation of thermal
energy in an open-channel flow. Detailed reviews on the
mechanics of both surface and hydraulic transfer were presented
in order to illustrate the limitations of such a differential
formulation. When these equations are applied to field situations, however, one must necessarily take account of both the
temporal and spatial scales for which the equations are to be
integrated for useful purposes. Consider a typical power
plant releasing waste water into a river at a varied but continuous rate. Near the release site a flowing mass of waste
water with elevated temperature and low density forms a distinct heat plume having a sharp interface with the cold
ambient water. The equation for conservation of thermal energy,
however satisfactory it may be in a differential body, is very
unwieldy to integrate over the region which encompasses such
sharp interfaces.

More direct approaches to the problem of the near-field
heat plume, which is heavily influenced by stratification and
jet momentum, are the ones based on the dynamics of densimetric
flow and jets (Silberman and Stefan, 1970). The convective
diffusion equation such as Eqs. (8-3), (8-10), (8-13), on the
other hand, is most appropriate for integration in the far-
field, where density and velocity gradients are small. It is
difficult at the present time to properly define the intermediate region where the two approaches join. According to the
study by Benedict and others (1971) on jet effects, this region
may be expected to occur at a point where the ratio of ambient
velocity to jet velocity has been increased to about 0.8. In
terms of density stratification, a local Richardson number,

$$\frac{g}{\rho} \frac{d\rho/dy}{(du/dy)^2}$$

should have been reduced to about 0.25, a value at which significant vertical mixing starts to break down the density
interface (Thorpe, 1968). These numbers were obtained from
specific studies and should not be construed as general rigid
criteria.

Use of Eq. (8-3) for three-dimensional field problems has
been rare because of the lack of information concerning the
effects of stratification and jet action on the distribution
of parameters such as velocity, u , and diffusion coefficients,
ε_i . The only known application of the three-dimensional solution to field problems has been carried out by the Vanderbilt

University group, Edinger and Polk (1969) and Polk, Benedict, and Parker (1972). Empirical diffusion coefficients, which were obtained by matching the field data with the analytical solutions, show that the transverse coefficients are much larger and the vertical coefficients much smaller than the values expected from typical flumes or uniform channels. These deviations appear to reflect the effect of stratification since a constant value of the diffusion coefficient was applied to an entire set of data, much of which came from the near and intermediate fields.

There are several analytical techniques available to solve three- or two-dimensional equations. For simple boundary forms and constant parameters, there are a large number of solutions satisfying various linear boundary conditions (Carslaw and Jaeger, 1959, Crank, 1956, and Sutton, 1953). In seeking new solutions, however, the Laplace transform combined with the Fourier transform and other integral transforms appear to be the favorite techniques used by workers (Cleary, McAvoy, and Short, 1971). When boundary forms are complicated and/or parameters are variable, numerical calculation is an important and attractive method of attack. In using finite-difference numerical techniques for a convective diffusion equation, one should be particularly aware of the numerical dispersion resulting from approximations of the convective term, which may easily and completely misguide workers in evaluating the magnitude of diffusion and dispersion coefficients (Bella and Dobbins, 1968). Recently some advantages of the finite-element method over the finite-difference method have been recognized by workers of ground water diffusion (Pinder and Frind, 1972). Applicability of this technique to surface water problems has not been fully investigated.

An Application of Yotsukura-Cobb Stream-Tube Method to the Two-Dimensional Problems. This particular method of describing the steady-state two-dimensional solute concentration was developed from the observation that the transverse cumulative discharge in a cross section is a more direct and appropriate variable than the transverse distance in characterizing the conservation of solute mass in a steady natural stream. By adopting the cumulative discharge as the transverse variable, one can eliminate troublesome lateral variations of the convective term, $u(z)$, from the equation for simple treatments by either numerical or analytical approximation. Application to nonconservative wastes is possible when the waste is soluble and decays according to the first-order reaction. As shown in Eqs. (8-10) and (8-29) of Section 8.2, the heat exchange, though physically a surface phenomenon, can be approximated as if it is a first-order reaction within a water body in the two-dimensional formulation. The following is a brief description of the method excerpted from the comprehensive report to be published later.

It will be convenient to redefine some variables for the sake of brevity. The variable $u(z)$ is the depth averaged longitudinal velocity, $D(z)$ the dispersion coefficient induced by vertical velocity gradients, $\varepsilon_z(z)$ the transverse diffusion coefficient, and T water temperature. In this chapter all symbols represent depth-averaged values. When the conservation of thermal energy is considered in a natural stream, the total depth, Y, is a variable with respect to Z even if the flow is steady and uniform. Under such a condition, a derivation similar to the one leading to Eq. (8-10) shows that

$$\frac{\partial T}{\partial t} + u(z) \frac{\partial T}{\partial x} = \frac{\partial}{\partial x}\left(D(z) \frac{\partial T}{\partial x}\right) + \frac{1}{Y(z)} \frac{\partial}{\partial z}\left(\varepsilon_z(z)Y(z) \frac{\partial T}{\partial z}\right) + \frac{H_T}{\rho C_p Y(z)} .$$

$$(8-34)$$

The notations are as defined in Section 8.2 except those redefined above.

Equation (8-34) is applicable to both thermally loaded temperature and natural temperature. An equation for excess temperature, that is the thermally loaded temperature minus the natural temperature, may be derived by subtracting from Eq. (8-34) a similar equation written for natural temperature, T_n. Prior to this, the surface transfer, H_T, is to be linearized according to Eq. (8-29). Defining the excess temperature, T_e, as the thermally loaded temperature, T, minus the natural temperature, T_n, and completing the subtraction, the equation for T_e is obtained as

$$\frac{\partial T_e}{\partial t} + u(z) \frac{\partial T_e}{\partial x} = \frac{\partial}{\partial x}\left(D(z) \frac{\partial T_e}{\partial x}\right) +$$

$$\frac{1}{Y(z)} \frac{\partial}{\partial z}\left(\varepsilon_z(z)Y(z)\frac{\partial T_e}{\partial z}\right) - \frac{K(t)T_e}{Y(z)} . \qquad (8-35)$$

If the release rate of waste heat is steady and Eq. (8-35) is applied at a large time t, the longitudinal dispersion term may be neglected. It is also seen that, if heat were conservative $(K = 0)$, the terms, $\frac{\partial T_e}{\partial t}$ and $\frac{KT_e}{Y}$, drop out of Eq. (8-35) and the resulting solutions are for a steady-state distribution. In order to utilize such steady-state solutions, assume that $Y(z)$ in the surface-transfer term is approximated by $\bar{Y}$, the width-averaged depth. Then it can be shown that

$$T_e (x,z,t) = T_e' (x,z) \exp\left(- \int_0^t \frac{K(t)}{\bar{Y}} dt\right) \qquad (8-36)$$

8-25

is a solution to a simplified form of Eq. (8-35), or

$$\frac{\partial T_e}{\partial t} + u(z) \frac{\partial T_e}{\partial x} = \frac{1}{Y(z)} \frac{\partial}{\partial z} \left(\varepsilon_z(z)Y(z) \frac{\partial T_e}{\partial z} \right) - \frac{K(t)T_e}{Y}$$

(8-37)

provided that T_e' is a steady-state solution to

$$u(z) \frac{\partial T_e'}{\partial x} = \frac{1}{Y(z)} \frac{\partial}{\partial z} \left(\varepsilon_z(z)Y(z) \frac{\partial T_e'}{\partial z} \right) .$$

(8-38)

As long as the discharge rates of river and waste heat are steady, Eq. (8-36) shows that the excess temperature T_e is simply obtained at a point (x,z) by multiplying a time-dependent loss factor to the steady state solution T_e'. Note, however, that Eq. (8-36) does not apply to the condition that K is nonzero constant and $\frac{\partial T_e}{\partial t}$ is zero in Eq. (8-37). For this case, it can be shown that there is a solution,

$$T_e(x,z,t) = T_e'(x,z) \exp\left(-\int_0^x \frac{Kdx}{Y\,U} \right) ,$$

(8-39)

provided that u in the decay term is approximated by $\bar{U}$, the cross-sectional average velocity.

No analytical solution is currently available for Eq. (8-38) in which $u(z)$ and $Y(z)$ vary transversely as in a natural stream. However, Yotsukura and Cobb (1972) found that an analytical approximation to Eq. (8-38) is quite feasible in such conditions. Defining the cumulative discharge as a new variable

$$q = \int_0^z uY dz ,$$

(8-40)

and replacing z with q, Eq. (8-38) is transformed into a form in which u and Y appear only in the diffusive flux term. By assuming furthermore that the variation of diffusivity in the transverse direction has small effects on the solution, Eq. (8-38) is approximated by

$$\frac{\partial T_e'}{\partial x} = \overline{\varepsilon_z uY^2} \frac{\partial^2 T_e'}{\partial q^2}$$

(8-41)

where the diffusion factor $\overline{\varepsilon_z uY^2}$ is a constant defined by

$$\overline{\varepsilon_z uY^2} = \frac{1}{Q} \int_0^Q \varepsilon_z uY^2 dq \qquad (8\text{-}42)$$

and Q is the total discharge and also the maximum value for the variable q .

An analytical solution to Eq. (8-41) for a line source extending from q_{s1} to q_{s2} , where $(q_{s2} - q_{s1})$ is equal to waste water discharge Q_s , is given by a set of the error functions as follows:

$$T_e'(\alpha,q') = \frac{T_{es}}{2} \left[\sum_{n=0}^{\infty} \sum_{j=1}^{2} \left\{ \mathrm{erf}\, \frac{\alpha(q_{s2}' + 2n + \delta_j q')}{\sqrt{2}} \right.\right.$$

$$\left. - \mathrm{erf}\, \frac{\alpha(q_{s1}' + 2n + \delta_j q')}{\sqrt{2}} \right\}$$

$$+ \sum_{n=1}^{\infty} \sum_{j=1}^{2} \left\{ \mathrm{erf}\, \frac{\alpha(q_{s2}' - 2n + \delta_j q')}{\sqrt{2}} \right.$$

$$\left.\left. - \mathrm{erf}\, \frac{\alpha(q_{s1}' - 2n + \delta_j q')}{\sqrt{2}} \right\} \right] \qquad (8\text{-}43)$$

Summation with respect to the index j is defined by $\delta_1 = +1$ and $\delta_2 = -1$. The symbols q' , q_{s2}' , and q_{s1}' are all fractional values relative to Q , T_{es} is the excess temperature at the waste release site, and α is a nondimensional parameter,

$$\alpha = \sqrt{\frac{Q^2}{2x\overline{\varepsilon_z uY^2}}} \quad . \qquad (8\text{-}44)$$

Yotsukura and Cobb verified by tracer experiments that Eq. (8-43) is quite satisfactory for a number of straight uniform natural channels. They also found that it is usable in a moderately meandering reach of the Missouri River. The non-dimensional diffusion coefficient, $\overline{\varepsilon_z/YU_*}$, was found to range from 0.23 for the straight channels to 0.7 for the Missouri reach. The symbol U_* designates the average shear velocity.

Calculation of the exponential decay term in Eq. (8-36) is easily done once K is given as a function of time according Eq. (8-28). As discussed previously, however, a proper choice of the reference temperature, T_R , must be such that T_R is as close as possible to expected water temperature T. In a typical short-term excess-temperature study in a stream, T_R may be represented best by the daily average natural temperature observed upstream from a waste discharge site (Yotsukura, Jackman, and Faust, 1972).

Application of the product solution for T_e, Eq. (8-36), to field problems consists of the following steps. First a river reach of concern is schematized by a flow system consisting of a fixed number of stream tubes with equal subdischarge ∇q. This is shown in Fig. 8-3. Note that all solid lines represent impervious boundaries through which no flow or diffusion takes place. Since Eq. (8-36) is applicable only to a uniform flow, the reach is then divided into a set of subreaches based on the cross-sectional conditions, the location of tributaries and islands, and also the desired locations of temperature calculation. In the stream-tube flow system, the longitudinal distance remains the same as in the actual river system.

Solutions to steady state "conservative" temperature, T'_e are calculated by means of Eq. (8-43) for each successive subreach by taking upstream temperature as a line source for

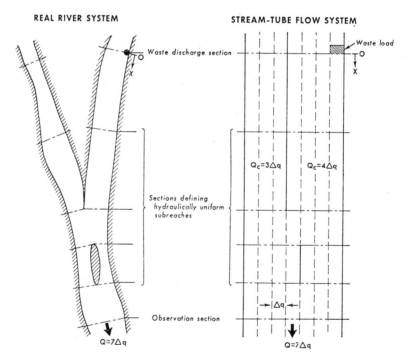

Fig. 8-3 Sketch of real river system and stream-tube flow system.

8-28

downstream temperature. However, since each upstream stream
tube tends to have different excess temperature in most
applications, repetitive use of Eq. (8-43) for each upstream
tube source is necessary. In such cases, the downstream
temperature is obtained by superposing contributions from all
upstream tubes in a given channel. The work is usually done
efficiently by the use of digital computers after the hydraulic
information is tabulated for each subreach from regular stream-
gaging data. A proper estimate of $\bar{\epsilon}_z$ is needed in solving
Eq. (8-43). This aspect will be discussed later.

In finding the exponential loss due to the surface dissipation, a choice is made of the actual times at which the
temperature is desired at a specified cross section. The travel
time from the waste discharge site to the section is determined
from hydraulic data and the time-dependent meteorologic data
are used in Eq. (8-28) to calculate the variations of $K(t)$ as
the water travels downstream from the discharge site. The
total loss, $\exp \left(- \int_0^t \frac{K(t)}{\gamma}\right)$, is calculated by means of finite-
interval integration for each section. The excess temperature
at a section for the desired time is then obtained by Eq.
(8-36). The calculated value of T_e may be added to the
natural temperature prevailing at the time for the section if
such information is available.

Field data from several stream sites were made available
for analysis by the U. S. Geological Survey in cooperation with
U. S. Atomic Energy Commission. Details concerning the data
collection and one-dimensional analysis are discussed in the
report by Jackman and Meyer, 1971. Among these data, those
observed at the Potomac River near the Dickerson Power Plant,
Maryland, were ideal for testing the present model because of a
marked nonuniformity in the transverse temperature distribution
for a distance of about 20 miles downstream. In other streams,
the transverse diffusion was complete within a few miles of the
discharge site. In all of the above field measurements, the
water temperature and the hydraulic and meteorologic variables
were observed at several cross sections downstream of the discharge sites at 2-hour intervals for a period of 24 hours.
Supplementary solar radiation data were obtained from the
National Weather Service stations when such measurements were
not conducted at the stream sites. As for the Potomac River,
supplementary data on water temperature and meteorologic data
were obtained from the Dickerson Power Plant and the National
Weather Service for 3 days preceding the actual 24-hour measurements. This was necessary because the heated water which was
observed at Seneca, 18 miles downstream from Dickerson, at the
end of the 24-hour measurement period had left Dickerson much
earlier than the commencement of the measurement and had been
exposed to substantial dissipation of heat under the

meteorologic conditions not covered by the measurements. All measurements were conducted by Geological Survey personnel.

The Potomac River data were analyzed most intensively because of its ideal nature. One of the central parameters sought in the analysis was the magnitude of the transverse diffusion coefficient $\bar{\varepsilon}_z$. By the trial and error matching of Eq. (8-43) with observed temperature and dye distributions at several downstream sections, it was found that $\bar{\varepsilon}_z/\bar{Y}U_*$ on the order of 0.6 was the optimum value. Since this agrees with the currently available information on $\bar{\varepsilon}_z$ in a natural stream, it was decided to use this value for all streams and all sub-reaches. It is worth noting that this optimum figure was derived from the observations at distances larger than 1,000 $\bar{Y}$ downstream from the waste discharge site so that the initial densimetric effect (Prych, 1970) on diffusion is estimated to be rather minor.

Another important aspect of the analysis was concerned with the natural temperature regime which would exist without heated discharges. For this purpose, the total heat exchange equation, Eq. (8-15), was applied in a Lagrangian sense to a body of moving water. A difference equation may be written as

$$\Delta T_n = \frac{\Delta t H_T}{\rho C_p \bar{Y}} . \qquad (8-45)$$

Comparison of the calculated to the observed value of T_n at hourly intervals was fair to satisfactory in most data and provided a justification for using Eqs. (8-15) and (8-28) for short-term calculations. Most of the coefficients in these equations were derived from the measurements on the order of a day or longer (Harbeck, 1953, 1962).

The results of the calculations are shown in Figs. 8-4 through 8-9. Figure 8-4 shows the comparison of observed and calculated natural temperatures derived from Eqs. (8-15) and (8-45). Figures 8-5 and 8-6 show the comparison of calculated and observed temperatures of the Potomac River in March and May 1969. The total discharge Q was about 5,000 cfs and heated discharge Q_s was about 10 percent of Q in both cases. Equations (8-36), (8-43), and (8-28) were used for the calculations. Figure 8-7 shows the result of the October Potomac River data. In this case, Q was about 1,800 and Q_s was 600 cfs. Since the heated discharge had higher velocity than the ambient discharge, the combined effect of jet action and densimetric effect produced very large diffusion at the cross section 0.83 miles downstream. In order to match the temperature distribution at this cross section, $\bar{\varepsilon}_z$ had to be

8-30

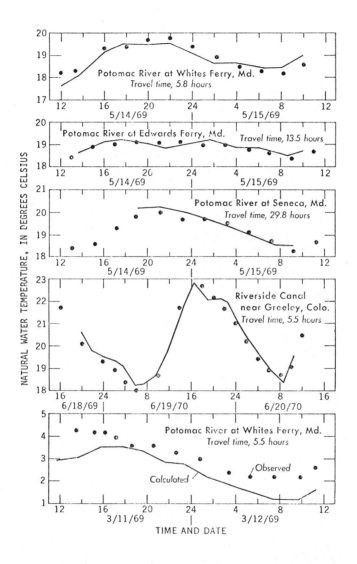

Fig. 8-4 Comparison of observed and calculated
natural river temperature.

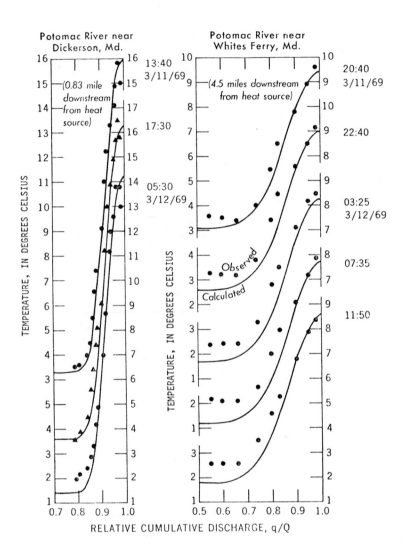

Fig. 8-5   Comparison of observed and calculated
temperature distribution in the transverse direction, Potomac River, March
1969.

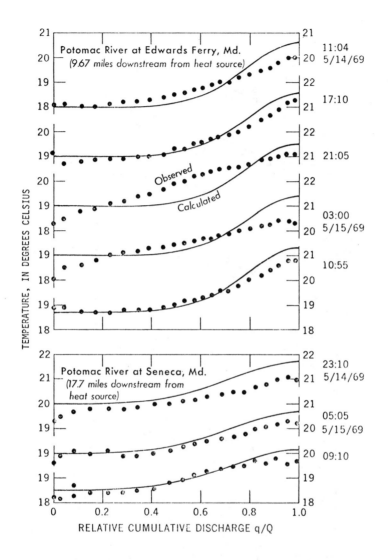

Fig. 8-6 Comparison of observed and calculated
temperature distribution in the transverse direction, Potomac River, May
1969.

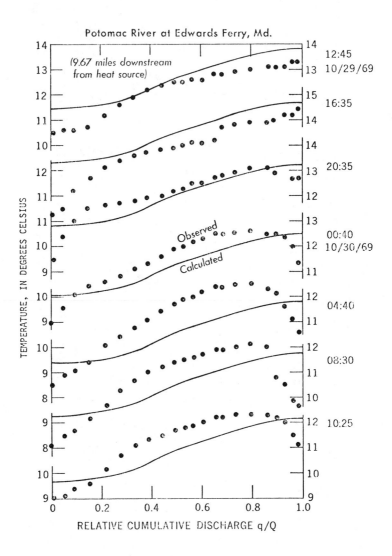

Fig. 8-7 Comparison of observed and calculated
temperature distribution in the transverse direction, Potomac River, October
1969.

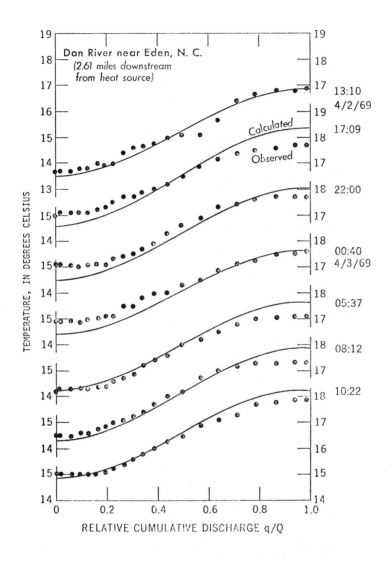

Fig. 8-8   Comparison of observed and calculated
temperature distribution in the transverse direction, Dan River, April 1969.

8-35

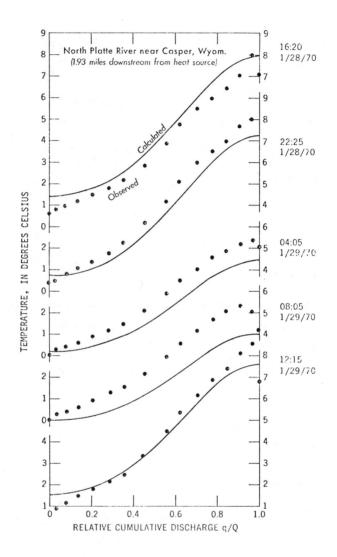

Fig. 8-9   Comparison of observed and calculated
temperature distribution in the transverse direction, North Platte River,
January 1970.

increased to about 20 times the value mentioned above. Figure 8-7 shows the results obtained by taking the calculated distribution at 0.83 miles as an initial condition and applying the regular value of $\bar{\epsilon}_z$ in subsequent reaches. The results are not as satisfactory as in March and May because of this effect. Also the effect of using the width-averaged $\bar{Y}$ in the surface-transfer term of Eq. (8-37) is apparent in several cases near the bank sides.

Figures 8-8 and 8-9 are similar comparisons applied to the data from Dan River near Eden, North Carolina, in April 1969, and North Platte River near Casper, Wyoming, in January 1970. In these rivers, the calculations were done such that the average observed temperature distribution at the section closest to the discharge site was used as the initial condition.

8.4 THE ONE-DIMENSIONAL PROBLEM

Simplifications and Solution Approaches. The one-dimensional form of the thermal-energy transfer equation has been given in Eq. (8-13). This equation was derived for a channel with constant depth, but it can be used to describe the energy transfer process in a river for which the velocity, depth, and temperature are not too variable in the cross section by simply using averaged values. Since this section will be concerned only with the one-dimensional case, Eq. (8-13) will be rewritten without the use of braces and overbars, and it will be understood that all quantities have been properly averaged in the cross section. Using the same reference temperature for Eq. (8-13) as will be used in the linearization of the surface exchange term and using one symbol, D, to represent the total dispersion coefficient, Eq. (8-13) becomes

$$\frac{\partial \Delta T}{\partial t} + U \frac{\partial \Delta T}{\partial x} = \frac{\partial}{\partial x} [D \frac{\partial \Delta T}{\partial x}] + \frac{H_T}{C_p \rho Y} . \qquad (8-46)$$

It will be assumed that the water temperature is uniform in the vertical direction so that the surface temperature can be considered to be equal to the local depth averaged temperature. Because mixing is so much more rapid in the vertical direction than it is in the transverse direction, this assumption does not seriously restrict the applicability of the equation. Finally, assuming that all meteorologic variables are independent of the z coordinate, that is across the width of the river, and combining Eq. (8-29) with (8-46)

$$\frac{\partial \Delta T}{\partial t} + U \frac{\partial \Delta T}{\partial x} = \frac{\partial}{\partial x} [D \frac{\partial \Delta T}{\partial x}] - \frac{K}{Y} \Delta T + \frac{H_R}{C_p \rho Y} . \qquad (8-47)$$

Equation (8-47) is probably the most general form of the one-dimensional equation which is also practical enough for most common uses.

If one is interested only in the distribution of excess temperature, that is the incremental effect of an artificial heat source, such as a power plant, on the natural temperature distribution within a stream, Eq. (8-47) simplifies significantly. The equation which described the distribution of excess temperature can be obtained from Eq. (8-47) in the same manner as Eq. (8-47) was obtained from Eq. (8-46). For this case, the last term, H_R , in Eq. (8-47) cancels (Jobson, 1972); and, the value of ΔT becomes the excess temperature. Since the value of H_R does not appear in the equation, the temperature excess can be predicted without knowledge of the absorbed radiation term provided only that the approximate natural temperature is known.

Equation (8-47) has the same form as the classical biochemical oxygen demand (BOD) equation in which ΔT is replaced by the BOD, K is replaced by the sum of the biochemical oxidation rate coefficient and the sedimentation rate coefficient for BOD, and $\frac{H_R}{C_p \rho Y}$ is replaced by the rate of inflow of BOD along the river. The biochemical oxygen demand equation has received wide attention.

By use of some simplifying assumptions, Bennett (1971) has shown how Eq. (8-47) can be transformed into a form which is much more amenable to solution. Using the method proposed by Bennett, assume U , D , and H_R are functions of time only and that K and Y are constant, then by use of the transformation

$$\Delta T = \lambda \exp \left[- \frac{K}{Y} t\right] + \exp \left[- \frac{K}{Y} t\right] \cdot {}_0\!\int^t \frac{H_R}{C_p \rho Y} \exp \left[\frac{K}{Y} \gamma\right] d\gamma .$$

$$(8-48)$$

Equation (8-47) becomes

$$\frac{\partial \lambda}{\partial t} + U \frac{\partial \lambda}{\partial x} = D \frac{\partial^2 \lambda}{\partial x^2} . \qquad (8-49)$$

Bennett (1971) has shown how this equation can be solved in a fast and convenient manner by use of a digital computer and a convolution integral approach.

Of course, if the depth and velocity are assumed to be independent of x and the longitudinal dispersion is ignored, Eq. (8-47) can be integrated directly for a steady state solution,

$$\Delta T = \frac{KH_R}{C_p\rho} + \left[\Delta T_o - \frac{KH_R}{C_p\rho}\right] \exp \left[-\frac{Kx}{UY}\right] \qquad (8-50)$$

in which ΔT_o is the temperature at the origin. Likewise, if one is interested only in the distribution of excess temperature, above or below the natural temperature, the equation which describes the excess temperature can be integrated to give the classical exponential dieaway curve (Jobson, 1972)

$$T_e = T_{eo} \exp \left[\frac{-Kx}{UY}\right] . \qquad (8-51)$$

The term which includes the incoming radiation has been completely eliminated.

Discussion of Previous Temperature Models. Equation (8-47) has been presented as a very general form of a one-dimensional temperature prediction model. A few of the previous temperature prediction models will now be discussed, and it will be shown that in general they represent specific cases of Eq. (8-47).

Probably the most widely known and widely quoted temperature prediction model is the one proposed by Edinger and Geyer (1965). This model will be referred to as the equilibrium temperature model. The equilibrium temperature model can be obtained from the present one by defining the reference temperature, T_R , in the surface exchange equation to be the equilibrium temperature, $E + 273.16$, and, allowing E to be an independent variable defined such that the quantity, H_R , Eq. (8-27), is zero. Except for the terms which result from the heat flux advected from the system by the evaporated water, which are usually small anyway, the total exchange is still given by Eq. (8-29) except that H_R remains zero due to the definition of the equilibrium temperature. Now using 273.16°K, i.e., 0°C, as the reference temperature in Eq. (8-3) so that the value of ΔT becomes the actual temperature as measured on the Celsius scale, and assuming the classical one-dimensional approach, the one-dimensional equation becomes

$$\frac{\partial\Delta T}{\partial t} + U \frac{\partial\Delta T}{\partial x} = \frac{\partial}{\partial x} \left[\epsilon_x \frac{\partial\Delta T}{\partial x}\right] - \frac{K}{Y} \left[\Delta T - E\right] \qquad (8-52)$$

in which E is an independent variable which must be found by solving Eq. (8-27) for E when the value of H_R is set equal to zero and $T_R = E + 273.16$. The introduction of the equilibrium temperature has been both unnecessary and inconvenient.

Because the amount of radiation which is absorbed from the sun and sky is an independent variable, any model must contain a term which describes this variable input. The reference surface exchange term, H_R , serves that purpose in the present model while the equilibrium temperature serves that purpose in the equilibrium temperature model. The value of H_R can be obtained directly from the meteorologic variables and Eq. (8-27) while the value of E must be obtained by use of the same meteorologic variables and a trial and error solution of Eq. (8-27) for T_R . This trial and error solution makes the equilibrium temperature model very cumbersome to use. In fact, it is almost impossible to use it unless the meteorologic variables are considered to be constant. In contrast fluctuations in meteorologic variables can be easily accounted for in the present model.

Another advantage of the present approach over the equilibrium temperature model is that in the present approach the reference temperature is constant and it can be selected arbitrarily. If the actual water temperature departs significantly from the reference temperature, large errors occur in the computation of the total surface exchange, H_T , because of the linearization process. The behavior of this linearization error with increasing temperature difference has been presented on Figs. 8-1 and 8-2. From these figures it was concluded that the difference should remain less than about ±8°C. The present approach allows one to choose the reference temperature arbitrarily, so that the linearization error may be minimized. On the contrary, the equilibrium temperature model uses the equilibrium temperature as a reference and this value is an independent variable over which the operator has no control. The actual water temperature is usually nearly constant throughout a day, while Edinger et. al. (1968, p. 1142) have shown that the diurnal fluctuation in the equilibrium temperature could easily be 50°C. The inadequacy of the equilibrium temperature model for predicting diurnal fluctuations in water temperature is immediately apparent. In order to limit the linearization error, time averaged values of meteorologic variables must be used in the equilibrium temperature model.

In conclusion, the proposed model is based upon the same physical principles as the equilibrium temperature model; and, therefore, the two models are almost identical in terms of physical correctness. However, the proposed model is more general and contains a more sophisticated method for the computation of the surface exchange terms while being simpler to apply and allowing the linearization errors to be controlled or at least estimated.

Dingman et. al. (1967, Dingman and Assur, 1969) have developed a model which was designed to be used to predict the length of an ice-free reach of river which could be maintained by a heat source. Their basic model can be obtained from

Eq. (8-46) by assuming steady state conditions, constant velocity, and by neglecting the longitudinal mixing term. With these assumptions Eq. (8-46) can be solved for x

$$x = C_p \rho Y U \int_{\Delta T_i}^{\Delta T_x} \frac{d(\Delta T)}{H_T} \qquad (8\text{-}53)$$

in which ΔT_i is the water temperature at the origin and ΔT_x is the temperature at a distance x from the origin. All water temperatures are assumed to be fully mixed in the cross section. Dingman et. al. assumed 273.16°K as a reference temperature so that ΔT is the actual water temperature as measured on the Celsius scale. This is a good choice for their purposes.

Dingman and Assur (1969) have presented the method which was used to linearize the surface exchange term, H_T, with respect to ΔT. They used one surface exchange equation for clear sky conditions and another for cloudy conditions. The linearization procedure will be illustrated by assuming clear sky conditions. The absorbed radiation term, H_N, was subdivided into its two components, the short-wave and the long-wave component; and, the magnitude of the long-wave component was computed from Brunt's equation using coefficients as determined by Anderson (1954, p. 92). Ignoring the short-wave component, their expression for the total surface exchange was

$$H_T = 0.97 \, \sigma \, T_a^4 \, [0.68 + 0.036 \, \sqrt{R_h} \, \sqrt{f(T_a)}]$$

$$- \varepsilon \, \sigma \, (T_R + \Delta T)^4 - \rho \, L_R \, \psi \, [f(T_R + \Delta T) - R_h \, f(T_a)]$$

$$- \beta \, \rho \, L_R \, \psi \, [(T_R + \Delta T) - T_a] \qquad (8\text{-}54)$$

in which R_h is the relative humidity expressed as a decimal quantity and the other terms are the same as have been defined in Eq. (8-27). The first term of Eq. (8-54) represents the net long-wave radiation which is absorbed by the water. The second term represents the back radiation, H_b. The third term represents the heat flux utilized by evaporation and is equivalent to the third term of Eq. (8-27). Dingman and Assur used an expression proposed by Rimsha and Donchenko (Dingman and Assur, 1969, p. 10) for the wind function. This expression is

$$\Psi = 0.021 + 0.0092(\Delta T + T_R - T_a) + 0.0102\ u_a \qquad (8\text{-}55)$$

in which u_a is the wind velocity in meters per second, and the units of Ψ are cm day^{-1} mb^{-1}. The fourth term in Eq. (8-54) represents the energy exchange due to conduction and is equivalent to the last term in Eq. (8-27). The heat flux advected from the system by the evaporated water, H_w, is ignored.

Although Eqs. (8-54) and (8-55) are complex functions of the absolute air and water temperatures, only a narrow range of temperatures is of interest say 0-20°C. Therefore, for given values of wind speed and relative humidity, it is reasonable to approximate Eq. (8-54) by use of an equation of the form

$$H_T = H_o + a_o T_a' + b_o \Delta T \qquad (8\text{-}56)$$

in which H_o is a constant which is a function of wind speed, short-wave radiation and other variables much as is the value of H_R in Eq. (8-27), a_o and b_o are constants which are functions of wind speed, relative humidity, etc., much like the value of K in Eq. (8-28), and T_a' is the air temperature measured on the Celsius scale. Dingman and Assur (1969) assumed that the values of b_o and a_o were equal in magnitude and opposite in sign so that H_T could be represented by

$$H_T = H_o + a_o(T_a' - \Delta T) \qquad (8\text{-}57)$$

where the reference temperature is 273.16°K. Assuming a relative humidity of 50% and the value of $\Delta T = 0$, which corresponds to a water temperature of 0°C, Dingman and Assur (1969) computed the value of H_T for a large number of air temperatures by use of Eqs. (8-54) and (8-55). From these values of H_T and T_a', they determined expressions for H_o and a_o in Eq. (8-57) as functions of the wind speed using the method of least squares. Because only the value of T_a' was varied in this fitting procedure, the value of a_o which Dingman and Assur determined represents the change in H_T which results from a unit change in air temperature. The purpose of Eq. (8-57) is to relate the surface exchange term, H_T, to the water temperature so that Eq. (8-53) can be integrated. It would appear that the value of b_o in Eq. (8-56) is needed instead of a_o and inspection of Eq. (8-54) illustrates that the relation between them is not constant but depends on the relative humidity and wind speed.

Equation (8-57) like Eq. (8-29) must contain one component which is independent of the water temperature and one component which is a function of the water temperature. The component of Eq. (8-57) which is independent of water temperature is made up of two terms, H_o and $a_o T_a'$. There is no necessity of separating these two terms; in fact, the representation in Eq. (8-57) is unfortunate because it conveys the mistaken impression that the most important driving force for the surface exchange term is the difference in temperature between the air and the water. Harbeck (1959, p. 29) has pointed out the fallacy of using this temperature difference as a driving force. Of course, the separation of the two terms which are both independent variables also makes the solution more cumbersome. Equations (8-57) and (8-29) were both developed to serve the same purpose. The coefficients in Eq. (8-57) must be determined independently for each location using averaged meteorological data, a constant relative humidity and a least squares analysis. The coefficients in Eq. (8-29) can be determined directly from meteorological data.

The final step in the development of the model was to substitute Eq. (8-57) into Eq. (8-53) and to integrate, which results in

$$x = \frac{C_p \rho UY}{a_o} \ln \left[\frac{H_o + a_o(\Delta T_x - T_a')}{H_o + a_o(\Delta T_i - T_a')} \right]. \qquad (8\text{-}58)$$

Substituting Eq. (8-29) into Eq. (8-53) gives

$$x = \frac{UY}{K} \ln \left[\frac{H_R + C_p \rho K \, \Delta T_x}{H_R + C_p \rho K \, \Delta T_i} \right]. \qquad (8\text{-}59)$$

The model of Dingman et. al. (1967) was developed for a specific purpose; it therefore lacks generality. It does represent a significant step forward in that it does not incorporate the equilibrium temperature concept, but it still confuses the problem slightly by implying that the driving force for excess heat dissipation is the difference between the air and water temperatures.

In a preliminary report (1968), the Tennessee Valley Authority has proposed a method of predicting the average water temperature of a fully-mixed stream. This method will be referred to as the TVA model. The basic equation of the TVA model is the same as that given by Eq. (8-46) except that it assumes a constant dispersion coefficient and has an additional term which could be used to account for lateral flow into or out of the river. Depending on the required accuracy and the temperature range of interest, TVA suggested that the total surface exchange be determined from either

$$H_T = C'' + B'' \Delta T + A'' \Delta T^2 \qquad (8\text{-}60)$$

or

$$H_T = C' + B' \Delta T \qquad (8\text{-}61)$$

in which the constants C'', C', B'', B', and A'' are determined from monthly averaged values of meteorologic data and the value of ΔT is the stream temperature as determined on the Celsius scale. Of course, Eq. (8-60) can more accurately represent the total surface exchange than can Eq. (8-61); but, its use complicates the solution of Eq. (8-46). The Tennessee Valley Authority (1968) has presented analytic solutions to various simplified versions of Eq. (8-46). Using the quadratic form of the total surface exchange term, Eq. (8-60), an analytic solution was presented for the steady state condition with zero dispersion, that is D and $\frac{\partial \Delta T}{\partial t}$ were assumed to be zero. Using the linear form of the surface exchange term, a more complete form of Eq. (8-46) could be solved analytically. For this case a solution was presented in which the values of B', U, and D were assumed constant and C' was assumed to be a sinusoidal function of time.

After the temperature range is determined, the values of the constants in either Eq. (8-60) or (8-61) should be determined by computing the "exact" surface exchange from monthly averaged meteorologic data for different water temperatures. The three water temperatures needed to determine the coefficients in Eq. (8-60) should represent the approximate maximum, minimum, and mean values of the expected water temperature. The "exact" surface exchange rate is determined as the net of the mean monthly value of H_N, plus the sum of the back radiation, evaporation and conduction terms which are determined by use of Eqs. (8-16), (8-20), and (8-22) respectively. The value of Ψ in Eqs. (8-20) and (8-22) is assumed to be a constant times the two-meter wind velocity and the heat flux advected from the system by the evaporated water is ignored.

The TVA model approaches the total surface exchange term in a manner which is very similar to that used by Dingman and Assur (1969). This eliminates the linearization about the equilibrium temperature and is therefore generally a more accurate approach than that of the equilibrium temperature model, and there is no reason why the approach cannot be used to predict diurnal temperature fluctuation. The concept of the reference temperature is not clearly evident in the TVA model; and, as a result, the accuracy of the approach is not easily determined. Equations (8-61) and (8-29) have the same form so that the values of C' and B' could also be determined by use of Eqs. (8-27) and (8-28). Although the ratio of C' to B' is defined as the equilibrium temperature in the TVA model, this equilibrium temperature is used only as an independent variable and, therefore, neither detracts from the accuracy of the model nor complicates its solution.

Morse (1970) has presented a stream temperature prediction model which is very similar to that proposed by the Tennessee Valley Authority. In this model Morse presented a numerical solution technique for Eq. (8-46) wherein the dispersion term is ignored and the total surface exchange term is given by Eq. (8-60). In essence the solution technique is a routing scheme which requires a minimum of information about the river's geometry. A knowledge of backwater profiles, discharge and cross-sectional areas, and widths is all that is necessary. Separate values of A", B", and C" are determined for each time period of a representative day. A representative day is composed of a fixed number of time periods during which conditions are assumed to be constant. For example, the conditions for the time period 0600-0900 would be obtained by averaging over many days the conditions which had occurred during this part of the day.

Morse determines the values of the constants A", B", and C" by use of a least squares analysis between the "exact" surface exchange and the assumed water temperature. Different values of these constants are determined for each period of the day. The "exact" value of the total surface exchange, H_T, is determined in the same manner as that proposed by the TVA model except that the meteorologic variables represent the average conditions which are expected to occur during a given period of the day instead of daily average values.

The model was applied to a 200 mile reach of the Columbia River during July, 1966 (Morse, 1970). On the average it predicted the water temperature to within 0.17°C while the total range in observed temperatures was 1.6°C. For this application of the model, the representative day was divided into 4 periods of 6 hours each. In August, 1969, the model was tested on an 8.77 mile stretch of the Little Deschutes River near LaPine, Oregon (Morse, 1971). The discharge of the Little Deschutes was about 200 ft^3 sec^{-1} (5.66 m^3 sec^{-1}), and the representative day was divided into 8 periods of 3 hours each. Figure 8-10 illustrates the results of this test when applied to a 5 mile reach. By use of these data, Morse (1971, p. 11) concluded that the wind function could be approximated by

$$\Psi = 2.8 \times 10^{-6} \, T_a' \, u_a \qquad (8-62)$$

in which T_a' is the air temperature in degrees Celsius, u_a

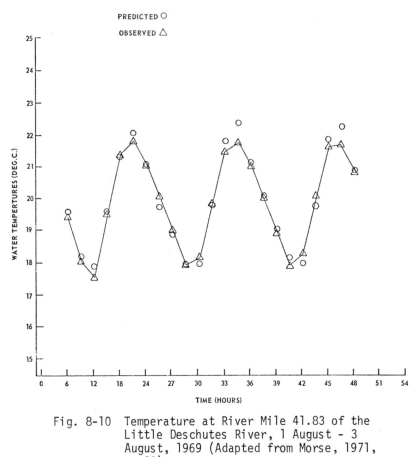

Fig. 8-10   Temperature at River Mile 41.83 of the
            Little Deschutes River, 1 August - 3
            August, 1969 (Adapted from Morse, 1971,
            p. 22).

is the wind speed in centimeters per second and ψ is the
evaporation rate in centimeters per day. The vapor pressures
must be measured in millibars.

Morse's model is very similar to the TVA model except that
it has been extended so that shorter time durations may be
analyzed. As illustrated by Fig. 8-10, the model appears to
describe the natural system reasonably well.

As mentioned earlier in Section 8.3, Jackman and Meyer
(1970) have used Eq. (8-51) in a preliminary analysis of some
heat dissipation data obtained downstream from 7 large heat
sources on rivers in the United States. Stream temperature
and discharge data were obtained at several cross sections and
selected meteorologic data were recorded for each reach downstream of the heat source. The objective of the project was to
provide a substantial body of data on stream temperatures below
the sites of large waste heat discharges for a selection of
stream types and for varying flow and climatic conditions.

Parker and Krenkel (1969, p. VI-19) have reviewed the stream temperature prediction models of Schroepfer, Raphael, Garrison and Elder, LeBosquet, Gameson et. al., Velz and Gannon, and Duttweiler as well as that by Edinger and Geyer. These models will not be reviewed here. However, in general they are even more restricted in nature than are the ones which have been discussed.

Estimate of Surface Transfer Coefficients. A temperature prediction model has been developed and several existing models have been discussed. These models are similar in that they all apply the conservation of thermal energy principle to the water system and, therefore, use some form of (8-1) as a starting point. There seems to be little doubt about the ability of Eq. (8-1) to describe the natural system. All models also depend upon the total surface exchange term which is generally incorporated as a boundary condition. Therefore, it would appear safe to say that the art of stream temperature modeling involves the solution of some simplified form of Eq. (8-1) with boundary conditions given by Eqs. (8-4) and (8-5). Because a fairly general form of this equation can be solved, at least numerically, the major obstacles to stream temperature modeling is the determination of the coefficients and inputs for Eqs. (8-1) and (8-4).

For the prediction of natural stream temperatures and even for the prediction of excess temperature distributions for distances which are far from the source, the spatial temperature gradients are small and so the effect of one troublesome coefficient, the diffusion or dispersion coefficient, is minimized. The results of Morse (1970, 1971) demonstrated that reasonably accurate natural temperature predictions can be made while completely neglecting the dispersion term. Because the physical processes involved in the surface exchange phenomenon are reasonably well understood, the problems associated with the determination of the total heat exchange term need be classified into only two areas. Those associated with the prediction or measurement of representative values of meteorologic parameters such as net incoming radiation, wind speed, air temperature, etc., and those associated with the determination of the proper values of empirical coefficients such as the wind function, the constant in Bowen's ratio, etc.

The instrumentation necessary for the measurement of the required meteorologic variables, while expensive, is reasonably well developed. Unfortunately these variables frequently vary quite rapidly both spatially and temporally while the model area is usually large, and the model time is quite long. Therefore, the determination of representative values of the parameters is very difficult. A discussion of the methods of obtaining these representative values is beyond the scope of this report.

Many empirical coefficients are necessary for the computation of the total surface exchange term, Eq. (8-29). The values of most of these, however, such as the Stefan-Boltzman constant, the latent heat of vaporization, etc., are very well established. Only the empirical wind function in the evaporation equation, Ψ , and the constant in Bowen's ratio, β , are open to serious question. Of these two, the empirical wind function is the most troublesome. There are two reasons for this; first the wind function appears in all except the radiation terms while Bowen's ratio appears only in the conduction term; and, second, when the wind function is determined from energy budger studies, it automatically contains the effect of Bowen's ratio. Probably for these reasons as well as because it has proven impossible to accurately determine the value of β from field data, the constant in Bowen's ratio is almost universally assumed to be 0.61 millibar per degree Celsius. The problems associated with the determination of the total heat exchange term generally are reduced to the determination of representative meteorologic variables and the choice of the empirical wind function.

Some of the expressions which have been used for the wind function will be presented in the sequel and an attempt will be made to present some of the supporting evidence for each expression. After the expressions for the wind function have been presented, the effect of this choice on the total surface exchange term and the surface exchange coefficient, K , will be demonstrated.

The empirical hydrodynamic approach to the evaporation problem was started by Dalton (Brutsaert, 1965, p. 19). According to Brutsaert (1965, p. 19), Dalton delivered a formal lecture in 1801 to the Manchester Literary and Philosophical Society in which he stated that evaporation is proportional to the difference in vapor pressure at the surface of the water and in the air. He also indicated that the constant of proportionality, which is defined as the wind function, Ψ , is affected by the wind velocity. Since that time a large number of experimental data have been collected, and many expressions for the wind function have been proposed. Most of these expressions have the general form

$$\Psi = A + B\, u_a \qquad (8\text{-}63)$$

in which A and B are coefficients which depend upon many variables and most were derived by use of data obtained from evaporation pans. Kohler (1954, p. 138) presents several reasonable reasons why the value of A in Eq. (8-63) should be larger for data obtained from evaporation pans than for data from a lake.

In 1931 Rohwer (1931) published the results of an extensive series of evaporation experiments. Based on data obtained from a wind tunnel, evaporation pans at elevations ranging from below sea level to about 15,000 feet, and an 85 foot diameter pond. Rohwer proposed the expression

$$\Psi = (0.110 - 4.14 \times 10^{-5} \text{ P}) (0.44 + 2.64 \times 10^{-3} u_a)$$

$$(8-64)$$

in which P is the atmospheric pressure in millibars, u_a is the wind speed at the ground level in centimeters per second and the evaporation is given in centimeters per day when the vapor pressure difference is expressed in millibars. The constants in Eq. (8-64) have been converted to a system of units which will be common to all the following equations.

In 1942 Meyer (Linsley et. al., 1958, p. 98) presented the formula

$$\Psi = 2.7 \times 10^{-2} + 7.5 \times 10^{-5} u_2 \qquad (8-65)$$

in which the units are the same as those for Eq. (8-64), and u_2 represents the wind speed at 2 meters above the surface. Meyer's equation was presented in terms of the wind speed measured 25 feet above the ground, but the coefficient in Eq. (8-65) has been adjusted for use with a 2-meter wind by assuming the ratio of the two wind speeds to be 1.24. The ratio 1.24 was obtained from the Lake Hefner data as presented by Marciano and Harbeck (1954, p. 49). It is desirable to present Meyer's equation in terms of the 2-meter wind speed so that its coefficients can be compared more easily to those in other expressions. At standard atmospheric pressure and zero wind speed, Rohwer's equation predicts 11 times more evaporation than is predicted by Meyer's equation. However, this comparison is not entirely fair because the wind speed in Rohwer's equation is the wind speed at the ground level and the relationship between this wind speed and the 2-meter wind speed is not clear. One would expect, however, that there would be a significant wind at 2 meters before a wind could be detected at the ground level.

Based upon a series of studies of evaporation from reservoirs, Harbeck (1962) proposed the relation

$$\Psi = \frac{1.92 \times 10^{-4}}{(A_r)^{0.05}} u_2 \qquad (8-66)$$

in which A_r is the area of the reservoir in acres. This relation was based on data obtained from reservoirs ranging in area from 1 to nearly 30,000 acres and Harbeck estimates the standard error of estimate of this relation to be 16 percent (1962, p. 104). For a reservoir area of 100 acres and a wind speed of 50 cm/sec, the approximate starting speed of a good anemometer, Meyer's equation predicts over 4 times as much evaporation as Harbeck's equation. However, at 1,000 cm/sec, the approximate maximum wind speed which is frequently encountered, Harbeck's equation predicts 50% more evaporation than does Meyer's equation. Both equations are plotted on Fig. 8-11 for comparison. The lines intersect at 346 cm sec^{-1} which is approximately the average wind speed encountered at Lake Hefner. Harbeck's equation is one of very few which is based field data, and therefore it is often used to determine the evaporation from lakes or reservoirs. However, it is extremely easy to visualize reasons why this wind function should not apply to evaporation from rivers. For example, the wind fetch for rivers is short, the stream turbulence probably effects the rate of evaporation, etc. Unfortunately it is virtually impossible to measure the rate of evaporation from rivers by use of any direct method such as the water budget method.

Shulyakovskiy (1969, p. 568) discusses the factors which control the value of A in Eq. (8-63) as it applies to evaporation from pans. The three factors are: (a) wind velocities which are less than the stall speed of the anemometer, (b) air flow disturbances resulting from the difference between the temperature of the water surface and the temperature of the land surrounding the water, and (c) free convection. Using

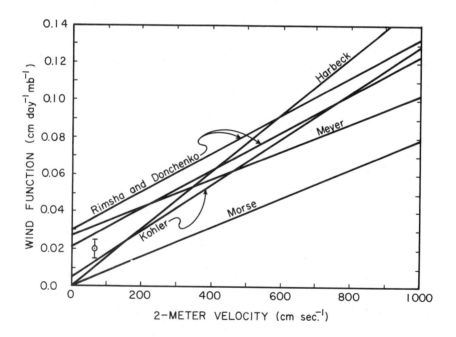

Fig. 8-11 Relationship between the 2-meter wind speed and the wind function.

8-50

a value of $B = 1.12 \times 10^{-4}$, which is larger than the value
proposed by Meyer [Eq. (8-65)] but smaller than the one proposed
by Harbeck for small lakes [Eq. (8-66)], and a measured
frequency distribution for low wind speeds, Shulyakovskiy
estimated that a stall speed of 100 cm/sec would result in an
apparent value of $A = 1.5 \times 10^{-2}$. The second factor, the
difference between the water surface temperature and the
temperature of the surrounding land, has been observed to affect
the wind currents over Lake Mead (Kohler, 1958, p. 10). The
third factor, free convection, is produced by unstable density
stratification of the air over the water and this stratification
is determined primarily by the difference between the water
surface temperature and the air temperature. Consequently,
Shulyakovskiy suggests that the value of A should be represented by the sum of a constant term and a term which is
dependent on the temperature difference between the air and
the water.

In 1957 Rimsha and Donchenko presented an expression for
the wind function which attempts to compensate for free convection. This expression, as reported by Dingman, Weeks, and Yen
(1968, p. 354) is

$$\Psi = 2.09 \times 10^{-2} + 9.15 \times 10^{-4}(\Delta T - T_a') + 1.02 \times 10^{-4} u_2$$

$$(8-67)$$

in which ΔT is the water temperature and T_a' is the air
temperature, both in degrees Celsius. The coefficients of
this equation were obtained by use of a least squares analysis
of calorimetric data taken adjacent to a Russian river under
wintertime conditions. Equation (8-67) is also plotted on
Fig. 8-11 for two different temperature differences. The upper
curve is for a 10°C temperature difference and the lower curve
is for a zero temperature difference.

Rimsha and Donchenko's equation has received a certain
amount of testing in the United States. In 1965 Dingman, Weeks
and Yen (1968) applied Dingman's model to a reach of the
Mississippi River in order to predict the lengths of ice-free
reaches below steam-power generating plants in the vicinity of
Minneapolis-St. Paul. They reported that observations of the
lengths of ice-free reaches were in good agreement with the
calculated values when Rimsha and Donchenko's equation was
used for the wind function. Dingman et. al. (1968, p. 359)
also used Kohler's equation for the wind function but found
Rimsha and Donchenko's equation clearly gave results which were
in better agreement with the observed lengths. Kohler's wind
function is given by

$$\Psi = 5.25 \times 10^{-3} + 1.229 \times 10^{-4} u_2 \qquad (8-68)$$

8-51

Weeks et. al. (1971) report the use of Dingman et. al. (1967) model to predict water temperatures downstream of the Dave Johnson Power Plant at Glenrock, Wyoming on the North Platte River. These tests were also conducted under wintertime conditions. They reported very satisfactory agreement between the observed and calculated temperature values when the wind function of Rimsha and Donchenko was used. The wind function of Kohler had a systematic tendency to underestimate the actual cooling. Weeks et. al. (1968, p. 1536) also report that Freysteinsson calculated water temperatures in Iceland under wintertime conditions using several wind functions. He apparently concluded that the Rimsha and Donchenko equation provided the best results but that further testing of the equation was desirable, particularly for wind velocities greater than 400 cm/sec.

Although the Rimsha and Donchenko equation appears to represent a compromise between the somewhat extreme forms of the Meyer and Harbeck equations (Fig. 8-11), it should be remembered that this expression was derived and tested only during winter and along rivers of approximately the same size and type.

The wind function suggested by Morse has been presented in Eq. (8-62). This expression was developed by use of data obtained on the Little Deschutes River and the air temperature during these runs was about $28^{\circ}C$ (Morse, 1971, p. 13). Therefore, an air temperature of $28^{\circ}C$ was assumed for plotting Eq. (8-62) on Fig. 8-11. Although this equation gave good results for the data from which it was derived, (Fig. 8-10) it is doubtful that it would be valid under differing conditions.

The Tennessee Valley Authority has reported an analysis of the stream temperature distribution downstream of Norris Dam on the Clinch River in eastern Tennessee, and this analysis allows a single independent although admittedly crude check on the wind function (TVA, 1968, p. 51). The water released from Norris Dam is colder than natural; therefore, it warms up as it travels downstream. The equilibrium temperature was defined in such a way that it was in fair agreement with the natural river temperature (TVA, 1968, p. 52). The difference between the measured water temperature and the equilibrium temperature can therefore be considered to be the excess temperature as defined in Eq. (8-51). The temperature excess is of course negative in this case. Multiplying the numerator and denominator of the exponent in Eq. (8-61) by the width of the stream, W , it becomes

$$\Delta T = \Delta T_o \exp(-KxW/Q) \qquad (8-69)$$

in which Q is the total discharge. The ratios $\Delta T/\Delta T_o$ were plotted as a function of xW/Q on semi-logarithmic paper and a straight line resulted. From the slope of this straight line, they estimated the value of surface exchange coefficient, K , to be 45.8 cm day^{-1} (TVA, 1968, p. 52). An analysis of the scatter of the data on the figure indicates that the maximum and minimum probable values of K are 54.8 and 36.9 cm day^{-1} respectively. All the data were representative of July conditions; therefore, the authors estimated the wind function by use of Eq. (8-28), the estimated value of K and the average meteorologic conditions existing in eastern Tennessee during the month of July. The National Atlas (USGS, 1970, p. 101) gives the following mean conditions for eastern Tennessee during the month of July: air temperature = 21.1 - 26.7^{o}C, relative humidity 70 - 80 percent, wind velocity 67 cm sec^{-1}. From these mean conditions the value of the wind function was found to be 0.0197. This value is shown plotted on Fig. 8-11 at a wind velocity of 67 cm sec^{-1}. The top and the bottom of the symbol represent the uncertainty of this value as determined from the maximum and minimum probable values of K . The representativeness of the meteorologic conditions found in the National Atlas as applied to the site may be questioned; however, Eq. (8-28) is not sensitive to the assumed values of air temperature and relative humidity. For example, within the range $10(50^oF) < T_a' < 37.8^oC (100^oF)$, and $50 < R_h < 90$ percent, the resulting value of the wind function varies by less than 1 percent.

Inspection of Fig. 8-11 indicates that this single point appears nearest to the Kohler equation. However, because a true representative wind speed for the reach is unknown, none of the equations can be discounted, except perhaps the Morse equation. The selection of an expression for the wind function will undoubtedly remain a matter of personal preference for many years. Therefore, this section is concluded by attempting to illustrate the effect of the wind function on both the surface exchange coefficient, K , and the reference surface exchange term, H_R . Of course the reference surface exchange term is closely related to the natural temperature of the system.

The dependence of the surface exchange coefficient on the wind function is illustrated on Fig. 8-12. The air temperature and relative humidity were assumed to be 30°C and 60 percent respectively in the construction of the figure. However, Eq. (8-28), from which Fig. 8-12 was constructed, is so insensitive to the assumed values of these parameters that the figure can be assumed representative of about any weather conditions. For all practical purposes the value of K can be assumed to be a function of only the wind function and the assumed reference temperature. Jobson (1972) has shown that the value of the surface exchange coefficient can be approximated by the expression

$$K = (7 + 522\Psi) \exp (0.035 \, T_R) \qquad (8\text{-}70)$$

in which the units of K are in cm day^{-1}, the units of Ψ are in cm day^{-1} mb^{-1}, and the reference temperature is expressed in degrees Celsius. Equation (8-70) approximates the values presented on Fig. 8-12 to within about 10 or 15 percent for values of $0 < \Psi < .2$ and $5 < T_a' < 40^\circ C$.

The behavior of the reference surface exchange term [Eq. (8-27)] is illustrated on Figs. 8-13 and 8-14. The ordinate of both figures is the reference surface exchange term, H_R , less the net absorbed radiation term, H_N . The net absorbed radiation term is an independent variable which is not a function of the water temperature. The reference exchange term is a linear function of the wind function and the relative humidity; therefore, straight line interpolation can be used. It is instructive to compare the magnitude of the ordinates of Figs. 8-13 and 8-14 to the maximum probable value of the net absorbed radiation term, H_N . The solar constant is 2880 cal day^{-1} cm^{-2} which represents an upper limit to which the instantaneous short wave radiation term may approach. The

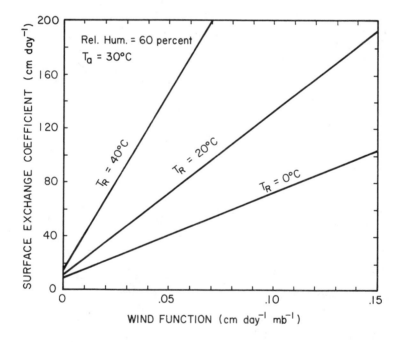

Fig. 8-12 The Surface Exchange coefficient as a function of the wind function.

maximum instantaneous long wave radiation term is on the order of 1000 cal day^{-1} cm^{-2}. The minimum values are on the order of zero and 300 cal day^{-1} cm^{-2} for the short and long wave terms respectively. An interesting point occurs on both Figs. 8-13 and 8-14. This is the intersection of all three curves at a point at which the reference exchange term is independent of the wind function and therefore of the wind speed. For a relative humidity of 80 percent, the point occurs for an air temperature of only 2.5°C above the water temperature. This intersection illustrates the futility of attempting to determine the wind function from an energy balance of a stream under certain meteorologic conditions.

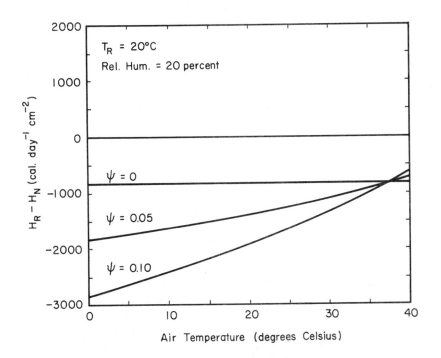

Fig. 8-13 Variation of the Reference Surface Exchange Term with the Wind Function and Air Temperature for a Relative Humidity of 20 percent.

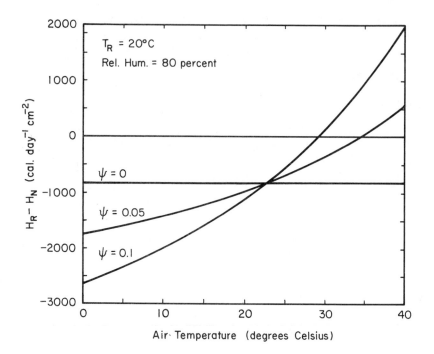

Fig. 8-14 Variation of the Reference Surface Exchange
Term with the Wind Function and Air Temperature for a Relative Humidity of 80 percent.

8.5 SUMMARY AND CONCLUSIONS

The problem of thermal pollution in rivers is of growing
concern to engineers as well as society in general. Because
the power generation industry is the dominant producer of waste
heat and because the national demand for electric energy
continues to grow, the amount of waste heat which must be
released to the environment will certainly continue to increase
at a rapid rate. Natural flowing water will always be the most
efficient means of dissipating excess heat provided that such
use does not seriously conflict with the requirements of other
uses. In order to take advantage of this economy in waste
disposal while meeting water quality criteria, man must be able
to predict the changes in water temperature which will result
from a planned activity. The purpose of this report has been
to present an approach to the prediction problem which inte-
grates the surface and hydraulic transfer mechanisms. The
densimetric or stratification aspect of the problem was not
discussed.

The three-dimensional problem was formulated for an open channel flow with uniform depth by writing the conservation equation for thermal energy in terms of turbulent convection and diffusion and by describing the surface transfer as a boundary condition. The two-dimensional problem was then derived by integrating the three-dimensional equation with respect to depth and it was shown that the surface and hydraulic transfer mechanisms are combined into one equation without the necessity of assuming a uniform water temperature. Finally the one-dimensional equation was developed by integrating the two-dimensional equation with respect to the width. The one-, two-, and three-dimensional equations are very much similar to, and no easier to solve than, the classical Fickian diffusion equation. However, in the present derivations, unlike other conventional derivations, the water temperature, and velocity are not assumed to be uniform in the cross section.

The heat flux at the air-water interface enters the conservation equation as a boundary condition, therefore, a knowledge of this flux is necessary before the equation can be solved. The usual expressions describing each of the physical processes were presented and summed to yield an expression for the total surface exchange. A linear approximation was then developed by expanding the expression as a Taylor series about an arbitrary reference temperature and retaining only two essential terms. The first term may be called the reference surface exchange term and the second term is linear in the temperature and contains the surface exchange coefficient. An analysis of the accuraty of the linearized expression indicated that it represents the non-linear expression with an accuracy which is consistent with the accuracy of the wind function, provided that the water temperature is within $\pm 8^{\circ}C$ of the reference temperature. This temperature range is large enough to make the linearized expression useful in analyzing most practical problems.

The mechanics of diffusion and dispersion have been reviewed in some depth in order to evaluate the physical significance of the diffusive terms. Recognizing that the diffusive terms are a major source of approximation to the otherwise exact equation for the conservation of thermal energy, limitations to the present formulation have been discussed from a hydraulic viewpoint. A summary on the magnitude of diffusion coefficients was also presented.

Application of the derived equations to field problems was presented in two separate sections; one for the three- and two-dimensional cases where hydraulic transfer is of importance and another for the one-dimensional problem where surface heat exchange is of major concern.

The three-dimensional equation was shown to be of limited value to near-field applications, because the effects of jet action and density stratification make an integration of the equation rather unwieldy for practical pusposes. Consequently literature on the practical use of three-dimensional equations is very limited even for the intermediate field. A discussion was given to a two-dimensional model for excess temperature prediction, namely, the one which combines the exponential heat decay with the Yotsukura-Cobb stream-tube method of describing a steady-state two-dimensional diffusion. Tests with the excess temperature data obtained from several streams show that the model is capable of predicting temperatures with an overall error of $1^{\circ}C$. The parameters such as the transverse diffusion coefficient and the surface transfer coefficient are in reasonable agreement with the currently available information. The model is an intermediate-field model and not usable in the immediate vicinity of effluent discharge sites. At far downstream locations, on the other hand, the model blends with the one-dimensional model.

For the prediction of natural temperature distributions, as well as excess temperatures in the far field, the one-dimensional equation provides an adequate model. The one-dimensional thermal equation is shown to have the same form as the biochemical oxygen demand (BOD) equation and the same treatment as given to the latter equation can be applied to the former equation. If the depth and velocity are independent of the longitudinal coordinate the equation can be integrated directly. Furthermore, if the excess temperature is needed the equation simplifies to the classical exponential dieaway curve. Excess temperature distributions can be predicted on the basis of wind speed information alone, providing that the approximate natural temperature is used as a reference temperature.

The one-dimensional equation was compared to the existing prediction models proposed by Edinger and Geyer (1965), Dingman et. al. (1967), Tennessee Valley Authority (1968), and Morse (1970). The major disadvantage of Edinger and Geyer's model is that it linearizes the surface exchange term in reference to the equilibrium temperature. This hypothetical temperature has a range of variation much larger than actual water temperatures have and produces large linearization errors unless long term average values are used. The other three.models all compute the total surface exchange for a number of different conditions using an expression similar to Eq. (8-27) and fit these computed values with an expression which is either linear or quadratic in the water temperature. Their approaches are similar to the one presented herein in that all avoid the use of the equilibrium temperature concept.

One of the major obstacles encountered in the application of the one-dimensional model is the selection of an expression for the wind function to be used in the evaporation equation. Several expressions were discussed, but because of the difficulty of checking them against field data, the selection of a proper equation will undoubtedly remain a matter of personal preference for some time. In order that the effects of this selection might be known, an illustration of the effect of the

wind function on both the surface exchange coefficient and the
reference surface exchange term was presented.

8.6 NOTATIONS

A	Coefficient in wind function, Eq. (8-63)
A"	Coefficient in heat flux equation, Eq. (8-60)
A_r	Surface area of reservoir, Eq. (8-66)
a_0	Coefficient in heat flux equation, Eq. (8-56)
B	Coefficient in wind function, Eq. (8-63)
B'	Coefficient in heat flux equation, Eq. (8-61)
B"	Coefficient in heat flux equation, Eq. (8-60)
b_0	Coefficient in heat flux equation, Eq. (8-56)
C_p	Specific heat of water under constant atmospheric pressure
C'	Coefficient in heat flux equation, Eq. (8-61)
C"	Coefficient in heat flux equation, Eq. (8-60)
D	Longitudinal dispersion coefficient; refer to each section for specific notations such as D, D_v, $\langle D_v \rangle$, D_h and $D(z)$
E	Equilibrium temperature
E_v	Rate of evaporation, Eq. (8-18)
$f(T_R + \Delta T)$	Saturation vapor pressure of air at the temperature $T_R + \Delta T$, Eq. (8-19)
$f'(T_R)$	First derivative of $f(T_R + \Delta T)$ evaluated at the temperature T_R
g	Acceleration of gravity
H_T	Total heat flux at the air-water interface
H_N	Heat flux due to radiation absorbed from the sun and the sky
H_b	Heat flux due to radiation emitted by the water
H_e	Heat flux due to evaporation
H_h	Heat flux due to conduction
H_w	Heat flux due to advection of evaporated water
H_R	Total heat flux at the reference temperature T_R
H_0	Coefficient in heat flux equation, Eq. (8-56)

K	Surface exchange coefficient of thermal energy
L_R	Latent heat of vaporization of water at the reference temperature T_R
L_t	Lagrangian time scale of turbulent water velocity
L_w	Characteristic width dimension for open channels
P	Atmospheric pressure
P_a	Vapor pressure of the air above the water, Eq. (8-18)
Q	Total discharge of an open channel flow
Q_s	Discharge of heated waste water
q	Cumulative partial discharge in channel cross section; refer to Section 8.3 for specific notations such as q , q_{s1} , q_{s2} , q'_{s1} , q'_{s2} , and q'
$R(\tau)$	Lagrangian correlation function for turbulent velocity
R_h	Relative humidity, Eq. (8-54)
S	Slope of the latent heat of vaporization curve with respect to water temperature, Eq. (8-20)
T	Temperature of water; refer to each section for specific notations such as T , T_{abs} , ΔT , $\overline{T}$, $\langle \overline{T} \rangle$, T' , $\overline{T}'$, T_e , T'_e , T_{es} , T_n , ΔT_n , ΔT_0 , ΔT_x and ΔT_i .
T_R	An arbitrary reference temperature on the absolute scale
T_a	Temperature of air measured on the absolute scale, Eq. (8-22)
T'_a	Temperature of air measured on the Celsius scale, Eq. (8-56)
t	Time
Δt	Time increment
U	Longitudinal velocity of water; refer to each section for specific notations such as U , $\overline{U}$, u_i , u , $\overline{u}$, u' , $\langle u \rangle$, $\overline{u}'$, and u_d
U_*	Cross-sectional average shear velocity
u_a	Wind velocity, Eq. (8-55)
u_2	Wind velocity at 2m above the water surface, Eq. (8-30)
W	Channel width
x_i	Space coordinate in the i-th direction (i = 1, 2, 3)

x	Longitudinal coordinate in the downstream direction
y	Vertical coordinate with origin at the water surface
Y	Total depth of water; refer to each section for specific notations such as Y, $\overline{Y}$, and $\langle Y \rangle$.
z	Transverse coordinate with origin at the channel center
α	Nondimensional diffusion parameter, Eq. (8-44)
β	Bowen ratio, Eq. (8-22)
ε	Emissivity of water for radiation flux, Eq. (8-16)
ε_i	Turbulent diffusion coefficient; refer to each section for specific notations such as ε_i, ε_{ij}, ε_x, ε_y, $\overline{\varepsilon_y}$, ε_z, $\overline{\varepsilon_z}$, $\overline{\varepsilon_i}$, ε_i', $\langle \varepsilon_i \rangle$, and $\overline{\varepsilon_i'}$
λ	Transform function of water temperature, Eq. (8-48)
ρ	Density of water
σ	Stefan-Boltzman constant for black body radiation, Eq. (8-16)
σ_v	Variance of transverse diffusion, Eq. (8-31)
σ_e	Excess variance of transverse diffusion due to densimetric effect
ψ	Wind function, Eq. (8-18)

REFERENCES

Al-Saffar, A. M., 1964, Eddy diffusion and mass transfer in open-channel flow; Ph. D. Dissertation, University of California, Berkeley, 138 p.

Anderson, E. R., 1954, Energy budget studies in water-loss investigations; Lake Hefner studies, Technical Report: U. S. Geol. Survey Prof. Paper 269, p. 71-120.

Aris, R., 1956, On the dispersion of a solute in a fluid flowing through a tube; Proc. Royal Soc. of London, vol. 235A, p. 67-77.

Batchelor, G. K., and Townsend, A. A., 1956, Turbulent diffusion; p. 352-399 in Surveys in Mechanics, edited by G. K. Batchelor and R. M. Davies, Cambridge University Press, 475 p.

Bella, D. A., and Dobbins, W. E., 1968, Difference modeling of stream pollution; Jour. of Sanitary Eng. Div., Am. Soc. of Civil Engineers, vol. 94, no. SA5, p. 995-1016.

Benedict, B. A., Polk, E. M., Yandell, E. L., and Parker, F. L., 1971, Surface jet and diffusion models for discharge of heated water; Proc. of the 14th Congress of the International Assoc. for Hydraulic Research, vol. 1, p. 183-190.

Bennett, J. P., 1971, Convolution approach to the solution for dissolved oxygen balance equation in a stream; Water Resources Research, vol. 7, no. 3, p. 580-590.

Bowen, I. S., 1926, The ratio of heat losses by conduction and by evaporation from any water surface; Physical Review, vol. 27, no. 6, p. 785.

Brown, G. W., 1969, Predicting temperature of small streams; Water Resources Research, vol. 5, no. 1, p. 68-75.

Brutsaert, W., 1965, Equations for vapor flux as a fully turbulent diffusion process under adiabatic conditions; Bulletin of International Association for Scientific Hydrology, vol. 10, no. 2, p. 19.

Carslaw, H. S., and Jaeger, J. C., 1959, Conduction of heat in solids; Oxford University Press, London, 2nd Edition, 510 p.

Chatwin, P. C., 1971, On the interpretation of some longitudinal dispersion experiments; Jour. of Fluid Mechanics, vol. 48, part 4, p. 689-702.

Cleary, R. W., McAvoy, T. J., and Short, W. L., 1971, Unsteady-state, three-dimensional model of thermal pollution in rivers; The 70th National Meeting of Am. Inst. of Chem. Engineers, paper 45a.

Crank, J., 1956, The mathematics of diffusion; Oxford University Press, London, 347 p.

Dagan, G., 1968, A discussion of the dispersivity tensor for a turbulent uniform channel flow; Tech. Report 801-2, Hydronautics Inc., Laurel, Md., 28 p.

Dingman, S. L., Weeks, W. F., and Yen, Y. C., 1967, The effects of thermal pollution on river ice condition, part I. A general method of calculation; Cold Regions Research and Engineering Lab., U. S. Army, Hanover, N. H., 34 p.

Dingman, S. L., Weeks, W. F., and Yen, Y. C., 1968, The effects of thermal pollution on river ice conditions; Water Resources Research, vol. 4, no. 2, p. 349-362.

Dingman, S. L., and Assur, A., 1969, The effects of thermal pollution on river ice conditions, Part II, a simplified method of calculation; Cold Regions Research and Eng. Lab. report no. 206, part II, Corps of Engineers, U. S. Army, Hanover, N. H., 10 p.

Edinger, J. E., and Geyer, J. C., 1965, Heat exchange in the environment; EEI Publ. no. 65-902, Edison Electric Inst., New York, N. Y., 259 p.

Edinger, J. E., Duttweiler, D. W., and Geyer, J. C., 1968, The response of water temperatures to meteorological conditions; Water Resources Research, vol. 4, no. 5, p. 1137-1143.

Edinger, J. E., and Polk, E. M., 1969, Initial mixing of thermal discharges into a uniform current; Center for Research and Training in the Hydrologic and Hydraulic Aspects of Water Pollution Control, Rep. 1, Vanderbilt Univ.

Elder, J. W., 1959, The dispersion of marked fluid in turbulent shear flow; Jour. of Fluid Mechanics, vol. 5, no. 4, p. 544-560.

Engelund, F., 1969, Dispersion of floating particles in uniform channel flow; Jour. of Hydraulic Div., Am. Soc. of Civil Engineers, vol. 95, no. HY4, p. 1149-1162.

Fischer, H. B., 1966, Longitudinal dispersion in laboratory and natural streams; Report No. KH-R-12, Calif. Inst. of Tech., Pasadena, 250 p.

Fischer, H. B., 1967, Transverse mixing in a sand bed channel; U. S. Geol. Survey Prof. Paper 575-D, 6 p.

Fischer, H. B., 1967, The mechanics of dispersion in natural streams; Jour. of Hydraulics Div., Am. Soc. of Civil Engineers, vol. 93, no. HY6, p. 187-216.

Fischer, H. B., 1969, The effect of bends on dispersion in streams; Water Resources Research, vol. 5, no. 2, p. 496-506.

Gerber, H. B., 1967, Bibliography on thermal pollution; Journal of Sanitary Eng. Div., Am. Soc. of Civil Engineers, vol. 93, no. SA3, p. 85-113.

Glover, R. E., 1964, Dispersion of dissolved or suspended materials in flowing streams; U. S. Geol. Survey Prof. Paper 433-B, 32 p.

Harbeck, G. E., Jr., 1953, The use of reservoirs and lakes for the dissipation of heat; U. S. Geol. Survey Circ. 282, 6 p.

Harbeck, G. E., Jr., Koberg, G. E., and Hughes, G. H., 1959, The effect of the addition of heat from a power plant on the thermal structure and evaporation of Lake Colorado City, Texas; U. S. Geol. Survey Prof. Paper 272-B, p. 7-49.

Harbeck, G. E., Jr., 1962, A practical field technique for measuring reservoir evaporation utilizing mass-transfer theory; U. S. Geol. Survey Prof. Paper 272-E, p. 101-105.

Hinze, J. O., 1959, Turbulence; McGraw-Hill Book Co., New York, 586 p.

Holley, E. R., and Harleman, D. R. F., 1965, Dispersion of pollutants in estuary type flows; Hydrodynamics Lab. Report no. 74, Mass. Inst. of Tech., 202 p.

Idso, S. B., and Jackson, R. D., 1969, Thermal radiation from the atmosphere; Journal of Geophysical Research, vol. 74, no. 23.

Ippen, A. T., Harleman, D. R. F., and Lin, J. D., 1960, Turbulent diffusion and gravitational convection in an idealized estuary; Hydrodynamics Lab. Tech. Rep. no. 38, Mass. Inst. of Tech., 33 p.

Jackman, A. P., and Meyer, E. L., 1971, Basic data on heat dissipation downstream from large heat sources; Symposium of the 5th Annual Midyear Meeting of the Health Physics Society.

Jaske, R. T., 1969, Thermal modification of river quality; Rep. BNWL-719, Pacific Northwest Lab., Richland, Wash., p. 6.

Jobson, H. E., 1968, Vertical mass transfer in open channel flow; Ph. D. Dissertation, Colo. State Univ., 204 p.

Jobson, H. E., 1972, The dissipation of excess heat from water system; Jour. of Power Div., Am. Soc. of Civil Engineers, (in press).

Keefer, T. M., 1971, The relation of turbulence to diffusion in open-channel flows; Ph. D. Dissertation, Colo. State Univ., 141 p.

Koberg, G. E., 1964, Method to compute long wave radiation from atmosphere and reflected solar radiation from a water surface; U. S. Geol. Survey Prof. Paper 272-F, p. 107-136.

Kohler, M. A., 1954, Lake and pan evaporation in water-loss investigations; Lake Hefner studies, Tech. Report; U. S. Geol. Survey Prof. Paper 269, 138 p.

Kohler, M. A., 1958, Wind patterns over Boulder Basin; water-loss investigations: Lake Mead studies; U. S. Geol. Survey Prof. Paper 298, p. 8-11.

Linsley, R. K., Jr., Kohler, M. A., and Paulhus, J. L., 1958, Hydrology for engineers; McGraw-Hill Book Co., Inc., New York, p. 98.

List, R. J., 1966, Smithsonian meteorological tables; Smithsonian Institution, Washington, D. C., 6th edition, 527 p.

Marciano, J. J., and Harbeck, G. E., Jr., 1954, Mass-transfer studies in water-loss investigations; Lake Hefner studies, Technical Report: U. S. Geol. Survey Prof. Paper 269, p. 46-70.

McQuivey, R. S., and Keefer, T. N., 1971, Turbulent diffusion and dispersion in open channel flow; Proc. of the First International Symposium on Stochastic Hydraulics, Univ. of Pittsburgh, p. 231-250.

Monin, A. S., 1959, General survey of atmospheric diffusion; Advances in Geophysics edited by Frenkiel and Sheppard, vol. 6, Academic Press, New York, p. 29-40.

Morse, W. L., 1970, Stream temperature prediction model; Water Resources Research, vol. 6, no. 1, p. 290-302.

Morse, W. L., 1971, Stream temperature prediction under reduced flow; Am. Soc. of Civil Engineers Annual and National Environmental Engineering Meeting, Reprint 1525, 30 p.

Okubo, A., 1970, Oceanic mixing; Tech. Rep. 62, Chesapeake Bay Inst. The Johns Hopkins Univ., 119 p.

Orlob, G. T., 1958, Eddy diffusion in open channel flow; Ph. D. Dissertation, Univ. of Calif., Berkeley, 151 p.

Parker, F. L., and Krenkel, P. A., 1969, Engineering aspects of thermal pollution; Vanderbilt University Press, 340 p.

Pien, C. L., 1941, Investigation of turbulence and suspended material transportation in open channels; Ph. D. Dissertation, Univ. of Iowa, 111 p.

Pinder, G. F., and Frind, E. O., 1972, Application of Galerkin's procedure to aquifer analysis; Water Resources Research, vol. 8, no. 1, p. 108-120.

Polk, E. M., Benedict, B. A., and Parker, F. L., 1972, Dispersion of thermal discharges in bodies of water; the 64th Annual Meeting of Am. Inst. of Chem. Engineers, Paper 22a.

Prych, E. A., 1970, Effects of density differences on lateral mixing in open-channel flows; Report no. KH-R-21, Calif. Inst. of Tech., 225 p.

Rohwer, C., 1931, Evaporation from free water surface; U. S. Dept. of Agriculture Tech. Bull. no. 271, 96 p.

Sayre, W. W., and Chamberlain, A. R., 1965, Exploratory Laboratory study of lateral turbulent diffusion at the surface of an alluvial channel; U. S. Geol. Survey Circ. 484, 18 p.

Sayre, W. W., and Chang, F. M., 1966, A laboratory investigation of open-channel dispersion processes for dissolved, suspended, and floating dispersants; U. S. Geol. Survey open-file report, 210 p.

Sayre, W. W., 1968, Dispersion of mass in open-channel flow; Hydraulics Paper no. 3, Colo. State Univ., 73 p.

Shulyakovskiy, L. G., 1969, Formula for computing evaporation with allowance for the temperature of the free water surface; Soviet Hydrology Selected Papers, Issue no. 6, p. 566-573.

Silberman, E., and Stefan, H., 1970, Physical (hydraulic) modeling of heat dispersion in large lakes, a review of the state of the art; Argonne Natl. Lab. ANL/ES-2, 111 p.

Sullivan, P. J., 1968, Dispersion in a turbulent shear flow, Ph. D. Dissertation, Univ. of Cambridge, 197 p.

Sutton, O. G., 1953, Micrometeorology; McGraw-Hill Book Co., New York, 333 p.

Taylor, G. I., 1921, Diffusion by continuous movements; Proc. London Math. Soc., A20, p. 196-211.

Taylor, G. I., 1954, The dispersion of matter in turbulent flow through a pipe; Proc. Royal Soc., London, vol. 223A, p. 446-468.

Tennessee Valley Authority, 1968, The water temperature regime of fully-mixed streams; Water Resources Research Lab. Report no. 15, Norris, Tenn., 64 p.

Thorpe, S. A., 1968, A method of producing a shear flow in a stratified flow; Jour. of Fluid Mech., vol. 32, pt. 4, p. 693-704.

U. S. Geological Survey, 1970, The national atlas of the United States of America; U. S. Dept. of Interior, Washington, D. C., p. 113.

Vanoni, V. A., 1946, Transportation of suspended sediment by water; Trans. Am. Soc. Civil Engineers, vol. 111, p. 67-133.

Weeks, W. F., Keeler, C. M., Parrott, W., and Levine, D., 1971, Wintertime dissipation of heat from a thermally polluted river; Water resources Research, vol. 7, no. 6, p. 1529-1537.

Yotsukura, N., Fischer, H. B., and Sayre, W. W., 1970, Measurement of mixing characteristics of the Missouri River between Sioux City, Iowa, and Plattsmouth, Nebr.; U. S. Geol. Survey Water Supply Paper 1899-G, 29 p.

Yotsukura, N., and Cobb, E. D., 1972, Transverse diffusion of solutes in natural streams; U. S. Geol. Survey Prof. Paper 582-C (in press).

Yotsukura, N., Jackman, A. P., and Faust, C. R., 1972, A note on the approximation of heat exchange at air-water interface; Water Resources Research (in press).

Chapter 9

SOME EFFECTS OF WASTES ON NATURAL WATERS

by

Peter A. Krenkel, Consulting Environmental and Water Resources
Engineer, Vanderbilt University, Nashville,
Tennessee

CHAPTER 9

SOME EFFECTS OF WASTES ON NATURAL WATERS

9.1 WATER POLLUTANTS AND WATER POLLUTION CONTROL

Introduction. Probably the most important aspect of waste disposal faced by the environmental engineer is the ultimate disposal of both the solid and liquid fractions of a treated waste material into the environment. Most wastes will eventually find their way into some phase of the hydrologic cycle, thereby having some impact on the environment. It is mandatory that the engineer insure that the effect(s) of these materials on the enivronemnt is (are) minimal. Good engineering practice dictates that waste materials be discharged into a receiving water in such a way that nature's ability to assimilate these wastes is utilized without having deleterious effects on water quality. Obviously, the ability of a water to accept waste materials without causing deleterious effects must be considered as a beneficial use of water. To do otherwise can only result in higher costs to the consumer and ultimately, to a lower standard of living for our society.

Unfortunately, the environment has become a political issue, and as is the case with most political problems, solutions are being based on political expediency rather than technical expertise. Current philosophy is to require treatment requirements on a rational engineering basis. For example, regulatory agencies are requiring chlorination of all effluents containing sanitary wastes, even though recent evidence indicates that the effect of the chloramines formed by the reaction between chlorine and certain organics may indeed cause adverse effects on aquatic life.

No one can disagree with a philosophy that protects the environment; however, to dictate zero discharge by congressional mandate, as is the case with current legislation is ludicrous and will ultimately lead to economic disaster. One only has to consider the economic advantage given to other countries by this practice in order to conclude that the ultimate effect on the economy of the United States will be disastrous. In addition, valid arguments can be given by the underdeveloped countries as to why they should not adhere to such strict environmental controls. After all, we have been insulting the environment for years to attain our economy, so why should they not have a similar opportunity.

Typical of the misinterpretation of our water problems by the lay press is the often quoted "water shortage" in the United States. Examination of water demand and supply predictions for the next few decades demonstrates that we will not run out of water in the near future; however, the water that we do have available to us must be subjected to adequate water quality management. The concept of consumptive use of water is obviously ignored. Of course, one must consider regional problems, inasmuch as there are some locations in the contiguous United States that do have water problems because of the small amount of precipitation occurring.

It is quite appropriate that this Institute on River Mechanics give some consideration to water quality management, inasmuch as the effects of hydraulic structures and other hydraulic engineering cuasing changes in flow regimes may indeed have a profound effect on water quality. The study of water quality management must include the hydraulic engineering discipline if rational solutions to our water quality problems are to be determined.

Proper insight into the fate of pollutants in our waterways can only be gained by adequate knowledge of the systems involved. For example, in order to determine the ability of a river to satisfactorily accept a waste discharge, hydraulic and hydrologic parameters that must be delineated include the hydraulic geometry, flow characteristics, the meteorologic characteristics, the detention times, the turbulence characteristics and the drought-frequency analysis. In addition, disposal of waste materials into other water bodies requires special expertise in the hydro-mechanics of estuaries, lakes and ground water. The paucity of data concerning the hydrodynamics of reservoirs and lakes is well known, yet numerous wastes are being discharged into these waters without adequate knowledge of their behavior or ultimate fate. The behavior of waste materials introduced into stratified flow conditions is also not well known, and yet, both ocean and lake environmnets are subjected to many waste water discharges.

Even the casual observer can conclude that if the many pollution problems associated with our receiving waters are to be subjected to rational study, the expertise of the hydraulic engineer is mandatory.

Classification of Pollutants. Klein (1962) has conveniently classified various types of pollution into four categories: Chemical, Physical, Physiological and Biological. The effects of each of these categories will be briefly discussed. It should be remembered that, depending on the intended use of the water, every stream will have a limit as to the amount of each of these types of wastes that can be satisfactorily assimilated into the aquatic environmnet.

Chemical: Chemical materials that may be discharged into a receiving water may be broadly classified into organic and inorganic pollutants.

Undesirable results from the discharge of inorganic materials include changes in pH of the waters caused by strong acids or bases, an increase in water corrosivity caused by soluble salts and toxicity caused by heavy metals or other toxic materials. A classical example of the effects of an inorganic waste discharge possessing both toxicity and oxygen demanding characteristics is the effluent from a sulfur dioxide scribbing tower, where the effects on the stream may include both a lowering of the pH and a decrease in the dissolved oxygen content of the river. Inert insoluble inorganics such as clays may also cause problems because of the possibility of sludge deposits on the river bottom and adverse effects on biological life. As is the case with organic pollution, the question as to how much of these kinds of pollutants may be satisfactorily assimilated by a receiving water must be answered.

The major consideration with respect to organic materials is of course, the depletion of dissolved oxygen and its resultant effect on the biota. Biochemical reactions and the exertion of an oxygen demand are the characteristics of organic wastes that are of most significance to the oxygen balance. Their effects and analysis will be discussed in detail in a later section. Typical of the reactions involved would be that of a simple sugar being oxidized by bacterial action to form CO_2 and water, as follows:

$$C_6H_{12}O_6 + 6O_2 \xrightarrow{\text{bacteria}} 6CO_2 + 6H_2O$$

The theoretical Biochemical Oxygen Demand (BOD) of this reaction may be computed to be 1.07 milligrams per gram, and while this value will probably not be obtained in the aquatic environ   t, the reaction exemplifies the phenomena involved.

Other organic materials and their concomitant effects of concern to water quality control include oils, with their tendency to form surface films, taste and odor producing substances such as phenols, and compounds of a toxic nature such as pesticides and cyanides. Of particular concern are the exotic refractory orgaincs that are known to restrict growth or cause death of fish and other aquatic life. No adverse effects on human health attributable to the presence of refractory contaminants in the United States has been reported, yet trace quantities of many of these pollutants are being detected in water. Although it is not known that their presence is harmful, it likewise is not known that their presence is safe. The real question is concerned with the longtime cumulative effects of these materials in drinking water; for example, detergents.

Physical: Under the category of physical pollutants are listed color, turbidity, temperature, suspended solids, foam and radioactvity. It is obvious that these parameters may be associated with various types of chemical pollutants and may be a result of chemical pollution rather than a pollutant per se.

While color is not necessarily harmful, it is obviously undesirable in drinking water and for certain industrial water uses. The removal of some types of color may cause problems at a water treatment plant and will increase the cost of treated water.

Turbidity is primarily caused by either colloidal material or very finely divided suspended matter which settles only with difficulty. Turbidity caused by the hydrous oxides of iron and manganese are quite objectionable in domestic water and may require special treatment for removal. Turbidity is not necessarily harmful to fish; however, the reduction in sunlight caused by a turbid water may decrease the productivity of a river. Turbidity considerations are becoming especially important with respect to dredging operations, both for navigation purposes and for aggregate production.

Temperature increase only recently has been considered as a serious pollutant in the United States. The tremendous growth in the use of cooling water for electrical generating stations has caused an ever-increasing awareness of the many possible effects of heated discharges on the environment. Because of the current relative importance of heated water to water pollution control, potential temperature effects will be extensively treated in a subsequent section.

Even relatively unpolluted waters carry suspended materials originating from erosion processes. However, a significant quantity of suspended matter may be contributed by various waste discharges. This material may be organic or inorganic and may cause damage to biological life, result in a reduction in assimilative capacity by reducing photosynthesis and retarding benthic activity, and in general, cause nuisance conditions to be formed.

In addition to the previously mentioned physiological considerations of detergents, the resultant foam produced in many receiving waters is most objectionable from an aesthetic standpoint. Also, the surface active properties of synthetic detergents may cause a reduction in the rate of oxygen gas absorption, thus diminishing the self-purification capacity of the receiving water.

Radioactivity present in a stream may originate from natural or background sources, from fallout, or from a waste discharge. It may be found incorporated in silts or sludges, in biological life, or dissolved water. Within recent years, developments in nuclear science and technology have stimulated many applications of radioactive materials. Concurrent with these developments, increasing amounts of radioactive wastes are being produced and discharged to the environment. Because of the many unique pollutional aspects of radioactivity, proper control of radioactive wastes at the source is imperative.

Physiological: Taste and odor problems may be caused by a multitude of substances and are among the most troublesome to the water pollution control engineer because of public complaints. To the layman, odors arising from a river are indicative of pollution; the more offensive the odor, the greater the degree of pollution. Taste and odor are particularly objectionable in waters used for drinking or food processing purposes, as palatability is a function of the taste of the water and/or food.

Extremely minute quantities of some substances can impart objectionable taste to a water. For example, chlorophenols can be tasted at a concentration of 0.002 milligrams per liter of phenol, and hydrogen sulfide can be smelled at a concentration of 0.0011 milligrams per liter.

It should also be noted that many of these taste and odor producing compounds have the ability to taint fish. Thus, a very small quantity of phenol in the water may completely eliminate the use of fish for food, only because of the bad taste imparted to the fish by the chemical.

Biological: Probably the most important of all water pollution control considerations are those concerned with public health. In fact, the single most important process in the water treatment plant is disinfection, which helps to insure the absence of pathogenic organisms in the drinking water.

The etiological agents of water borne diseases include virus, bacteria, protozoa, and the helminths. Bacterial borne diseases include cholera, typhoid fever, paratyphoid fever and bacillary dysentery. Infectious hepatitis and poliomyelitis are viral borne and have been shown to be transmitted by water. Amoebic dysentery is an example of a water borne disease carried by a protozoan and schistosomiasis exemplifies a water borne disease caused by the helminths. It is interesting to note that because of adequate water supply and pollution control activities, no other profession can claim to have had such a dramatic influence on the course of history as Sanitary Engineering. One needs only to consider the 1892 Cholera epidemic in Hamburg, Germany, where 17,000 cases of cholera resulting in 8,065 deaths occurred in two months because of inadequate water pollution control.

When considering biological forms of pollution, one must not overlook biological growths caused by the discharge of waste materials into a receiving water. Excessive growths of algae and fungi are many times the result of waste discharges and may be considered as secondary biological pollution, possibly causing problems of a greater magnitude than the original pollutant.

Pollution Control Standards. Obviously, before the assimilative capacity of a receiving water can be determined, the intended use of the water must be delineated and standards for water quality adopted. In considering these standards, the effect(s) of the pollutant(s) in question must be ascertained and the economic aspects of proposed treatment methods investigated.

Two general types of standards have been used to control water pollution; those that set stream standards for receiving waters and those that set effluent standards for waste discharged. Likewise, stream standards are of two classifications and effluent standards are of two classes.

Stream standards may be dictated by dilution requirements or standards of receiving water quality. The standards of receiving water quality may depend on the establishment of threshold values for various pollutants or depend on the beneficial use for which the water is intended.

Effluent standards may restrict the strength or amount of pollutants that can be discharged, or may specify the degree of treatment required. It should be noted that the most reasonable approach is a combination of both stream standards and effluent standards. The current bill before the congress (1972) does not consider either approach and instead, dictates zero discharge (total recycle) by 1985. This regulation is not only impractical, but if enforced, will place U.S. industry on a non-competitive basis in the world market.

Waste Characterization. Obviously, prior to the determination of potential effects of a waste discharge on the receiving water the nature and quantities of each source must be delineated. In order to gain insight into those factors that may be harmful to aquatic life, it is instructive to note some of the materials that may cause harm to aquatic life.

As has been previously noted, the introduction of bio-degradable organic material into a waterway may cause depletion of the water's oxygen content. If this depletion causes oxygen levels to fall below those required in order to sustain aquatic life, lethal or sub-lethal effects may occur. Thus, it is imperative that the oxygen utilization characteristics of a waste material be defined. Probably the three most common methods for determining the oxygen demand of a wastewater are the Biochemical Oxygen Demand (BOD), the Chemical Oxygen Demand (COD), and the Total Organic Carbon (TOC). The BOD measures the oxygen utilized by bacteria in stabilizing a waste, the COD measures the oxygen required to stabilize a waste by chemical oxidation and the TOC is a measure of the total organic carbon present in a wastewater. Thus, for a realistic evaluation of the oxygen depletion that might occur in a river, the BOD is probably the most indicative measurement. A mathematical description of the BOD exertion will be presented in a subsequent section.

Another parameter that may be indicative of oxygen depletion is nitrogen, inasmuch as the conversion of organic nitrogen to the stable nitrate form may require significant oxygen. One only has to consider the stoichiometric quantities of oxygen required to oxidize ammonia nitrogen to nitrite nitrogen to nitrate nitrogen in order to place this parameter in its proper perspective. With the increased waste treatment requirements, the nitrogen is placed into the receiving water in an easily assimilable form and in addition, the nitrogen bacteria will also be present. Thus, waste characterization must include a determination of oxygen demanding nitrogen compounds. It should also be noted that nitrogen may play a significant role in euthrophication acceleration, just as nitrogen is considered to be a limiting nutrient.

9-6

Of equally significant importance is the delineation of possibly toxic materials. These may include metals, salts, certain organics and physical changes in the water such as temperature and turbidity. Significant changes in pH must also be investigated because of the sensitivity of certain organisms to pH variations. As previously mentioned, the solids concentration in the water may have a deleterious effect on the biota and thus total, dissolved, settleable and suspended solids must be determined.

One other aspect that should be considered is the possible synergistic effect of certain materials. For example, zinc becomes such more toxic in the presence of copper and its toxicity also increases with an increase in temperature. A classic example of synergism is the addition of cyanide by one source and the contribution of acid by another. The result, hydrogen cyanide, is a well known toxic material.

One other parameter of water quality requiring elucidation is bacteriological safety. If a wastewater containing sanitary wastes or wastes with bacteria of public health significance therein is introduced, an estimate of the concentration of these bacteria in the receiving water must be made. It should be noted that the tests utilized only indicate "potential" hazard from pathogenic bacteria (the coliform test), and do not necessarily indicate a health hazard.

It is obvious that proper assessment of a waste contribution must be based on concentration of a particular contaminant and an associated flow rate. It is therefore mandatory that a reasonable determination of flow be made so that wastewater contributions can be estimated on a mass basis.

Benificial Uses of Water. Since the intended use of the water should dictate its quality requirements, a knowledge of water allocation for specific purposes is mandatory. The major uses of water are as follows:
   A. Domestic water supply
   B. Industrial water supply
   C. Agricultural water supply
   D. Stock and wildlife watering
   E. Propagation of fish and other aquatic life
   F. Shellfish culture
   G. Swimming and bathing waters
   H. Boating and aesthetic enjoyment
   I. Water power and navigation
   J. Transport, dispersion and assimilation of wastes
Even though drinking water may not possess the highest quality requirements, it is usually considered as the highest use of water. Of prime concern is the bacteriological quality of the water inasmuch as the potential of water as a carrier of pathogenic organisms is well known (cholera, typhoid fever, etc.). In addition to bacteriological safety, a domestic water supply should be both palatable and potable. There should be no toxic substances, it should be a neutral pH and relatively soft.

Standards for industrial water supplies are difficult to define, inasmuch as different industries have different quality requirements. Prime requisites for industrial water supplies are constant quality and constant quantity. It is interesting to note that over 70 percent of the industrial use of water is for cooling purposes. While cooling water does not have particularly stringent quality requirements, water utilized for boiler feedwater probably possesses the most strict water quality criteria.

Agriculture presently uses the major portion of the water supply in the contiguous United States, and while overall quality is not restrictive, certain parameters must be controlled if arable lands and reasonable productivity are to be maintained. Probably the most important impurity in water with respect to irrigation is the sodium content, inasmuch as high concentrations of sodium placed onto certain kinds of soils can cause impermeable conditions to result. Proper irrigation practice requires knowledge of the sodium adsorption ratio (SAR), which is defined as

$$ SAR = \frac{Na^+}{\left(\dfrac{Ca^{++} + Mg^{++}}{2}\right)^{1/2}} \qquad (9-1) $$

where cations are expressed in milliequivalents per liter (meq/l); The Exchangeable Sodium Percent (ESP), which is defined as

$$ ESP = \frac{100\ (-0.0126 + 0.01475\ SAR)}{1 + (-0.0126 + 0.01475\ SAR)} ; \qquad (9-2) $$

the salt tolerance of the crops; the soil permeability and infiltration rate and the drainage conditions. Obviously, one should not use any water for irrigation without thorough studies of these factors.

It should also be noted that suspended solids in wastewaters may also cause problems as will the presence of Boron. Thus, even though utilization of wastewaters for irrigation may initially appear to be attractive, examination of these factors may prove the practice to be undesirable.

Probably the most important water quality considerations for stock and wildlife watering are possible toxicity and salinity. On the other hand, the propagation of fish and other aquatic life is the basis for many existing water quality standards. Parameters of importance include oxygen, pH, CO_2, NH_3, temperature, suspended solids, toxic materials and salts. The previously mentioned synergistic effects of many of these impurities must also be considered. Shellfish culture requirements are primarily concerned with the ability of these organisms to accumulate materials because of their large pumping rates. In addition to previously mentioned impurities, bacterial and viral contamination of the water must also be considered.

Remaining water use requirements are primarily concerned with aesthetics, with the exception of swimming and bathing waters, which should contain no toxic materials and should be free from pathogenic organisms. Aesthetic considerations include visible floating or suspended solids, slimes, blooms, odor, oil, foaming, and excessive acidity or alkalinity.

9.2 WASTE ASSIMILATIVE CAPACITY

Introduction. One of the most important considerations in studies of waste assimilative capacity is the stream's ability to maintain an adequate dissolved oxygen concentration. The determination of the spatial and time distribution of dissolved oxygen is called the oxygen balance. While the methodology for performing an oxygen balance is still somewhat primitive, some means of determining the organic waste assimilative capacity is necessary to aid in water pollution control activities. Several advances in theoretical concepts and field estimation of oxygen balance parameters have been made in recent years. It is the purpose of this discussion to illustrate these techniques, and demonstrate that a combination of an understanding of theoretical concepts and engineering judgement will usually allow an adequate oxygen balance to be made. It should be emphasized that while this discussion is concerned with the ability of a river to accept organic waste materials, a waste assimilative capacity can be defined for other pollutants, such as temperature, acidity, salts, etc.

Phases of the Study. By definition, the waste assimilative capacity is that amount of material that can be placed into a receiving water, under the worst possible conditions, that will not cause significant deleterious effects. Therefore, the geophysical characteristics of the river must be ascertained. These may include cross sectional data, depth, temporal and spatial distribution of flows, evaporation, transpiration, and the temperature of both air and water.

Since dilution plays a major role in the waste assimilative capacity of a river, a drought-frequency analysis must be used to determine the flows at which critical conditions will exist in the river. In the United States, the design flow for waste assimilative capacity studies is many times taken as the 10 percent or 5 percent flow. That is, that flow that will be equaled or exceeded 90 percent of the time or 95 percent of the time respectively. If controlled flow is practiced on the river, care must be taken in interpreting the results, as the conditions may not always follow the distribution expected.

Flow Through Times. It is essential that detention times in the river be known in order that collection, analysis interpretation and projection of data can be logically pursued.

Observations should be conducted at three or more flow conditions in order that a time of travel versus discharge curve can be developed. This curve can then be used to extrapolate to any desired stream flow.

Methods available for time of flow studies include the use of fluorometric, colorimetric, conductimetric or radioactive tracers; floats; and river cross-section analysis. If cross-sectional areas are determined, it is recommended that they be taken at 500 foot intervals or as close as economy permits.

Figure 9-1 demonstrates the type of curve that will be of value to waste assimilation capacity studies. Figure 9-1 was derived from data taken on the Coosa River in Georgia by noting the time of passage of the peak concentration of Rhodamine "B" dye at each station. Also shown is the detention time based upon channel storage. The discrepancy in the observed and calculated values can be explained by turbulent diffusion theory.

Reactions Occuring in the River. While a simplified approach may be taken in stream analysis, the following oxygen sources and sinks should be investigated and included in the model, if found to be significant:

A. Reaeration
B. Deoxygenation (nitrogenous and carbonaceous)
C. Photosynthesis
D. Sedimentation
E. Benthos demand
F. Wind effects on reaeration
G. Respiration of aquatic plants
H. Immediate chemical oxygen demand
I. BOD and O_2 by convection

The simplest case, as will be subsequently demonstrated, is where only natural reaeration and carbonaceous oxidation occur. Thus, if these reactions are found to be the major ones, the other factors can be ignored unless future conditions dictate that they must be considered.

Field Studies. In order to rationally examine the receiving water for its ability to satisfactorily assimilate waste materials, it is mandatory that the field information obtained be as accurate as possible. Thus, the actual field studies are among the most important phases of water quality investigations and should be carefully planned and conducted.

It should be noted that while it is ideal to obtain an infinite number of observations, limitations of time, money, personnel and facilities will require a compromise between the ideal investigation and a realistic one.

Objectives of Water Quality Studies. The following objectives should be considered when planning for water quality studies:

A. Determination of the natural water quality of the river

B. Adequate measurement of the effects of existing waste discharges on water quality and water utilization

C. Sufficient data on waste loads, water quality and stream characteristics to allow projection of the data to predict water quality and effects of waste discharges under future conditions

D. Ascertainment of corrective measure required to protect the receiving water for its intended utilization.

Preliminary Planning. Assemble and review all available maps, information and reports concerned with the water body under consideration. Using this information and before going to the field, prepare a brief preliminary plan of operation for the subsequent field reconnaissance. The following items should be included in the preliminary plan:

A. Locations and estimation of strengths of known sources of waste discharges

B. Location of areas of water use and designation of legitimate water uses

C. Plan of major rivers showing tributaries and water resource developments such as dams and diversions

D. Possible sampling stations

E. Estimate of sampling frequency and number of samples to be taken at each station

F. Required laboratory determinations,

G. Existing gaging stations and locations of points where additional flow data are needed

H. Other hydrologic and hydraulic data required and possible means of ataainment

I. Potential laboratory locations

J. Supplies and equipment

K. Personnel requirements

L. Estimate of cost

Preliminary Field Operations. It is highly desirable to spend time in the field prior to the survey to obtain preliminary information and make preparations for the actual field investigation. The following outline describes the procedures that should be followed:

A. Local Contacts: Discuss project with local agencies and individuals who use or have knowledge of the river and acquire all available maps, reports, operating records and verbal information.

B. Sources of Wastes: All sources of wastes should be inventoried in accordance with standard procedures.

C. River:

1. Observe the entire reach of water involved by wading, walking the bank and by boat.

2. Note especially the points of waste discharge and dispersion patterns, visible evidence of pollution confluences, mixing of tributaries, stream flow characteristics, approximate widths and depths, locations of prospective sampling stations, and apparent water usage.

3. Collect bottom samples of biological organisms and bottom deposits and observe evidence of algae.

(a) Bottom organisms indicate degree of pollution.
(b) Bottom deposits indicate the extent of sludge deposits.
(c) Algae demonstrates the need for technique to differentiate between atmospheric reaeration and photosynthesis as a source for dissolved oxygen.
4. Time of Travel: Proceed as previously indicated.
5. Select and identify sampling stations:
(a) For dissolved oxygen evaluation on most streams, sampling locations should include one station just above each major waste discharge, stations at about half-day intervals for two days travel time below waste sources, and stations at one day intervals for an additional three or four days time of travel.
(b) For coliform evaluation, the stations should be similar to (a) except that the downstream stations at one day intervals should extend to a total of 10 to 20 days time of water travel below waste sources.
(c) In very small or very turbulent streams, the sampling stations should obviously be located at closer intervals.
(d) At the confluence of tributary streams, locate one station at the mouth of the tributary and one station just above the confluence.
(e) Stations should be located near points of important water use, if possible.
(f) At stations where waste and water are well mixed, sample at the midpoint of the stream; however, if inadequate mixing occurs, quarter-points should also be sampled.
(g) Identify stations adequately.
(h) Determine access to sampling stations and estimate the time of sampling.
D. Preliminary Stream Samples:
1. Collect one or more sets of stream samples for preliminary analysis.
(a) Dissolved oxygen results will assist in establishing necessary sampling stations.
(b) Coliform and BOD tests will facilitate selection of proper dilutions to be used.
(c) Determination of other constituents will help to select proper laboratory procedures and determine the size of sample portions necessary for analysis.
Final Planning. Using the preliminary plan and the knowledge gained from preliminary field investigations, a reasonable and practical plan for the field studies can be developed. In developing the final operational procedures the following considerations should be made:
A. Period of Field Operations:

1. The time period selected should be at a time of the year when past experience indicates that the stream flows are relativley stable.
2. For an oxygen balance, choose a period of drought flow.
3. Sampling daily or on alternate days is usually preferable to a period of around the clock intensive sampling, but a combination of both may be best.
   B. Sampling:
      1. Sewage:
         (a) Collect samples around the clock at 15 minute to one hour intervals for three to seven days.
         (b) Composite sample portions in proportion to flow for three to four equal time periods of each day.
      2. Industrial Wastes:
         (a) For well known processes with little variation, equal sample portions collected at one-half to one hour intervals and composited for eight hours or for a complete cycle of operation on three to five days should be adequate.
         (b) For little known and variable processes, detailed and prolonged sampling amy be necessary. Ideally, samples should be collected at 5 to 15 minute intervals and composited in proportion to flow for six to 24 hour periods for seven or more days or complete cycles of operation.
      3. Stream:
         (a) If stream flow, waste discharge, or photosynthesis vary widely throughout the day, sample around the clock for at least one or two days to establish the daily cycle of variation in waste constituents and effects.
         (b) In most streams, grab samples each day or on alternate days for two weeks will probably be adequate.
   C. Laboratory Operations:
      1. Select principal determinations that will yield necessary information and reject determinations that would be interesting but not contribute to the solution of the problem.
      2. Make certain that work assigned to the laboratory is reasonable by coordinating plans with the laboratory supervisor.
      3. Ship samples that do not need to be analyzed in the field to a headquarters laboratory.
Miscellaneous Considerations. The methodology presented assumes that there is no limit to time, personnel, equipment and money available for the investigation. Obviously, the field investigations must be adjusted to comply with these factors. The final plan must supply the maximum information with minimum cost.

All key personnel should be included in a planning session where the problems, objectives and filed operations are elucidated. Accurate and immediate recording of all observations should be encouraged and the investigation should be reviewed daily for possible revisions of the operating plans.

Mathematical Modeling. The most accurate oxygen balance would consider each of the factors previously outlined. However, many of these factors are most difficult to determine, and unless unusual conditions are present, a good estimate of the oxygen balance may many times be obtained by assuming that the principle reactions occurring in the self-purification process are those of the Biochemical Oxygen Demand and Reaeration.

It is generally accepted that the rate of absorption of gas into a liquid follows a first order rate process and therefore is proportional to the oxygen deficit. This can be expressed as:

$$\frac{dD_2}{dt} = K_2 D_2 \qquad (9-3)$$

where:

$D_2 = (C_s - C_t)$ = oxygen deficit in mg/l

K_2 = Reaeration coefficient

C_s = Kp at a given temperature

K = Henry's Law Constant

p = Partial pressure of oxygen

C_t = Concentration of oxygen at time "t"

The rate of BOD exertion can also be expressed as a monomolecular reaction as follows:

$$\frac{dL}{dt} = -K_1 L \qquad (9-4)$$

where:

L = Concentration of BOD in mg/l

K_1 = BOD rate constant

The total change in deficit with respect to time is then:

$$\frac{dD}{Dt} = \frac{dD_1}{dt} + \frac{dD_2}{dt} = K_1 L - K_2 D \qquad (9-5)$$

Integrating equation (9-5) with the appropriate boundary conditions yields:

$$D_t = \frac{K_1 L_a}{K_2 - K_1} (10^{-K_1 t} - 10^{-K_2 t}) + D_a 10^{-K_2 t} \qquad (9-6)$$

where:

D_t = oxygen dificit at time "t" in mg/l

L_a = Ultimate first stage BOD in mg/l

K_1 = BOD rate constant using log base 10

K_2 = Reaeration rate constant using log base 10

It is seen that if all of the parameters in equation (9-6) are accurately known, and if the initial assumptions regarding the neglection of other oxygen balance parameters are valid, then a prediction of stream conditions can be made for a point downstream from a waste discharge, and the effect of the waste discharge on the oxygen assets of the stream can be evaluated.

While the oxygen sag curve is useful in many cases, its limitation should be recognized and the oxygen balance parameters neglected should be considered.

Thomas (1961) states the following valid criticisms and limitations for the formulation:

A. The sag curves, when fitted to stream D.O. and B.O.D. data have yielded such a wide range of values of the parameters K_1, K_2, L_a as to suggest that some important factors have not been taken into account in the formulation or that the variables that are included have not been incorporated in the correct mathematical form.

B. The formulation requires information from laboratory analysis of the rate of B.O.D. other than the 5-day 20^0C value, and information from such long-time B.O.D. tests, it is felt, may not be applicable to streams because of the inherent differences between the aquatic environment of streams and laboratory bottles.

C. The formulation requires that flow times to the various sampling points be measured; these measurements are often difficult to make and may be highly non-precise.

In spite of these statements, one may conclude that the fundamental concepts underlying the formulation are essentially correct and should be retained. It is now in order to examine the various components of the oxygen balance to determine the methodology involved in their determination and the validity in omitting them from the mathematical model.

Biochemical Oxygen Demand: The determination of the BOD and its rate constant, K_1, has been traditionally performed in the laboratory. However, it is obvious that the rate of BOD exertion in quiescent laboratory bottles is not necessarily the same as in a dynamic river. The value of K_1 is not only affected by mixing, but by deposition, absorption and scour that may occur in the river under consideration. Therefore, a rational procedure for the determination of the rate of carbonaceous BOD exertion in a river is to measure the BOD at successive downstream stations, and then to determine the rate constant from the slope of a plot of the log of the BOD versus time of passage or distance. In general, the rate constant for an untreated waste will be more than 0.15 per day. It should be noted that long term laboratory BOD tests must be run in order to ascertain ultimate carbonaceous BOD values. A plot that might be obtained is shown on Fig. 9-2(a). Figure 9-2(b) illustrates the effect of a discharge containing volatile settleable solids (Krenkel, et al., 1969).

9-15

Reaeration Coefficient: Probably the most difficult to determine of the parameters needed for the oxygen balance is the reaeration coefficient, K_2. Many theories have been proposed; however, the determination of this factor still leaves much to be desired. Probably the only universal agreement regarding a mathematical model describing aeration is with respect to equation 9-3. It should be noted that the problem in estimating aeration capacities lies in defining the rate coefficient K_2.

Streeter[2](1925), in his classical work on the oxygen sag analysis, used an indirect (and incorrect) method to calculate K_2. If all the terms except K_2 are known, trial values of K_2 are assumed and the resulting curve is compared with the observed oxygen profile.

Streeter also found that the following equation closely approximated the observed data in a given stretch of river:

$$K_2 = \frac{C\bar{u}^n}{h^2} \qquad (9-7)$$

in which $\bar{u}$ is the mean stream velocity and C and n are constants for the particular length of river in question, and depend only on the physical conditions that affect turbulence. Although this empirical relationship is valid for a given situation, a reaeration coefficient must be determined in situ, and therefore negates that practical application of the equation. It is obvious that the velocity alone cannot account for the absorption phenomenon, for systems of a constant velocity may easily be visualized, but with completely different turbulence and mass transfer characteristics.

O'Connor (1958) proposed equations based on the turbulent characteristics of a stream as follows:
For isotropic flow

$$K_2 = \frac{[D_m\bar{u}]^{1/2}}{2.31[h]^{3/2}} \qquad (9-8)$$

and for non-isotropic flow

$$K_2 = \frac{480\ D_m^{0.5} S_e^{0.25}}{h^{1.25}} \qquad (9-9)$$

Isotropic trubulence was assumed to exist for Chezy coefficients greater than 17, and non-isotropic turbulence for values less than 17. Some inconsistencies in the method developed by O'Connor raise doubt as to its general validity. The values obtained using these formulations do not always agree with actual observations, and should be used with caution.

Investigations by Krenkel and Orlob (1963) revealed the following empirical equation for K_2 corrected to a temperature of 20°C:

$$K_2 = 1.138 \times 10^{-5} \, D_L h^{-2.32} \qquad (9-10)$$

where D_L is the longitudinal mixing coefficient and h is the depth of water undergoing reaeration in a laboratory flume.

Thackston and Krenkel (1966) extended this work to include several rivers in the Tennessee Valley Authority system and derived the following equation for K_2 at 20°C:

$$K_2 = 0.000125 \, (1 + F^2)^{\frac{1}{2}} \frac{u_*}{h} \qquad (9-11)$$

where:
F = Froude No. $\dfrac{\bar{u}}{\sqrt{gh}}$
u_* = Shear Velocity = $\sqrt{hS_e g}$

Churchill (1962), using what are probably the most extensive and accurate measurements of river reaeration available, relied entirely on statistics to arrive at the following equation for K_2 at 20°C:

$$K_2 = 5.026 \, \bar{u}^{-0.969} h^{-1.673} \qquad (9-12)$$

Finally, Langbien (1967) proposed the following equation for K_2 which was based on an extensive literature review:

$$K_2 = 3.3 \, \bar{u} \, h^{-1.33} \qquad (9-13)$$

Temperature Effects: It is well known that temperature affects the aeration process significantly. It has been shown experimentally that the value of the absorption velocity constant K_2, varies with temperature as follows:

$$K_{20} = K_{2(T')} \, (1.016)^{(20-T')} \qquad (9-14)$$

or approximately 1.6 percent per degree centigrade near 20°C. It should also be noted that gas solubility in water decreases with increasing temperature, a fact that partially offsets the temperature effect on the rate constant.

Photosynthesis: The addition of dissolved oxygen by photosynthesis can be quite significant; however, oxygen furnished via photosynthesis should not be relied upon because there is no assurance that it will be available during critical low flow periods or during the night. In an investigation by Camp (1963), oxygen production by photosynthesis was found to be considerable higher than oxygen supplied by atmospheric reaeration. In order to determine the production of oxygen in the euphotic zone, the light and dark bottle technique is commonly used.

This method involves the collection of water samples at pre-selected depths at each station, portions of which are placed in clear glass and in opaque bottles and immediately suspended at the test depth and exposed for a given period, usually from 24 hours to several days. Another portion is immediately analyzed for its dissolved oxygen content. At the end of the incubation period, the bottles are analyzed for dissolved oxygen concentration. The loss of oxygen from the dark bottle represents BOD, while the change in oxygen in the light bottle, a result of both BOD and photosynthesis. The final dissolved oxygen concentration difference represents oxygen produced by photosynthesis during the incubation period.

Bottom Deposits: Bottom deposits may exhibit a quite significant oxygen demand if conditions are such that the sludge can accumulate over long periods of time. Particular care must be taken with this demand if the water is relatively slow moving, such as in lakes, ponds, or estuaries. Camp (1963) proposes the following formulation to account for BOD of bottom deposits in the absence of settling out of BOD:

$$Hp = \frac{dL_d}{dt} = 2.3 \, K_4 L_d \qquad (9\text{-}15)$$

Where:

- Hp = areal demand in gms. per square meter per day
- H = stream depth in meters
- p = rate of addition of BOD to overlying water in ppm per day
- L_d = total areal BOD of the bottom deposits in gm per square meter at any time t after decomposition has started
- K_4 = areal demand rate constant $\sim$0.003

The delineation of benthic oxygen uptake rates is difficult because of the non-homogeneous nature of river bottoms. It is possible to measure these rates either "in situ" or in the laboratory; however, utilization of previously established rates determined by other workers is probably more practical. Typical values of oxygen uptake rates by sludge deposits may be expected to vary from one to ten grams per square meter per day.

Velz (1958) has shown rather dramatic effects of sludge deposits and claims that this factor accounts for many of the discrepancies noted in reported oxygen balance studies. He also states that when the river velocity is less than 0.6 fps, deposition can be expected to occur, while 1.0 to 1.5 fps may cause resuspension.

Nitrification: While nitrification has not usually been a significant factor in the past, increasing treatment requirements may very well result in oxygen depletion by nitrification

being a major consideration in the oxygen balance. When
secondary treatment is instigated, the quantity of easily
oxidizable carbonaceous material is reduced and a large number
of nitrifying organisms may be introduced into the receiving
water. Nitrification can then proceed rapidly and cause
significant oxygen depletion due to the conversion of ammonia
to nitrites and then to nitrates.

The process is an autocatalytic one and may be described
by:

$$\frac{dc}{dt} = \pm KC \ (N - C) \qquad (9\text{-}16)$$

where:
    C = concentration of ammonia or nitrate
    N = concentration initially present
    K = reaction rate coefficient
The rate coefficient can be determined by river measurements
as with the BOD, only in this case, either the nitrite or the
nitrate concentration is measured with distance or time of flow.

Other Considerations: Other factors that might be
considered include longitudinal dispersion, aeration via wind
action, immediate oxygen demand and awuatic plant respiration.
However, with the exception ot an immediate oxygen demand and
aquatic plant respiration, these factors are ususally negligible.
The presence of an immediate oxygen demand is apparent and
special techniques must be used to measure aquatic plant
respiration.

Performing the Oxygen Balance. The classical oxygen sag
curve has been presented with its limitations and a discussion
of the various parameters involved. Obviously, several
approaches to the determination of the waste assimilative
capacity could be made on the basis of the information presented
thus far. The results of the application of the simple model to
a river are shown on Figure 9-2(c).

If application of the simple model is not successful, the
model may be modified to include other parameters found to be
significant. Typical of these models is that proposed by Camp
(1965), which includes photosynthesis and benthos demand:

$$D_t = \frac{K_1}{K_2 - K_1 - K_3} [L_a - \frac{p}{2.3(K_1 + K_3)}] \ [10^{(K_1+K_3)t} - 10^{-K_2 t}] \ +$$

$$\frac{K_1}{K_2} [\frac{p}{2.3 \ (K_1 + K_3)} - \frac{a}{2.3 \ K_1}] \ (1 - 10^{-K_2 t}) + D_a 10^{-K_2 t} \qquad (9\text{-}17)$$

Many of the objections that are apparent in the basic
Streeter-Phelps model may be overcome by the use of a statistical approach. Because the regression equation is determined
from observed data, the effects of those factors which are not
directly considered will be reflected in the values of the
regression coefficients of the variables which are included.

9-19

If the conditions prevailing at the time of the collection of the basic data remain constant, a regression equation may be expected to predict the allowable pollution load with a fairly high degree of accuracy. It should be noted that extrapolation of a regression equation beyond the range of the observed data is not well advised.

Discussion: It should be noted that all of the many methods proposed for performing the oxygen balance have been used with some degree of success. It is apparent that a decision must be made as to which method is applicable to a given situation. Therefore, the investigator must carefully evaluate the characteristics of the receiving water and judiciously choose his method of analysis. Obviously, the simplest technique that will yield the desired accuracy is the methodology that should be adopted.

The investigator should also make a comprehensive evaluation of all water resources developments planned for the area in question. As will be demonstrated subsequently, changes in the flow regime may have a dramatic effect on waste assimilation capacity.

9.3 THERMAL POLLUTION

Introduction. Potential problems from the addition of waste heat to our waterways ahve only recently been recognized. It is the purpose of this discussion to place the concern over this artificial addition of heat in its proper perspective. It should be stated immediately that past experience to this point in time has not demonstrated a serious problem from thermal pollution. However, the projections of power production for the next few decades indeed indicate that a potential problem does exist.

Figure 9-3, which is a description of the projected power requirements for the next few decades for the United States demonstrates the problem. Examination of this figure demonstrates that we will indeed face a dilemma unless reasonable precautionary measures are taken. The potential heat additions to our waterways are exemplified by the fact that within the next few years, our major source of power must come from nuclear sources. This presents a two-fold problem, inasmuch as nuclear power plants will reject some 50 percent more heat than an equivalent sized fossil fuel plant and furthermore, in order to economically justify the use of nuclear fuel, the plants are of a much larger size. Thus, not only do we have more heat rejected to the environment per unit of electricity produced, but we have a much larger unit at a single location producing electricity.

It is interesting to note that contrary to popular belief, a recent study in the Northwest indicated that only 1.5 percent of the estimated 6 percent load growth per year was attributable to population growth. The remainder of the load demand was attributed to an increase in per capita consumption. Taking this concept somewhat farther, the ecologists suggest that a restriction of "luxury" uses of electricity will help to resolve the problem. If we examine the estimated electrical energy requirements for the south central region of the United States for 1990, and if we assume that the use of freezers, dishwashers, disposals, and clothes dryers were banned, we would find only a 2 percent reduction in electrical energy utilization. If we also dropped the use of air-conditioners, we would find then, a total of only a 7 percent reduction. This somewhat oversimplifies the situation, but the implications are obvious.

Effects of Heated Discharges on the Receiving Water. When the heated water from a power plant reaches the recipient, it may result in a stratified flow condition. This man-made stratification has several implications with regards to water quality. Mixing between the upper and lower layers is inhibited. Thus, oxygen replacement through the natural forces of stream self-purification cannot take place in the lower layer of water. Because of this lack of mixing, organic wastes discharged into the lower layer are not allowed the benefit of that portion of the stream flow in the upper layer. Thus, there is less dissolved oxygen available, less dilution, and a more concentrated biochemical oxygen demand exertion in the lower layer. The overall results will be a reduction in the river's waste assimilative capacity.

Temperature effects on the self-purification capacity of a river include a lowering of the dissolved oxygen content of the water with an increased temperature, an increase in the metabolic activity of the microorganisms, an increase in the reaeration rates in the river, and an overall reduction in the river's waste assimilative capacity. Figure 9-4 demonstrates the change in both the reaction rate coefficient for reaeration and the reaction rate coefficient for deoxygenation with temperature. Studies in both Europe and the United States have indicated a considerable loss in the waste assimilative capacity of a river caused by the introduction of heated waters to a river (Krenkel et al., 1965). It should be noted that if the temperature in a river is increased, the dissolved oxygen sag point will occur sooner and it will be more pronounced.

Biological Effects of Heat. Restrictive requirements are being placed on new powerplants throughout the United States. Therefore, it is instructive to note the reasons for these new restrictions, which are quite costly to the consumer. One must first examine the potential effects on the biota that are caused by the addition of waste heat to a receiving water.

These possible effects include an increase in respiration and growth, direct death by reaching the thermal death point, and indirect death by associated phenomena caused by a raising of the temperature. These indirect effects include stress or death due to lower oxygen concentrations, a disruption of food supply by effects on food chain organisms, decreased resistance to toxic materials and disease, increased subjectivity to predation, and synergism with toxic materials. In addition, a desirable species of fish may be replaced by more tolerant species that are more able to withstand the increased temperatures. It should also be noted that there must be some sublethal effects which are not known and are not determinable in normal laboratory testing procedures. The temperature also has some other effects with respect to organisms other than fish. For example, an increase in temperature tends to promote the growth of blue-green algae, which are the problem organisms in filter plants and may add to the BOD and release odors. A population shift in benthic organisms has also been noted inasmuch as Physa-acuta and Oligochaetae have shown a decided increase below powerplant discharges.

The tolerance of organisms to temperature fluctuations should also be recognized, inasmuch as sudden changes in temperature are much more harmful to aquatic life than the converse (Speakman and Krenkel, 1971). It is interesting to note that even though the present philosophy of the regulatory agencies is to place quite restrictive limitations on the discharge of heated water, our knowledge of the effects of heated discharges on aquatic life are quite meager. For example, at a meeting in 1968, the director of the Water Quality Laboratory of the Environmental Protection Agency in Duluth stated: "The recent emphasis on water quality standards has made apparent the importance of establishing valid and precise water quality requirements for aquatic life. Our present state of knowledge precludes the establishing of criteria for even the common water quality parameters such as temperature, oxygen, and hydrogen ion concentration." Nothing has changed with regards to our knowledge since this date.

Corrective Measures. By using conventional hydrologic techniques, it is possible to perform an energy balance and predict the rate of dissipation of a heated discharge in a given receiving water. If these calculations demonstrate that the temperatures will be excessive and possible detrimental to aquatic life, several alternatives are available. Cooling ponds can be used if land is available and the efficiency of these ponds in the cooling of water can be increased by the use of sprays. If these kinds of devices are not feasible, a cooling tower may be used, several types being available. In any case, the prime objective in the design of a cooling tower is to introduce maximum contact at the air-water interface. Probably the most common type of cooling tower that will be seen in the near future will be the hyperbolic natural draft tower. In this tower, the chimney shape creates its own draft and while the initial cost is higher, it is balanced by savings in power, longer life and less maintenance when compared to a mechanical draft tower. The use of dry cooling towers should also be mentioned, although it is highly improbable that this type tower, which operates similarly to an automobile radiator, will be used on a wide scale in the near future. The reason for this is primarily associated with high cost. In addition, we do not presently have dry cooling towers capable of cooling waters from the very large powerplants that are being constructed.

The use of cooling towers, while seemingly attractive to the environmentalists, poses many problems. These include possible changes in the climate, an increased consumptive use of water, potential fogging and icing, and additional energy requirements. In fact, it is interesting to note that cooling towers cause a 5 to 8 percent reduction in the efficiency of a powerplant and this is in the order of magnitude of the increase in power consumption for one year.

Since cooling towers cannot be continuously operated without a consumptive loss of water, blowdown must be practiced and additional water added. This means an increased use of our water and a different kind of pollution which is contained in the blowdown waste. Estimates for the hyperbolic natural draft cooling towers are somewhere between 8 and 11 dollars per kilowatt capacity.

Beneficial Uses of Heated Water. A discussion of the thermal pollution problem should include some mention of the possibilities of using waste heat in a beneficial manner. Such a use should be both economical and capable of using most of the warm water discharge during all periods of the year. Examination of the various proposals for waste heat utilization demonstrates that none of them meet either criteria.

Among the possibilities mentioned is space heating which is reportable used in several cities in the world. However, examination of these facilities demonstrates that in most cases, the powerplant in question has additional capacity to supply the heat for the areas being subjected to district heating. In addition, the question as to what should happen to this waste heat during summer months has not been resolved. Frost protection for crops has been mentioned as has the use of warm water irrigation for crops. It should be noted however, that the water is not always needed for this purpose and the discharge from a 1,000 megawatt plant would require 100 to 200 square miles of land for disposal.

The use of waste heat for aquaculture has some potential and is being attempted in several locations in the world. Unfortunately, the powerplants are not always located in an area where this farming can be practiced and it usually will not utilize all of the heat emanating from the plant.

One other possibility that has been mentioned is to use the waste heat in conjunction with a waste treatment plant. Examination of this possibility demonstrates it to be highly impractical inasmuch as the additional hydraulic load introduced by the water from the powerplants would make the sizing of the waste treatment plant totally impractical and in addition, the additional heat would not make the rate of oxidation attractively increased.

9.4 EUTROPHICATION

Introduction. The acceleration of eutrophication of many of our water bodies is current cause for concern, both to engineers and to the public. It should be noted; however, that some misunderstanding concerning this topic has become apparent. Eutrophication is a natural process which occurs as a result of the geological aging of a lake. A lake will progressively go from an oligotrophic state to a mesotrophic state to a eutrophic state and ultimately will be completely filled in as shown on Fig. 9-5. In order to understand the nomenclature, one only needs to examine the origin of the Greek works, where trophein means to nourish, oligo means few, meso means intermediate, and eu means well. Thus it can be seen that eutrophication is a natural process and the effect of man's activities is to accelerate this natural process. As a lake ages, enrichment by nutritive materials is increased. These nutrients may originate from precipitation, ground water inflow, and in general from the contiguous drainage basis. As a lake ages, plants accumulate along with sediment and thus extinction of a lake could be considered to be a result of enrichment, productivity, sedimentation and decay.

Limiting Nutrient Concept. A nutrient may be defined as a substance that is necessary for growth or reproduction of an organism. There are some 21 essential elements that are known to be required for the sustenance of algae. However, those that are thought to be in limiting concentrations have in the past been considered to be either nitrogen or phosphorus. In fact, usually accepted concentrations that are said to be limiting for these elements are 0.3 milligrams per liter for nitrogen and 0.01 milligrams per liter for phosphorus. Recent work by the Athens Laboratory of the Environmental Protection Agency has demonstrated that carbon may be the limiting nutrient in some instances (Kerr et al., 1970). This concept, which appears to be substantiated by other workers, has wide implications for the water pollution control field. For example, the dollars that have been spent in research and development for phosphorus and nitrogen removal facilities could well be used for other purposes if carbon is the limiting nutrient. It is interesting to note Table 9-1, which shows a nutrient balance for phosphorus and nitrogen in Lake Mendota inasmuch as this table demonstrates that even if the nitrogen and phosphorus contributions from municipal and industrial wastewater were eliminated, there would still be sufficient quantities of these materials to cause eutrophication acceleration, if in fact, these were the limiting nutrients.

It is obvious that if we are to solve our water pollution control problems with respect to eutrophication, every effort should be made to resolve this apparent controversy between scientific workers as to whether or not carbon is the limiting nutrient.

TABLE 9-1 ESTIMATED NUTRIENT SOURCES FOR LAKE MENDOTA
(After Lee et al.)

Source	Annual Contributions (in pounds)		Estimated Contributions (in percent)	
	Nitrogen	Phosphorus	Nitrogen	Phosphorus
Municipal and Industrial Waste Water	47,000 (Total)	17,000 (Total)	10	36
Urban Runoff	30,300 (soluble)	8,100 (soluble)	6	17
Rural Runoff	52,000 (soluble)	20,000 (soluble)	11	42
Precipitation on Lake Surface	97,000	140 – 7,600	20	2*
Ground Water	250,000	600	52	2
Nitrogen Fixation	2,000	--	0.4	--
Marsh Drainage	?	?	--	--
Total	478,300	47,000*		

* Result based on 1,000 pounds per year of phosphorus in precipitation on the lake surface.

Sources of Nutrients. It should be noted that in most of our lakes, nitrogen and phosphorus may already be contained in the sediments. Therefore, it would appear that these elements should not be in scarce quantity for the production of algae, if required. The prime source of phosphorus with respect to wastewater discharges, is detergents, inasmuch as considerable quantities of phosphorus are contained in household detergents which are ultimately discharged to our waste treatment plants. As previously noted, the nitrogen and phosphorus balance made on Lake Mendota indicates taht the percentage contribution from this source, while significant, does not indicate the entire story. The contribution of nitrogen from groundwater is seen to be 52 percent, which obviously is of concern to the eutrophication acceleration problems of Lake Mendota. One other aspect that should be considered is the seasonal variation of the growth of phytoplankton in a lake. Figure 9-6 demonstrates the relative size of phytoplankton population with season. It is seen that the period of concern with respect to excessive plant growth is from late spring until fall. Thus, perhaps some modification in the frequency of treatment processes would be reasonable with respect to this aspect of eutrophication acceleration control.

Measurement of Eutrophication. One of the problems in defining the degree of eutrophication in a lake is its measurement. Several analytical techniques have been proposed for this measurement and include the standing crop of algae and aquatic plants, the amount of suspended solids, the amount of chlorophyll, the volume of algae, the number of algal blooms, and photosynthesis. Perhaps the most widely used measurement is to determine the number of "objectionable blooms" of algae. In this measurement, a bloom is frequently defined as containing 0.5 to 1 million cells per liter. Another method of assessing lake eutrophication is the oxygen concentration in the hypolimnion. In fact, the oxygen depletion in lakes deep enough to stratify is probably the most widely used index depicting oligotrophic and eutrophic lakes. Light penetration has also been used as a measure of eutrophication as has the aquatic plant nutrient content and the sediment composition.

Effects of Eutrophication. Excessive growth of plants can have a significant adverse effect on water quality. It may cause an increased chlorine demand, it may cause problems with coagulation in the water treatment plant, it may cause clogging of the rapid sand filters, and probably the most significant effect is a possible taste and odor problem. The color and turbidity resulting from algae may also be a problem.

With regards to recreational uses of water, the excessive growth of aquatic plants may make a lake aesthetically undesirable, inasmuch as the thickness of the plant growths may make water utilization for recreational purposes impossible. In addition, excessive eutrophication may cause a change in the fish population, perhaps substituting a less desirable type fish for one that is desirable. A case point would be Lake Erie, in which, while the total productivity is probably higher, the kinds of fish are not as desirable as in previous years.

Possible Corrective Measures. As stated by Lee (1970), lake eutrophication can be controlled or its effects minimized by reducing the nutrient input to the lake, by increasing the nutrient output from the lake, by immobilizing nutrients within the lake and by controlling excessive growths of algae within the lake.

If phosphorus and nitrogen are truly the limiting nutrients to eutrophication acceleration, then the emphasis in water pollution control should be on the removal of these substances at the waste treatment plant. However, if carbon is the limiting nutrient, then the process becomes somewhat simpler, inasmuch as carbon removal on the average, is less expensive than the removal of nitrogen and phosphorus. It might also be noted that an obvious solution to the contributions of phosphorus would be to eliminate this element from detergents. However, one only needs to recall the recent controversy over the substitution of nitrilotriacetic acid (NTA), where it was finally decided that this material as a substitute for phosphorus in detergents was unsatisfactory because of its toxicity.

Other possibilities would be the diversion of wastewaters, where the wastewaters would be bypassed from the lake in question, such as in Lake Tahoe. It should also be possible to dredge lake sediments to remove nutrients but the cost of this process would leave some question as to its practicability. Flushing lake waters has also been attempted but lakes rarely have large enough quantities of nutrient poor water available for this purpose. Chemical control can also be utilized for the control of algae but there are some problems with this procedure. One other process that has been mentioned is harvesting the algae and aquatic weeds near the shore. This procedure is probably also not practical.

One other possibility that should be mentioned because of current interest is the use of certain kinds of fish that utilize phytoplankton for food. While these fish do exist, recent experiences in Poland have demonstrated that the fish themselves will eventually lead to the destruction of other, more desirable species.

9.5 MERCURY IN THE AQUATIC ENVIRONMENT

Introduction. Mercury has traditionally been of public health concern, primarily because of the vapors emanating from the metallic elemental form. In fact, the basis of industrial hygiene limitations on mercury concentrations have primarily been based on this vapor. These limits are 0.1 milligrams per cubic meter of air for metallic vapor and 0.01 milligrams per cubic meter of air for organic vapors. As will be discussed subsequently, the problem of mercury in water was not recognized until the last decade. It is interesting to note in this regard that the only country having mercury standards for drinking water was Russia when the current crisis arose, these limits being 5 parts per billion in drinking water.

In the early 1950's, fishermen around Minamata Bay, Japan, were stricken with a mysterious neurological illness. It was also found that other animals were affected, such as fish, cats and birds. The symptomatic effects were finally traced to high concentrations of organic mercury contained in fish in the Bay and which were found to be contributed by a chemical plant in the area. A similar problem was noted later in Niigata, Japan, where additional deaths and cases occurred. The total number of people that died or were seriously disabled was 121, both in Niigata and Minamata Bay.

To place these incidnets in proper perspective; however, it should be noted that the concentration of mercury in the shell fish was in the order of 41 parts per million in Minamata as contrasted with concentrations in the order of 1 to 2 parts per million in the southeastern United States. Furthermore, the ingestion of fish in Japan is quite different from that in the United States, being in the order of 84 grams per day per capita in Japan and 17 grams per capita per day in the United States. One other aspect of the Japanese incidents is the fact that the fish and the shell fish that were incriminated also contained significant concentrations of other heavy metals. It is common knowledge that the toxicity of many metals is synergistic with other metals.

The next focus on the mercury problem occurred in Sweden in the early 1960's, when ornithologists began to notice a decline in the bird population. This decline was attributed to the utilization of phenyl mercuric acetate (PMA) as a fungicide and subsequent ingestion of the seeds by the bird population and by fish. In 1967, Sweden banned the sale of fish from 40 lakes and rivers. The use of PMA as a fungicide was also banned during the 1960's.

In 1969, a Ph.D. student in Canada noted unusually high concentrations of mercury in fish taken from Lake Saint Claire in that country. Subsequently, it was found that several lakes in Canada were contaminated with mercury and there were at one time one million pounds of fish that were burned in Canada because they exceeded the recommended 0.5 part per million limit of mercury.

The scene switched to the United States in 1970 when there were several water bodies closed in the southeast. Pickwick Lake, which is a large recreational area bordering on Tennessee, was closed in 1970, as was a portion of the Mobile Tombigbee Waterway. While the concentrations of mercury in the fish were not high relative to those found in Japan, they did exceed the FDA 0.5 part per million limitation.

Several other incidents, although not related to the water problem, should be mentioned. Outbreaks of organic mercurial poisoning occurred in Iraq and in Pakistan and in Guatamala during the 1950's and 1960's. It should be pointed out however that these outbreaks were totally unrelated to water, the ingestion of seed treated with PMA being the culprit. In addition, in New Mexico in 1969, a family who had obtained PMA treated seed fed this seed to their hogs. The hogs subsequently became sick, the farmer slaughtered them and fed them to his family and subsequent to eating the meat, several of the family became permanently disabled from the so-called "Minamata disease." This incident is an excellent example of the irresponsibility demonstrated by our news media, inasmuch as a major network presented a "special" demonstrating this incident of mercury poisoning, and to the laymen, the implication was that the incident was related to water contamination.

Sources of Mercury. Mercury is a very ubiquitous material, occurring quite frequently in nature in many locations. The contributions on a world-wide basis from natural sources have been shown to be much larger than those contributed by man. In fact, recent evidence indicates that the mercury concentrations that have recently been revealed in fish have been in fish for years before the current concern. The major source of mercury causing local problems has been from the chloralkali plants, which use mercury as one of the cells in the manufacture of caustic and chlorine.

Mercury is used in many industrial processes and in many instances will ultimately find its way into the sewer. Therefore, it would be expected that sewage sludge would contain significant concentrations of mercury and sediments in the vicinity of wastewater outfalls would demonstrate higher than normal levels of mercury, which has been found to be the case. Higher than normal levels of mercury have been found in locations adjacent to ship docks, where mercury has been used as a fungicide in the treatment of lawns, and in general in many areas that may eventually contribute the mercury to some portion of the hydrologic cycle. The real crux of the matter is to define the seriousness of the problem and to place the sources and sinks of mercury in their proper perspective. This problem becomes quite serious when it is recognized that one entire industry has been closed down because of excessive mercury concentrations in sword fish and other industries and individuals have been affected economically.

Biological Transformation. One of the reasons that mercury was previously not considered to be a problem was the fact that it was thought to be innocuous once it was introduced into a waterway. Subsequent to the experiences in Japan and Sweden, Swedish workers found that any form of mercury could be converted by microorganisms to the toxic methylmercury form.

It should be noted that methylmercury is many times more toxic to man than is the metallic form and thus is the form of mercury of concern with regards to water pollution control. It is also significant to note that methylmercury will concentrate in the fetus, thus possibly leading to damage to newborn children even though the mother shows no symptoms of the Minamata Disease.

Originally, the process of the methylation of mercury by bacteria that occurs in the bottom sediments was thought to be anaerobic. Subsequent investigations have shown that the process is aerobic but will occur at a much slower rate in the absence of oxygen. In general, it has been found that the methylation process is a detoxification one for the bacteria. That is, the bacteria find that the elemental form of mercury is toxic and that the methylmercury form is not, although the converse is true for humans.

Many factors have been found to affect the rate of methylation in sediments, although quantification of the process is lacking. For example, it has been shown that at a high pH, the predominant form of mercury produced is in the dimethyl form, which does not pose an immediate problem in the aquatic environment, and at lower pH's, the toxic monomethylmercury form is present, which is of concern. It is also thought that organic materials affect the methylation rate inasmuch as higher rates of methylation have been noted near organic waste discharges.

The problem essentially is one of the microorganisms in bottom sediments producing methylmercury, the fish absorbing this into their tissue and concentrating it and then man ingesting the fish and the methylmercury contained therein.

Mercury and other heavy metals have been shown to primarily be concentrated in the size fraction of sediment less than 16 microns. Furthermore, in normal environmental conditions, it is quite difficult for this material to release itself from the fractions onto which it is adsorbed. It is therfore seen that the problem is quite closely associated with sediment transport. In fact, it is interesting to note that subsequent to the closure of Pickwick Lake, the only mechanism by which the mercury could have traversed to Kentucky Lake being by sediment transport.

Analysis. Many problems are present with the analysis of mercury. The usual methodology today for total mercury involves the use of flameless atomic absorption spectroscopy and this methodology can detect approximately 0.2 parts per billion of mercury. However, the method is not generally thought of as being totally reliable inasmuch as varying results are obtained at different laboratories. This is not to say that experienced laboratories cannot arrive at reasonable quantitative results, but that the control methods should be based on a standard method of analysis, which we do not presently have.

Since the concern over mercury is with respect to methylmercury, it would appear reasonable that control should be based on methylmercury content. Unfortunately; however, there

are not very many laboratories in the United States that have
the capability to perform methylmercury analysis. The assumption is made that all of the mercury in fish is methylmercury
and it is on this basis that the total mercury analysis is used
by the regulatory agencies for control. It is possible to
analyze for methylmercury by using a gas chromatograph and
competent laboratory technicians can determine organic mercury
at concentrations to 0.5 parts per billion.

Toxicology. This discussion would not be complete without
some comments concerning the toxicology of mercury. In this
regard, it should be noted that the present FDA standards in
the United States for fish are 0.5 parts per million, the basis
being primarily the experiences of Japan and Sweden. In Sweden
the limit has been placed at 1 part per million, with the
recommendation that fish should not be consumed more than one
time per week. In Japan, a recommendation is that not more
than two millograms of mercury be ingested per kilogram of body
weight for a normal person and 0.5 milligrams per kilogram of
body weight for a pregnant woman.

Methylmercury concentrates in the brain, liver, kidneys,
and in the fetus. It is detectable in hair, blood and urine,
although analysis of the blood is the best indication of
methylmercury poisoning. The symptoms include a numbness in
the extremities, slurred speech, unsteady gait, exaggerated
reflexes, constriction of the vision field and mental
disturbance.

It is particularly significant to note that recent work
ahs suggested that the major portion of mercury contained in
fish is not methylmercury (Krenkel et al., 1972). If this is
in fact the case, it demonstrates again the need for a rational
approach to environmental problems, inasmuch as many people
have been affected by a loss in revenue and the general economic
picture with respect to fish has been drastically reduced. It
is my opinion that the regulatory agencies should use methylmercury analysis as a base for determining whether or not a
fish is safe rather than the currently utilized total mercury
analysis.

Remedies. If the mercury problem is truly shown to be
hazardous, then some approach should be taken to correct the
situation in the water bodies where it has been shown to be
of significance. Possibilities include dredging the sediments
from the lake, eliminating the oxygen to create the sulfide,
laying a covering on the bottom of the lake, changing the pH,
etc.

Some of these possibilities have been attempted by the
Swedish workers, the most notable attempt being with regards
to dredging of the lakes. The Swedes, on two occasions,
dredged out the sediments from affected waterways and subsequently found that the mercury concentrations in fish were
higher than before. The reason proposed was that when the
anaerobic sediments, where the mercury was tied up as the

9-31

sulfide, were released to the air, the mercury was converted to the ionic form and the sulfide to sulfate. The bacteria were then able to convert the mercury to the toxic methylmercury form and the rain subsequently washed out this material into the waterway, where it was absorbed by the fish. The Tennessee Valley Authority has suggested that the sedimentation rates in the reservoirs affected will ultimately place a covering over the mercury containing sediments that will render them innocuous to the aquatic environment. It should be noted in th this regard that the choloralki industries have stopped significant discharges of mercury to the aquatic environment.

9.6 SUMMARY

The problems of water pollution have been presented in a very brief form and implications with regards to the environment have been elucidated. A simplified methodology for the determination of the ability of a river to accept organic waste materials has been presented and the role of the hydraulic engineer demonstrated. Also, several pertinent current problems of water pollution have been discussed and again, the role of the hydraulic and hydrologic engineer illustrated.

It is hoped that from this necessarily brief discussion of water pollution and its control that some insight has been given into the problems facing today's society. It should be emphasized that there are solutions to these problems that are reasonable. On the other hand, priorities should be attached to all of the problems facing society and water pollution problems should be solved on a rational basis, coupled with the priority assigned to them with regards to our other social problems.

REFERENCES

Camp, T.R., Water and Its Impurities; Reinhold Press, 1963.

Churchill, M.A., The Prediction of Stream Reaeration Rates; TVA, Chattanooga, Tennessee, 1962.

Klein, L. River Pollution, 2: Causes and Effects; Butterworths, London, 1962.

Kerr, P.C., et al, The Interrelation of Carbon and Phosophorus in Regulating Heterotrophic and Autotrophic Populations in Aquatic Ecosystems; Southwest Water Lab., Environmental Protections Agency, Athens, Georgia, July 1970, Water Pollution Control Research Series 16050 FGS 07/70.

Krenkel, P.A. et al, Mechanisms of Mercury Transformation in Bottom Sediments; Tech. Rep. No. 27, Dept. of Environmental and Water Resources Engineering, Vanderbilt University, Nashville, Tennessee, January 1972.

Krenkel, P.A. and Orlob, G.T., Turbulent Diffusion and the Reaeration Coefficient; Transaction, Amer. Soc. of Civil Engineers, Vol. 128, part III, 1963.

Krenkel, P.A., Cawley, W.A., and Minch, V.A., The Effect of Impounding Reservoirs on River Waste Assimilation Capacity; Journal Water Pollution, Control Federation, Sept. 1965.

Krenkel, P.A. et al, Stream Analysis and Thermal Pollution; World Health Organization, 1969, Copenhagen, Denmark.

Langbien, W.B. and Durum, W.H., The Aeration Capacity of Streams U.S.G.S. Circular 542, Washington, D.C., 1967.

Lee, G.F., Eutrophication; University of Wisconsin Water Resources Center, Eutrophication Information Program, OCC. Paper No. 2, September, 1970.

O'Connor, D.J. and Dobbins, W.E., Mechanism of Reaeration in Natural Streams; Transactions, ASCE, Vol. 123, 1958, p. 641

Speakman, J.N. and Krenkel, P.A., Ouantification of the Effects of Rate of Temperature Change on Aquatic Biota; Nat'l Center for Research & Training in the Hydraulic and Hydrologic Aspects of Water Pollution Control, Vanderbilt University, Nashville, Tennessee, May 1971.

Streeter, H.W., A Study of the Pollution and Natural Purification of the Ohio River; Public Health Bulletin 146, U.S. Public Health Service, 1925.

REFERENCES - (Continued)

Thackston, E.L. and Krenkel, P.A., Longitudinal Mixing and
    Reaeration in Natural Streams; Tech. Rep. No. 7, Sanitary
    and Water Resources Engineering, Vanderbilt University,
    Nashville, Tennessee, 1966.

Thomas, H.A., Jr., The Dissolved Oxygen Balance in Streams;
    Proceedings, Seminar on Waste Water Treatment and Disposal,
    Boston Society of Civil Engineering, 1961.

Velz, C.J., Significance of Organic Sludge Deposits; Proc.,
    Oxygen Relationships in Streams; Public Health Service,
    Cincinnati, Ohio, March 1958

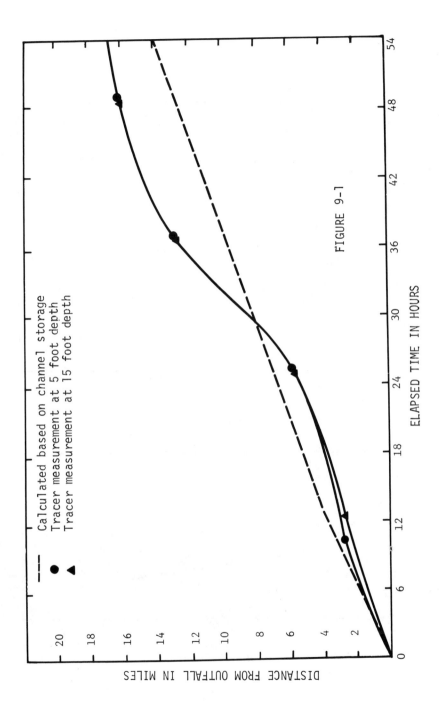

FIGURE 9-1

Legend:
- Calculated based on channel storage
- Tracer measurement at 5 foot depth
- Tracer measurement at 15 foot depth

X-axis: ELAPSED TIME IN HOURS (0, 6, 12, 18, 24, 30, 36, 42, 48, 54)

Y-axis: DISTANCE FROM OUTFALL IN MILES (2, 4, 6, 8, 10, 12, 14, 16, 18, 20)

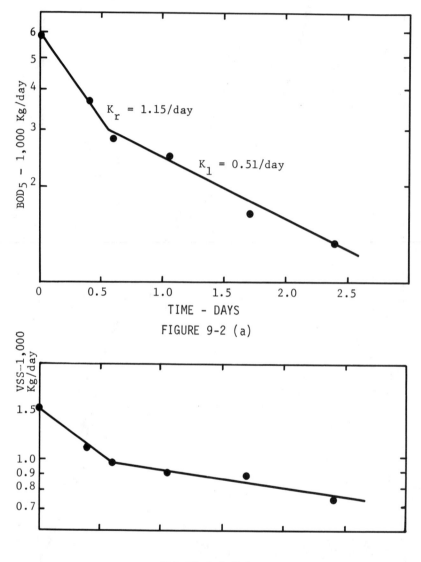

FIGURE 9-2 (a)

FIGURE 9-2 (b)

9-36

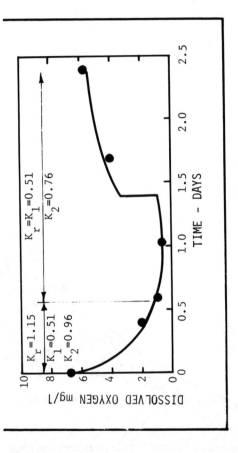

FIGURE 9-2 (c)

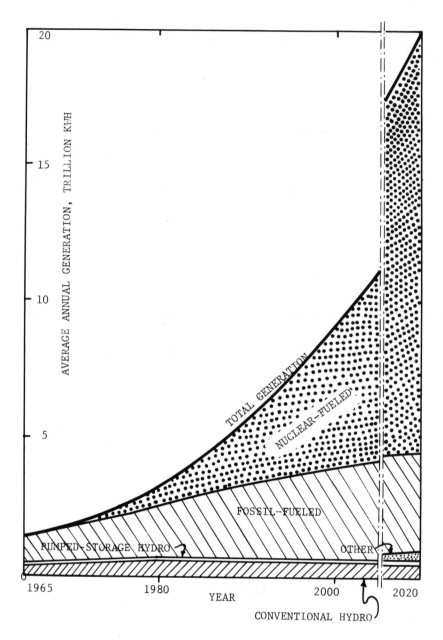

FIGURE 9-3

9-38

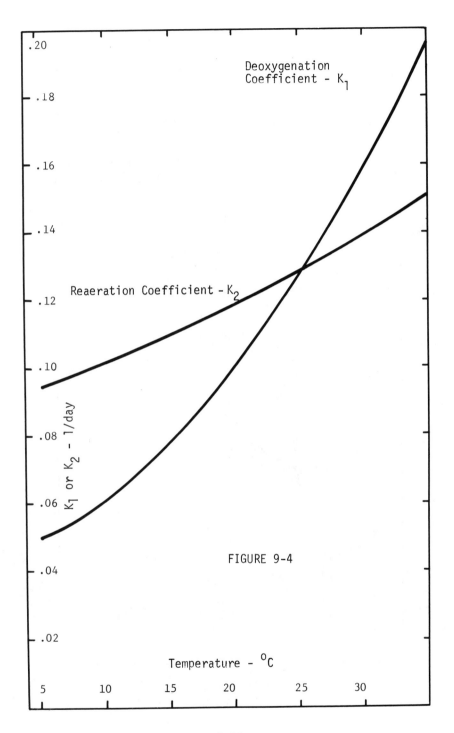

FIGURE 9-4

9-39

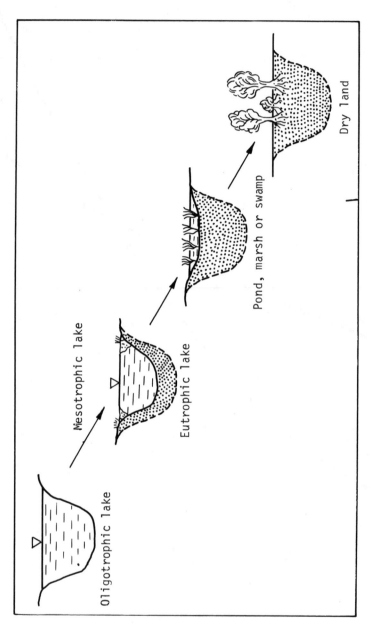

FIGURE 9-5   Eutrophication--the process of
aging by ecological succession

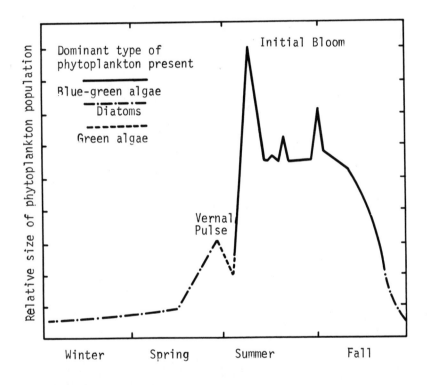

FIGURE 9-6 Hypothetical curve of seasonal changes
of phytoplankton in a eutrophic lake

Chapter 10

HEATED SURFACE DISCHARGES INTO
FLOWING AMBIENT STREAMS AND LAKES

Edward Silberman, Director of St. Anthony Falls Hydraulic
Laboratory, University of Minnesota,
Mississippi River at 3rd Avenue, S.E.,
Minneapolis, Minnesota

Chapter 10

HEATED SURFACE DISCHARGES INTO
FLOWING AMBIENT STREAMS AND LAKES

10.1 INTRODUCTION

Every new kilowatt of steam-electric generating capacity requires provision for dissipating 1.5 to 2 kilowatts of heat equivalent at or near the generating site. This heat is generally not readily usable and must be wasted to the environmnet. The transfer is accomplished by cooling the steam condensers with water. For a modern 1000 megawatt nuclear plant, 1800 cfs of water raised $17^\circ F$ might be required as an example. Newer technologies for producing less waste heat to replace existing steam generating plants are still perhaps 30 years from full development according to a National Academy of Sciences report (1971).

Cooling water can be provided in various ways. Recycling through open or closed cooling towers or through cooling ponds is possible. However, the most economical method for large plants where natural water bodies are available has been the once-through cooling system wherein water is withdrawn from the water body, pumped through the condensers, and returned to the water body at higher temperature. For economic and other reasons, this method will probably continue to be used for many new power plants where environmental constraints can be satisfied.

The returned cooling water, because of its increased temperature, ahs experienced physical and chemical changes, and these changes have implications for the life forms which depend on the water. In order to assess the possible effects, as well as to position cooling water intakes and outfalls to avoid recirculation, it is desirable to be able to predict the temperature pattern in the water surrounding the outfall. The regions of largest temperature change which occur near the outfall are usually of first concern, but even small increases which occur farther away may be important, especially if there is another plant contributing to heating in the same area.

This chapter reviews the present understnading and some calculation methods for making such predictions. It is limited to outfalls from surface cnaals as opposed to submerged outfalls.

Discharge from a surface canal usually results in higher surface temperatures, and hence more rapid transfer of heat from the water to the atmosphere, than does discharge from a submerged outlet. A submerged outlet produces more rapid mixing and dilution of the warm water prior to its appearance at the surface. Thus a larger volume of water may be heated near the outlet than in the surface canal case, but to a lower temperature. Surface canals are generally more economical than submerged outlets, but limits on maximum temperature rise may restrict their use.

10-1

10.2 ANALYTICAL CONCEPTS

Physical Basis for Analysis. Two kinds of physical occur-
rences are involved in the prediction of temperature increase
in a body of water produced by a heated discharge from a surface
canal. These are additional heat transfer to the atmosphere
through the water-air interface and dilution of the heated
flow by spreading and mixing with the ambient receiving water.
(Ultimately, however, all heat added to fresh water bodies must
be dissipated to the atmosphere by the surface-heat-transfer
process. Heat loss through the earth containing the water body
is ver small and is negligible for computational purposes).
 Although research needs to be done on both these mechanisms, the surface heat transfer phenomenon is probably better
understood at the present time than is the dilution phenomenon.
Furthermore, in the important region near the outlet, surface
heat transfer is generally of much less importance than dilution in cooling the effluent. In any event, it is necessary to
make the dilution calculations in order to determine what surface area is subject to heat transfer and what surface temperature drives the transfer. (Conversely, it is necessary to know
or assume something about the surface heat transfer in order to
calculate the dilution).
 Surface heat transfer can be evaluated for present purposes
using

$$q = \varrho c_p k(T - T_e) \qquad (10-1)$$

where q is the heat transferred per unit time from unit surface
area, positive from water to air; T is the surface temperature,
variable in space and time; and T_e is the equilibrium temper-
ature--that surface temperature at which no net heat transfer
would occur--also variable with time. Both T and T_e are
measured as excess temperatures with respect to the ambient
temperature. The density of the ambient water is ϱ and its
specific heat is c_p. The coefficient k and T_e depend on such

meteorological factors as solar radiation, back radiation, wind,
and wet and dry bulb air temperatures. Empirical methods for
their determination are discussed in Brady, et al. (1969). T_e,
on the average over a day, is close to the ambient temperature
T_a when no artificial heat is added, but may differ by several
degrees, positive or negative, at any given time. Typical heat
transfer rates near a warm water canal outlet are of the order
of 150 BTU per ft. square per day per degree F Temperature
difference.
 The total heat transfer over a period of time can be
obtained by integrating q over the entire surface area and the
required time period. For steady conditions, the total heat
transfer will equal the heat input from the condensers for the
same period. Steady conditions are never really achieved
because of such factors as night and day, variable cloud cover,

10-2

variable winds, and even variable plant load. Nevertheless, it is useful to calculate for extreme conditions on the basis of mean-steady transfer over a relatively short time interval (say several hours), assuming that the rate of change of the several variables will not influence the calculations.

With the simplified concept of surface heat transfer discussed above, it is feasible to proceed to calculate the flow of heated water from a canal into a lake or river. A general scheme is visualized as sketched in Fig. 10-1. This also establishes the coordinate system. The factors to be considered are the canal cross-sectional shape, its orientation and dimensions, and the mean velocity and temperature of the warm water in the canal; the local current velocity, direction, and temperature in the receiving body of water; the wind, if any; and the slope of the bottom near the canal outlet. The bottom and shores of the lake or river are assumed to be sufficiently remote, except for the slope near the canal outlet, not to influence the discharge. In Fig. 10-1 a mean velocity can be defined by

$$\overline{U}(s) = \int_{-1}^{+1} \int_{-1}^{0} U(s,n,z) \; d(\frac{z}{h}) d\frac{n}{b} \qquad (10\text{-}2)$$

and a mean temperature by

$$\overline{T}(s) = \int_{-1}^{+1} \int_{-1}^{0} T(s,n,z) \; d(\frac{z}{\lambda_v h}) d(\frac{n}{\lambda b}) \qquad (10\text{-}3)$$

Characteristics of Warm Water Discharges.
    I. Buoyant Surface Plumes. Of the many physical and chemical changes produced by heating water 15° to 30°F above the ambient temperature, density decrease is probably the most noticeable. The change is small, less than one-half percent for a 30°F rise, but even such small changes produce important static buoyancy forces. In the absence of strong turbulent mixing, the buoyancy results in a vertical rise of the bottom of a warm water layer accompanied by horizontal spreading at the surface. This process forms a buoyant surface plume whose spread is illustrated in Fig. 10-2. Simultaneously, the warm water cools through heat transfer to the atmosphere in accordance with Eq. (10-1) and, at a lesser rate, by heat diffusion to the ambient water. Hayashi and Shuto (1967), among others, have presented theoretical calculations and experimental confirmation for this situation.
    II. Non-Buoyant Jets. On the other hand, the water flowing from a warm water canal with small density difference can be considered a half-jet with a plane of symmetry at the free surface. Temperature, then, is merely a marker of the water emitted from the canal. The paper by Tamai, et al. (1969), for

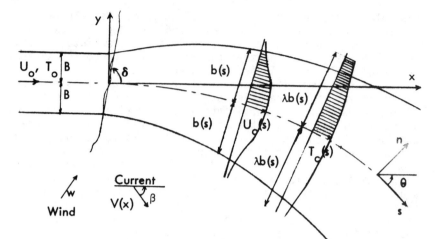

a. Plan

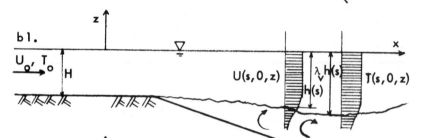

b1.

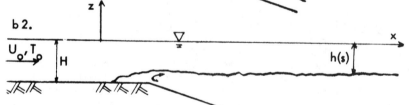

b2.

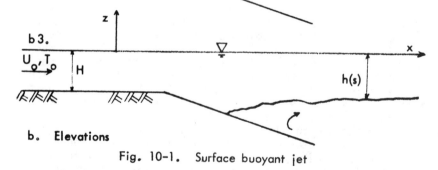

b3.

b. Elevations

Fig. 10-1. Surface buoyant jet

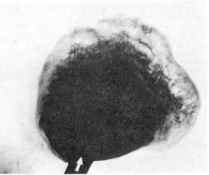

Fig. 10-2. Buoyant surface plume

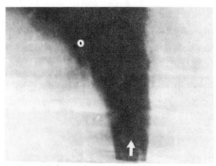

Fig. 10-3. Submerged jet (in cross flow)

Plan

Elevation

RUN 67

Fig. 10-4. Surface buoyant jet

example, takes this position for the region near the outfall.
With this assumption, the available information on submerged
jets as summarized by Abramovich (1963) can be applied to warm
water discharges. Of primary interest for the present purpose
is the entrainment process which draws ambient fluid into the
jet. Figure 10-3 illustrates this process. At the scales of
depth (say 10 ft) and velocity (say 1 fps or more) at which warm
water discharges occur, the flow is turbulent. Entrainment results from the turbulent shear flow near the edges of the jet.

Using established three-dimensional turbulent jet theory,
the discharge can be divided into a zone of flow establishment
near the outlet and a fully developed turbulent half-jet farther
out. The former region has embedded within it the remnants of
the original canal flow surrounded by a new flow regime produced
by shear with the ambient fluid. Shear gradually erodes the
embedded flow so that farther downstream than 6 to 10 times the
depth, the original flow has disappeared. Thereafter the flow
is fully developed jet flow.

In the absence of complicating phenomena, both regions of
the flow can be assumed to be self similar--that is, mean flow
properties treated dimensionlessly do not vary in the flow direction, only normal to it. In both regions, theory then shows
that the outer boundaries of the jet, however they are defined
and probably without regard to cross-sectional shape, spread
proportionally to their distance from an arbitrary origin. The
spread can be written

$$b = b(0) + \alpha s \qquad (10\text{-}4)$$

where b is the width defined in a suitable manner, $b(0)$ is an
initial width, s is the distance along the jet centerline, and
α is the experimentally determined coefficient of proportionality
which depends not only on the region of the flow, but also on the
definition of b. For a half-circular jet with b defined as the
distance from the centerline to where the velocity is half the
centerline velocity, experiments have established $\alpha \simeq 0.22$.
Also, the velocity of entrainment turns out to be directly
proportional to the centerline velocity of the jet, so that

$$v(s) = KU_c \qquad (10\text{-}5)$$

where $v(s)$ is the entrainment velocity normal to the jet axis.
In a fully developed, circular, turbulent jet, a typical experimental value for K is 0.057. Actually, α and K are related to
each other once the shape of the dimensionless velocity profile
and the cross sectional shape are chosen, and experimental values
are not required for both factors. When the velocity profile
and α or K are known, the flow in the jet can be calculated at
each s so that the rate of ambient fluid entrainment and dilution due to mixing can be calculated without knowing specific
details about the mixing process.

Studies have also been made of the temperature distribution in a submerged jet for the case in which the temperature does not change the density. Experimental dimensionless temperature profiles turn out to be of the same form as the velocity profiles but the temperature appears to spread more rapidly--α is greater in Eq. (10-4) when written for temperature profiles. With a known empirical spread rate for the dimensionless temperature profile, the assumed form of the temperature profile, and the calculated rate of entrainment of ambient fluid it is possible to calculate the temperature distribution in a non-buoyant half-jet.

III. __Surface Buoyant Jets.__ A discharge of warm water from a surface canal is generally a composite of these two phys- ical phenomena, the one produced by buoyancy and the other by turbulent jet mixing. It ia appropriately called a surface buoyant jet. Figure 10-4 illustrates the surface buoyant jet.

It can be reasoned that such a jet will spread laterally more rapidly than would be the case of either a buoyant surface plume or an unheated submerged jet separately, but it is not so clear how vertical spread will behave. In fact, the depth of a surface buoyant jet may increase, decrease, or remain approxi- mately constant depending on certain parameters which vary with distance along the jet. Likewise, temperature drop can be seen to be a result of both surface cooling and dilution effects due to entrainment; the net effect should be the sum of the two.

Not only are the jet properties influenced by density dif- ferences, but the flow establishment region may be entirely dif- ferent from that of a buoyant plume or a non-buoyant half-jet. In fact, the flow near the exit of a warm water canal has many similarities to varies flow in open channels. Some possibili- ties are sketched in the vertical plane of Fig. 10-1. There are corresponding possibilities in the horizontal plane. What oc- curs depends on whether depth control is exercised from upstream or downstream. Stefan (1970) and Koh (1971) discuss this subject.

The shape of the horizontal interface between the warm and ambient water and whether control is from upstream or downstream are determined largely by the water depth in the canal relative to the depth of the warm water in the receiving body far from the canal exit and by the value of the densimetric Froude number at the canal exit. The densimetric Froude number at the exit, Fr_{Do}, measure the relative importance of inertia and buoyancy forces.

$$Fr_{Do} = U_0/(g \frac{\Delta \varrho}{\varrho} H)^{\frac{1}{2}} \qquad (10-6)$$

Here, U_0 is the mean velocity in the canal, H is the water depth in the canal near its exit, $\Delta \varrho$ is the difference in density between the canal water and receiving water which is at density ϱ, and g is the acceleration due to gravity. For

$Fr_{Do} \lesssim 1$, control is downstream as shown by Harleman (1961), and the bottom of a warm water jet may appear as shown in Fig. 10-1b2 (with Fig. 10-1b1 as a limit). For $Fr_{Do} > 1$, control is upstream and the bottom flow may appear as in Fig. 10-1b1 or Fig. 10-1b3; far from the outlet, control will transfer to downstream--how far from the outlet depends on Fr_{Do}. Between the outlet and the position where downstream control takes over, there may be stable or unstable waves at the bottom of the warm water layer or even an inverted hydraulic jump. Other factors which may influence the transition from upstream to downstream control are the bottom slope (Fig. 10-1b3) and the angle the canal makes with the shoreline contours.

From these considerations of the outlet region it can be seen that only in some circumstances can a calculation be carried continuously from the canal into the receiving body of water. (Specifically, this can be done only when either $Fr_{Do} \lesssim 1$ or $Fr_{Do} \gg 1$.) The concept of a zone of flow establishment in the sense applied to non-buoyant jet flow is not valid for most heated water discharges at intermediate Fr_{Do}. In this region of surface buoyant jet establishment the mixing, entrainment, and jet thickening depend on too many variables to make for read ready calculation. Usually physical modeling is necessary, a subject to be discussed subsequently.

IV. Turbulent Mixing. If the receiving body of water is already in turbulent motion, as is the case with any large body of water, but especially rivers, it is possible that the ambient turbulent mixing will outweigh that produced by shear of the warm water layer, overcoming the static buoyancy of the layer. Such a situation is not likely to arise near a canal outlet, because even with discharge into a river, the shore restricts the river speed there, and the discharge velocity may be relatively large compared to the local river speed. However, farther away the ambient turbulence may become the predominant factor along with surface heat transfer. When this stage if reached in a river, the surface buoyant jet may disappear, the warm water being mixed almost uniformly throughout the depth of the flow as described by Wunderlich and Fan (1971), although lateral spread and surface cooling may still be detected. Computations for spreading can now be carried on as for a non-buoyant contaminant. This subject is discussed in a preceding chapter.

V. Regions of the Flow. Considereing the preceding discussions, it is convenient to divide the flow from a warm water canal into the following regions, beginning at the canal exit: outlet, near field, far field.

In the outlet region for $1 < Fr_{Do} \ll \infty$, the warm layer adjusts in thickness to accommodate the downstream thickness requirement. There is considerable instability present in the process, as previously indicated, and this results in immediate dilution. Stefan's and Hayakawa's (1972) theoretical calculation of dilution in the extreme case of a two-dimensional inter-

10-8

nal hydraulic jump shows that maximum dilution may not exceed the order of 100 percent. In the general three-dimensional case there will probably still be strong vertical dilution, although possibly less than in the two-dimensional case. Thus the near field may begin after considerable initial dilution whose magnitude may be difficult to specify. Also, the position at which the near field begins--the place where downstream control becomes effective--cannot readily be specified.

In some cases, the outlet and near field can be considered together; this is especially true if a hydraulic model is constructed for a specific site. It is also true even for an analytical model if $Fr_{Do} \lesssim 1$, as previously noted. (If $Fr_{Do} \gg 1$, the computation can also be carried out in the outlet region.) When the outlet is studied separately from the near field, the near field is unconstrained by the specific geometry of the outlet, and more general analytical results can be obtained than when the two are lumped together.

It is not necessary to make a clear demarcation between near field and far field. The far field is finally characterized by the preponderance of ambient turbulence in the mixing process. For small ambient turbulence in the far field may actually be a buoyant surface plume. In the far field, surface heat transfer is far more important than it is in the near field. Eventually, the far field disappears because of heat transfer to the atmosphere. In fact, the far field may merge with a pre-existing stratified flow in a large lake and its exact extent may never be known. Both the generalized near field and the far field lend themselves to analytical treatment, and the methods of calculation will be discussed presently.

Before proceeding further, it will be useful to enlarge the definition of densimetric Froude number introduced in Eq. (10-6). Beyond the outlet canal,

$$Fr_D = \overline{U}(s)[g\frac{\Delta \varrho(s)}{\varrho} h(s)]^{-\frac{1}{2}} \qquad (10-7)$$

where $\overline{U}$ is as defined in Eq. (10-2) and $\Delta \varrho$ and h are mean values of density difference and warm layer thickness at a distance s from the outlet. It can be seen that for very large values of Fr_D, the phenomenon can be expected to be largely jet-like (Fig. 10-3), since inertial forces predominate. For smaller values near unity, buoyant spread governs (Fig. 10-2). It is apparent that Fr_D varies along the jet as $\overline{U}$, h and $\Delta \varrho$ vary; it is an important parameter in further calculations.

It should be noted that mixing and entrainment at the horizontal interface depned more on local parameters than on the mean properties in Eq. (10-7). Local buoyancy and inertia forces at an interface can be written $g(\Delta \varrho/\Delta z)(\Delta z/\varrho)$ and $\Delta z(\Delta U/\Delta z)^2$ per unit mass, respectively, where Δz is the small vertical distance over which ϱ changes by $\Delta \varrho$ and U by ΔU. In dealing with local influences, it is customary to define the ratio of buoyancy to inertia as a Richardson number, Ri:

$$Ri = g(\partial \varrho / \partial z)/\varrho(\partial U/\partial z)^2 \qquad (10-8)$$

If Δz is identified with h and ΔU with the mean excess jet velocity U compared to ambient fluid at rest, a buld Richardson number is obtained which is identical with the inverse square of the densimetric Froude number. It can be reasoned that small Richardson numbers relate to jet entrainment conditions while large values near unity relate to buoyant spreading. These relations are substantiated by the experimental work of Ellison and Turner (1959).

Without analyzing any of the other factors that may be important, it is rather apparent that near a discharge canal outlet Fr_D is likely to be larger than unity (or Ri number considerably smaller) because of the large $\partial U/\partial z$ near the interface. Far away, the velocity and velocity gradient near the interface will have decreased due to spreading and Fr_D will have decreased (or Ri increased). Far field and near field are distinguished by the differences in entrainment and cooling processes associated with changes in Fr_D or Ri.

In separating the flow field into regions for analytical purposes, its essential continuity msut not be forgotten. Boundary conditions in the near field, such as depth of the warm water layer, are determined by the far field and initial conditions in the far field, such as surface temperature distribution, are determined by the near field.

VI. Ambient Currents. Figure 10-1 provides for a current in the receiving body whose speed and direction vary with distance from the outlet. The momentum of the entrained ambient fluid must be added vectorially to the initial momentum of the warm water layer to obtain the final speed and direction of the streamlines in the surface buoyant jet. With any significant current, the resulting streamlines will be far from parallel. However, in making computations, the entrained momentum is usually assumed to be distributed so that all the streamlines in the jet turn at the same rate. Thus the other streamlines are assumed to be parallel to each other and to the central streamline which marks the jet trajectory. The spread, entrainment, and cooling of the non-curved buoyant jet are applied to the jet moving along the curved trajectory to make the concept of Fig. 10-1 workable. This implies that the ambient current is not excessively large compared to U_c.

When the ambient current momentum is superimposed on that of the surface buoyant jet, the ration of inertial to buoyant forces changes and a new definition of densimetric Froude number is required. Stefan (1971) proposes

$$Fr_D{}^* = [\overline{U}(s) - V(x) \cos(\beta + \theta)][g\frac{\Delta \varrho(s)}{\varrho} \lambda_v h(s)]^{-\frac{1}{2}} \qquad (10-9)$$

An ambient current can influence a jet in other ways than through direct momentum exchange. As the current flows under the jet, separation eddies may form on the far side, creating a pressure force tending to further change jet momentum. This force is usually represented by a drag coefficient, much as though the jet were a solid body. Pressure forces of this nature also tend to destroy the symmetry of the jet. As long as the momentum of the entrained ambient fluid is properly accounted for, there is no interfacial shear as a separate force along the jet.

VII. Influence of Wind. Wind has several effects on a surface buoyant jet. First, through surface stress, it may produce currents through much of the depth of the receiving body. However, if the wind has blown for only a short time or has changed direction, its effect may be felt only on the surface, distorting the cross-sectional shape of the jet. In general, wind stress can be expected to penetrate the jet to the same depth as it penetrates the ambient fluid.

Second, wind increases the surface cooling rate, both directly by increasing k in Eq. (10-1) and indirectly by creating waves. The waves increase surface area and produce turbulence which increases ambient mixing and entrainment in the far field. Calculations without wind effects are always more conservative than those allowing for wind.

A third effect of wind is of interest. If wind stress deflects a surface layer toward a shoreline, the warm water may accumulate and be forced to greater depths there than elsewhere in the jet because of the static head. This will eventually produce a warm water counterflow under the original warm layer, thickening the entire layer and reducing its speed. Because of its reduced Fr_D, such a layer eventually becomes more stable than the original layer. Such transient phenomena as wind usually cause the far-field warm layer to be thicker than would otherwise be estimated, but also cause it to disappear more rapidly than calculated.

VIII. Solid Boundaries. Lateral boundaries may influence the rate of spread and the direction of a surface buoyant jet in both the near and the far field. Unsymmetrical boundaries within the field of motion of the jet produce differential pressures on the boundaries of the jet, with lower pressures toward the closer boundary. This will cause the jet to deflect toward the closer boundary. Symmetrical boundaries generally parallel to the jet may have an influence much like that in a two-dimensional diffuser, drawing the jet alternately to one boundary and then the other at irregular intervals in time and space. Meandering of the jet should increase the rate of entrainment. Additionally, the presence of a solid boundary would result in a reverse flow between the boundary and the jet, again increasing the entrainment.

Bottom boundaries sloping away from the outlet at a flat angle may influence the initial depth of the jet by constraining

the jet to cling to the bottom for some distance uptil it separates as illustrated in Fig. 10-1. Slopes steeper than about
1:3 probably have no effect of this kind. When the flow in a
surface buoyant jet is attached to a bottom slope, frictional
forces on the bottom must be accounted for in the jet momentum.
A discharge canal crossing a flat beach at an angle to the beach
contours could produce a very unsymmetrical jet because of the
varying separation across the canal bottom. The flow from such
an outlet region would be very difficult to calculate. Bottom
slopes are not of much consequence farther out in the near
field or in the far field.

IX. Winter Versus Summer Conditions. It has been tacitly
assumed so far that ambient temperatures are well above the
freezing point of water, the usual case of interest. There are,
however, interesting cooling water discharge problems that occur
in ice-covered lakes and rivers during winter. It should be
recognized that water attains its maximum density near $39^{O}F$,
whereas water in contact with ice is near $32^{O}F$ and is lighter
than the warmer water on which it floats.

In winter, condenser cooling water may be returned to the
source at near $60^{O}F$. Since the corresponding density is considerably less than that of water near $32^{O}F$, there will be an
initial surface buoyant jet, more than likely approaching the
buoyant plume condition because of the large density difference.
This will be accompanied by an open water area. However, in
cooling, the jet will eventually reach temperatures near $39^{O}F$,
attaining densities greater than those of the water adjacent to
the surrounding ice. At this point the jet will dive under the
ice, leaving an insulating water layer near $32^{O}F$ above it. The
place of diving can be considered the end of the near field in
an ice-covered situation. The open area is relatively small
compared to the summer extent of the near field because of the
much greater rate of surface heat transfer. This is illustrated
in a paper by Carlsson (1970).

In its plunge beneath the surface, the warm water entrains
cold water in a manner similar to that of a rising warm water
jet from a submerged outlet in summer. The mixed water finds
its new level in accordance with its temperature and forms the
far field. The far field is much different from that found
under summer conditions, since it is no longer in contact with
the atmosphere. It loses heat very slowly by conduction through
the ice and bottom, but cools mostly by mixing and entrainment
of adjacent fluid. The warm water layer flows as a bottom or
intermediate density current and can be expected to be detectable
at much greater distances from the canal outlet than under summer conditions. After sufficient mixing, it is possible for the
warm water to have distributed itself over the depth of the
water body and weakened the ice far from the outlet canal.

Calculation in the far field of a river during winter can
be based on available knowledge about submerged jets in a coflowing stream as outlined in Abramovich (1963). On a lake, a

static stratified layer will form. This reasoning also applies when the water surface does not freeze, but its temperature is less than 39°F.

Calculations in the Near Field.

I. Basic Assumptions. The calculation of a surface buoyant jet involves solving the equations of conservation of mass, momentum, and thermal energy as outlined in Schlicting (1968), for example, using appropriate boundary conditions. Rather than solving the equations for all points in the flow field, it is feasible to solve them by integrating mass, momentum, and heat flow through successive cross sections, finding the variation of the several integrals with distance from the outlet. The following assumptions facilitate the calculation (see Fig. 10-1):

A. The flow is mean steady.

B. Density is determined by temperature, the relation being known, and density enters the equations only through its effect on buoyancy. Hence, the kinematic continuity equation replaces mass conservation.

C. The warm water flow is entrapped in the ambient current so that the spread, entrainment, and cooling of the non-curved buoyant jet can be superimposed on the curved trajectory as explained in Part I of the preceding section. Excess velocity $U(s,n,z)$ and temperature $T(s,n,z)$ can be defined as that velocity and that temperature which would exist if there were zero ambient current, uniform ambient temperature, and no curvature of the trajectory.

D. The profiles of velocity excess made dimensionless with $U_c(s)$ are similar with s and symmetrical about n = 0. (They are not necessarily related to the velocity profiles in the canal.) This is not a very good assumption with cross current and wind, but it must be accepted in order to make calculation possible with reasonable effort.

E. The profiles of temperature excess made dimensionless with $T_c(s)$ are similar with s and symmetrical about n = 0. Again, this is not a particularly good assumption.

F. The jet cross-sectional shapes are similar with s and symmetrical about n = 0, although the aspect ratio may change.

G. The jet grows by entrainment of ambient fluid. Entrainment is governed by proportionality between the entrainment velocity normal to the jet and the centerline velocity.

H. Similarity is not altered by external forces such as those due to wind or bottom friction.

After profile shapes have been selected to represent the similarity assumptions, numerical values for the integrals of continuity, momentum, and heat flow can be calculated once and for all. These integrals are of the form

$$I_1 = U_c bh \int_{-1}^{+1} \int_{-1}^{0} \frac{U(s,n,z)}{U_c} \, d\!\left(\frac{z}{h}\right) d\!\left(\frac{n}{b}\right) \qquad (10\text{-}10)$$

10-13

$$I_2 = U_c{}^2 bh \int_{-1}^{+1} \int_{-1}^{0} \frac{U^2(s,n,z)}{U_c{}^2} \, d(\frac{z}{h}) \, d(\frac{n}{b}) \qquad (10\text{-}11)$$

$$I_3 = U_c T_c \lambda b \lambda_v h \int_{-1}^{+1} \int_{-1}^{0} \frac{U(s,n,z)}{U_c} \frac{T(s,n,z)}{T_c} \, d(\frac{z}{\lambda_v h}) \, d(\frac{n}{\lambda b}) \qquad (10\text{-}12)$$

The integrals enter the equations of conservation with the coefficients U_c, T_c, b, and h, all of which depend only on s. Thus, there is a set of three equations for four unknowns. The fourth unknown involves an equation or equations for spreading rate or entrainment rate and for change in aspect ratio of the jet cross section. Solution of these auxiliary equations brings additional terms into the conservation equations for entrained fluid, entrained momentum, and dilution of heat.

There are also boundary conditions of various kinds which need to be introduced into the equations through terms in addition to I_1, I_2, and I_3. In the heat conservation equation, a term must be included for surface heat transfer. In the momentum integral equation, terms representing current drag, wind stress on the surface, bottom shear where the jet is attached to the bottom, and gravitational forces associated with the sloping water surface produced by variable buoyancy need to be considered. Usually there are two momentum equations--one in the jet direction and one normal to it tending to deflect the jet.

The difficulty in using these equations to pass from the canal exit to the near field is that all of the similarity functions may change discontinuously when s passes through the outlet region.

II. Some Illustrative Computational Results. It is proposed to summarize three sets of calculations based on the above plan and assumptions: those of Stolzenbach and Harleman (1971), Stefan (1971), and Motz and Benedict (1970,1972). Others have established calculation methods, but these are generally more restricted in one or more aspects than the three referred to. Hayashi and Shuto (1967), already referred to, limit their analysis to buoyant plumes. Koh (1971) limits his to two dimensions with finite width, eliminating lateral spread. Wada (1969) does not assume universal similar profiles, but makes other assumptions for eddy viscosity and mixing coefficients that permit numerical calculation of the equations. All of these, and others, produce interesting insights in their own right, but do not lead to directly useful general computational procedures.

Stolzenbach and Harleman (1971): The computation begins with the non-buoyant jet case in which the similarity profiles, jet shape, and basic entrainment parameters are established. The velocity and temperature profiles are taken in power law form.

$$U(s,n,z) = U_c(s) \left[1 - (\frac{n}{b})^{\frac{3}{2}}\right]^2 \left[1 - (\frac{-z}{h})^{\frac{3}{2}}\right]^2 \qquad (10\text{-}13)$$

$$T(s,n,z) = T_c(s) \left[1 - (\frac{n}{b})^{\frac{3}{2}}\right] \left[1 - (\frac{-z}{h})^{\frac{3}{2}}\right] \qquad (10\text{-}14)$$

The smaller power on the temperature profile assumes that the more rapid spread of heat than of momentum found in the non-buoyant case also applies to the buoyant case. The jet shape is assumed to be rectangular, but the width b and the depth h grow at different rates depending on horizontal and vertical entrainment rates. Horizontal entrainment is taken from the non-buoyant spread, Eq. (10-4), with $\alpha = 0.22$. Vertical entrainment is obtained from the horizontal value using a semi-empirical relation established from the arguments of Phillips (1966) and the data of Ellison and Turner (1959). It is essentially

$$\alpha_z = \alpha \exp\left[-\frac{5.0}{Fr_D^2}\right] \qquad (10\text{-}15)$$

where α_z is the vertical spread coefficient and Fr_D is as given in Eq. (10-7). Observe that Eq. (10-15) yields zero vertical entrainment for $Fr_D \to 0$ and equal horizontal and vertical entrainment for $Fr_D \to \infty$ (the non-buoyant jet case).

The calculation proceeds from the given outlet cross section in steps in s assuming a continuous stepwise change in centerline values of velocity and temperature and of cross-sectional depth and width. The width and depth may grow at different rates as governed by Eq. (10-15). The integration in each cross section is carried out in four parts to permit the inclusion of a flow establishment region like that occurring in non-buoyant jets. The parts are the core, the fully developed turbulent part, and the transition parts with part core and part fully developed turbulence in the horizontal and vertical planes. In the establishment region, although the total spread is taken from the core and is calculated from continuity and momentum. Hence, the spread of the jet is not as rapid in this region as in the fully developed region farther downstream.

Calculations are carried out without and with cross currents (variable with x) and without and with bottom slopes following the canal exit. No current drag or wind shear is included, but accelerative forces due to water surface slope are accounted for. Calculations are reported for various initial aspect ratio channels from nearly square to very deep.

The calculations are compared with the authors' laboratory experimental results for ranges in $s/(BH)^{1/2}$ between zero and 50 to 100. Comparisons are made principally for $T_c(s)/T_0$ and $h/(BH)^{1/2}$, but there are also some for $b/(BH)^{1/2}$. In the experiments, h and b are obtained from temperature measurements; no velocity measurements were made. The authors record the fact that no constants used in the calculations had to be evaluated from the data--they were all taken from previous basic experiments by others. Comparisons for temperature are fair for most cases. As is pointed out by the authors, surface heat transfer was unimportant in the cooling process compared to dilution for the distances to which these computations were carried. Comparisons for depth were generally poor to close to the outlet, but tended to improve farther away. The poor showing near the outlet is believed to be associated with the transition from upstream to downstream control. Neglect of this transition makes the early entrainment too small and subsequent entrainment too large.

Stefan (1971): Stefan's method of calculation is not very different in principle from that of Stolzenbach and Harleman. Similarity profiles are of Gaussian form,

$$U(s,n,z) = U_c(s) \exp\left[-\frac{1}{2}\left(\frac{n}{b}\right)^2\right] \exp\left[-\frac{1}{2}\left(\frac{-z}{h}\right)^2\right] \quad (10\text{-}16)$$

$$T(s,n,z) = T_c(s) \exp\left[-\frac{1}{2}\left(\frac{n}{\lambda b}\right)^2\right] \exp\left[-\frac{1}{2}\left(\frac{-z}{\lambda_v h}\right)^2\right] \quad (10\text{-}17)$$

Here, also, the temperature profile is expected to spread faster than the velocity and the ralative rate is controlled by $\lambda > 1$. Stefan suggests $\lambda_v = \lambda = 1.05$ for the buoyant jet. The jet shape is taken as elliptical with semiaxes b and h which grow at different rates depending on entrainment and spread. For calculation and measurment purposes, Stefan assigns to the width and depth in Eqs. (10-10) through (10-12) the values 3b and 3h, three standard deviations of the profiles. Stefan takes the horizontal entrainment velocity as $K_H U_c$ with $K_H = 0.059$ from earlier work on non-buoyant jets. He then draws on the experiments of Ellison and Turner (1959) to obtain a factor by which the horizontal entrainment velocity is to be multiplied to obtain vertical entrainment velocity. This is

$$K_V/K_H = 1.0 - 1.33 \log(6.32/Fr_D^*) \quad (10\text{-}18)$$

where Fr_D^* is as given by Eq. (10-9). The relation is such that for $Fr_D^* \approx 6.3$, the vertical and horizontal entrainments are equal (non-buoyant jet) and for $Fr_D^* = 1.1$, the vertical entrainment is completely suppressed (buoyant surface plume).

The width and depth calculations are dependent on buoyant spread as well as on entrainment. Stefan calculates the growth in b due to spread as

$$\left.\frac{db}{ds}\right|_{\text{Buoyancy}} = C/Fr_D \quad (10\text{-}19)$$

and calculates the shrinkage in h so as to just maintain the calculated entrainment rate at each cross ection,

$$\left.\frac{dh}{ds}\right|_{Buoyancy} \simeq -\frac{h}{b}\left.\frac{db}{ds}\right|_{Buoyancy} \qquad (10\text{-}20)$$

Thus the elliptical cross section spreads faster in width than in depth. Numerical values for C are not available from previous research.

Stefan's calculations proceed from the exit cross section in steps in s about equal to H, assuming continuous stepwise changes in profiles and cross-sectional shape with s. No flow establishment zone is provided for, the flow being fully developed turbulent throughout the jet. Calculations are carried out without and with uniform cross flow and wind stress. The wind force term in the momentum equation is obtained by multiplying the wind shear stress (from an empirical formula) by the surface area between cross sections: thus the effect is spread uniformly over the depth of the jet. Current drag and buoyancy forces due to water surface slope are also accounted for. No provision is made for a bottom slope at the canal exit.

Sample calculations are carried out in the report for two canal shapes, one semicircular and the other with the horizontal axis four times the depth. There were two initial densimetric Froude numbers, 3.75 and 15.0. The calculations show the effects of wind or cross currents on trajectory shape, entrainment, centerline temperature decay, and depth of the jet. Some comparisons were made with his own laboratory experiments conducted without cross currents or wind: the experiments carried from the exit to $s/(BH)^{1/2} \simeq 42\text{-}1/2$. In the calculations, the constant C which appears in Eq. (10-19) is taken from the experimental data: its value if found to lie between 1.25 and 2.5, the former value arising from velocity spread measurements and the latter from visual observation of dyed warm layers. Stefan's temperature predictions are inferior to those of Stolzenbach and Harleman: Stefan attributes his difficulties to failure to provide for a flow establishment zone in the calculations and to the accumulation of heat in the receiving tank during some of the experimental runs. Depth measurements scatter about the predicted values, but the results are probably comparable to those of Stolzenbach and Harleman. Stefan measured both temperature and velocity profiles and verified that the Gaussian shape was acceptable for calculation and that λ_v was of order unity.

Motz and Benedict (1970, 1972): The calculation method used by Motz and Benedict differs in perhaps three significant ways from those of Stolzenbach and Harleman and of Stefan. First, they assume no vertical entrainment, so that the jet spreads only horizontally. This corresponds to Stefan's $Fr_D^* \lesssim 1.1$ in Eq. (10-9). Second, they do not attempt a

10-17

continuous calculation from the canal exit into the near field; rather, the calculation starts from an artificial origin related to the real canal by laboratory empirical data. And third, entrainment and drag due to ambient currents are to be obtained from new experiments rather than from previous work on non-buoyant jets and on entrainment related to Richardson number. Otherwise, this calculation method depends on the same assumptions as the others.

Gaussian profiles are used in the horizontal plane, the velocity and temperature excess profiles being identical. Vertical velocity and temperature profiles are flat over the depth of the jet, and velocities and temperatures are ambient below the jet. The depth remains constant throughout due to the absence of vertical entrainment. Hence the cross section is rectangular. Horizontal spread is determined by proportionality between the entrainment velocity and the excess centerline velocity, the proportionality being constant throughout the length of the jet. (This is the K_H of Stefan.) The proportionality constant is not assigned in advance, however.

As in the other models, calculation proceeds stepwise in s according to a numberical technique after the continuity, integral momentum, and integral thermal energy equations have been written in each cross section. Aside from the momentum entrained by lateral mixing with the ambient current, the only external force term in the momentum equations is the drag of the cross current; this is introduced through a drag coefficient C_D to be evaluated from experimental data. Because vertical entrainment in absent, there should probably be an interfacial shear term at the bottom of the jet, but this is not provided for; nor are wind effects or acceleration due to water slope accounted for. Bottom slope effects need not be included, since the calculation begins at some distance from the canal exit. The heat conservation equation neglects surface heat transfer.

Motz and Benedict use laboratory experiments to determine the transfer of control from upstream to downstream. They take the end of the zone of flow establishemnt as the farthest distance from the canal exit at which $T_c = T_0$. They begin by assuming a uniform temperature profile at the canal exit which transforms to the Gaussian similarity profile; this makes b(0)= 1.6 B to satisfy conservation of heat (with no entrainment or heat loss). Laboratory data then lead to empirical curves which can be written

$$s_E/b(0) \simeq 0.6 \ (V/U_0)^{-0.766} \qquad (10\text{-}21)$$

$$\theta(0)/\delta \simeq 0.9 - 0.7 \ V/U_0 \qquad (10\text{-}22)$$

where s_E is the length of the establishment zone between the canal exit and s = 0 and the other quantities are as defined in Fig. 10-1. The laboratory experiments were also used to calculate values of K_H and C_D, but consistent results could not be obtained. However, it was shown that considerable latitude is permissible in selecting these constants. Temperature profiles measured in the laboratory conformed to the Gaussian profiles in the horizontal plane, while vertical entrainment was an order of magnitude less than the horizontal, assumed.

Motz and Benedict applied their calculation method to some field measurements in rivers in which temperatures were read at several cross sections and for which canal input flow quantity, direction, and temperature were known. Equations (10-21) and (10-22) were used to establish the origin for calculations, while the field measurements were used to obtain K_H and C_D. Then the jet spread and temperature decay were calculated. For most of the data, laboratory and field, K_H is in the range 0.13 to 0.49; this is considerably larger than the value of 0.059 used by Stefan, but in the Motz and Benedict work there is a broad interfacial area in which no entrainment is acknowledged, while Stefan considered entrainment over the entire perimenter. One field experiment did yield $K_H = 0.04$. C_D values from the field work ranged from 0.3 to 0.6, but in the laboratory they ranged up to 3.9. K_H and C_D are related to each other, and errors in one lead to errors in the other.

III. Summary of the Near Field Calculations. The preceding three claculation models indicate that assumptions A through H listed earlier probably lead to useful procedures for computation of surface buoyant jets. The exact assumptions for profile shapes and jet cross section are not important. However, calculations through the transition region where flow control passes from upstream to downstream, called the flow establishment region by Motz and Benedict, are acceptable only in special circumstances. This region needs further laboratory study for the general three-dimensional case. One question that might be asked is whether the Motz and Benedict definition of the establishment zone as extending as far as $T_c = T_0$ is adequate. Laboratory models of specific sites will probably always be desirable in the outfall region.

Beyond the flow establishment region, any of the models can be used with some success. The Motz and Benedict model, however, is limited to cases in which $Fr_D^* \geq 1.1$, Eq. (10-9), since vertical entrainment is neglected. Also, the neglect of accelerative forces produced by the sloping water surface leaves something to be desired in that model. The Stefan model presumably permits evaluation of the effect of wind, but no comparisons were made with experiments. None of the authors made calculations to compare with the experimental data obtained by the other authors. The main need for further research on the fully developed surface buoyant jet is associated with numerical values for measuring the entrainment process.

Calculations in the Far Field. The far field is the continuation of the surface warm water layer from the near field. At this stage, the layer has reached the point of nearly constant thickness and small, slowly-changing temperature and velocity excesses as shown by the near field computations. The same basic equations apply as in the near field, with the results from the near field calculations forming the starting conditions for the far field. (Also, it should be noted, the far field thickness has to be fed back to the near field to locate the transition point from upstream to downstream control.)

One major difference in the far field, as already noted, is that ambient turbulence may be as important as or more important than the jet-generated shear turbulence. Ambient turbulence, therefore, contributes to horizontal spread of the warm water layer, and the spread rate will be different, and will be calculated by a different process, then in the near field. On the other hand, vertical entrainment is largely suppressed in the far field because the Richardson number near the interface is of order unity. Thus the equation of continuity will contain different terms in the far field than in the near field. The momentum and heat transport equations will be similar to the earlier versions, the momentum change due to entrainment now being modified by the altered entrainment rates. In the heat transport equation, surface heat transfer can no longer be neglected, since this is, after all, the ultimate mode of dispersal for the excess heat.

The entrainment attributable to ambient turbulence can be calculated from the kinematic eddy viscosity and turbulent Prandtl number of the ambient water, assuming that turbulent transfer is by a gradient process. For each specific site these quantities would have to be measured by means of heat or dye dispersion tests conducted in the field; universal values cannot be assigned. Furthermore, the measured values will vary with wind, especially, and other factors. As an alternative to conducting dispersion tests, it would be possible to measure turbulent mean transfer properties directly with a hot-film anemometer or other electronic device; however, this would entail much more tedious work than dispersion tests. In any event, using the above field data, horizontal entrainment can be calculated by recourse to the basic non-buoyant jet equations as outlined by Abramovich (1963). Bansal (1971) can be referred to for calculations of dispersion coefficients in rivers, for example.

If it is further assumed that there is no vertical entrainment, as already proposed, vertical profiles in the far field can be taken as flat; that is, there is assumed to be no vertical variation of temperature or velocity from the surface value down to the interface.

Using the above procedures and retaining the similarity assumption, the calculation of the far field becomes two-dimensional much as in Motz and Benedict (1970) except that surface heat transfer must be accounted for. In fact, since Motz and Benedict determined entrainment rates from field data, they may very well have incorporated ambient turbulent entrainment into their reported results.

There are no recorded calculations of far field behavior in the literature, nor are the limits of the far field predictable, since the velocity and temperature excesses decay exponentially. The most to be expected of far field calculations might be predictions of warm layer thickness and general plots of isotherms indicating the surface area that might experience $1^{\circ}F$, $2^{\circ}F$, etc., temperature rises.

10.3 HYDRAULIC MODELING

Modeling. A physical phenomenon whose details cannot be observed directly can be usefully studied by means of models. The buoyant surface jet is such a phenomenon. Models are also useful because they permit experiments to be conducted before large sums of money are committed to prototype construction and, especially, because the input parameters in a model can be changed at will, whereas to make the same observations in the prototype under natural conditions, long periods of waiting would be required to obtain a significant range of input conditions.

In Part 10-2, some numerical mathematical models were examined. In this part, analog modeling in the form of hydraulic or physical modeling is to be considered. An analog model solves a set of equations which approximately describe the basic phenomenon by reference ot another physical occurance whose performance is approximately described by the same set of equations, but which is more readily accessible than the original. In the case of a hydraulic model of a surface buoyant jet, the equations to be solved are essentially those that were established for numerical solution in Part 10-2.

Hydraulic modeling has been applied to warm water discharge from thermal power plants since the early 1950's. It was recognized from the beginning that modeling thermal discharges presented some new problems in hydraulic modeling and required reconsideration of some old ones. One of the latter was the problem of distortion of horizontal relative to vertical scale. Some of the former involved the effect of stratification on model-prototype relations and the modeling of heat transfer at the air-water interface. Unfortunately, not all the rules are well established yet because of the difficulty in obtaining prototype data that are applicable to comparison with model predictions. A similar problem exists, of course, with respect to mathematical modeling.

Hydraulic modeling is especially useful in studying the outlet region of a heated surface discharge, because mathematical modeling generally cannot be readily applied there. Approximations as to the extent of the outlet region and the dilution occurring therein can be obtained from a hydraulic model. Motz and Benedict (1970, 1972), whose work was reviewed

in Part 10-2, did exactly this. A hydraulic model is also useful where lateral or bottom boundaries occur in other regions
of the flow from a warm water canal; a mathematical model is
too difficult to operate in those circumstances.

Even in situations in which mathematical models can be
applied with confidence, it is sometimes desirable to operate
a hydraulic model. For one thing, the hydraulic model makes the
effects of changing certain parameters directly visible. This
is useful to both the scientist who is studying physical principles and to the layman who needs to see in very concrete form
the proposal which he is being asked to accept. A hydraulic
model may also be useful for producing estimates of certain
parameters which are required in a mathematical model, such as
the spread of warm water due to density differences. Hydraulic
modeling of the far field is difficult, however, because the
far field usually encompasses such large areas that vertical
exaggeration or distortion of the model scale is necessary, and
this involves some incompatible conditions. Distortion is not
required under similar circumstances in a mathematical model.

At the present state of knowledge it is probably useful to
study a proposed warm water discharge from a surface canal using
a hydraulic model for the outlet region and mathematical models
of the type described in Part 10-2 for the near and far fields.
The hydraulic outlet model can be constructed at undistorted
scale; this makes possible proper representation of both turbulent jet entrainment and buoyant spread while maintaining
geometrical similarity to the prototype. If the available area
is large enough, part or all of the near field can also be contained in the hydraulic model. However, adequate model scale
should not be sacrificed to include too much of the region
beyond the outlet, since the near field can frequently be
treated as well by a mathematical model. Because hydraulic
modeling of the far field involves scale distortion, it should
be avoided if possible. However, if the far field (or the near
field) contains complicated boundaries, or perhaps a cold water
intake, a hydraulic model may be necessary.

Silberman and Stefan (1970) have prepared a comprehensive
review on the subject of hydraulic modeling of heat dispersion
in large lakes.

Hydraulic Modeling Laws. The laws of modeling can be established by writing the basic equations of continuity, momentum,
and heat transport in dimensionless form for both the warm
layer and the ambient fluid. If the canal depth H and its mean
velocity U_0 are chosen as reference length and velocity and the
initial density difference $\Delta\varrho/\varrho|_0$ as reference density differ-
ence, the force and stress terms in the equations will have
coefficients in the form of a densimetric Froude number, a
Reynolds number, and other dimensionless force ratios depending
on which forces are included in the basic equations. To assure
that the model is operating in the same manner as the prototype,
the dimensionless equations should be the same for both. If

10-22

the model is made geometrically similar to the prototype, all fixed lengths will be the same in model and prototype when referred to the reference length; that is,

$$H_m/H_p = H_r; \quad B_m/B_p = H_r \qquad (10\text{-}23)$$

where the subscripts m and p refer to model and prototype, respectively, and subscript r refers to the ratio of model to prototype quantities. The only further requirement for similarity is that all the dimensionless force coefficients be equal in the two realizations. Thus, considereing the initial densimetric Froude number defined in Eq. (10-6),

$$\frac{U_{o,m}}{U_{o,p}} = U_r = \sqrt{\frac{\Delta Q/Q|_{o,m}H_m}{\Delta Q/Q|_{o,p}H_p}} = \left(\left.\frac{\Delta Q}{Q}\right|_r H_r\right)^{\frac{1}{2}} \qquad (10\text{-}24)$$

It is necessary to include the gravitational force in the equations of motion near the outlet, especially, because of the free surface slope. This introduces the ordinary Froude number, Fr, and the requirement that it be the same in model and prototype, so that

$$Fr = U_o/\sqrt{g\,H_o} \quad \text{and} \quad U_r = \sqrt{H_r} \qquad (10\text{-}25)$$

assuming that the gravitational constant is the same in model and prototype. To satisfy both Eq. (10-24) and Eq. (10-25),

$$\left.\frac{\Delta Q}{Q}\right|_r = 1 \qquad (10\text{-}26)$$

One of the dimensionless force coefficients that is prominent in the equations is the Reynolds number, $U_o H/\nu$, where is the kinematic viscosity of the fluid. Not much range in is available in the fluids which could be used in a hydraulic model, so water is usually used for its ready availability. Thus, if the density differences are kept reasonably small in the model, Eq.s (10-23) and (10-24) do not permit equality of Reynolds numbers to be obtained. It is generally believed that Reynolds number effects can be avoided by making the model Reynolds number large enough that the model surface buoyant jet will be everywhere turbulent as in the prototype. For a wide canal,

$$Re = U_o H/\nu > 600 \qquad (10\text{-}27a)$$

could meet this requirement. Perhaps a better criterion would be the congruency relation for lock exchange flow proposed by Frazer, et al. (1968). This would result in

10-23

$$(g \, \frac{\Delta Q}{Q})^{\frac{1}{2}} H^{\frac{5}{2}} (L_o \nu)^{-1} > 150 \qquad (10\text{-}27\text{b})$$

where L_0 would be the length of the outlet region in the case of an outlet model. With Eq. (10-6), this can be written

$$Re = U_o H/\nu > 150 \, \frac{L_o}{H} \, Fr_{D,o} \qquad (10\text{-}27\text{c})$$

The distance L_0 depends on $Fr_{D,o}$ and the depth of the warm water layer downstream; examination of the model experimental results reviewed in Part 10-2 suggests, very roughly, $L_0/(BH)^{1/2} < 20$. Equation (10-27c) would usually require a larger Reynolds number than Eq. (10-27a).

Another force that might appear in the equations is that due to surface tension, γ. This is measured by a Weber number, $We = U_0(\varrho H/\gamma)^{1/2}$; it is always negligible in the prototype and can readily be made negligible in the model by avoiding too small a model scale.

In the outlet region, such quantities as surface heat transfer and ambient turbulence of the receiving body can be safely neglected. The far field, where they are important, will be dealt with later. To assure the same relation between vertical and horizontal entrainment in model and prototype, the local Richardson numbers, Eq. (10-8), must be the same everywhere. As shown in Part 10-2, this is equivalent to having the same Fr_D and hence the same $Fr_{D,o}$, and is already provided for in Eq. (10-24). Since horizontal spread may be the result of buoyancy as well as entrainment, it is necessary to write

$$\frac{db}{ds} = \left.\frac{db}{ds}\right|_{\text{Entrain.}} + \left.\frac{db}{ds}\right|_{\text{Buoyancy}} = \alpha + \frac{C}{Fr_D} \qquad (10\text{-}28\text{a})$$

according to Eqs. (10-4) and (10-19). Since α and C are presumably universal and Fr_D is the same in model and prototype, horizontal spread will be the same in both. Similarly,

$$\frac{dh}{ds} = \left.\frac{dh}{ds}\right|_{\text{Entrain.}} + \left.\frac{dh}{ds}\right|_{\text{Buoyancy}} = \alpha\left(\frac{K_V}{K_H}\right)^{\frac{1}{2}} - \frac{C}{Fr_D} \frac{h}{b} \qquad (10\text{-}28\text{b})$$

using Eq. (10-20) and the argument leading to Eq. (10-18). Since K_V/K_H is determined by Fr_D from Eq. (10-18), vertical spread will also be the same in model and prototype.

Another scale ratio that may be important in the outlet region involves the bottom roughness in a canal which runs onto a sloping beach as shown in Fig. 10-1b3. A turbulent Reynolds number alone will not insure the correct point of separation in the model. It is not possible to state rules governing the roughness in this case. (It is simpler to model a prototype with a steep slope, because the place of separation is not a variable.)

As was pointed out in Part 10-2, the depth of the end of the outlet region cannot be established by studying the outlet region, but must come from solution of the remainder of the near field. An outlet model will give as many different results as there are different depths imposed at its end. With warm layer thickness at the end of the outlet model assigned, satisfaction of Eqs. (10-23) through (10-27) will generally lead to satis- factory modeling of an outlet region.

The near field region of a surface buoyant jet can be modeled by the same laws as the outlet region if ambient turbu- lence and surface heat transfer can still be ignored. In fact, since the water surface slope is likely to be relatively unim- portant in the near field, the condition given by Eq. (10-25) and hence Eq. (10-26) can be neglected; the $\Delta Q/Q$ ratio then becomes a free parameter. However, care must be exercised not to increase $\Delta Q/Q$ so much by increasing temperature that surface heat transfer does become important in the model. The depth at the end of a near field model must come from the far field and cannot be determined from the model alone. The near field may extend from one thousand to several thousand feet from the outfall.

If ambient turbulence is to be accounted for and is attrib- utable to river flow, it can be represented by making the water surface slope in the model river the same as in the prototype. Using a friction factor f to define hydraulic gradient,

$$S = \frac{H_L}{L} = \frac{f}{4R_H} \frac{\overline{V}^2}{2g} \; ; \quad \frac{S_m}{S_p} = S_r = f_r \frac{\overline{V}_r^2}{H_r} \qquad (10\text{-}29a)$$

where H_L is the head loss over a unit of flow length L, R_H is the hydraulic radius of the river channel, and $\overline{V}$ is the mean velocity in the river. Since river flow is generally modeled by the Froude law, Eq. (10-25) can be used in Eq. (10-29a) to obtain

$$f_r = 1 \qquad (10\text{-}29b)$$

Lake turbulence would be difficult to model. It is believed that it can be ignored in a near field model in the absence of strong waves or currents, but this subject is presently under investigation.

Surface heat transfer in the dimensionless thermal energy equation appears in the form of a Stanton number which can be written

$$St = \frac{qLb}{Qc_p \, T \, \overline{U} \, hb} \qquad (10\text{-}30)$$

where L is a unit of length in the flow direction. Using Eq. (10-1) for q and specifying identical Stanton numbers in model and prototype, Eq. (10-30) leads to

$$k_r(T - T_e)_r L_r = U_r T_r H_r \qquad (10\text{-}31a)$$

where $k_r = k_m/k_p$ and so on for the other ratios. Using Eq. (10-24), this can be written

$$k_r \frac{(T - T_e)_r}{T_r} = (\frac{\Delta \varrho}{\varrho})_r^{\frac{1}{2}} \frac{H_r^{\frac{3}{2}}}{L_r} \qquad (10\text{-}31b)$$

If $L_r = H_r$, $(\Delta o/o)_r = 1$, and T_0 is the same in model and prototype (as it frequently is), the equation reduces simply to

$$\Delta T_{e_r} k_r = (H_r)^{1/2} \qquad (10\text{-}31c)$$

where $\Delta T_{e_r} = (T - T_e)_m/(T - T_e)_p$. In this case the atmosphere above the model has to be manipulated to satisfy Eq. (10-31c) once H is chosen. It is apparent that there is more danger of having too much heat transfer from a model water surface than too little.

If it is necessary to study the far field in a hydraulic model, an undistorted model is usually out of the question because of the large surface area that has to be represented. The far field may extend several miles from the outfall. In that event, Eq. (10-23) must be relaxed, foregoing complete geometric similarity. In the dimensionless equations H/B = H/L will now appear, and in comparing model and prototype the ratios $H_r/B_r = H_r/L_r > 1$ occur and are called the distortion. The distortion should be held to a minimum, certainly not more than 10. If the model is to be useful, it is still necessary to represent spread of the warm water, ambient turbulence, and surface heat transfer as nearly correctly as possible. This requires satisfaction of Eqs. (10-24) and (10-31b) as well as an ambient turbulence condition like Eq. (10-29b) for a river. It is very difficult to model the ambient turbulence correctly in a lake, and even Eq. (10-29b) leaves something to be desired in a river model, because the spectrum of turbulence really determines the transfer properties, and this is impossible to reproduce at small scale. What can be done in a lake model is to make the kinematic eddy viscosity and turbulent Prandtl number in the model correspond as nearly as possible to measured or estimated prototype values. The model flows whould be nonitored using hot film or equipment with similar capabilities.

In a far field model, the minimum depth of the warm water layer would be determined by the Reynolds number as expressed, perhaps, by Eq. (10-27b) with h replacing H and a length from the inlet of the model to the beginning of the far field replacing L_0; the ratio $\Delta o/o$ would be measured at the beginning of the far field. Examination of Eqs. (10-28a) and (10-28b) shows that only horizontal spread could be satisfactorily modeled in a distorted model. However, in view of the near uniform thickness of the far field warm water layer, this is probably all that would be required. If the distorted model has the same T_0 and ambient temperature as the prototype, so that Eq. (10-26) is satisfied, Eq. (10-31b) becomes

$$\Delta T_{e_r} k_r = H_r^{3/2} / L_r \qquad (10\text{-}31d)$$

and the model atmosphere needs to be manipulated to meet this condition. It might be noted that for a vertical scale of 1:100 and a distortion of 10, the ratio given by Eq. (10-31d) is unity.

If the boundaries in a wide river are being modeled, the head loss past each section of the boundary--an island, for example--should be modeled according to the vertical scale. Using the friction law expressed in Eq. (10-29a), the modeling requirement becomes

$$f_r L_r = 1 \qquad (10\text{-}29c)$$

Such modeling does not guarantee correct turbulence, however, as was indicated above.

If Eqs. (10-24), (10-26), and (10-31d) are satisfied and suitable ambient turbulence is established, a distorted model of the far field can be used to study spread and cooling of the warm water layer.

Hydraulic Modeling Techniques. One parameter which is involved in the modeling of surface buoyant jets, but not in modeling non-buoyant flows is the ratio $\Delta o/o$. Even though the value of this ratio in a warm water canal dishcarge is established by the initial temperature excess in the canal, it need not be so established in a model; salinity is also sometimes used for the purpose. In a saline model, fresh water represents the warm water inflow and saline water the ambient receiving water. (Any other combination of miscible light and heavy fluids, such as helium and air, could be used, but most of the others are not very practical.)

One advantage of using salinity is that it can be determined from conductivity, which has a more nearly linear variation with density than does temperature. On the other hand, a conductivity probe is a somewhat more complicated device to build and operate than the simple thermocouple or thermistor probe which is commercially available for temperature measurement; also, when temperature is used it is possible to acquire surface temperatures over a large part of the model area in very little time using the infrared technique described by Hindley, et al. (1971), for example. Establishing density differences using salinity is practical when excessive quantities

10-27

of heat might otherwise be required in a large model. Further more, salinity models are not subject to ambient density changes caused by heat loss (or gain) through the tank walls or bottom, whereas temperature models need to be insulated to protect against these changes. Since salinity models do not experience surface heat transfer, they would be most useful in outlet and near-field situations where surface heat transfer in the proto-type is usually negligible anyway. However, the components of models based on salinity deteriorate rapidly because of corrosion.

Whether temperature or salinity differences are used to create density differences in a model, several precautions need to be taken. These center around the need to maintain a homo-geneous and steady ambient density in the model tank for the duration of an experiment. If this is not done, it will be nearly impossible to maintain a constant reference value of $\Delta \rho / \rho$ and, therefore, to adequately model the entrainment of ambient fluid. There would be no problem if the entire proto-type could be modeled at an undistorted scale using the laws previously outlined. When only a part of the prototype can be modeled in a single model, however, the discharge from the model has to be controlled carefully so as to maintain a steady state--i.e., constant surface water level, constant warm layer thickness, and constant ambient density near the discharge. These quantities should be continuously monitored. Usually the first two can be readily controlled by a weir or siphons, but these devices do not remove water and heat or salinity in the same proportion as would occur in the warm layer if it proceeded to its natural boundaries in the prototype. Hence, the density gradually changes in a model tank, and the experiment should be halted after a specified percentage of change has occurred in $\Delta \rho / \rho$. If there is a current coflowing with the surface buoyant jet, so that more water has to be wasted than merely the input warm water, there is less of a problem with ambient density change.

A further complication arises if the lateral boundaries cannot be placed sufficiently far apart in the model. In such a case, provision should be made for some of the ambient water to be drawn off laterally so that the warm surface layer can spread without hindrance. The water removed has to be replaced by a distributed inflow at ambient temperature or salinity. As with a coflowing current, the situation may actually be somewhat improved by cross currents, for then the cross flow input and output can be controlled in the same manner as the buoyant itself. Again, the experiment should be discontinued when the reference value of $\Delta \rho / \rho$ varies by a specified percentage. It is not possible at this time to set bounds for the minimum width or depth in an experimental tank to avoid wall effects. These depend, of course, on the initial densimetric Froude number. In the experiments by Stefan (1971), the warm layer thickness never exceeded twice the canal depth in a tank whose

depth was somewhat greater than 10 times the canal depth. The
tank width was 34 times the canal width, and lateral spread did
not seem to be influenced for a downstream distance of at least
10 or 12 canal widths, possibly more. In the experiments,
$0.6 < Fr_{Do} < 3.75$.

It is usually practical and economical to recirculate warm
water in a model, heating the recirculated water to restore its
temperature. In a saline model, concentrated brine needs to be
added to the ambient fluid to maintain its salinity, while the
fresh water in the jet is usually wasted.

Wind effects are difficult to model. If real winds are
used, surface heat transfer will be too great in a model in
which temperature is used to create density differences; this
will not be the case in a saline model. In addition, there is
little information on which to base wind modeling. Some of the
studies which look toward modeling ocean waves, such as that of
Wu (1971), may be useful. If the surface wind stress that
occurs at the model scale can be calculated, this stress can
possibly be applied using a distribution of vertical spinning
disks with horizontal axes lying just above the surface. Alternately, a distribution of short, moving belts lying on the
surface could be used.

One of the principal problems with a far field model is
satisfaction of Eq. (10-31d) for surface heat transfer; in some
near field models where Eq. (10-31c) applies, its satisfaciton
may cause even more of a problem. It is desirable to control
the atmosphere over the model to satisfy these equations. This
can be done by enclosing the space over the model and providing
air conditioning equipment to control atmospheric temperature
and humidity. Provision of radiant heat may also be desirable,
but this can probably be dispensed with if k and T_e in Eq. (10-1)
are well controlled by temperature and humidity. When a model
is constructed within an otherwise enclosed space, the atmosphere over the model can be enclosed expeditiously by hanging
curtains of polyethylene sheet with air spaces between the
sheets. When the model atmosphere is controlled it is especially
necessary to insulate the side and bottom walls of the tank.

The other principal problem with a far field model is control of ambient turbulence. If this is not determined by river
flow, it may be necessary to introduce turbulence using an artificial device--for example, pairs of spinning, counter-rotating
cylinders with vertical axes. With artificial generation,
turbulence should be monitored using a hot film anemometer or
similar device.

The references already referred to in Part 10-2 can be
consulted for application of some of these and other techniques.
Further discussion of model techniques pertinent to surface
buoyant jets can be found in Silferman and Stefan (1970) and in
Jain, et al. (1971). Other model study reports of interest
include those of Neale (1971) and Hindley, et al. (1971), but
these do not apply directly to the conditions herein.

In heat dispersion model work, temperature (or conductivity) alone is usually used to mark the extent of the spreading layer. However, when basic physical principles are being studied, it is also desirable to acquire velocity data. Special instrumentation is required for this because in the model, spread velocities are frequently of the order of a few hundredths of fps. Stefan and Schiebe (1968) describe a tethered sphere instrument for the purpose, but is is very tedious to use.

10.4 FIELD EXPERIENCE

Problems in Obtaining Field Data. It is desirable to obtain data on warm water discharges to lakes and streams for several purposes. These include learning more about the physical phenomena, validating modeling methods, and verifying specific model predictions. The latter purpose is frequently served with a minimum of field data: an aerial infrared survey or a few point measurements of temperature have frequently sufficed. The former two require much more detailed data, and there have veen very few field surveys which serve those purposes well.

Many problems are involved in making good field surveys. Tokar (1971) outlines some of these in the summary of his report, a portion of which follows:

"The occurrence of transient phenomena in lakes is able to continuously distort plume configurations. It is therefore unlikely that temperature and current measurements made by boat traverses or by point-by-point sampling over prolonged periods of time are sufficiently meaningful to delineate the temporal and spatial structure of a thermal plume and the surrounding ambient waters. The suitability of boat data-acquisition methods can be significantly improved if field survey methods can be reduced in time to one-half hour or less to complete a survey. Further improvements in field methods will come about when boat surveys are supplemented with data acquired from permanently and strategically placed in situ sensors recording on a continuous basis. Obviously, some tailored combination of boat acquisition methods which can yield considerable spatial information, together with a coarse network of continuously recording, permanent, in situ instrumentation yielding temporal truth, would be desirable. Unfortunately, the use of permanently located in situ instrumentation grids will probably continue to be utilized for thermal-plume investigations because this type of equipment is often quite expensive; the deployment of such equipment maintenance problems are to be anticipated."

"Further refinements in plume survey investigations can be achieved using airborne remote-measurement techniques such as infrared imagery, spectral dye dispersion studies, and drogue studies. There has already been some activity using airborne techniques on large lakes. However, except for a few notable exceptions, this work has been of either a reconnaissance or a pioneering nature. Airborne measurements by themselves are no panacea, however, because for the most part they yield water-surface or near-surface conditions which must be supplemented by in situ measurements taken either from a boat or from permanently located instrumentation. The whole field of airborne remote sensing is rapidly developing on many fronts, but, as it presently stands, such measurements continue to be relatively expensive for comprehensive thermal-plume investigations, particularly if quantitative results are sought."

The airborne measurements mentioned by Tokar probably have more utility in the far field than elsewhere, because there the warm layer is of relatively uniform thickness. Only a few in situ measurements are necessary in the far field to get much information from the airborne measurements. It should also be noted that most of the field data that is recorded has been obtained in the far field and farther reaches of the near field, and little has been obtained in the outlet region.

One problem that arises in any attempt to get field data to validate model experiments is the need to find field conditions which correspond closely to those assumed in the model study. In some cases there have actually been geometric changes in the design between the model studies and the field surveys. But even without such a complication, when all the equipment and personnel required to make a comprehensive survey have been assembled, the wind may change, distoring the plume beyond recognition from the model study; or it may begin to rain; or the plant load may inadvertently decrease part-way through a survey.

Another problem is that much field data is obtained without an adequate plan in mind. A complete survey should include as much of the data outlined in Table 10-1 as it is possible to get.

The time required to take the data must be held to a minimum; this can be facilitated by using more than one crew. For consistent data, it is probably wise to begin a field survey around solar noon and conclude within two hours or less. A cloudless or completely cloud-covered sky is desirable, and winds should be light. It is much more time-consuming to obtain data in the outlet region than elsewhere because of the unsteadiness of the flow there. This unsteadiness is associated with the large-scale turbulence of the entrainment process and perhaps also with variable feedback from the far and near fields. Continuous readings from at least one fixed sensor near the bottom of the warm layer or from a vertical column of fixed sensors in the outlet region during the time required for a survey are very desirable. Scarpace and Green (1972) reproduced a graph of temperature variation with time from a lake record at 9 ft depth which may be in the outlet region; this shows fluctuations of up to $5^{\circ}F$ in a matter of seconds.

Obtaining the average ambient temperature in a lake is not as easy as it may appear. The problem is that the lake may have some natural stratification, and the addition of waste heat and its dissipation throught the surface are continually changing

Table 10-1. Suggested Plan for Field Data Surveys

Item	Remarks
Plant Data	
Avg. heat rejection at condenser	
Avg. temp. in canal at exit	Should be nearly constant for about 24 hrs. preceding and during survey
Avg. water flow in canal	
Meteorological Data	
Dry bulb temp.	Measurements continuous or at hourly intervals
Wet bulb temp.	
Wind speed and direction	Measurements at 3 to 6 hr. intervals for 24 hrs preceding and during survey
Sky cover	
Avg. short wave solar radiation	
Ambient Water Data	
Avg. ambient temp.	Measurements at beginning and end of survey
Avg. current distribution, speed and direction	
Survey Data	
Time of each major part of data	
Vertical temp. profiles	Measurements at surface, 2 ft, 4 ft, 6 ft, 10 ft, and at 5 ft intervals thereafter to bottom or no change
Canal exit	Profiles at 50 ft intervals across exit
Outlet region	Profiles on 50 ft grid spacing
Near field	Profiles on 200 ft grid spacing
Far field	Profiles on 1000 ft grin spacing
Infrared temp. survey	
Vertical velocity profiles	Measurement by current meter at the same points as temp.
Surface velocities	By drogue, perhaps using air photos
Dye dispersion	From air photos

that stratification and the "natural" temperature that goes with it. Stefan, Chu, and Ho (1972) have analyzed this problem. In a river it is usually acceptable to use an average temperature measured upstream of the discharge point beyond the spreading region.

Although obtaining the other data called for in Table 10-1 requires considerable development of techniques, probably there are no other subtle problems like those associated with obtaining ambient lake temperatures or true temperatures in an outlet region.

Some Case Studies. Most of the data available from field surveys of thermal discharges into lakes have been reviewed and analyzed by Tokar (1971). Tokar's charts should be examined for information on the general isotherm patterns associated with thermal discharges. As already mentioned, most of these data are from the far field or the outer part of the near field.

Figures 10-5 and 10-6 show isothermal patterns in horizontal and selected vertical planes for a typical low densimetric Froude number (<1) discharge from a surface canal into a lake. The lake is actually a wide place in the St. Croix River lying between Minnesota and Wisconsin, but because of the width, the average river current is only about 0.03 fps as against an average flow velocity in the canal of about 0.4 fps (550 cfs discharge). Data obtained from field notes supplied by Northern States Power Company are available for several surveys at this site; this one set has been selected both because it is reasonably typical and because it shows an interesting effect attributable to the wind whose direction and speed are shown in Fig. 10-5. The wind was stronger than shown earlier in the day. The isotherms in Fig. 10-5 show that the warm water was driven against the far shore, where it "piled up" and was forced down to create a warmer water region far from the outlet than at the outlet at the 5 ft depth. Some remnants of the warmer water along the far shore can still be found at the 10 ft depth, not shown, but none at lower depths. Other surveys with winds from the south show a similar "piling up" effect against the point of land jutting from the Wisconsin shore north of the discharge point. With southeast and north winds, no "piling up" occurs. The figures show how rapidly the warm water spreads laterally at this small densimetric Froude number.

Stefan and Schiebe (1971) measured both temperature and velocity profiles along the projection of the canal centerline shown in Fig. 10-5 at a later date, and one of their profile sets is shown in Fig. 10-7. The temperature profile is reasonably similar to the one shown in Fig. 10-6, considereing the lower maximum temperature of the Stefan and Schiebe profiles. The velocity profiles are somewhat similar to the temperature profiles.

An interesting aspect of the warm layer thickness can be observed in the centerline profiles: there appears to be a sharp increase in thickness as measured by temperature at about

10-33

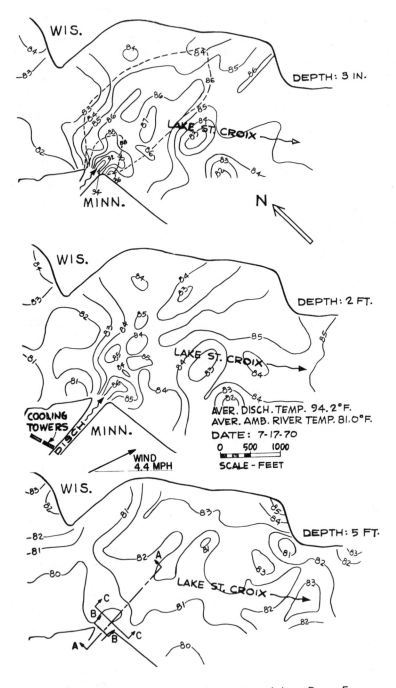

Fig. 10-5. Typical isotherms in a lake, Deg. F

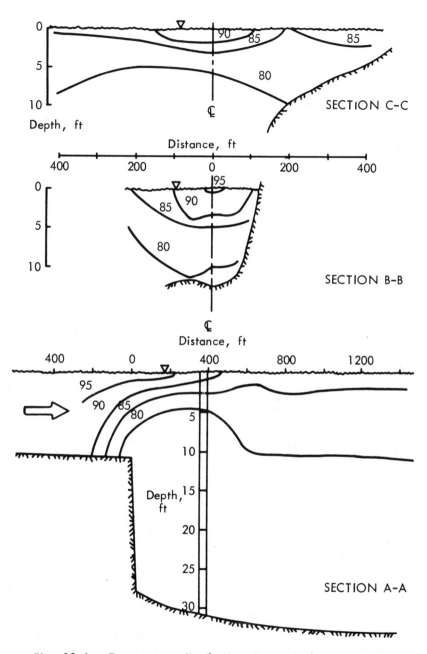

Fig. 10-6. Temperature distributions in vertical cross sections corresponding to Fig. 10-5, Deg. F

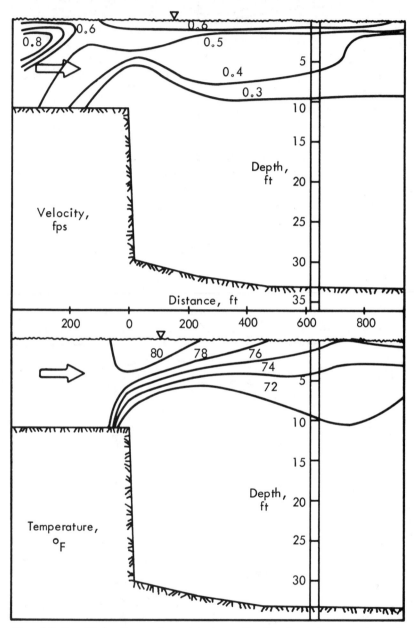

Fig. 10-7. Velocity and temperature distribution along projected centerline of discharge channel

600 feet from the canal exit and a similar increase as marked by the velocity even closer to the outlet. This thickening appears to be associated with mixing in the outlet region, where major vertical dilution occurred. It should be recalled from Part 10-2 that the thickening is probably associated with the downstream control exercised by the cooling process in the lake. There is undoubtedly a good deal of unsteadiness associated with this thickening process, as already noted, and only simultaneous measurements could define a true instantaneous profile. Scarpace and Green (1972) have observed from infrared surveys that surface isotherms appear to move in waves away from a warm water exit, and this observation may be associated with the unsteadiness of the outlet region.

It might be noted that the unsteadiness in the outlet region may well be the property which makes the assumption of similarity and profiles of Gaussian form applicable in analyzing the flow on a mean-steady basis as discussed in Part 10-2. The unsteadiness makes it impossible to obtain other than average values in most field data, and averages would not be satisfactory for comparison with a more precise theory if there were one.

A model study applicable to the warm water discharge shown in Fig. 10-5 was conducted by Silberman and Stefan (1964) prior to construction of the power plant. The model was distorted and used salt and fresh water. Unfortunately, the canal outlet in the model was about 500 feet farther downstream and entered the lake in a more southeasterly direction (28° difference) than the prototype canal shown in Fig. 10-5. Also, there was no wind in the model study and little more than half the lake current shown in the figure, although lake current effects must be almost negligible. To get some comparison between model and prototype, two isotherms obtained from the model were transposed onto Fig. 10-5 by changing their origins and rotating them bidily. The results are shown as broken lines on the upper diagram of the figure.

Another useful kind of field measurement relates to the determination of ambient turbulence properties of lakes without heat addition. This information is sueful in computing the far field. Several measurements of this kind have been carried out in the Great Lakes; the work of Jones and Kenney (1971) is an example.

Unfortunately, few data are available on thermal discharges into rivers. Most of what has appeared in the literature is from studies sponsored by the Tennessee Valley Authority or by others in the southeastern United States. Motz and Benedict (1970) summarize some of this, especially as regards the far field, in their paper previously referred to. Polk, et al. (1971) reproduced some of the data for the outlet region and near field. Some of the figures in their paper should be examined for the general form of the isotherms. Some velocity profiles are also shown. Sonnichsen (1971) made measurements in the Columbia River at Hanford, Washington, mostly far field, to determine dispersion without and with warm water discharge.

There are several published sets of data for warm water discharges to estuaries. The paper by Hindley, et al. (1971) is one of these, but is limited to surface temperature measurements by an infrared technique. Others have accumulated more complete data sets in estuaries; Carter (1968) is an example. There are also several published accounts of temperature measurements in cooling ponds, of which a paper by Thompson (1971) is quite complete; however, estuarial and cooling pond situations are not directly applicable to the present topic. There have also been observations of installations with submerged outlets, but these are very dissimilar, especially in the outlet region, to the surface buoyant jet case.

10.5 SUMMARY

In summary, it can be said that analytical work, hydraulic model studies, and the collection of field data have served to produce a good working knowledge of the principal physical phenomena occurring in heated surface discharges. Predictions of prototype behavior can be made with some success using a combination of hydraulic and mathematical modeling. However, the accuracy which can be obtained in predicting prototype behavior is not really known. Uncertainty is the result of both the assumptions that have to be made in the modeling and the difficulty in obtaining field data which correspond to model assumptions. In gathering field data, two problems that loom large are the inherent instability in the outlet region and the need to maintain steady plant discharge and meteorological conditions during and for several hours preceding a field survey. Among the model assumptions causing problems are those dealing with wind action on the jet trajectory and similarity; with boundary conditions in the outlet region; and with ambient turbulence of the receiving water in the far field. The fewer the assumptions that have to be made regarding these problems, the better the prediction.

10.6 NOTATIONS

B width of canal, ft

b width of velocity profile, ft

C_D drag coefficient of jet due to ambient current

c_p specific heat, BTU, $slug^{-1}$, $^{o}F^{-1}$

$exp[\ ]$ exponential function

Fr Froude number, $U(gh)^{-1/2}$

Fr_D densimetric Froude number, $U(g\frac{o}{o} h)^{-1/2}$

Fr_D* densimetric Froude number with ambient current

f friction factor

g acceleration due to gravity, ft, $\sec^{-2}$

H depth of canal, ft

h depth of velocity profile, ft

K proportionality constant for velocity of jet entrainment

K_H proportionality constant for velocity of jet entrainment in horizontal plane

K_V proportionality constant for velocity of jet entrainment in vertical plane

k surface heat transfer coefficient, ft, $\sec^{-1}$

L length of flow region, ft

n transverse coordinate; see Fig. 10-1

q surface heat transfer, BTU, ft^{-2}, sec

R_H hydraulic radius, ft

Re Reynolds number, $U_0 H^{-1}$

S slope of free water surface

s longitudinal coordinate; see Fig. 10-1

s_E length of establishment zone, ft

St Stanton number, $\alpha L b (o c_p T \bar{U} h b)^{-1}$

T excess temperature over ambient temperature in receiving water, ^{0}F

T_e equilibrium temperature, measured as excess over ambient, ^{0}F

U excess velocity in jet in s-direction over ambient current, fps

V ambient current velocity, fps; see Fig. 10-1

v entrainment velocity in n- or z-direction, fps

W wind velocity, fps; see Fig. 10-1

We Weber number, $U_0 (oH)^{1/2} {}^{-1/2}$

x coordinate in canal discharge direction; see Fig. 10-1

y coordinate normal to x in horizontal plane; see Fig. 10-1

z vertical coordinate; see Fig. 10-1

α proportionality constant for horizontal spread of jet due to entrainment

α_z proportionality constant for vertical spread of jet due to entrainment

β angle between ambient current and x-axis, deg; see Fig. 10-1

γ surface tension, lb, ft^{-1}

δ angle between shoreline and x-axis, deg; see Fig. 10-1

θ angle between s- and x-axis, deg; see Fig. 10-1

λ ratio of width of temperature profile to width of velocity profile

λ_V ratio of depth of temperature profile to depth of velocity profile

ν kinematic viscosity of ambient water, ft^2, $\sec^{-1}$

ϱ density of ambient water, slug, ft^{-3}

$\Delta\varrho$ decrement in density of warm water relative to ambient water, slug, ft^{-3}

Subscripts:
- c   centerline value
- m   model
- o   initial conditions
- p   prototype
- r   ratio of model to prototype quantities

An overbar represnets a mean value.

REFERENCES

Abramovich, G.N., 1963, The Theory of Turbulent Jets:
Massachusetts Institute of Technology Press, Cambridge,
Massachusetts.

Bansal, M.K., 1971, Dispersion in Natural Streams; Journal of
Hydraulics Division, ASCE, Vol. 97, No. HY11, Nov 71,
pp. 1867-1886.

Brady, D.K., Graves, W.L., Jr., and Geyer, J.C., 1969, Surface
Heat Exchange at Power Plant Cooling Lakes; Johns Hopkins
University, Report No. 5, Project RP-49, 154p.

Carlsson, B., 1970, Thermal Effect of Heated Effluents in Lake
Mälaren; Nordic Conference on Hydrology, Stockholm, Sweden.

Carter, H.H., 1968, The Distribution of Excess Temperature From
a Heated Discharge in an Estuary; Johns Hopkins University
Chesapeake Bay Inst. Tech. Report No. 44, Oct 68, 39 pp.

Ellison, T.H. and Turner, J.S., 1959, Turbulent Entrainment in
Stratified Flows: Journal Fluid Mech., Vol. 6, Pt 3,
pp. 423-448.

Frazer, W., Barr, K.I.H., and Smith, A.A., 1968, A Hydraulic
Model Study of Heat Dissipation at Longannet Power Station;
Proc., Inst. of Civil Engineers, 39, Jan 68, pp. 23-44.

Harleman, D.R.F., 1961, Stratified Flow; Ch. 26 of Streeter, V.
L., Ed., Handbook of Fluid Dynamics, McGraw-Hill, New York.

Hayashi, T. and Shuto, N., 1967, Diffusion of Warm Water Jets
Discharged Horizontally at the Water Surface: Proc. 12th
Congress, IAHR, Colorado State University, Sept. 67, Vol.
4, pp. 47-59.

Hindley, P.D., Miner, R.M., and Cayot, R.F., 1971, Thermal
Discharge: A Model-Prototype Comparison; Journal Power
Div., ASCE, Vol. 97, No. PO4, Dec. 71, pp. 783-798.

Jain, S.C., Sayre, W.W., Akeampong, Y.A., McDougall, D., and
Kennedy, J.F., 1971, Model Studies and Design of Thermal
Outfall Structures, Quad-Cities Nuclear Plant; Iowa Inst.
of Hydr. Res., Iowa City, IIHR Report No. 135, Sept. 71,
101 pages.

Jones, I.S.F., and Kenney, B.C., 1971, Turbulence in Lake Huron:
Water Resources Research, Vol. 5, pp. 765-776.

Koh, R.C.Y., 1971, Two-dimensional Surface Warm Jets; Jr. Hyd.
Div. ASCE, Vol. 97, No. HY6, June 71, pp. 819-836.

Motz, L.H. and Benedict, B.A., 1970, Heated Surface Jet
    Discharged Into a Flowing Ambient Stream; Vanderbilt Univ.,
    School of Engineering, Aug. 70, 207 pages.

Motz, L.H. and Benedict, B.A., 1972, Surface Jet Model For
    Heated Discharges; Journal Hyd. Div., ASCE, Vol. 98, No.
    HY1, Jan. 72, pp. 181-199.

National Academy of Sciences, 1971, Potential Technological
    Advances and Their Impact on Anticipated Water Require-
    ments; Report to National Water Commision, June 71, 246 p.

Neale, L.C., 1971, Chesapeake Bay Model Study for Calvert
    Cliffs; Journal Power Division, ASCE, Vol. 97, No. PO4,
    Dec. 71, pp. 827-839.

Phillips, O.M., 1966, The Dynamics of the Upper Ocean; Cambridge
    University Press, Cambridge, England.

Polk, E.M., Jr., Benedict, B.A., and Parker, F.L., 1971, Cooling
    Water Density Wedges in Streams; Journal Hydr. Div., ASCE,
    Vol. 97, No. HY10, Oct. 71, pp. 1639-1652.

Scarpace,F.L. and Green, T., III, 1972, The Use of a Thermal
    Line Scanner in the Remote Sensing of Water Pollution;
    Univ. of Wisconsin Sea Grant Program Report No. 13, 11 p.

Schlichting, H., 1968, Boundary Layer Theory; 6th Ed., McGraw-
    Hill, New York.

Silberman, E. and Stefan, H., 1964, Effects of Condenser
    Cooling Water Discharge From Projected Allen S. King
    Generating Plant on Water Temperatures in Lake St. Croix;
    Univ. of Minnesota, St. Anthony Falls Hydr. Lab., Proj.
    Report No. 76, 88 p.

Silberman, E. and Stefan, H., 1970, Physical (hydraulic) Model-
    ing of Heat Dispersion in Large Lakes: A Review of the
    State of the Art; Argonne Natl. Lab., Report No. ANL/ES-2,
    Aug. 70, 110 p.

Sonnichsen, J.C., Jr., 1971, Lateral Spreading of Heated
    Discharge; Journal Power Division, ASCE, Vol. 97, No. PO3,
    July 71, pp. 623-630

Stefan, H., 1970, Stratification of Flow From Channel into Deep
    Lake; Journal Hydr. Division, ASCE, Vol. 96, No. HY7,
    July 70, pp. 1417-1434.

Stefan, H., L971, Three-Dimensional Jet-Type Surface Plumes in Theory and in the Laboratory; Part I of Surface Discharge of Heated Water, U.S. Environmental Protection Agency, Water Pollution Control Research Series, Report No. 16130, FSU 12/71.

Stefan, H., Chu, C-S, and Ho, Wing, 1972, Impact of Cooling Water Discharge on Lake Temperatures: A Case Study; Journal Power Div., ASCE, Vol. 98, June 72.

Stefan, H. and Hayakawa, N., 1972, Mixing Induced by an Internal Hydraulic Jump; Water Resources Bulletin, AWRA, June 72.

Stefan, H. and Schiebe, F.R., 1968, The Measurement of Low Fluid Velocities with the Aid of a Tethered Sphere; Water Resources Research, Vol. 4, No. 6, pp. 1351-1357.

Stefan, H. and Schiebe, F.R., 1971, Field Measurements in a Three-Dimensional Jet-Type Surface Plume; Part III of Surface Discharge of Heated Water, U.S. Environmental Protection Agency, Water Pollution Control Research Series, Report No. 16130 FSU 12/71.

Stolzenbach, K.D. and Harleman, D.R.F., 1971, An Analytical and Experimental Investigation of Surface Discharges of Heated Water; Massachusetts Institute of Technology, Dept. of Civil Engineering, Report No. R71-10, Feb. 71, 212 p.

Tamai, N., Wiegel, R.L., and Tornberg, G.F., 1969, Horizontal Surface Discharge of Warm Water Jets; Journal Power Div., ASCE, Vol. 95, No. PO2, Oct. 69, pp. 253-276.

Thompson, D.M., 1971, Hazelwood Power Station - Data Collection and Analysis of Cooling Pond Performance; Proc. Fourth Australasian Conf. on Hydraulics and Fluid Mechanics, Monash Univ., Melbourne, Autralia.

Tokar, J.V., 1971, Thermal Plumes in Lakes: Compilations of Field Experience; Argonne Natl. Lab., Report No. ANL/ES-3, Aug. 71, 169 pages.

Wada, A., 1969, Numerical Analysis of Distribution of Flow and Thermal Diffusion Caused by Outfall of Cooling Water; Proc. 13th Congress, IAHR, Kyoto, Japan, Vol. 3, pp. 335-342.

Wu, Jin, 1971, Anemometer Height in Froude Scaling of Wind Stress; Journal Waterways, Harbors and Coastal Engineering Division, ASCE, Vol. 97, No. WW1, Feb. 71, pp. 131-137.

Wunderlich, W.O. and Fan, L-N., 1971, Criteria for Fully-Mixed
    Temperature Regime in Streams; Proc. 14th Congress, IAHR,
    Paris, France, Vol. 1, pp. A29-1 to A29-8.

Chapter 11

FISH BEHAVIOR RELATED TO THERMAL POLLUTION

by

Harold K. Hagen, Associate Professor, Department of Fishery and
Wildlife Biology, College of Forestry and
Natural Resources, Colorado State University,
Fort Collins, Colorado

Chapter 11

FISH BEHAVIOR RELATED TO THERMAL POLLUTION

In common with many environmental concerns, the impact of
thermal pollution in an aquatic ecosystem has received a great
deal of publicity in recent years. Because the aquatic community is not as easily observed as the terrestrial and because
an emotionally aroused public can be fueled as easily on conjecture as they can on fact, there is a considerable amount of
false information about damage and potential damage from thermal
pollution.

There are many excellent publications regarding studies or
symposia that have been related to the influence of heated
effluents on fish. Alabaster (1964), Alabaster and Downing
(1960), Brett (1956, 1958, 1960), Garside and Tait (1958),
Mihursky and Kennedy (1967), Ferguson (1958), Jones (1964),
Coutant (1970), Levin, Birch, Hillman and Raines (1970), Krenkel,
Parker and Eds (1969). These are but a few of the available
publications. There are in addition many investigations being
completed at the present time and many of these are long term
involving highly sophisticated sensing and recording equipment
as well as multivariate design. It is this last factor that is
so important in obtaining a true understanding of fish behavior
as related to thermal pollution. In the natural environment
one single variable is seldom valid by itself nor is it capable
of prolonged or independent measurement. If good baseline
data are to be established for setting limits of thermal discharge they must be obtained from multivariate studies. Along
with this need is a need to focus more on how fish themselves
signal a response to thermal changes and what they do to
compensate rather than on what man presumes the effects might be.

Considering the fact that there are thousands of species of
fish that can and will come into direct contact with various
forms of thermal pollution it would be impossible to study the
peculiarities of each species' life history and establish
standards to insure their total protection. A few key species,
representative of general groups, have been studied in both
field and laboratory situations for more than two decades and
several useful guidelines have been established from these data
and observations. Obviously each new potential source of pollution will demand its own modifications based on the dynamics
of the ecosystem and the species of fish involved.

11.1 BASIC PROBLEMS OF TEMPERATURE ACCLIMATION IN FISH

Because cold blooded animals cannot change their body temperature by losing water vapour in expired air or in sweat as a
warm blooded animal can, they are severely handicaped in an
environment that might be subjected to rapid or extreme thermal
fluctuations. Any temperature changes in the water surrounding

fish is immediately communicated through the gills and circulatory system to the entire body of the animal. In many animals, including marine mammals, an insulation of the integument by adipose tissue or thickened epidermal cells will prevent too rapid a response to thermal change. This is impossible in most fish since the blood must be exposed directly to the water at the gill surface to maximize the oxygen exchange. Because oxygen is very limited in water as contrasted to air, any insulation of the gill would result in severe limitations of the respiratory process.

When a fish is placed in warm water, the body temperature of the fish must rise accordingly or it will be in immediate danger of heat death. Just what heat death actually is and what the sequence of physiological responses are in a fish' body are not well known. It may result from an inactivation of enzymes, a coagulation of cell proteins, a failure of the central nervous system in coordination or most likely a combination of all these factors. There are, of course, great variations in response to heat (or cold) in individual groups of fish. Some have developed a number of adaptive structures. There are many species which are actually quite heat tolerant. In most instances this tolerance is accomplished through a much lower than normal metabolic rate. This usually means a more sluggish or semi-motile fish such as a sucker or catfish. Whether these species are more or less desirable from mans' point of view becomes an important point in considering the consequences of heat pollution. From the ecological viewpoint the vacating of ecological niches must always be considered in any temperature variation.

Fish obviously have a low temperature tolerance as well as high and they can be acclimated to live at temperatures much below normal. Cold death points in fish are usually at or near freezing points of water but in fish acclimated to high temperatures it could be several degrees above freezing.

Brett (1956) has attempted to determine the relative tolerances of several species of fish by establishing a trapezium bounded by acclimation and real temperatures. By measuring the surface areas of observed resistance and tolerance zones he has developed a scale of high to low tolerance based on "square degrees." Chum salmon for example, with a "square degree" score of 468 would be low while a catfish scoring above 1000 square degrees would be highly tolerant. Jones (1964) has gathered thermal death point and acclimation data from a number of European and American sources. Many of these data are presented in Table 1. It should be noted that as the acclimation temperature is increased the expected increase in thermal death point follows but it is highly variable among species. Speckled trout, for example, acclimated from 5C to 25 C increase the thermal death point by 1.6 C while a more tolerant species such as the goldfish shows a 7.8 C death point increase over a similar 20C increase in acclimation temperatures.

Table 11-1   Thermal Death Points of Fish Related
to Acclimation Temperatures

Fish (common name)	Acclimation temp. (°C)	Thermal Death Point (°C)
Bluegill	15	30.7
Brook Stickleback	25-26	30.6
Brown trout- fry	5-6	22.5
"	20	23.0
yearling	?	25.91
Parr	?	29
Carp	20	31-34
Catfish (brown bullhead)	15	31.8
Chinook salmon- fry	15	25
"	20	25.1
Chum salmon- fry	15	23.1
"	20	23.7
Coho salmon- fry	15	24.3
"	20	25.0
Common shiner	15	30.3
Common sucker	15	29.3
Creek chub	15	29.3
Fathead minnow	10	28.2
"	20	31.7
"	30	33.2
Golden shiner	15	30.5

Table 11-1   (Continued)

Fish (common name)	Acclimation temp. (°C)	Thermal Death Point (°C)
Goldfish	10	30.8
"	20	34.8
"	30	38.6
Guppy	30	34.0
Largemouth Bass	20	32.5
"	30	36.4
Perch	?	23-25
Pumpkin seed Sunfish	25-26	34.5
Rainbow trout	?	28.0
Roach	20	29.5
"	25	30.5
"	30	31.5
Salmon (Atlantic) grilse	?	29.5-30.5
parr	?	32.5-33.8
Speckled trout	5	23.7
"	10	24.4
"	15	25.0
"	20	25.3
"	25	25.3
Tench	?	29-30

11.2 LETHAL LIMITS; INVOLUNTARY PHYSIOLOGICAL RESPONSE

The classic assay for examining temperature as a lethal factor in fish is the LD-50 or lethal temperature dose necessary to kill 50% of test animals. Under strict laboratory conditions this limit is not terribly difficult to determine. Trout and other salmonid fishes, for example, are apt to reach the LD-50 level at temperatures near 86F (30°C). When field conditions are considered, however, the situation can be much different. The thermal history of an individual fish or a group of fishes will be important. If fish have been gradually acclimated to either higher or lower temperatures than normal they may have developed a tolerance that would exceed a former maximum upper or lower acclimation point or ultimate incipient lethal level. The rate of acclimation in fish is nearly always faster in the upward or higher temperature than it is in the lower. A fish, for example, that has adjusted to a steadily increasing temperature over a matter of hours or days, may not be able to readjust to lower temperatures again without going through a much larger period of re-acclimation to a former low temperature. In some species it could take a month or more. Thus the laboratory determined LD-50 level is at best a general guideline. Some investigators (Alabaster 1964) have calculated likely lethal effects by determining the maximum acclimation possible in a few species and have subtracted this figure from known lethal values to more clearly show sensitivity of the fish. It should be remembered that there are many other factors in a natural environment that can either buffer for or against rapid changes in temperature. Even the amount and type of aquatic vegetation can be an important consideration.

Thermal shock is commonly produced in fish where there has been little or no acclimation time possible. The seriousness of the shock will, of course, depend largely on the degree of temperature difference but it will also depend upon the species of fish involved. A carp or related fish, which has a lower metabolic rate than a trout and consequently a lower oxygen demand will not likely succumb to thermal shock as rapidly and chances for adjustment are increased. From a fisheries management viewpoint, the implications of possible thermal shock in a mixed population becomes obvious.

Less obvious and certainly less thoroughly researched is the problem of disorientation and coordination in fishes subjected to sub-lethal levels of thermal shock. The concept commonly referred to as C.T.M. is the thermal point in which locomotor activity becomes so disorganized that the fish will lose its ability to perform some life sustaining functions. An example not uncommonly seen is in fish stocking operations where transported fish are stocked into waters of higher temperature. Fish will be observed "spinning" at the surface or at times rushing in to shore or stranding themselves in shallow waters where they are subject to predation or loss from other than direct thermal causes.

Some direct effects of temperature increase on fish would be in reproduction and other stages in the life history. In many fish species reproductive cycles are dependent upon temperature variation. Even a change of one or two degrees can trigger or suppress reproductive activities. After eggs have

been deposited and fertilized, most fish species are dependent
upon relatively uniform temperatures for development. In species
where long incubation periods are normally required a sudden or
prolonged increase in temperature can cause mutation or possibly
a weakened embryo with a low survival potential. In instances
where short incubation periods are required even slight temperature increases can accelerate development to such an extent
that the entire spawn can be destroyed. The method of thermal
injection becomes an important consideration related to the type
of egg laying or nesting involved. A pelagic or surface drift-
ing egg or larvae is thus much more vulnerable to surface lam-
inated heat layers than a species that would build a nest in the
bottom gravels. In species where guarding the nest is necessary
for survival, such as found in the sunfish (Centrarchidae)
desertion by the male is common with temperature variation.

Problems in basic fish metabolism associated with temperature are both numerous and complicated. Oxygen consumption will
increase very rapidly in relation to temperature increases in
most species of fish while the ability of water to retain dissolved oxygen decreases. At the same time there is a tendency
for substances toxic to fish to be either more soluble or more
rapidly dispersed.

The growth of fish is also closely related to temperature
and will, of course, have a much narrower set of limits than
the lethal boundaries. In most species the food consumption
and growth rate will increase in a sigmoid pattern in response
to temperature increases but in many instances after a leveling
is reached, any increase in temperature will cause a decrease
in feeding and growth, or both, with a resulting, often rapid,
decrease in body weight and stamina. At such a stage many fish
are vulnerable to a wide variety of water borne diseases or
parasites. It is obvious that any temperature change in the
aquatic environment will have an ultimate effect on any fish
population present.

11.3 VOLUNTARY RESPONSE OF FISH TO THERMAL LOADING

As indicated previously the involuntary response of fish to
temperature increases are several and to some degree predictable.
The voluntary responses are less well known but are of equal
importance if wise decisions are to be made in regard to posi-
tioning and regulating thermal discharges into river systems.
How predictable they might be remains to be proved.

The results of several ecological studies to date (Levin,
Birch, Hillman, Raines, 1970; Churchill and Wojtalik 1969) have
suggested that with only a few exceptions, there has been no
major damage to fish or the aquatic environment from existing
power plants, the main source of high thermal discharges. Fish
have been found to possess a distinct ability to detect zones
that would be lethal to them and in most instances can avoid

them if provided an alternative. Fish have also shown an immediate awareness of benefits that can be derived from an artificial change in stream temperature patterns. Increased food
production provided in some instances by either warmer or less
fluctuating temperatures, especially in winter seasons, has
resulted in large congregations of fish in heated waters. There
has been little evidence to show that these congregations have
been responsible for any real increase in growth since the
impact of larger numbers of consumers may well exceed the increase in primary production in many instances. Congregations
of fish do allow greater harvest by fishermen, which may or
may not be desirable but at the same time it favors predation
and the possibility for spreading disease.

Of major concern in thermally polluted waters is the possible blockage of migrations by either anadromous or catadro-
mous fishes. Most concern is directed to young fishes, which
may be swept into cooling systems or directly into thermal
discharges. Data suggest that even small fish will usually
avoid lethal zones or suffer no drastic mortality when swept
through some cooling systems (Levin et al. op. cit.). Although
data are few on behavioral reaction of adult migrants there
are no data that indicate fish would not or could not avoid
regulated discharges in migratory streams. It is possible that
the National Technical Advisory Committee recommendation that
passageways for migration should contain preferably 75 per cent
of the cross-sectional area and/or volume of flow of the stream,
is more than necessary provided the zones of heat are maintained
at the surface or can be contained within narrower limits.

11.4 YELLOWSTONE INVESTIGATIONS

During the winter of 1964, the author was a member of a
study team from the State University of New York Atmospheric
Science Division. In observing the aquatic life in the Firehole
River, he became intrigued by the dynamics of heated effluents
entering the river and the response of the floral and faunal
communities. In 1965, a grant from the Office of Water Resources and the cooperation of the U. S. National Park Service
and the Bureau of Sport Fisheries and Wildlife permitted a
more extensive investigation and resulted in the production of
a M. S. thesis (Argyle 1966) in which many of the data for
this report are compiled.

It seemed probable that this river which had been subjected
to constant thermal pollution from a variety of sources and
through a wide range of discharge points for many centuries
would be a better study area for true impact of heated water
than any laboratory. The endemic animal populations from these
climax communities should indicate a more normal behavioral
response than those under artificial laboratory conditions.
Granted, of course, were the limitations of more difficult and

non-continuous observation. Three major study areas were selected on the Firehole River (Figure 1). The Fountain Freight Bridge Station was typical of many small but very hot springs (192F) that flow directly into the river in a single discharge point. The Excelsior Geyser produces one of the major thermal flows entering the Firehole. Its discharge of 9 Cfs is approximately 75 percent of the total thermal discharge of the Midway Geyser Basin. The third station, Ojo Caliente Spring (Figure 2), which is located in the upper section of the Lower Geyser Basin, was selected because of its multiple channel discharge and the fact that its drop over a relatively steep bank caused thermal water to create turbulence at the point of entry. Water flow from this spring was 0.214 Cfs at a temperature of 180.5 F.

Perhaps the most important immediate finding was the frequency and stability of thermal stratification (Figure 3). Much of the literature has indicated that although hot waters would flow for a time on the surface, there was no stratification as such and that mixing would prevent this from occurring, Jones (1964). Quite the contrary the majority of the very hot waters from springs and geysers separated upon entry into two distinct layers, top and bottom in most shallow and moderate depths. Fountain Freight Bridge Station demonstrated this immediate layering very clearly. Figure 4 shows the rapid separation as well as the immediate degradation of the heat layers which was most rapid on the bottom layer. In injections over deep water only the top layer was formed. The only exceptions were in areas of heavy turbulence at the point of entry or in some exceptionally shallow areas. This separation had been reported as early as 1927, Liddell (1927). Others who have more recently commented upon it have included Markowski (1959); Alabaster (1964); Duttweiler et.al. (1961); Churchill and Wojtalik (1969). Most authors, however, did not measure the depths of the layering, its stability under various conditions or the behavior of fish in areas of stratification.

Fish and many of the invertebrates of the Firehole River seemed very much aware of the stability of the heated water layers and maintained themselves often with seeming unconcern only inches from scalding temperatures. Although layering is generally a function of volume and surface area it was found in several instances that very resistant stratification could occur where there was no more than twelve inches in depth. In one such station near the Fountain Freight Road Bridge, the heat intolerant scud (Gammarus sp.) and unidentified snails lived among the foliage of dense mats of pondweed (Potomogeton sp.). These animals were seen to move up along the vegetation to within an inch of the surface. The healthy green pondweeds pushed upwards until they reached within one or two inches of the stratified layer. At this point they turned brown but as

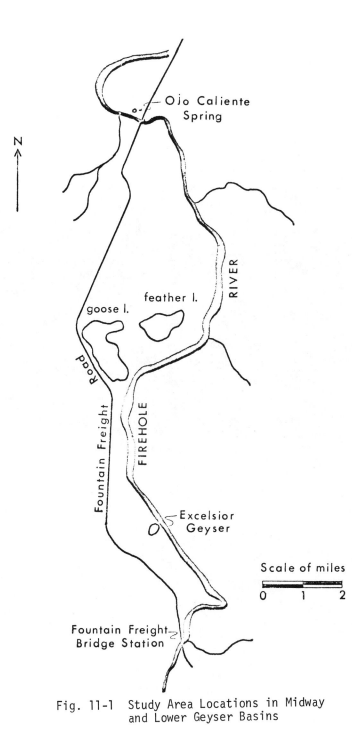

N

Ojo Caliente
Spring

feather I.

goose I.

RIVER

Road

Fountain Freight

FIREHOLE

Excelsior
Geyser

Scale of miles

0   1   2

Fountain Freight
Bridge Station

Fig. 11-1   Study Area Locations in Midway
and Lower Geyser Basins

11-9

Fig. 11-2 Ojo Caliente Spring in
           the Lower Geyser Basin

Fig. 11-3 Finding the Frequency and Stability
of Thermal Stratification

11-11

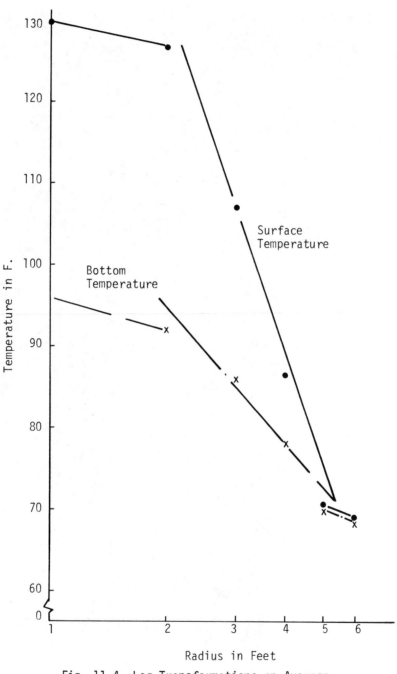

Fig. 11-4 Log Transformations on Average
Surface and Bottom Temperatures

the foliage was pushed even further upward into the last 18 millimeters or less from the surface they immediately turned white from the scalding waters (131 F). Small brown trout Salmo trutta linnaeus were observed entering this zone apparently to within an inch of the surface as they searched out and fed upon the scud. Had this layering not been exceptionally stable, a climax community such as this could not have been produced.

In another instance, fingerling trout believed to have been both rainbow Salmo gairdneri Richardson, and brown were observed feeding at the upper end of a pool which was immediately below the point of entry for effluents of the Giant Geyser. As hot waters from an eruption poured into the river, the fish stopped feeding, dropped a few inches below the surface until the wedge of hot water had passed, and then immediately started feeding on the surface again. The surface wedge was traced with a Stoll-Hardy radiometer and found to be completely dissipated in less than five hundred feet from the point of entry, with no apparent or measureable mixing despite its passage over a shallow riffle area.

Additional winter observations also proved rewarding. It was found that the layering observed and measured in the summer had not changed nor had the biotic communities. It was interesting to find that rainbow trout avoided the coldest water of the winter season and concentrated in zones where there was a modified thermal influence. Brown trout, on the other hand, showed little preference. Electro fishing tests showed them to be equally abundant in the 38 F water above the Old Faithful Geyser Basin and in the 50 F water in and below the first geyser basin.

In addition to the Firehole River, observations were made on the inlet to Shoshone Lake, Witch Creek, a tributary of Heart Lake and a small tributary of Yellowstone Lake. Behavior responses were observed in the Cutthroat trout Salmo clarki (Girard); Speckled dace Apocope osculus carringtoni (Cope); Utah chub Gila atraria (Girard); Longnose sucker Catostomus catostomus (Forster); and the Utah sucker Catostomus ardens (Jordan and Gilbert). Behavior related to thermal influences was similar to those observed in the rainbow and brown trout. All seemed well aware of the boundary zones of the stratified waters and were able to quickly and easily avoid them even when frightened.

In smaller streams such as Witch Creek, where some thermal discharges approached twenty percent of the stream flow, the boundary zones were still distinct enough so that the fish could pass freely up and down the stream. Simon (1962) has reported that the speckled dace and the Utah sucker of Witch Creek are able to withstand temperatures well above 80 F. Although these observations are no doubt accurate it was found that these species would stay in mid depth zones below these temperatures when possible.

11-13

The amount and degree of turbulence present at the point of thermal entry into the river was, as stated previously, important in determining how the heated water disperses and how fish will be affected. Where there was considerable turbulence or where multiple flows enter in sequence mixing did occur from top to bottom and stratification was not present unless the effluent was very hot (150 F or above). The effect of this turbulence in achieving mixing is demonstrated in Figures 5 and 6, showing surface and bottom water temperatures. Even here, however, the lack of stratification may not be totally due to mixing from turbulence since soil temperatures (Figure 6) indicate the presence of very hot waters below the soil surface that could be a factor in preventing the stratification. Fish tended to avoid these areas. Where inflow was in quiet or moderately turbulent water the separation into two factions, a surface and bottom layer, was almost immediate. Once formed, the wedge of hot surface water was exceptionally difficult to break down even if the wedge passed over a very turbulent zone. Fish appeared to be much aware of these differences and they followed the boundaries freely and without difficulty.

In the area of the Ojo Caliente Spring, dragonfly larvae (Odonata) intent upon emerging to the surface were observed to ascend vegetation or climb up the rhyolite and sinter under-banks until they reached the scalding surface layer. Here they hesitated for a time and then moved up into the very hot layer to be immediately scalded to death. This was the only instance in all observations where any animal form failed to avoid the lethal zones of hot water. Because there was some shifting of very hot water zones and because layering was not as definite as in less turbulent zones the animals might have become confused or could not move away in time.

Depth appears to be a decisive factor in determining how rapidly thermal water disperses as well as the degree of stratification. In all cases where stratification occurred, heat loss to the atmosphere was very rapid and in all instances where it occurred the elevation in stream temperature was much less than it was in areas where complete or partial mixing had occurred.

It was very evident that a steep temperature gradient resists mixing better than a low temperature gradient. Hot waters (above 120 F) almost always formed the bonded layers unless turbulence was severe. Moderate to low temperature inflows often mixed immediately with the cold river waters even though turbulence was not extensive. In all observations where inflow temperatures were within 20 F or less of ambient stream temperatures there was no stratification.

Lateral dispersion of thermal waters in the Firehole River was governed primarily by river current velocity but was in part related to temperature gradient. Very hot waters tended to be resisted more by the current and were kept closer to the shoreline. As the gradient in temperature decreased the heated

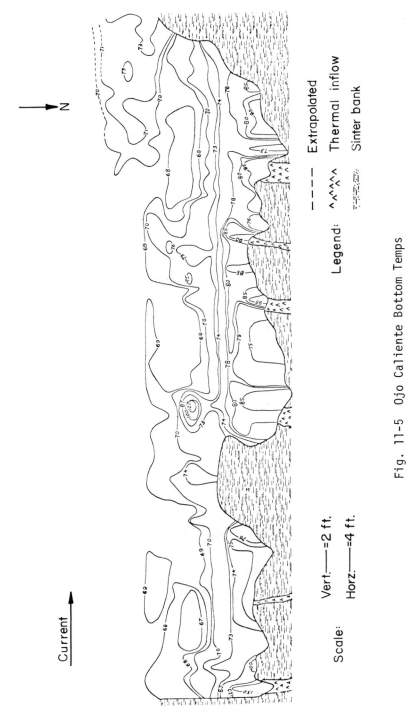

Fig. 11-5 Ojo Caliente Bottom Temps

Legend: — — —   Extrapolated
          ∧∧∧∧∧   Thermal inflow
          ≡≡≡≡≡   Sinter bank

Scale: Vert.——=2 ft.
         Horz.——=4 ft.

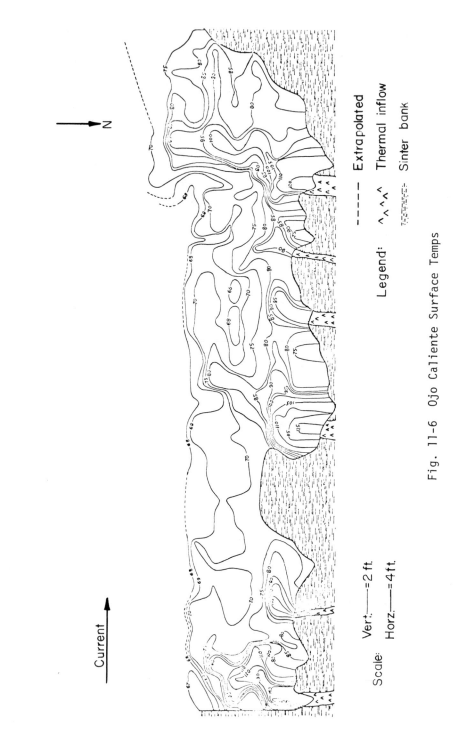

Fig. 11-6 Ojo Caliente Surface Temps

Legend: − − − − −   Extrapolated

^ ^ ^ ^   Thermal inflow

Sinter bank

Scale: Vert.——=2 ft.

Horz.——=4 ft.

Current

N

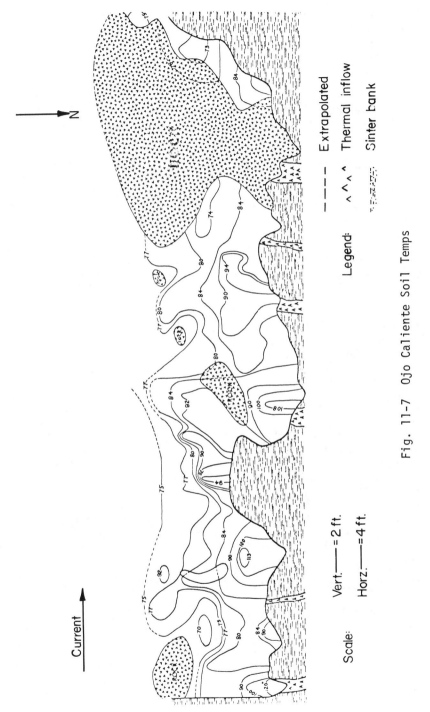

Fig. 11-7 Ojo Caliente Soil Temps

Legend: — — — Extrapolated

∧ ∧ ∧ Thermal inflow

Sinter bank

Scale: Vert. —— = 2 ft.

Horz. —— = 4 ft.

water tended to fan out in the form of a wedge spreading over a larger portion of the river. This observation was similar in findings in T.V.A. studies on Widdows Creek and other areas, Churchill and Wojtalik (1969), although they did not have the high temperatures found on the Firehole. Trout observed passing through these areas were just as apt to pass under the stratified zone next to shore as they were to move out and around the lateral boundary. Slight differences in density and viscosity no doubt contributed to the resistance to the very hot water.

In one study section on the inlet to Shoshone Lake, where a low temperature inflow entered on the west bank of the stream and a much higher gradient inflow entered almost opposite, fish were observed to move away from the low temperature boundary zone and pass under the stratified warmer water area. Depth of the stream was nearly uniform across the transect. Mixing was very evident in the west side zone and resulted in a temporary rise of approximately 1.5 F in the water column near that shore.

These limited studies in the Yellowstone area have indicated the extreme variation and complexity of thermal flow patterns into a lotic environment. It is obvious that monitoring and more observations in a naturally polluted environment are needed in the modeling of any lotic system where large thermal discharges are anticipated. It would appear that heated discharges in most situations can be modified in ways that will mitigate dangers to valuable fish and invertebrate populations at all stages of their life history. The fact that the highest temperatures produced the least pollution and the fastest dissipation of heat in many study areas is worthy of consideration and further study. This is especially important in view of the constant demands by regulatory agencies to bring any thermal effluent to as near ambient as possible. In the design of most power plant cooling devices one of the most repeated goals is to achieve rapid mixing of the discharge waters with the ambient to reduce the volume and surface area affected by temperature differences. This does not appear to be the least damaging solution as far as the natural aquatic ecosystem in Yellowstone is concerned. There is no reason to assume, however, that the situation in the Firehole is applicable to the majority of the lotic environments where thermal pollution has or will occur.

11.5 FISH RESPONSE TO ENVIRONMENTAL CHANGE

Man has a reasonably good idea of what the thermal tolerance limits of some species of fish are under many conditions. A direct response from the affected animal is, however, more apt to be accurate and timely in the case of thermal or other stress. Although our technology finds us well equipped and experienced in establishing base line studies before a thermal pollution occurs and we have no difficulty in assessing damage after kill or injury has taken place, we are painfully deficient in methodology for studying fish behavior that will signal or inform us of beginning or potential dangers so that we can prevent any damage from occurring. With this in mind, two investigations have been attempted in measuring direct response from fish when subject to thermal pollutants.

11.6 TENSOR SIGNALS

Periodically through the past decade there have been reports or claims that fish are capable of producing a low frequency vibration that would be similar to the vibrations produced by a tensing or pulling of a muscle, or cord. The reasons that they have not been fully detected in the past has been due primarily to the use of antennae in water of a di-pole construction incapable of receiving the signal. By using a simple single antenna, an amplifier, an oscilloscope and a tape recorder a number of experiments were conducted to see if the so called tensor signal could be detected and how it might be used in behavioral fish studies.

Having proved to his own satisfaction that tensor signal production from fish is a fact and potentially a very important area for study, the author attempted to use these signals as a measure of thermal and other forms of stress.

Tensor signals can be recorded on an oscilloscope or through proper amplification they can be recorded on tape for immediate or delayed listening. Normal behavior patterns of fish are usually accompanied by tensor sound signals. This increases at night or when fish are found in either deep or turbid water where vision is reduced. Each signal is different for each species of fish and will differ in intensity with the immediate behavior. Feeding response and a response to fright for example will be obviously much different.

By carefully excluding background noise, which is amazingly prevalent and complex in water, the true signals can be recorded for measurement and study. To date only two species of fish have been tested for heat response. These are the rainbow trout Salmo gairdneri Richardson and the fathead minnow Pimephales promelas Rafinesque. In both species there has been a reasonably clear identifying signal produced when temperatures have either been raised suddenly or when they have been gradually increased to a level near the suspected tolerance levels. It has been interesting to find that the response from individual fish is quite variable. This range in response must be considered should the technique ever be used for either monitoring of an area of potential pollution or if the technique is modified for laboratory evaluations of tolerance limits.

Good engineering skills will have to be incorporated into further investigations to find better ways of clearing background noise under field conditions as well as more rapid methods for separating and evaluating the signal. Physiological investigations are also needed to determine exactly where and how the signal is produced and what effects such factors as stamina or possibly disease would have on the strength and validity of the signal.

11.7 RADIO TELEMETRY

A second possible technique for recording fish response to thermal stress has been tried on a limited scale. This has resulted from an attempt to avoid the problem of individual fish sensitivity to heat and thus the wide range of signal response.

The development of very small radio transmitters for tracking fish movements has been progressing at both the University of Wyoming and at Colorado State University. By chance, an unintentional insertion of a holding pin was made into the pericardial cavity of a fish at the University of Wyoming. Instead of the anticipated continuous signal from the transmitter a rhythmic pulsing was heard on the receiver. At the time the investigator did not know what had occurred. Similar testing at Colorado State University proved that the signals were actually heartbeats of the fish. Although this offered no value in tracking studies it did suggest a possible use in the rapid detection of thermal or other pollution in the water.

Because the blood supply of the fish is constantly exposed to the external environment through the gill surfaces, any small change in environmental heat can cause a change in circulation rate or at least a response from the heart. This occurs even though the circulation of fish is very sluggish as contrasted to a warm blooded animal. The response of an increased heart beat can be transmitted by radio to a receiving station on shore for taping and interpretation.

Limited tests to date indicate some considerable possibility with this technique. Very small transmitters can be produced and when they are imbedded into styrofoam or other buoyant materials they can be carried easily by even very small fish without injury. Battery life for the transmitters can be extended by reducing the transmitting range. In the studies that have been completed so far, radio life has been extended to forty-five or more days and it is likely that this can be improved greatly without much added weight.

The advantage of the radio telemetry over the tensor signal of fish would be the possibility of a more immediate response to change in water quality than would a dependency on the fish to make a voluntary response. There is also the possibility of confusion of behavioral signals among fish, at least until such time that the definite response patterns of tensor vibrations are more clearly defined.

The major disadvantages of this system are the loss of tags and the constant threat of malfunction of the transmitters.

This later problem could be somewhat mitigated by the release of several test animals at one time or by having a ready source of new fish that could be tagged and released as soon as transmission was interrupted or failed. Tag loss under laboratory and limited field tests to date has been minimal. Several fish have been held for as long as six months without injury or loss, which is far longer than the present battery life expectancy.

Another disadvantage would be the limitation on size of fish. Fingerling or fry could not be tagged and these fish are often the most important to monitor in potential pollution situations.

It would appear that a combination of the two systems might be worthy of consideration. If the tensor signal proves to be of practical value there is little doubt that the technology needed to make more accurate recordings of the various signals could be developed.

It is possible that fish response to toxic materials in water could be transmitted in the same manner as heat detection. No investigative attempts have been made as yet in this area.

These two techniques may prove to have no real or practical value in monitoring fish behavior in relation to thermal pollution. In the process of their thorough examination, however, other devices or techniques might be found that will accomplish the objective.

REFERENCES

Alabaster, J. S., 1964, The effect of heated effluents on fish, p. 261-292. In J. S. Alabaster (Ed.) Advances in water pollution research: Vol. I, Proceedings of the International Conference held in London, Sept. 1962. The Macmillian Co., New York.

Alabaster, J. S., and A. L. Downing, 1960, The behavior of roach (Rutilus rutilus (L) in temperature gradients in a large outdoor tank: Proc. 8th session Indo-Pacific Fish. Coun. December 1958, Section III - Symposium on Fish Behavior, p. 49-71.

Argyle, R. L., 1966, Thermal dispersion of lotic waters of Yellowstone National Park: M.S. thesis, Colo. State University, June 1966, 122 p.

Berger, B. B., 1961, Does production of power pollute our rivers? Power Eng., 65(3):p. 60-61.

Brett, J. R., 1956, Some principles in the thermal requirements of fishes: Quart. Rev. Biol. 31(2):p. 75-87.

_____, 1958, Implication and assessments of environmental stress: In: The Investigation of Fish-Power Problems, University of British Columbia, p. 69-83.

_____, 1960, Therman requirements of fish---three decades of study, 1940-1960: In: Biological Problems in Water Pollution. 2nd Seminar 1959, Robert A. Taft Sanitary Engineering Center, Tech. Rept. W60-3, p. 110-117.

Churchill, M. A., and T. A. Wojtalik, 1969, Effects of heated discharges: The T.V.A. experience, Nuclear News, Sept. 1969, p. 80-86.

Coutant, C. C., 1962, The effect of a heated water effluent upon the macro-invertebrate riffle fauna of the Delaware River, Proc. Penn. Acad. Sci., p. 58-71.

Duttweiler, D. W., F. J. Jeffers, A. L. Kowal, W. M. Reyes, J. J. Lentz and W. M. Sanders, 1961, Heat dissipation in flowing streams: Johns Hopkins Univ. Dept. San. Eng. and Water Resources, report of the 1960-61 Advanced Seminar, 122 p.

Edinger, J. E., and J. C. Geyer, 1965, Heat exchange in the environment: Johns Hopkins Univ. Dept. San. Eng. and Water Resources, 253 p.

Ferguson, R. C., 1958, The preferred temperature of fish and their mid-summer distribution in temperate lakes and streams: J. Fish. Res. Bd. Canada 15(4): p. 607-624.

Garside, E. T., and J. S. Tait, 1958, Preferred temperature of rainbow trout (Salmo gairdnerii Richardson) and its unusual relationship to acclimatization temperature, Canad. J. Zool. 36, p. 564-567.

11-22

Jones, Erichsen, J. R., 1964, Thermal pollution: the effect
of heated effluents: Chapt. 13, Fish and River Pollution,
Butterworth and Co., London, p. 153-168.

Krenkel, P. A., and F. A. Parker, 1969, Biological aspects of
thermal pollution: Vanderbilt Univ. Press, 407 p.

Leclerc, E., 1964, Self-purification of fresh water streams as
affected by temperature and by the content of oxygen,
nitrogen and other substances: p. 51-62, In: J. S.
Alabaster (Ed.) Advances in water pollution research:
Vol. I., Proceedings of the International Conference
held in London, Sept. 1962, The MacMillian Co., New York.

Levin, A. A., T. J. Birch, R. E. Hillman and G. E. Raines,
1972, Thermal discharges: Ecological effects: In:
Environmental Science and Technology, Vol. 6, No. 3,
March 1972, p. 224-230.

Markowski, S., 1959, The cooling water of power stations: a
new factor in the environment of Maine and fresh water
invertebrates: J. Animal Ecol., 28: p. 243-258.

Mihursky, J. A., and V. S. Kennedy, 1967, A water temperature
criteria to protect aquatic life: In: A Symposium on
Water Quality Criteria to Protect Aquatic Life, Amer.
Fish. Soc. Special Publ., No. 4, p. 20-32.

Simon, J. R., 1962, Yellowstone fishes: Yellowstone Library
and Museum Assn., publ. Western Litho-Print Inc.,
Billings, Montana, 49 p.

Chapter 12

AGRICULTURAL IMPACT ON WATER QUALITY
IN WESTERN RIVERS

by

Gaylord V. Skogerboe, Associate Professor of Agricultural
Engineering, Colorado State University,
Fort Collins, Colorado

Chapter 12

AGRICULTURAL IMPACT ON WATER QUALITY
IN WESTERN RIVERS

12.1 INTRODUCTION

Irrigation is one of the most important agricultural practices developed by man, with irrigation being practiced in some
form since the earliest recorded history of agriculture. The
economic base for many ancient civilizations was provided by
irrigation. Indians of the western hemisphere were irrigating
crops long before the discovery of the New World (Rohn, 1963).
Much of the economy of the western United States depends on
irrigation, which has been the dominant factor in the development of land and water resources in the arid and semi-arid
regions of the western states. Irrigation is practiced on about
10 percent of the total cropped land in the United States, but
this land produces approximately 25 percent of the Nation's
total crop value. (National Technical Advisory Committee,
FWPCA, 1968). Irrigation farming not only increases productivity,
but it also provides flexibility which allows shifting from the
relatively few dryland crops to many other crops which may be
in greater demand. Irrigation contributes to strengthening
other facets of a region's economy in that it creates employment opportunities in the processing and marketing of agricultural products.

The practice of irrigation has detrimental effects on
environmental water quality, just as do many other of man's
activities. It has long been recognized that the quality of
water draining from irrigated areas was materially degraded
from that of the irrigation water applied. Agriculturists
have viewed this as a natural consequence of the many processes
involved, and little attention has been given to the possibility that progress could be made toward controlling or allev-
iating the quality degradation caused to our water resources.

The agricultural impact on water quality is a major concern in the West because of two primary reasons. As compared
with the more humid areas of the East, western rivers are
more fully utilized, with large quantities of water being diverted for agriculture. Secondly, many of the western agricultural soils are high in natural salts, which have not been
leached through recent centuries because of sparse rainfall.

Irrigation return flow constitutes a large portion of the
flow in many streams of the western United States. Some degree
of salt concentration due to irrigation has been accepted as
the price for irrigation development. However, there are areas
where quality degradation has been a serious matter for some
time. As pressures on water resources increase, there is a
mounting concern for proper control of such serious water
quality deterioration. The need for more precise information
as a basis for wise action has been brought sharply into focus.

There is a great dearth of information concerning the exact role of irrigation return flows in surface and groundwater quality problems.

Many of the irrigated lands, particularly in western arid areas, contain large quantities of salt and are therefore classed as saline soils. Some lands are high in exchangeable sodium and are referred to as being sodic. Crop production is reduced on one-quarter of the irrigated lands in the western United States due to saline soils. Salinity is a hazard to half of the irrigated acreage in the West. California, which has a greater acreage of irrigated land than any other state, also contains the largest acreage of salt-affected soils. The states of South Dakota, Nevada, Hawaii, Utah, and Colorado have more than one-third of the irrigated lands being affected by highly saline soils.

The impaired crop production mentioned above is not limited to the western United States, but is a major problem in many areas of the world. The portions of the world facing the greatest population pressures are the same areas which have the least amount of additional land available for agriculture. In such areas, increased food production must come from more intensive farming with consequent increased yields. Although there is a great need to increase the productivity of such lands, agricultural production is being damaged due to rising groundwater tables and increased salinity in the soils and groundwater supplies. Bower (1966) has estimated that more than a third of the world's irrigated land is plagued by salt problems.

Whether concerned about reducing water quality degradation resulting from irrigated agriculture, or maintaining the agricultural productivity of existing croplands throughout the world, many of the solutions are identical. In each case, improved water management practices are needed, particularly in the application of water on the farm.

The National Academy of Sciences (Committee on Pollution, 1966) has made projections for water requirements in this country at the turn of the century. Essentially, their studies show a need for doubling the efficiency of water use by irrigation in order to satisfy future needs.

12.2 WATER QUALITY PROBLEMS

Whenever water is diverted from a river for irrigation use, the quality of the return flow is degraded. The return flow mixes with the natural flows in the river. This mixture is then available to downstream users to be diverted to satisfy their water demands. This process of diversion and return flow may be repeated many times along the course of a river. In the case of the original diversion, if the increase in pollutants contained in the return flow is small in comparison to the total flow in the river, the water quality would probably not be degraded to such an extent that it would be unfit for use by the next downstream user.

If the quantity of pollutants in the return flow is large in relation to the river flow, then it is very likely that the water is not suitable for the next user unless the water is treated to remove objectionable constituents. Since water is diverted many times from the major rivers, the river flows show a continual degradation of quality in the downstream direction. As the water resources become more fully developed and utilized, without controls, the quality in the lower reaches of the river will likely be degraded to such a point that the remaining flows will be unsuitable for many uses, or previous uses of the waters arriving at the lower river basin no longer will be possible.

Usually, the quality of water coming from the mountainous watersheds in the West is excellent. At the base of the mountain ranges, large quantities of water are diverted to valley croplands. Much of the diverted water is lost to the atmosphere by evapotranspiration (perhaps one-half to two-thirds of the diverted water), with the remaining water supply being irrigation return flow. This return flow will either be surface runoff, shallow horizontal subsurface flow, or will move vertically through the soil profile until it reaches a perched water table or the groundwater reservoir, where it will remain to be pumped or be transported through the groundwater reservoir until it reaches a river channel.

That portion of the water supply which has been diverted for irrigation but lost by evapotranspiration (consumed) is essentially salt-free. Therefore, the irrigation return flow will contain most of the salts originally in the water supply. The surface irrigation return flow will usually contain only slightly higher salt concentrations than the original water supply, but in some cases, the salinity may be increased significantly. Thus, the water percolating through the soil profile contains the majority of salt left behind by the water returned to the atmosphere as vapor through the phenomena of evaporation and transpiration. Consequently, the percolating soil water contains a higher concentration of salts. This is referred to as the "concentrating" effect.

As the water moves through the soil profile, it may pick up additional salts by dissolution. In addition, some salts may be precipitated in the soil, while there will be an exchange between some salt ions in the water and in the soil. The salts picked up by the water in addition to the salts which were in the water applied to the land are termed salt "pickup." The total salt load is the sum of the original mass of salt in the applied water as the result of the concentrating effect plus the salt pickup.

Whether irrigation return flows come from surface runoff or have returned to the system via the soil profile, the water can be expected to undergo a variety of quality changes due to varying exposure conditions. Drainage from surface sources consists mainly (there will be some precipitation runoff) of surface runoff from irrigated land. Because of its limited

contact and exposure to the soil surface, the following changes
in quality might be expected between application and runoff:
(a) dissolved solids concentration only slightly increased;
(b) addition of variable and fluctuating amounts of pesticides; (c) addition of variable amounts of fertilizer elements;
(d) an increase in sediments and other colloidal material; (e)
crop residues and other debris floated from the soil surface;
and (f) increased bacterial content.

    Drainage water that has moved through the soil profile
will experience different changes in quality from surface runoff. Because of its more intimate contact with the soil and
the dynamic soil-plant-water regime, the following changes in
quality are predictable: (a) considerable increase in dissolved
solids concentration; (b) the distribution of various cations
and anions may be quite different; (c) variation in the total
salt load depending on whether there has been deposition or
leaching; (d) little or no sediment or colloidal material;
(e) generally increased nitrate content unless the applied
water is unusually high in nitrates; (f) little or no phosphorus
content; (g) general reduction of oxidizable organic substances;
and (h) reduction of pathogenic organisms and coliform bacteria.
Thus, either type of return flow will affect the receiving water
in proportion to respective discharges and the relative quality
of the receiving water.

    The quality of irrigation water and return flow is deter-
mined largely by the amount and nature of the dissolved and
suspended materials they contain. In natural waters, the
materials are largely dissolved inorganic salts leached from
rocks and minerals of the soils contacted by the water. Irrigation, municipal and industrial use and reuse of water concentrates these salts and adds additional kinds and amounts
of pollutants. Many insecticides, fungicides, bactericides,
herbicides, nematocides, as well as plant hormones, detergents,
salts of heavy metals, and many organic compounds, render
water less fit for irrigation and other beneficial uses.

12.3 MAJOR PROBLEM AREAS

    The major water quality problem areas in the western
United States resulting from irrigated agriculture are shown
in Fig. 12-1. The problems will become more critical in each
area as the demand for water continues to increase.

    Colorado River Basin. The variety of water quality problems
resulting from irrigation return flow can be illustrated with
a few examples. The major water quality problem in the western
United States is salinity, with the Colorado River Basin being
one of the more serious problem areas. In addition to the
problems caused by large quantities of good quality water being
transported outside of the Basin, there is a tremendous problem
due to salt pickup by the irrigation return flows passing
through the soil profile and over saline shale beds before
returning to the river. Also, there are a number of mineral-

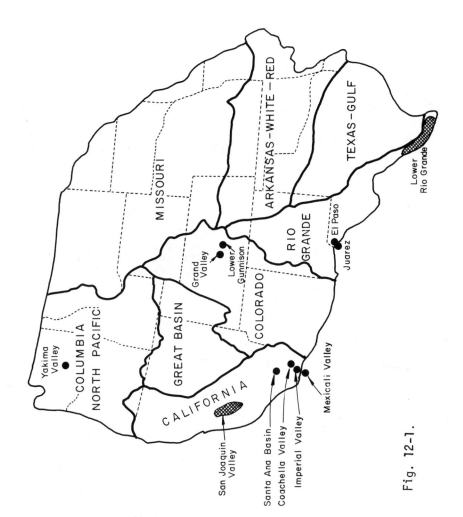

Fig. 12-1.

ized springs which further aggravate the salinity problem. The
highest rates of salt pickup among the irrigated valleys within the basin occur in Grand Valley, Colorado and Castle Valley,
Utah where the rate is about 8 tons of salt a year for each
irrigated acre. Salt pickup rates of roughly 6 tons per acre
per year result from irrigation in the Uncompahgre River Valley
and Lower Gunnison River Valley, with both valleys being
located in Colorado. High rates of salt pickup also occur at
Big Sandy Creek Basin in Wyoming, Ashley Valley in Utah, and the
Duchesne River Basin in Utah. Of the total salt load reaching
Hoover Dam, the Environmental Protection Agency (1971) estimates
that 37 percent is the result of salt pickup from deep percolating irrigation return flows.

The Colorado River Board of California (1970) has made
predictions of future salinity at Parker Dam (diversion point
for the Metropolitan Water District of Southern California)
and Imperial Dam (diversion point for All-American Canal which
serves Imperial and Coachella Valleys) based upon anticipated
upstream water development (Fig. 12-2). By the year 2000, the
projected salinity levels at Parker Dam and Imperial Dam will
be 1110 ppm and 1340 ppm, respectively, whereas the present
levels are 740 ppm and 850 ppm. The estimated damages to California by the turn of the century could amount to $40 million
per year (Colorado River Board of California, 1970). In addition, Arizona and the Republic of Mexico would also suffer
severe damages.

Imperial and Coachella Valleys, Southern California. The
high concentrations of salt in the water supply to Imperial
Valley, combined with problems of tight soils and high summer
temperatures, result in many difficulties for the farmer in
growing a crop. The biggest problem is maintaining a salt
balance in the root zone. A salt balance for the valley as a
whole was first achieved in 1949. The option of using sprinkler irrigation is unavailable to the Imperial Valley farmer
in many instances because the combination of salt and water
deposited on a leaf in one rotation of the sprinkler has dried
and left only the salt, with consequent toxic effects due to
salt concentration and absorption, before the sprinkler can
complete another rotation. Salt toxicity results in the demise
of plant foliage. Because of the tight soils, with consequent
low infiltration rates, there is a real difficulty in getting
enough water to pass through the root zone to assure that
there is no salt accumulation in the root zone, which would
result in lower crop yields. Cultural practices play a critical role in the infiltration of the irrigation water into the
soil profile. Also, seed bed preparation is very critical.
Changing the depth of seed placement one-half inch may result
in the seed not germinating due to rapidly changing salinities
in the soil solution with depth as a result of furrow irrigation.

The annual quantity of irrigation return flow from Imperial
Valley is 900,000 acre-feet, while Coachella Valley returns
100,000 acre-feet. The return flows from these two areas are

essentially the total inflow to the Salton Sea, which is approximately one million acre-feet per year. Of the total diverted
to the valley, a minimum of 10-15 percent is required for
leaching in order to maintain a favorable salt balance in the
root zone. The leaching requirement of 10-15 percent would
be satisfactory if equilibrium conditions existed. In practice, in order to gain on salt removal, a greater amount of
leaching is required. The Imperial Irrigation District estimates the leaching requirement to be 20 percent to accomplish
present levels of salt removal wherein the total annual quantity of salts removed is greater than the annual quantity of
salts brought into the valley. Increasing salinity levels in
the Colorado River will also increase the required leaching
fraction. Based upon salt measurements of the inflow and outflow waters, calcium and magnesium carbonates and gypsum are
being precipitated in the soil, while sodium and potassium
chlorides are being removed from the soil. The precipitation
and exchange of salt ions occur because the Colorado River water
is high in calcuim, bicarbonate, and sulfate. The necessity
for maintaining a salt balance is somewhat alleviated by the
high proportion of dissolved salt that is gypsum, which pre-
cipitates as an innocuous salt in the soil profile.

Salt balance studies have been reported for Coachella
Valley, which is located on the north and west side of the
Salton Sea, by Bower, Spencer, and Weeks (1969). The 60,000
acres of irrigated land is served by the Coachella Branch of
the All-American Canal, which diverts water from the Colorado
River at Imperial Dam. Part of the Coachella Canal is concrete-
lined and water diverted from the canal is transported in concrete pipelines to the individual farms, with the water being
measured throughout the system. The delivery and use of large
amounts of water from the Colorado River beginning in 1948
resulted in high groundwater levels developing in the valley.
To alleviate this situation, tile drainage was installed.
Presently, more than half of the lands have tile drainage. The
studies showed that a salt balance (the annual tonnage of
salts leaving the irrigated area, which enters the Salton Sea,
is equal to or exceeds the annual tonnage of salts entering
the valley from the Coachella Canal) was achieved when half of
the irrigated land had tile drainage and the leaching fraction
was 30 percent.

The irrigation return flow from Imperial Valley and Coachella Valley has a unique role related to water quality problems in the Salton Sea. At the time the Salton Sea was formed,
in the period 1905 to 1907, it had essentially the same salinity as the Colorado River. Prior to this time, free salt was
being mined in the area inundated by the Salton Sea. The
present salinity of Salton Sea is approximately 40,000 ppm.
At the time the salinity approached that of the ocean, the
California Department of Fish and Game transplanted salt-water
sport fish into the Salton Sea. For some time, these sport
fish had difficulty surviving due to a lack of forage fish.

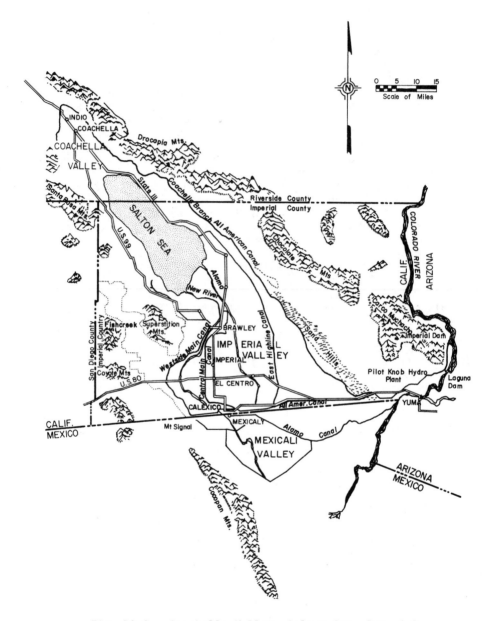

Fig. 12-2.   Coachella Valley, Salton Sea, Imperial
Valley, and Mexicali Valley.

Finally, a forage fish, the Corvino from Mexico, was found
which would survive in the Salton Sea. Now, with salinities
reaching higher levels than the ocean, it looks like much of
this salt-water sport fishing will be lost. There is some talk
of desalination. Eventually, the Salton Sea will assume many
of the characteristics of Great Salt Lake. Reducing the quantity of irrigation return flow reaching the Salton Sea would
only aggravate the present problems.

Wellton-Mohawk District, Arizona. Attempts to develop irrigation in the Wellton-Mohawk District of the Gila River Valley
were unsuccessful until Colorado River water diversion was
authorized by the Gila Project in 1947. The Gila River proved
an undependable supply as upstream development progressed, and
irrigation from wells failed as water levels declined and the
ground water quality deteriorated from continual evapotranspiration and recirculation (Moser, 1967). Soon after the introduction of Colorado River water, the drainage problem became
serious and was solved by the selective placement of wells to
remove the poor quality groundwater. A concrete-lined channel
was constructed to convey the poor quality drainage from the
valley without creating further drainage and salinity problems
in the lower lands. Although this was a more expensive scheme,
it was justified on the basis of benefits derived from preventing
further salt damages to productive lands. Further benefits were
derived by conveying the saline drainage waters to the Colorado
River downstream from Morelos Dam, the diversion point for
irrigation water going into Mexico. If at some future time
the quality of the Wellton-Mohawk drainage water improves
sufficiently, it may again be used as a portion of Mexico's
supply. Until that time, the Mexican water quality is being
protected by having the saline drainage water bypass Morelos
Dam. This is cited as an example of diversion away from a portion of a river system for the purpose of controlling the
quality of the water resources in the basin. Another example
of conveying drainage waters to a discharge point other than
the river system is in the San Joaquin Valley of central
California.

Rio Grande Basin. Salt balance studies have been conducted
in the Rio Grande Basin for a number of years. The results of
a 20-year study were reported by Wilcox (1962) and are summarized in Table 1. Several diversions for irrigation occur along
the Rio Grande (Fig. 12-3) between Otowi Bridge near Santa Fe,
New Mexico and Fort Quitman, Texas below El Paso. The four
main irrigated areas at the time of the study were as follows:
(a) 80,000 acres between Otowi Bridge and San Marcial; (b)
15,000 acres between Caballo Dam and Leasburg Dam; (c) 70,000
acre between Leasburg Dam and El Paso; and (d) 85,000 acres
between El Paso and Fort Quitman. A close correlation exists
between the irrigated areas, decreased discharge, and increased
salt load of the river. While the discharge is decreased to
one-fifth its original value, the dissolved solids concentration
is increased almost 10-fold and the total salt load is almost

12-9

Table 12-1. Mean annual discharge and dissolved solids, Rio Grande.[1]

Station	Discharge 1,000 acre-ft	Dissolved Solids ppm	Dissolved Solids 1,000 tons
Otowi Bridge, N.M.	1,079	221	324
San Marcial, N.M.	853	449	520
Elephant Butte Outlet, N.M.	790	478	514
Caballo Dam, N.M.	781	515	547
Leasburg Dam, N.M.	743	551	557
El Paso, Texas	525	787	562
Fort Quitman, Texas	203	1,691	467

[1]Adapted from Wilcox (1962).

doubled. Although the salt balance appears favorable between all stations except El Paso and Fort Quitman, much more detailed information is required before positive statements regarding the salt status of the irrigated soils could be made. The overall effects have been almost totally attributed to the use of water for irrigation. The sources of salts returned to the river have not been identified. The dangers of such general-ized conclusions can readily be seen. More detailed investigations will be required in order to suggest suitable and adequate control measures.

The high salinities encountered in the Rio Grande have resulted in agricultural damages to El Paso Valley because the more salt-sensitive crops cannot be grown in this area. The Mesilla Valley, which is roughly 40 miles upstream, has a wider range of crops that can be grown because of better quality water. The Hudspeth Irrigation District, which is located below El Paso, has encountered serious problems due to high concentrations of sodium salts, which drastically affect crop production.

Long-term projections for El Paso show that municipal and industrial water needs will require all of the flows in the Rio Grande, but it is presently anticipated that a large amount of this future water demand will have to come from groundwater supplies. The problem is compounded by the rapid growth rate of Juarez, which is located across the river from El Paso in the Republic of Mexico. Degradation of groundwater quality due to irrigation return flows moving through the soil profile could result in additional treatment costs when such water supplies are used to satisfy municipal and industrial water requirements. At the same time, studies are needed to evaluate the role of irrigation return flows in recharging the groundwater basin.

Agricultural lands in the lower Rio Grande Basin experience some of the same cultural problems encountered in Imperial Valley, namely tight soils and poor quality water. Irrigation return flows are not subject to reuse except in drought years when farmers pump from the drainage canals to supplement their supply. Consequently, there has been no real concern for the quality of drainage waters. A large part of the irrigated area is tile-drained to control groundwater levels and about

80 percent of the drainage water from the Texas side does not return to the river, but drains directly eastward to the Gulf Coast. No information is available regarding the quantity of nitrates, phosphates, or pesticides being carried to the Gulf by this route. Drains from the Mexican side do return to the Rio Grande and are of very poor quality. This occurs below Falcon Reservoir which supplies irrigation water to both Texas and Mexico. Careful farm water management and special cultural practices are required in order to move salts below the root zone and insure a productive agriculture. The quality problems requiring further study for possible control are those resulting from nutrient and pesticide transport to the drainageways and eventually into the Gulf of Mexico.

A recent study in the lower Rio Grande Valley of south Texas (Casbeer and Trock, 1969) has shown the need for institutional reform to promote efficient water resource utilization. The institutional influences that were shown to hinder improved water management practices were antiquated water rights doctrine and an unusually large number (34) of water control and irrigation districts in a three-county area. The major recommendations for reform included: (1) negotiable water rights; (2) consolidation of water districts into one master district; and (3) rehabilitation of outdated delivery and drainage facilities. Similar reforms could well be recommended for many of the irrigated valleys of the western states.

Central Valley of California.

Sacramento Valley. The Sacramento Valley represents quite a different problem with respect to irrigation return flows, as opposed to the San Joaquin Valley. The annual flow of the Sacramento River is somewhere between 14 and 18 million acre-feet per year. There are one million acres of irrigated land in the valley. The quality of the water supply is very good. The Sacramento River outflow provides dilution and flushing for the Delta area of the San Francisco Bay system. In order to maintain the quality of water within the Delta, the State does not want to allow further degradation of the Sacramento River, along with controlling waste discharges into the Delta. The California State Water Resources Control Board intends to maintain the quality of the Sacramento River.

The Sacramento Valley is a major rice producing area. Rice is planted by airplane, fertilized by airplane (phosphates are applied prior to planting on dry ground), and insecticides are applied by airplane. The major pollutants resulting from these practices are nitrates, phosphates, and pesticides.

One of the present problems concerning the Delta area of the Central Valley is that a portion of the water supply is being diverted by the State Water Project from the Sacramento River Basin to southern California. Limited drainage problems in Sacramento Valley are occurring because of increased irrigation provided by additional surface water supplies being used on the west side of the valley. These surface water

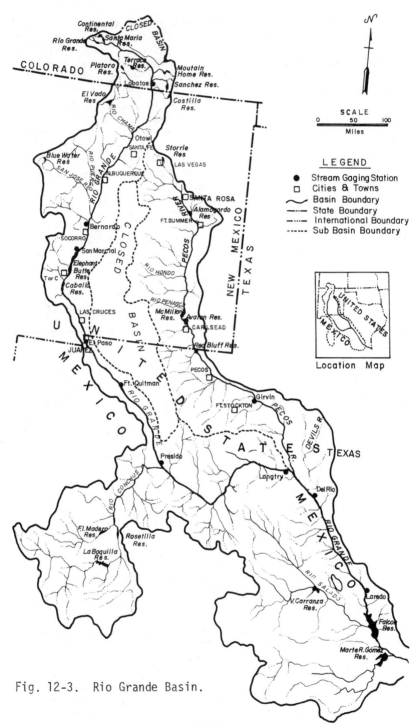

Fig. 12-3. Rio Grande Basin.

supplies are replacing the former pumped water supplies in some areas. At the present time, there are approximately 50,000 acres which have high water tables resulting from excessive water application.

San Joaquin Valley. In contrast to the Sacramento Valley to the north, the San Joaquin Valley experiences considerably greater water quality degradation in its irrigation return flows. The valley contains about 8 million acres of irrigable land of which about half is presently irrigated and approximately half of that acreage has a potential drainage problem. This comprises about 40 percent of the irrigable land of the State, but without water imports, has available only one-sixth of the State's water resources. Importation of water from the north resulting from the California State Water Project, the Federal Delta-Mendota Canal, and the San Luis Project has allowed vast new acreage to be placed under irrigation (Pillsbuty and Johnston, 1965), particularly on the arid western side of the valley. The irrigation water applied is of good quality with a total salinity of less than 500-700 ppm. Due to the high concentration of natural salts and native nitrates in the soils, drainage from the area will have salinities as high as 20,000 ppm, which may be reduced to the 3,000 ppm range after 50 years of irrigation and its concomitant leaching of the soil profiles. This severe water quality degradation precludes the reuse of the drainage water and has forced the consideration of drainage canals to convey the irrigation return flows to the ocean via San Francisco Bay. Portions of a federally constructed San Luis Drain have already been completed but are not yet conveying drainage waters. Farm tile drainage systems, which are not extensively used at the present time, return either to the San Joaquin River or are pumped back into the canal delivery system.

A unique problem exists in the San Joaquin drainage waters due to the relatively high nitrate content. A few studies to date have indicated the major source in this area to be natural nitrates in the soils and to a lesser extent, applied fertilizers. The possibility of damage to San Francisco Bay by release of these nitrates prompted extensive studies into potential treatment measures that might be used for their removal. Algae stripping and biological denitrification methods have been shown to be feasible solutions. Other researchers, working with submerged tile drains, have achieved a smaller degree of success. The cost of treatment is still high and further studies will no doubt be conducted before a final decision on the treatment scheme to be used will be made. The economic and legal problems involved may very well turn out to be the major blocks to solving the problem. Economists have investigated the abilities of the irrigators to bear the costs of state-federal drains to convey irrigation return flows out of the valley. It is doubted that farmer acceptance of these added costs will be achieved until they are forced to do so. This still leaves the added cost of treatment to be considered and a further decision regarding proper and just allocation of those costs.

Under our present system, controlling practices on-the-farm is virtually impossible unless some means can be developed whereby there will be economic incentives for reducing water pollution. Extensive demonstration and education programs will be required to promote acceptance of improved farm management practices. This is true not only in the San Joaquin Valley, but in other critical problem areas as well. Control of leaching practices through improved water management in the newly irrigated fringes of the valley may be necessary to protect the lower lying lands from excessively saline groundwater seepage. Detailed salt mass balance studies will be required to evaluate the greatest long-term benefits and to protect those lands placed in jeopardy by the problem of increased salinity in drainage waters. These also are required to develop and recommend potential salinity control measures that could be most effective in protecting the quality of surface and groundwater resources. Some trade-off between the need for crop production and the need for reduced pollution may be necessary.

Columbia River Basin. The water quality problems resulting from irrigation return flow are extremely varied in the Columbia River Basin. Problems involving nitrates, phosphates, nematodes, sediments, and pesticides are prevalent in this region. Attempts to undertake solutions to these problems are important, particularly since the problems will increase in complexity as the water supplies become more fully utilized.

Yakima Valley, Washington. One of the major areas of irrigation return flow quality problems is the Yakima Valley. There are presently approximately 400,000 acres of land under irrigation in the valley, with the potential for another 300,000 acres to be irrigated if the water supply were made available to some of the higher lands. An extensive irrigation return flow study in the Yakima River Basin (Sylvester and Seabloom, 1963) has shown the major water quality problems resulting from irrigation. The following discussion summarizes the findings of that study.

The Yakima River drains an area of 6,120 sq. mi., including over 400,000 acres of land irrigated for the production of a variety of crops (Fig. 12-4). It has a mean annual flow of 3,900 cfs which is partially regulated by six reservoirs in the headwaters. Natural water quality variations occur with changes in the rate of runoff and reservoir releases. In the lower 80 miles of the valley, the summer flow of 1200 to 2000 cfs consists almost entirely of irrigation return flow, and during the irrigation season, the entire flow of the river is diverted several times for irrigation use. The study revealed that irrigation return flow was the major factor influencing the overall quality of the Yakima River and that leaching and subsurface drainage were responsible for the increased salinity and change in ionic composition of

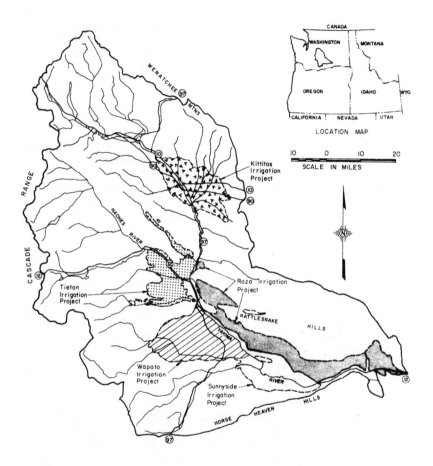

Fig. 12-4. Irrigation Development in the Yakima Valley

salts in the river. Thus, irrigation return flows were the major contributors to the 10-fold increase in dissolved solids, from 40-50 ppm in the headwaters to 400-500 ppm below the irrigated areas. Much worse water quality degradation results from sediment transport and nutrient releases to the river. Over-irrigation and fertilizer applications in excess of crop requirements were found to be the major causes of water quality degradation downstream. Increased turbidity (suspended solids) was particularly bothersome to downstream irrigators and one of the main reasons why sprinkler methods are not used more extensively. Improved water and fertilizer management practices were suggested as major factors in improving the quality of irrigation return flows in the entire valley area. The lack of adequate control over water delivery and water use results in over-irrigation. Although the water allotment is from three to three and one-half acre-feet per acre, the actual use was found to be as much as four to six acre-feet per acre per season.

Faulkner and Bolander (1970) have investigated the transportation of nematodes in surface irrigation return flow, as well as the establishment of plant parasitic nematodes upon host plants. Their findings in Yakima Valley showed that plants irrigated with surface irrigation return flow became heavily infested with parasitic nematodes. At the same time, plants irrigated with groundwater supplies did not become infested.

In summary, the major water quality problems occurring in the Yakima River Basin and other irrigated areas in the State of Washington are: sediment transport, nitrates, salinity (only in localized areas), nematodes, phosphorus on sediments, high bacterial (coliform) content in surface return flows, and increased temperature of surface return flows.

Snake River Valley. Irrigation return flows from the three million acres of irrigated land in the Snake River Basin present no really serious salinity problems. If the total potential of eight million irrigable acres were developed, water quality problems could develop. The chief reason for the quality of flow in the Snake River being maintained satisfactorily is that several large natural springs flow into the river downstream from the major irrigated areas. The Thousand Springs area below Twin Falls, Idaho contributes an average inflow of 4.3 million acre-feet per year. The quality of this inflow is very good (even better than Snake River water diverted above Twin Falls at Milner Dam) and results in a large dilution effect.

A recent study by Carter, Bondurant, and Robbins (1971) of the water-soluble nitrate, phosphate, and total salt balance on a large irrigation tract in the Twin Falls area is an excellent example of the type of investigations needed in many irrigation return flow problem areas. Typical information from such studies includes: quality and quantity of applied water, surface runoff, and subsurface drainage; fate of applied water; and the source of water quality problems from irrigation return flows.

The major problems arising from this large tract were the nitrate-nitrogen contributed by subsurface drainage and sediment transport in surface return flows. The subsurface drainage water from the area contained lower total salt concentrations than irrigation water diverted at many locations in the Colorado and Rio Grande River basins. In areas not served by a canal system, some salt problems have developed from pumping ground-water with salt concentrations as high as 3,000 micro-mhos (electrical conductivity).

Examples of excessive water usage in areas of ample supply are the unusually high water duties allotted. In the Burley, Idaho area, the water duty (acre-feet of water diverted during the irrigation season for each acre of land) is approximately 6.5 acre-feet per acre per irrigation season; in the Rupert area, it is roughly 9 acre-feet per acre; and in the Rigby area of the upper Snake, the water duty goes as high as almost 13 acre-feet per acre. These are totally unrealistic when it is realized that crops (in Twin Falls tract, for example) require from 23 inches (spring grain) to 42 inches (irrigated pasture) estimated evapotranspiration for the entire year (Carter, Bondurant, and Robbins, 1971). In some rivers, the large quantities of seepage and deep percolation losses may benefit downstream water users because the return flows may coincide with periods of low streamflow and high water demands by crops. These problems fall within the realm of water management and serve to illustrate some of the antiquated institutional con-straints in approaching optimum development of water resources. Although a number of irrigated valleys having high water diver-sion rates do not presently create serious water quality pro-blems, such practices become more critical as the water resources of the river basin become more fully utilized.

Odessa, Wahington area. The Odessa area in the State of Washington has pumped domestic water from a shallow aquifer which occurs at depths of about 200 feet. Later, wells were drilled for purposes of supplying water to irrigated lands. These irrigation wells were drilled into deeper aquifers at depths of 400 to 700 feet below the ground surface. The return flows from the irrigated lands have now contaminated the shallow domestic wells. The drilling of irrigation wells began as a means of supplemental water supply for irrigation, but the area is now being more intensively irrigated and higher cash value crops are being grown. Also, the small lakes in the area are used for irrigation, but recreational potentials may be lost because of deteriorating water quality due to irrigation return flows.

The East High Project of the Columbia Basin, which would consist of approximately 500,000 acres of irrigated land, would also add to the problem in the Odessa area. The present problems in this area due to the development of groundwater supplies, and the consequent problem of irrigation return flows, would be considerably aggravated by the additional irrigation of 500,000 acres of new land.

Horse Heaven Hills, Washington. The Horse Heaven Hills
area, which is located south of the Yakima River, has approximately 200,000 acres that could be easily placed under irrigation. Another 300,000 acres could be potentially placed
under irrigation. The last 300,000 acres would create more
of an irrigation return flow problem because this area consists of rolling hills and consequently would be faced with
sediment erosion. These lands also contain over 6 million
tons of leachable soil salts, which would be removed in
drainage waters upon irrigation development. This is a
typical problem for many of the agricultural lands in Washington which might be placed under irrigation in the future.

Lower Columbia Basin. A significant problem in the
sandy soil areas of the lower Columbia River Basin is the
early season irrigation for wind erosion control. This sandy
area encompasses roughly 100,000 to 200,000 acres. Sprinkler
irrigation is used to apply 3-5 inches of water from the time
of pre-plant until early leaf stage for potatoes and beets.
Much of the fertilizer applied prior to planting is leached
from the root zone before any significant plant growth occurs.

The problem of high nitrates in groundwater came into
focus in the lower Columbia River Basin during 1962, when two
cases of nitrate poisoning were reported. Subsequent analysis
of well-water in this area by the U.S. Bureau of Reclamation
disclosed that the water supplies from many wells contained
nitrate concentrations ranging from 50 to 500 ppm. The
source of this nitrate, whether it be from fertilizers or
natural soil deposits, must be investigated before any recommendations on water or fertilizer practices can reasonably be
initiated.

Santa Ana Basin, Southern California. The University of
California, both at Riverside and Davis, has been deeply involved
in studies in the Santa Ana River Basin. There are roughly
300,000 acres of irrigated land in the basin. The Santa Ana
Water Planning Agency requested that a survey be made of nitrogen
inputs in the valley, where the nitrogen is going, what nitrate
problems exist, and recommend management practices to improve
these problems.

The problems consist of water and fertilizer management
on these irrigated lands, municipal-industrial wastewaters,
as well as the disposal of animal wastes on the land.

With respect to fertilizer efficiency, there are some
examples of vegetable crops in Santa Ana Basin where 300 to
400 pounds of nitrogen per crop per acre are needed but the
application rate is more nearly 1,000 pounds of nitrogen per
acre, with some cases as high as 1,700 pounds of nitrogen per
acre. The higher usages of nitrogen are usually related to
higher water usage as well. Thus, nitrogen efficiency can be
related to water use efficiency, as well as management efficiency, with excessive water application leading to excessive
leaching of plant nutrients before they can be utilized by
the crop.

The basin is divided into two portions, an upper basin and a lower basin. This basin is divided by a natural dike almost at the county line (Orange County). Also, there is a reservoir located near this dike. The groundwater table is fairly deep, but the salinity of this groundwater is increasing with time. The planning agency is very concerned about this increased salinity. It would be desirable to control the amount of salts and nitrates reaching the groundwater and, consequently, the amount of salts and nitrates reaching the reservoir at the county line. This reservoir has been the water supply for appreciable groundwater recharge in Orange County.

Bear River, Utah. The headwaters of the Bear River are located in Utah. The river travels into the southwest portion of Wyoming, thence flows across southeastern Idaho and returns to northern Utah, where it terminates in the Great Salt Lake and is lost by evaporation. In the meantime, the flows have been diverted a number of times for irrigation. Flood irrigation is practiced on much of the upstream lands, with downstream users being dependent upon the return flow. Before reaching the Great Salt Lake, the flows of the Bear River pass through the Bear River Migratory Bird Refuge near Brigham City, Utah. The quality of the flows traveling through the refuge has been deteriorated due to irrigation return flow, surface water evaporation, and evapotranspiration by phreatophytes. The quality problem becomes serious during periods of low flow when most of the water is irrigation return flow. Although the irrigation return flow is essential, from a quantity standpoint, during periods of low flow, the poor quality of this water limits its usefulness.

Carson River, Nevada. The Carson River (Fig. 12-5) has some similarities to the Bear River. The headwaters of the Carson River are in the Sierra Nevada Mountains. The flow is generally in an easterly direction. Large quantities of water are diverted at the base of the mountains to irrigate forage crops in Carson Valley. Eventually, the flows returning to the river are stored in Lahontan Reservoir, which is one of the earlier U.S. Bureau of Reclamation projects, just upstream from Fallon, Nevada. The stored waters are used to irrigate lands in the Fallon area, with the water duty (acre-feet of water diverted during the irrigation season for each acre of land) being very high. Consequently, the water table in the area is very near the surface and large populations of phreatophytes are supported (Bain and Marlar, 1970).

The irrigation return flows are conveyed to the Carson Sinks, where the water is lost by evaporation. This sink area is managed as a waterfowl refuge. At the present time, quality problems in the refuge resulting from irrigation return flow are not as severe as encountered in the lower Bear River, but future water demands, as well as Indian water rights, can be expected to change this situation considerably. A balance will have to be reached between requirements for improved

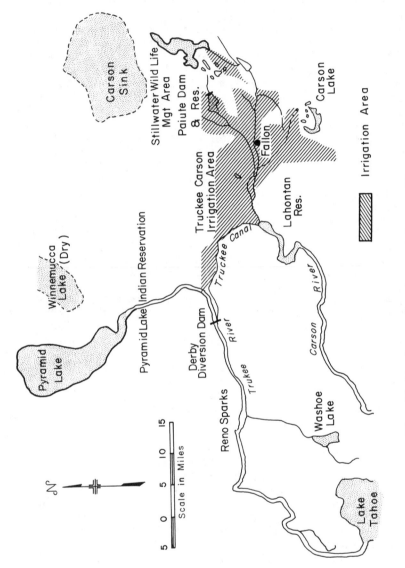

Fig. 12-5. Lower Truckee and Carson Rivers.

irrigation water management to release water supplies to satisfy Indian water rights, along with allowing a sufficient quantity of irrigation return flow having a satisfactory water quality to meet waterfowl needs in the refuge.

Upper Missouri River Basin. There are numerous examples of irrigation return flow quality problems throughout the Upper Missouri River Basin. Most of the quality problems that can be cited are the result of increased salinity, but this is largely due to a combination of two factors. First of all, the water supplies are fairly plentiful, which tends to mask quality degradation. Secondly, there is a real lack of documented studies regarding irrigation return flow quality in this region of the United States. The present knowledge on quality problems is the result of irrigation system failures or recent investigations undertaken for the purpose of expanding irrigated agriculture.

The State of Nebraska has plentiful water supplies and considerable potential for increasing its irrigated acreage. At the present time, more than 4 million acres of land are being irrigated in Nebraska. The present growth rate is approximately 250,000 acres of new irrigated land per year. Nebraska has 16 million acres of heavy soils amenable to surface irrigation and another 18 million acres of sand hills. At the same time, 8 million acre-feet of water per year is leaving the state. Thus, this water could be made available to new irrigated lands.

The water supply for much of the irrigated acreage in Nebraska is pumped from groundwater basins. Water reuse systems are rapidly coming into existence in lower Nebraska (Lincoln to Hastings) because of groundwater pumping costs. The cost of a water reuse system has been estimated to be comparable to a pumping lift of 50 or 60 feet. Many farmers in this area are now pumping groundwater 100 feet.

Presently, the major irrigation return flow quality problem in Nebraska is the result of inefficient water use on a USBR project in the Tri-County area. The groundwater table has risen 100 feet in the last 20 years, until it is now near the ground surface, with resultant losses in agricultural productivity. The cost of surface water in this area is much lower than for pumping groundwater, which is at least part of the reason for the inefficient water use.

There are a number of examples of irrigation project failures, or near failures, in Wyoming. The Riverton Project has suffered from sodic conditions, which now make land reclamation economically unfeasible for many farms. Much of this problem could have been alleviated if canals had beed lined, on-the-farm water management practices instituted, and drains constructed at the initiation of the project.

Areas in North Dakota and South Dakota, which are experiencing irrigation development, will face many salinity problems. Many of these lands are underlain by soils high in natural salts. Because of soils having low permeability, drainage will be required for many of these irrigation projects to insure their success. At the same time, irrigation return flow quality problems will increase substantially.

The Garrison Diversion Unit in North Dakota may be cited as an example. The plan for development involves the diversion of Missouri River water from Garrison Reservoir into the Red River of the North Basin to irrigate ultimately a total of one million acres. The lack of adequate prediction techniques precludes valid estimates of the impact of the irrigation return flows on the quality of Red River water. At the insistence of irrigators and water district personnel, the original plans were revised to include lined canals and pipeline distribution systems. Advantages of the revised plan include: adaptability to sprinkler methods and reduced land preparation costs; increased water control and water-use efficiencies; reduced weed control requirements; limited subsurface drainage needs; and lower operation and maintenance costs. No estimates of improved quality of return flows due to these revised plans (vs. original plan) were suggested, although some improvement would no doubt result. The need for prediction capabilities in newly irrigated areas is again emphasized.

12.4 CONCLUSIONS

The practice of irrigation has detrimental effects on environmental water quality, just as do many other of man's activities. Usually, the quality of water draining from irrigated areas is materially degraded in several ways as compared with the water applied. However, irrigation can also produce beneficial water quality effects through denitrification, phosphate reduction in subsurface return flows, and biological improvements. Irrigation return flows are of special concern because irrigated agriculture is the largest consumer of our water resources.

At the present time, about 48 million acres of land are irrigated in the United States, with all but 5 million acres being located in the 17 western states. Crop production is reduced on one-quarter of the irrigated lands due to saline soils, while salinity is an immediate hazard to half of these irrigated lands. Throughout the world, a third of the irrigated land is plagued by salt problems.

The major water quality problem resulting from irrigated agriculture is the salt transported to ground water reservoir and rivers by irrigation return flow. Other problems include the movement of sediments, variable amounts of fertilizers and pesticides, phosphates (which may come from fertilizers), and increased bacterial content in surface return flows. Subsurface return flows frequently show considerable increase in salts, including nitrates, but show a reduction in bacteria.

Presently, the major irrigation return flow quality problem areas are the San Joaquin Valley, Colorado River Basin, and Rio Grande Basin. Of these three areas, only the Colorado

12-22

River Basin has had a reconnaissance study undertaken to determine the salinity sources and to define, in a general manner, potential control measures. Studies on irrigation return flow have been conducted in the San Joaquin Valley, while very little attention has been given to irrigation return flow in the Rio Grande Basin. In addition to these major problem areas, there are numerous other locations throughout the West with recognized irrigation return flow problems, including the Yakima Valley in Washington; the Carson and Humboldt rivers in Nevada; the Santa Ana River Basin in California; the Sevier River in Utah; the South Platte River in Colorado; the Bear River in Utah and Idaho; the Platte River in Nebraska; the Pecos River in New Mexico and Texas; the Columbia River Basin in Idaho, Oregon, and Washington; and the Arkansas River Basin in Colorado, Kansas, Oklahoma, and Arkansas. Actually, potential water quality problems exist wherever irrigation is practiced.

REFERENCES

Bain, R.C., Jr., and Marlar, J.T., 1970, Water quality control problems in inland sinks; Water Quality Management Problems in Arid Regions, Report 13030 DYY 6/69, Edited by James P. Law, Jr. and Jack L. Witherow, Robert S. Kerr Water Research Center, Federal Water Quality Administration, U.S. Dept. of Interior, Ada, Oklahoma. October.

Bower, C.A., 1966, Irrigation salinity and the world food problem; Presented before a joint meeting of the Crop Science Society of America and Soil Science Society of America, August 22 at Stillwater, Oklahoma.

Bower, C.A., Spencer, J.R., and Weeks, L.O., 1969, Salt and water balance; Coachella Valley, California; Journal of the Irrigation and Drainage Division, ASCE, Vol. 95, No. IR1, p 55-63. March.

Carter, D.L., Bondurant, J.A., and Robbins, C.W., 1971, Water-soluble NO_3- Nitrogen, PO_4- Phosphorus, and total salt balances on a large irrigation tract; Soil Science Society of America Proceedings, Vol. 35, No. 2, p 331-335. March-April.

Casbeer, T.J., and Trock, W.L., 1969, A study of institutional factors affecting water resource development in the lower Rio Grande Valley, Texas; Texas A&M University, Water Resources Center, Tech. Report No. 21, College Station, Texas. September.

Colorado River Board of California, 1970, Need for controlling salinity of the Colorado River; Report submitted by the staff of the Colorado River Board of California to the members of the Board, Sacramento, California. August.

Committee on Pollution, National Academy of Sciences-National Research Council, 1966, Waste Management and control; Publication 1400, Report submitted to the Federal Council for Science and Technology, Washington, D.C.

Environmental Protection Agency, 1971, Summary report; The Mineral Quality Problem in the Colorado River Basin, Regions VIII and IX.

Faulkner, L.R., and Bolander, W.J., 1970, Agriculturally-polluted irrigation water as a source of plant-parasitic nematode infestation; Journal of nematology, Vol. 2, No 4, p 368-374. October.

Moser, T.H., 1967, Drainage by pumped wells in Wellton-Mohawk District; Journal of the Irrigation and Drainage Division, ASCE, Vol. 93, No. IR3, p 199-208. September.

National Technical Advisory Committee, FWPCA, 1968, Agricultural uses; Water Quality Criteria, U.S. Govt.
Printing Office, Washington, D.C.

Pillsbury, A.F., and Johnston, W.F., 1965, Tile drainage
in the San Joaquin Valley of California; University of
California Water Resources Center, Pub. No. 97, Los
Angeles.

Rohn, A.H., 1963, Prehistoric soil and water conservation on
Capin Mesa, Southwestern Colorado; American Antiquity,
28, No. 4, p 441-455.

Sylvester, R.O., and Seabloom, R.W., 1963, Quality and significance of irrigation return flow; Journal of the
Irrigation and Drainage Division, ASCE, Vol. 89, No. IR3,
p 1-27. September.

Wilcox, L.V., 1962, Salinity caused by irrigation; Journal
of the American Water Works Association, Vol. 54, No. 2,
p 217-222. February.

Chapter 13

DISPERSION OF CONTAMINANTS ATTACHED
TO SEDIMENT BED LOAD

by

Hsieh W. Shen, Professor of Civil Engineering, Colorado
State University, Fort Collins, Colorado

and

Hin-Fatt Cheong, Graduate Research Assistant, Department of
Civil Engineering, Colorado State University
Fort Collins, Colorado

Chapter 13

DISPERSION OF CONTAMINANTS ATTACHED TO SEDIMENT BED LOAD

13.1 INTRODUCTION

Contaminants such as herbicides, pesticides and radio-isotopes can attach to sediment particles and move as bed load in a flow. Unlike those contaminants which are dissolved in the flow and moved rapidly by the flow velocity, these bed load particles with contaminants, attached are dispersed rather slowly and can be a health hazard. Since sediment movements are a stochastic process, the dispersion of contaminated top soil will be approached stochastically. This study is limited to cohesionless soil.

Stochastic models describing the unidirectional movement of a sediment particle which advances in a series of alternate rest and transport periods have been proposed by a number of investigators, notably Einstein (1937), Hubbell and Sayre (1964), and Yang and Sayre (1971). Shen and Todorovic (1971). (For a detailed discussion, see Hung and Shen, Appendix B, River Mechanics Volume II). Current theoretical and experimental evidence indicate that the step lengths are gamma distributed with the shape parameter varying between one and three, and the rest periods are exponentially distributed. The analysis discussed here is within the above framework to investigate the concentration distribution function describing the dispersion of contaminated particles released instantaneously and continuously from a line source in the bed of a straight channel with steady, uniform flow.

13.2 INSTANTANEOUSLY RELEASED SOURCE

Assume a straight alluvial channel where the flow is steady and uniform. Consider a large number of contaminated particles having identical transport characteristics as the sand grains forming the bed to be released simultaneously in the bed at a time $t = 0$ and at a station $x = 0$. The concentration distribution function (Yang and Sayre, 1971) describing the longitudinal dispersion of the contaminated particles is (see also River Mechanics Volume II, Appendix B, Eq. B-41).

$$f_t(x) = K_1 e^{-K_1 x - K_2 t} \sum_{n=1}^{\infty} \frac{(K_1 x)^{nr-1} (K_2 t)^n}{\Gamma(nr) \, n!} \tag{13-1}$$

where K_1, K_2 and r are defined by the following probability density functions:

$$
f_X(x) = \begin{cases} \dfrac{K_1^r}{\Gamma(r)} x^{r-1} e^{-K_1 x} , & x \geq 0 \\ 0, & \text{otherwise} \end{cases} \tag{13-2}
$$

$$
f_T(t) = \begin{cases} K_2 e^{-K_2 t} , & t \geq 0 \\ 0, & \text{otherwise} \end{cases} \tag{13-3}
$$

where X and T are random variables describing the step lengths and rest periods of a single particle which moves downstream in an alternate sequence of steps and rest periods. $f_t(x)$ indicates the amount of contaminants per unit length downstream at x and time t when a unit amount (either gravimetric or volumetric) of contaminants is injected instantaneously at $x = 0$ and $t = 0$. Experimental evidence indicates that r is between one and three.

Decay of Concentration at $x = 0$. It is interesting to note that the area under the curve $f_t(x)$ is $(1-\exp(-K_2 t))$, so that the decay of the concentration level at the source is exponential with time.

Movement of Mass Center. Under the conditions of steady, uniform flow, the time rate of movement of the mass center, $\bar{x}$, is essentially constant. For the distribution function of Eq. (13-1):

$$
\bar{x} = \int_0^\infty x f_t(x)dx = \frac{r K_2 t}{K_1}
$$

and

$$
\frac{d\bar{x}}{dt} = r \frac{K_2}{K_1} . \tag{13-4}
$$

Neither the relationship between the sediment transport rate and the rate of movement of $\bar{x}$ nor the variation of K_1, K_2 and r for different flow conditions are well understood at present. Einstein (1937) attempted to relate the rate of movement of the mass center with the sediment transport rate as follows:

For uniform sediment sizes

$$
\frac{d\bar{x}}{dt} \sim q_s^{2/3}
$$

and, for non-uniform sizes

$$\frac{d\overline{x}}{dt} \sim q_s$$

where q_s is the sediment transport rate in liters per meter per unit time. Sayre and Hubbell (1965) suggested the following relationship between the mass center and sediment discharge:

$$q_s = \gamma_s (1-\alpha')d\frac{\overline{x}}{t}$$

where q_s is the sediment transport rate per unit width, γ_s is the specific weight of the sediment, α' is the porosity of the bed, and d is the depth of the zone of particle movement. However, the evaluation of d requires a knowledge of bedforms which is not known.

Migration of the Concentration Distributions. One can discuss the movement and attenuation of the concentration peak by considering first the case of $r = 1$. Equation (13-1) may be written as

$$f_t(x) = K_1 e^{-K_1 x - K_2 t} \left[\frac{\sqrt{K_2 t}}{\sqrt{K_1 x}}\right] I_1(2\sqrt{K_1 K_2 xt}) \qquad (13-5)$$

where $I_1(\ )$ is the modified Bessel function of the first kind of order one. When $f_t(x)$ is differentiated partially with respect to x and the set to zero, one can let $y = 2\sqrt{K_1 K_2 xt}$ and thus:

$$\frac{\partial f_t(x)}{\partial x} = \frac{\partial}{\partial x}\left[K_1 K_2 te^{-K_1 x - K_2 t}\frac{I_1(2\sqrt{K_1 K_2 xt})}{\sqrt{K_1 K_2 xt}}\right]$$

$$= 2K_1 K_2 te^{-K_1 x - K_2 t}\frac{\partial}{\partial y}\left[\frac{I_1(y)}{y}\right]\frac{\partial y}{\partial x}$$

$$-2K_1^2 K_2 te^{-K_1 x - K_2 t}\frac{I_1(y)}{y}$$

$$= 2K_1 K_2 te^{-K_1 x - K_2 t}\left[\frac{\sqrt{K_1 K_2 t}}{\sqrt{x}}\frac{I_2(y)}{y} - \frac{K_1 I_1(y)}{y}\right]$$

$$= 0$$

13-3

$$\frac{\sqrt{K_1 K_2 t}}{\sqrt{x_p}} \, I_2(y_p) - K_1 I_1(y_p) = 0$$

$$\therefore \; \frac{\sqrt{K_2 t}}{\sqrt{K_1 x_p}} = \frac{\sqrt{x}}{\sqrt{x_p}} = \frac{I_1(y_p)}{I_2(y_p)} \tag{13-6}$$

where $y_p = 2\sqrt{K_1 K_2 x_p t}$ and x_p is the position along x where the turning point of $f_t(x)$ is located at any time t. Equation (13-6) was also given by Hubbell and Sayre (1964). To examine the position of the mode after a very long dispersion time, one may make use of the following recurrence equation for modified Bessel functions.

$$I_0(y_p) - I_2(y_p) = \frac{2}{y_p} \, I_1(y_p) \; .$$

Substitution of Eq. (13-6) and rearrangement gives

$$\frac{I_0(y_p)}{I_1(y_p)} = \frac{I_2(y_p)}{I_1(y_p)} + \frac{2}{y_p}$$

$$= \sqrt{\frac{K_1 x_p}{K_2 t}} + \frac{1}{\sqrt{K_1 K_2 x_p t}} \; . \tag{13-7}$$

After a sufficiently long dispersion time, the mode is also at a considerable distance downstream of the source. When y_p is sufficiently large for the following asymptotic approximation to hold

$$I_n(y_p) \approx \frac{e^{y_p}}{\sqrt{2\pi y_p}}$$

where $I_n(\;)$ is the modified Bessel function of the first kind of order n; it can be seen from Eq. (13-6) that $(K_1 x_p)$ and $(K_2 t)$ are of the same order in magnitude. It is clear that Eq. (13-7) reduces to

$$\sqrt{\frac{K_2 t}{K_1 x_p}} \approx 1 \quad \text{or}$$

$$x_p \approx \bar{x} \tag{13-8}$$

at large dispersion times.

After a sufficiently long time has elapsed, the position of the peak concentration is almost coincidental with the location of the mass center. However, when y_p is sufficiently small for the y_p terms with powers of two and higher in the ratio $I_1(y_p)/I_2(y_p)$ to be negligible, one obtains

$$\frac{I_1(y_p)}{I_2(y_p)} = \frac{2}{y_p} \left[\sum_{K=0}^{\infty} \frac{(\frac{y_p}{2})^{2K}}{K!(K+1)!} \right] \Bigg/ \left[\sum_{K=0}^{\infty} \frac{(\frac{y_p}{2})^{2K}}{K!(K+2)!} \right] \sim \frac{4}{y_p} \;. \tag{13-9}$$

From Eq. (13-6),

$$\frac{\sqrt{K_2 t}}{\sqrt{K_1 x_p}} \sim \frac{4}{y_p} \quad \text{or}$$

$$K_2 t \approx 2 \tag{13-10}$$

which indicates that no peak of $f_t(x)$ exists for a dimensionless time scale less than two. With intermediate values of y_p, the attenuation of the peak under the condition imposed by Eq. (13-6) is given by:

$$\frac{f_t(x_p)}{K_1} = \frac{I_1^2(y_p)}{I_2(y_p)} \exp\left[-\frac{y_p}{2} \left\{ \frac{I_1(y_p)}{I_2(y_p)} + \frac{I_2(y_p)}{I_1(y_p)} \right\} \right] \tag{13-11}$$

which is shown in Fig. (13-1) by the curve for $r = 1$. To show this, we have from Eq. (13-5):

$$f_t(x_p) = K_1 e^{-K_1 x_p - K_2 t} \frac{\sqrt{K_2 t}}{\sqrt{K_1 x_p}} I_1(2\sqrt{K_1 K_2 x_p t})$$

$$= \frac{y_p}{2x_p} I_1(y_p)e^{-K_1x_p-K_2t} \quad . \tag{13-12}$$

Note that

$$K_1x_p+K_2t = K_1x_p(1 + \frac{K_2t}{K_1x_p})$$

$$= K_1x_p(1 + \frac{\bar{x}}{x_p})$$

$$= K_1x_p(1 + \frac{I_1^2(y_p)}{I_2^2(y_p)}) \quad . \tag{13-13}$$

From Eq. (13-6)

$$\frac{\sqrt{K_1K_2t}}{\sqrt{x_p}} = \frac{K_1I_1(y_p)}{I_2(y_p)}$$

$$2x_p = \frac{y_p}{K_1} \frac{I_2(y_p)}{I_1(y_p)} \quad . \tag{13-14}$$

From Eqs. (13-13) and (13-14)

$$K_1x_p+K_2t = \frac{y_p}{2} \frac{I_2(y_p)}{I_1(y_p)} \left[1 + \frac{I_1^2(y_p)}{I_2^2(y_p)} \right]$$

$$= \frac{y_p}{2} \left[\frac{I_2(y_p)}{I_1(y_p)} + \frac{I_1(y_p)}{I_2(y_p)} \right] \quad . \tag{13-15}$$

Substitution of Eqs. (13-14) and (13-15) into Eq. (13-12) gives the desired result.

For sufficiently large t, $\bar{x} = K_2t/K_1 \approx x_p$ and $y_p \approx 2K_2t$. Equation (13-11) takes on the asymptotic solution

$$\frac{f_t(x_p)}{K_1} \simeq \frac{e^{y_p}}{\sqrt{2\pi y_p}} \exp [-y_p]$$

$$\simeq \frac{1}{\sqrt{4\pi K_2 t}} \qquad (13\text{-}16)$$

in agreement with a similar result by Hubbell and Sayre (1964).
At large dispersion times, the peak concentration varies
inversely as the square root of the dispersion time. At
smaller and intermediate dispersion times, the decrease in the
peak concentration is even more rapid as shown in Fig. (13-1).

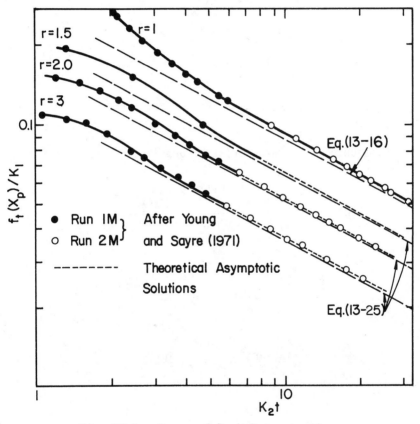

Fig. 13-1. Decay of Peak Concentration.

It will be shown that for sufficiently large t, Eq.
(13-1) may be approximated by a Gaussian curve with mean $\bar{x}$
and variance σ^2 where

13-7

$$\bar{x} = \int_0^\infty x f_t(x)\,dx = \frac{rK_2 t}{K_1} \qquad (13\text{-}17)$$

and

$$\sigma^2 = \int_0^\infty (x-\bar{x})^2 f_t(x)\,dx = \frac{r(r+1)K_2 t}{K_1^2} \quad . \qquad (13\text{-}18)$$

By virtue of the fact that the absolutely convergent infinite series of Eq. (13-1) consists of non-negative terms, $f_t(x)$ is approximately a probability density function as t gets very large. Introducing the following transformed variables

$$x_* = K_1 x$$

$$t_* = K_2 t$$

$$\sigma_* = K_1 \sigma \qquad (13\text{-}19)$$

$$\xi_* = \frac{x_*}{\sigma_*}$$

the expansion of the characteristic function, $\phi_{\xi_*}(u)$, of ξ_* is

$$\phi_{\xi_*}(u) \cong \sigma_* \sum_{n=1}^\infty \int_0^\infty \frac{e^{-\sigma_* \xi_* + iu\,\xi_*} (\sigma_* \xi_*)^{nr-1}}{\Gamma(nr)}$$

$$\frac{e^{-t_*} t_*^n}{n!}\, d\xi_*, \quad i = \sqrt{-1}, \quad t_* \gg 1$$

$$= \sum_{n=1}^\infty \left(1 - \frac{iu}{\sigma_*}\right)^{-nr} \frac{e^{-t_*} t_*^n}{n!}, \quad \left|\frac{iu}{\sigma_*}\right| \ll 1$$

$$= \sum_{n=1}^\infty \left\{ \left[\frac{t_*}{(1 - \frac{iu}{\sigma_*})^r}\right]^n \frac{1}{n!} \exp\left\{ - \frac{t_*}{(1 - \frac{iu}{\sigma_*})^r} \cdot \left(1 - \frac{iu}{\sigma_*}\right)^r \right\} \right\}$$

13-8

$$= \sum_{n=1}^{\infty} \left\{ \frac{1}{n!} \left[\frac{t_*}{(1 - \frac{iu}{\sigma_*})^r} \right]^n \exp \left\{ - \frac{t_*}{(1 - \frac{iu}{\sigma_*})^r} \cdot \sum_{s=0}^{\infty} \binom{r}{s} \left(\frac{-iu}{\sigma_*} \right)^s \right\} \right\} \quad ,$$

$$\binom{r}{s} = \frac{r!}{s!(r-s)!}$$

$$= \exp \left\{ - \frac{t_*}{(1 - \frac{iu}{\sigma_*})^r} \cdot \sum_{s=1}^{\infty} \binom{r}{s} \left(\frac{-iu}{\sigma_*} \right)^s \right\} \cdot$$

$$\sum_{n=1}^{\infty} \frac{1}{n!} \left[\frac{t_*}{(1 - \frac{iu}{\sigma_*})^r} \right]^n \exp \left[\frac{-t_*}{(1 - \frac{iu}{\sigma_*})^r} \right]$$

$$= e^{-t_*(1 - \frac{iu}{\sigma_*})^{-r} \sum_{s=1}^{\infty} \binom{r}{s} \left(\frac{-iu}{\sigma_*} \right)^s} \cdot$$

$$\left\{ 1 - \exp \left[\frac{-t_*}{(1 - \frac{iu}{\sigma_*})^r} \right] \right\}, \quad t_* \gg 1 \quad . \tag{13-20}$$

For sufficiently large t_*, the second term within the parenthesis becomes negligibly small for $|\frac{iu}{\sigma_*}| \ll 1$, and the cumulant generating function is

$$\log_e \phi_{\xi_*}(u) = -t_* (1 - \frac{iu}{\sigma_*})^{-r} \sum_{s=1}^{\infty} \binom{r}{s} \left(\frac{-iu}{\sigma_*} \right)^s \tag{13-21}$$

$$= \frac{rt_*}{\sigma_*} (iu) - \frac{r(r+1)t_*}{\sigma_*^2} \frac{u^2}{2} + \frac{r(r+1)(r+2)t_*}{3!} \left(\frac{iu}{\sigma_*} \right)^3$$

$$+ \text{"OM"} (t_*/\sigma_*^s), \quad s = 4, 5, \ldots$$

("OM" is the order of magnitude). Since $\sigma_*^2 = r(r+1)t_*$,

$$\log_e \phi_{\xi_*}(u) = \frac{rt_*}{\sigma_*}(iu) - \frac{u^2}{2} + \text{"OM"} \left(t_*^{1-\frac{s}{2}}\right), \quad s = 3,4,5,\dots$$

$$(13\text{-}22)$$

For sufficiently large t_*, the skewness and all the higher cumulants become vanishingly small to give

$$\log_e \phi_{\xi_*}(u) = \frac{rt_*}{\sigma_*}(iu) - \frac{u^2}{2}.$$

$$(13\text{-}23)$$

The concentration function can therefore be approximately represented by a Gaussian curve with mean and variance given by Eqs. (13-17) and (13-18) after a long dispersion time has elapsed.

$$f_{t_*}(x_*) \simeq \frac{1}{\sqrt{2\pi r(r+1)t_*}} \exp\left[-\frac{1}{2}\frac{(x_*-rt_*)^2}{r(r+1)t_*}\right].$$

$$(13\text{-}24)$$

The concentration function is also highly skewed at early dispersion times but it progressively becomes more symmetrical. For any $r \geq 1$, the asymptotic expression for the attenuation of the peak is

$$\frac{f_t(x_p)}{K_1} \sim \frac{1}{\sqrt{2\pi r(r+1)t_*}}$$

$$(13\text{-}25)$$

and the asymptotic expression for the position of the peak is

$$x_p \sim \frac{rK_2 t}{K_1}.$$

$$(13\text{-}26)$$

Thus, in general, after a sufficiently long time (say $t_* > 10$), the peak concentration decreases inversely as the square root of the dispersion time (Fig. 13-1), and the longitudinal position of the mode approaches the mass center of the distribution function (Fig. 13-2).

Envelope of the Concentration Distributions. The curves of $f_t(x)$ with x as the abscissa for different times are shown in Figs. (13-3) and (13-4). Figure (13-3) is based on the experimental values of dx/dt and $d\sigma^2/dt$ of Run 1M obtained by Yang and Sayre (1971) for a selected value of $r=1$ with K_1 and K_2 computed from Eqs. (13-4) and (13-18) where

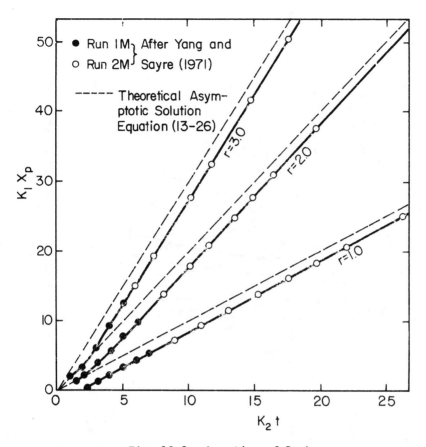

Fig. 13-2. Location of Peak x_p.

$$\frac{d\sigma^2}{dt} = \frac{r(r+1)K_2}{K_1^2} \quad . \tag{13-27}$$

Similarly, Fig. (13-4) is based on the results of Run 2M. Runs 1M and 2M represent that lowest and highest rates of dispersion, respectively. Pertinent hydraulic data for both runs are given in Table 13-I.

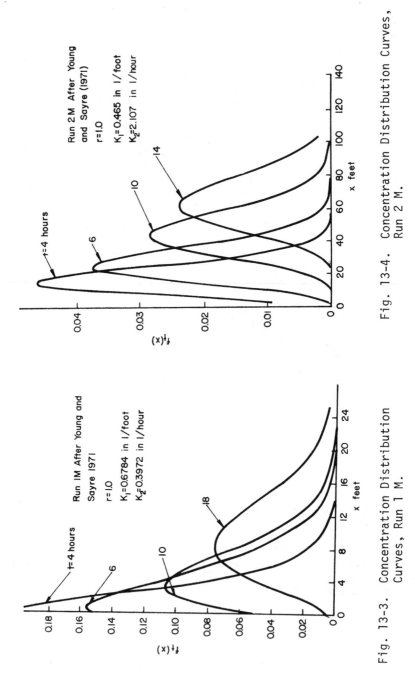

Fig. 13-3. Concentration Distribution
Curves, Run 1 M.

Fig. 13-4. Concentration Distribution Curves,
Run 2 M.

13-12

TABLE 13-I. Hydraulic Data for Runs 1M and 2M

Run No.	1M	2M
Water Surface Slope x 10^2	0.088	0.212
Water Discharge (cfs)	1.140	1.690
Normal Depth (ft)	0.518	0.521
Velocity of Water (ft/sec)	1.100	1.630
Bedform	Ripples	Dunes
Total Sediment Conc. (ppm)	60.2	871
Total Sediment Discharge (lb/sec)	0.00429	0.0918
Size of Tracer (mm)	0.30-0.35	0.30-0.35
Velocity of Tracer (ft/hr)	0.585	4.700
Rate of Spread of Tracer (ft^2/hr)	1.724	20.200

It is interesting to note that the envelopes of $f_t(x)$ with $r = 1, 2$ and 3 for each run appear to collapse into a single curve. An equation of the form $F_*(f_*,x_*,t_*) = $ constant may be imagined as defining a curve in the f_*-x_* plane for each fixed value of t_*. An envelope of a family of curves in the f_*-x_* plane is a curve C with the property that for each point P of C, there is a curve of the family through P tangent to C. The standard method of finding envelopes C of $F_*(f_*,x_*,t_*) = $ constant which are not themselves curves of the family is to eliminate t_* from the equation

$$F_*(f_*,x_*,t_*) = \text{constant} \tag{13-28}$$

and

$$\frac{\partial F_*(f_*,x_*,t_*)}{\partial t_*} = 0 \quad . \tag{13-29}$$

For the case of $r = 1$, by introducing the following change of variables, $u = \sqrt{2K_2}t$ and $a = \sqrt{2K_1}x$, we have from Eq. (13-5)

$$f_* = e^{-\frac{u^2+a^2}{2}} (\frac{u}{a})I_1(au) = 0 \quad .$$

then

13-13

$$F_*(f_*,a,u) = f_* - e^{-\frac{u^2+a^2}{2}} \left(\frac{u}{a}\right) I_1(au) = 0 .$$

Substituting into Eq. (13-29)

$$\frac{\partial F_*(f_*,a,u)}{\partial u} = e^{-\frac{u^2+a^2}{2}} \left[\left(\frac{u^2-2}{a}\right) I_1(au) - u I_2(au)\right] = 0 \tag{13-30}$$

so that

$$\frac{u^2-2}{au} I_1(au) = I_2(au) . \tag{13-31}$$

Recalling the following recurrence equation for modified Bessel functions,

$$I_2(au) = I_0(au) - \frac{2}{au} I_1(au) .$$

Equation (13-31) becomes, after some rearrangement,

$$u^2 = \frac{au I_0(au)}{I_1(au)} . \tag{13-32}$$

For $au > 10$, $I_0(au) \approx I_1(au)$ and the point of tangency between the envelope and the curve $f_*(x)$ is given approximately by $x_* = t_*$. With this approximate solution to Eq. (13-31), the approximate envelope is

$$f_t(x_e) = K_1 e^{-2K_1 x_e} I_1(2K_1 x_e) . \tag{13-33}$$

Note from Eq. (13-32) that $t_* > x_*$ and the curve given by Eq. (13-33) is uniformly lower over x than the envelope. The deviation between the two curves decreases with x.

As shown in Fig. (13-5), the actual total travelled distance $x(t)$ of a sediment particle is bounded by the two functions $x_u(t)$ and $x_L(t)$. $x_L(t)$ represents the lower bound for $x(t)$ by assuming that the particle is transported with instantaneous velocity at the end of each rest period while $x_u(t)$ represents the upper bound for $x(t)$ by assuming that the jth jump takes place at the end of the (j-1)th rest period. Consequently, the difference between $x_u(t)$ and $x_L(t)$ is not more than a step length and the inequality $rt_*/x_* > 1$ holds. The ratio rt_*/x_* approaches unity uniformly with time.

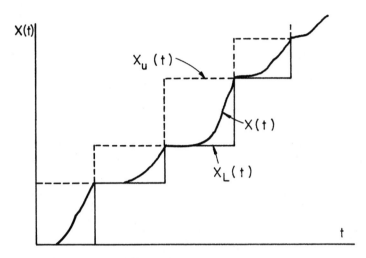

Fig. 13-5. Graphical Representation of the Movement of a Single Particle.

One may determine approximately the envelopes of $f_t(x)$ for other values of r greater than unity by using

$$r_o t_* = x_*, \quad r_o \geq 1 \qquad (13-34)$$

as the approximate solution to Eq. (13-29) in which $r = r_o$. One obtains from Eq. (13-29) for any $r \geq 1$,

$$\sum_{n=1}^{\infty} \frac{x_*^{nr-1} e^{-x_*-t_*}}{\Gamma(nr)} \left[\frac{t_*^{n-1}}{(n-1)!} - \frac{t_*^n}{n!} \right] = 0 . \qquad (13-35)$$

Let

$$\Delta = e^{-x_*-t_*} \sum_{n=1}^{\infty} \frac{x_*^{nr-1} t_*^{n-1}(n-t_*)}{\Gamma(nr)\, n!} \qquad (13-36)$$

13-15

The exact solution to Eq. (13-35) yields $\Delta = 0$. Thus, Δ is the residual for any approximate solution to Eq. (13-29). Table II shows the residuals when Eq. (13-34) is used as the approximate solution to Eq. (13-29) for $r_0 = 1$, 2 and 3.

TABLE 13-II. Residuals Arising from the Approximation.
$$r_0 t_* = x_*$$

r_0	Δ			
	$t_* = 1$	$t_* = 2$	$t_* = 3$	$t_* = 4$
1	0.0933	0.0283	0.0146	0.0093
2	0.0370	0.0100	0.0070	------
3	0.019	0.0040	0.0001	------

The procedure of using Eq. (13-34) to derive an approximation to the envelope of $f_t(x)$ is worthy of mention since it provides a quick and simplified solution to the problem, especially when r takes on a non-integral value for which a direct closed form solution is not possible. Depending upon the value of r, not much sacrifice on accuracy is involved when t_* exceeds five. However, this technique yields a curve that is uniformly lower than the envelope. The deviation between the two curves diminishes with distance. Moreover, the technique provides a better approximation for higher values of r. For each run, the approximate curves for $r = 1$, 2 and 3 appear to collapse into a single curve, and no significant differences are discernible except at very small values of x as shown in Fig. (13-6).

The asymptotic form of Eq. (13-33) is,

$$\frac{f_t(x_e)}{K_1} \sim e^{-2x_*} e^{-2x_*} \cdot \frac{e^{-2x_*}e}{\sqrt{4\pi x_*}e} \sim \frac{1}{\sqrt{4\pi x_*}e} \qquad (13\text{-}37)$$

Since $a = u$, and $\bar{x} = K_2 t/K_1$, and from Eq. (13-8), we have

$$t_* = \bar{x}_* = x_{*e} \sim x_{*p} \qquad (13\text{-}38)$$

and

13-16

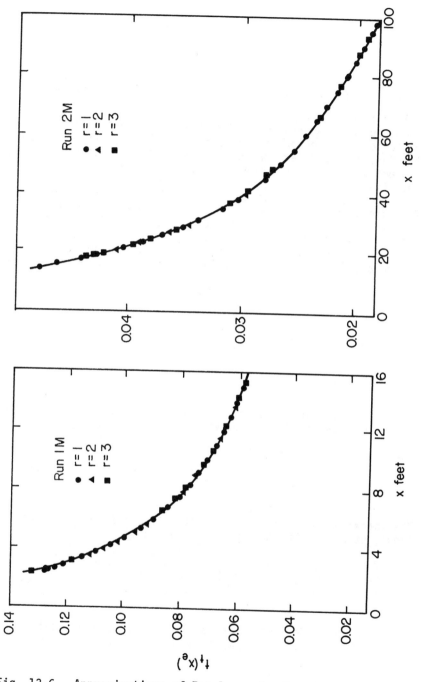

Fig. 13-6. Approximations of Envelopes for Runs 1M and 2M.

$$\frac{f_t(x_e)}{K_1} \sim \frac{1}{\sqrt{4\pi x_*}_p} \qquad (13\text{-}39)$$

In other words, the envelope of the family of curves $f_t(x)$ is almost tangent to the curves at their peaks after a long time has elapsed.

Contours of Constant Concentration as a Function of Time and Distance. Iso-concentration contours for different r values for Runs 1M and 2M are shown in Figs (13-7) and (13-8) respectively. The intercepts of each vertical line with a specified contour indicates the two limits of the critical zone where the concentration is above that particular limit. The intercepts of each horizontal line with a contour defines the limits of the critical time period when local concentrations exceed the specified level.

The movement of the mass centers for different values of r are also shown in Figs. (13-7) and (13-8). Since

$$\bar{x} = \frac{rK_2 t}{K_1} \qquad (13\text{-}40)$$

then

$$\bar{x}_* = K_1 \bar{x} = rt_* \qquad . \qquad (13\text{-}41)$$

An iso-concentration contour for the concentration C with $r = 1$ is given by Eq. (13-5) with $x_* = K_1 x$ and $t_* = K_2 t$.

$$\frac{C}{K_1} = e^{-x_* - t_*} \frac{\sqrt{t_*}}{\sqrt{x_*}} I_1(2\sqrt{t_* x_*}) \qquad . \qquad (13\text{-}42)$$

The intercept between the mass center line and the concentration contour $\bar{X}$ is, for $t_* = \bar{x}_*$, given by

$$\frac{C}{K_1} = e^{-2\bar{X}_*} I_1(2\bar{X}_*) \qquad . \qquad (13\text{-}43)$$

When the time under consideration is sufficiently large for Eq. (13-7) to hold, the asymptotic solution is

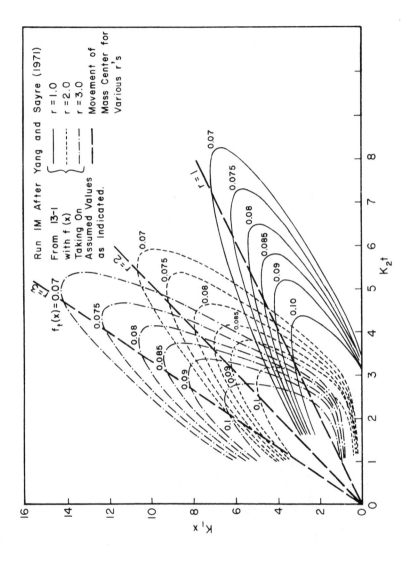

Fig. 13-7. Iso-Concentration Contours, Run 1M

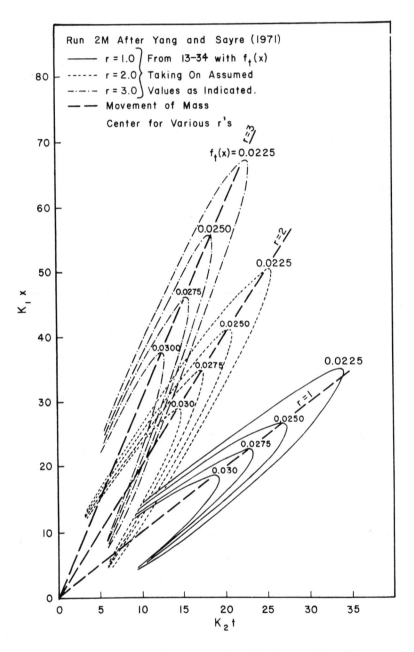

Fig. 13-8.   Iso-Concentration Contours, Run 2M

$$\frac{C}{K_1} \sim e^{-2X_*} \cdot \frac{e^{2\overline{X}_*}}{\sqrt{4\pi X_*}} \qquad (13\text{-}44)$$

$$\sim \frac{1}{\sqrt{4\pi X_*}} \qquad (13\text{-}45)$$

which shows that the intercept between the mass center line and the iso-concentration contour varies inversely as the square of the concentration after a long dispersion time, i.e.,

$$\overline{X}_* \propto \left(\frac{K_1}{C}\right)^2 \qquad . \qquad (13\text{-}46)$$

Approach to Normality of the Time-Concentration Functions. Time-concentration curves at different downstream locations are shown in Figs. (13-9) and (13-10). Figure (13-9) is based on the experimental values of $d\overline{x}/dt$ and $d\sigma^2/dt$ of Run 1M obtained by Yang and Sayre (1971) for a selected r value of 1 with K_1 and K_2 computed from Eqs. (13-4) and (13-27).

Figure (13-10) is similarly obtained from the results of Run 2M. The time-concentration curves are highly skewed near the source and progressively become more symmetrical downstream and ultimately tends to normality far downstream. The proof is quite straight forward for the case when r equals unity. Let $x_* = K_1 x$ and $t_* = K_2 t$. The time-concentration function with $r = 1$ is

$$f_{x_*}(t_*) = \sum_{m=0}^{\infty} \frac{e^{-x_*} x_*^{m}}{m!} \frac{e^{-t_*} t_*^{m+1}}{(m+1)!} \qquad . \qquad (13\text{-}47)$$

Clearly, $f_{x_*}(t_*)$ is a probability density function of t_* obtained from randomized Gamma densities. Define s_*^2 to be the second central moment of the time-concentration function and let $\tau_* = t_*/s_*$. The characteristic function of τ_* is

$$\phi_{\tau_*}(u) = \sum_{n=1}^{\infty} \frac{e^{-x_*} x_*^{n-1}}{(n-1)!} \int_0^{\infty} \frac{e^{-s_*\tau_*+iu\tau_*}(s_*\tau_*)^n}{n!} d(s_*\tau_*) ,$$

$$i = \sqrt{-1} , \quad x_* \gg 1$$

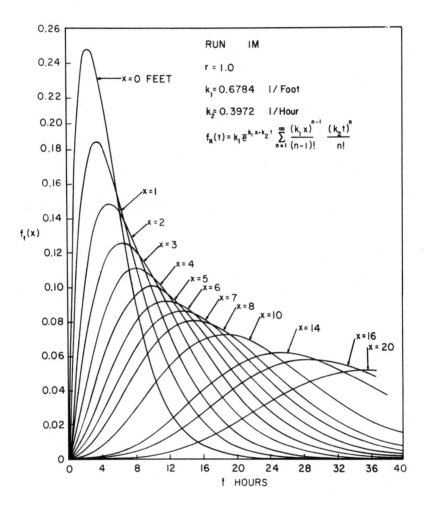

Fig. 13-9. Time Concentration Functions, Run 1 M.

13-22

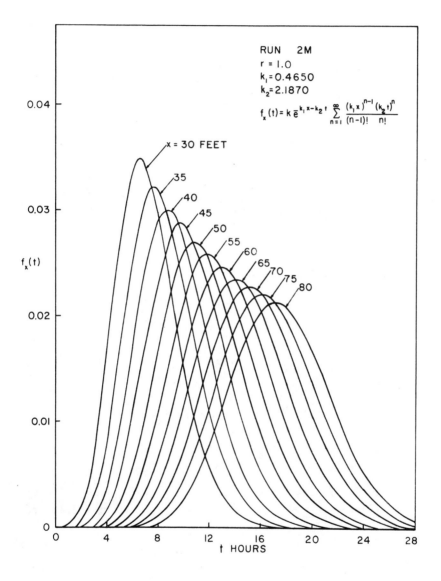

Fig. 13-10. Time Concentration Functions, Run 2 M.

13-23

$$= \sum_{n=1}^{\infty} \frac{1}{(1 - \frac{iu}{s_*})^{n+1}} \frac{e^{-x_*} x_*^{n-1}}{(n-1)!}$$

$$= \sum_{m=0}^{\infty} \frac{1}{(1 - \frac{iu}{s_*})^{m+2}} \cdot \frac{e^{-x_*} x_*^m}{m!}$$

$$= \frac{1}{(1 - \frac{iu}{s_*})^2} \sum_{m=0}^{\infty} (\frac{x_*}{1 - \frac{iu}{s_*}})^m \frac{1}{m!} e^{-x_*}$$

$$= \frac{1}{(1 - \frac{iu}{s_*})^2} \exp \left\{ \frac{ix_* u}{s_*(1 - \frac{iu}{s_*})} \right\} \quad .$$

The cumulant generating function is

$$\log_e \phi_{\tau_*}(u) = -2 \log_e (1 - \frac{iu}{s_*}) + x_* (\frac{iu}{s_*})(1 - \frac{iu}{s_*})^{-1}$$

$$= (x_* + 2)(\frac{iu}{s_*}) + (x_* + 1)(\frac{iu}{s_*})^2 + (x_* + \frac{2}{3})(\frac{iu}{s_*})^3 + \dots$$

$$+ (x_* + \frac{2}{m})(\frac{iu}{s_*})^m + \dots \quad , \text{ for } |\frac{u}{s_*}| \ll 1 \quad .$$

Since $s_*^2 = 2(x_* + 1)$,

$$\log_e \phi_{\tau_*}(u) = \frac{(x_*+2)}{\sqrt{2(x_*+1)}} (iu) - \frac{u^2}{2} + \text{"OM"} (x_*^{1-\frac{m}{2}}), \quad m = 3,4, \dots$$

$$(13-48)$$

As x_* becomes sufficiently large, the cumulants higher than the second become vanishingly small and

$$\log_e \phi_{\tau_*}(u) \approx \frac{x_*+2}{\sqrt{2(x_*+1)}} (iu) - \frac{u^2}{2} \quad , \quad x_* \gg 1 \qquad (13-49)$$

which is the log-characteristic function of a Gaussian distribution random variable. The moments of the time-concentration function can be determined from the cumulants. They are

$$M_1 = x_* + 2$$

$$M_2 = 2x_* + 2$$

$$\frac{M_3}{M_2^{2/3}} = \frac{3x_*+2}{\sqrt{2}\ (x_*+1)^{3/2}}$$

(13-50)

where M_j is the jth central moment of the time-concentration function. Consequently, for sufficiently large x_*, the time-concentration function for $r = 1$ can be represented approximately by the Gaussian curve

$$f_{x_*}(t_*) \simeq \frac{1}{\sqrt{4\pi(x_*+1)}}\ \exp\ [-\frac{(t_*-x_*-2)^2}{4(x_*+1)}]$$

(13-51)

and the asymptotic expression for the attenuation of the peak is

$$f_{x_*}(t_*)_p = \frac{1}{\sqrt{4\pi(x_*+1)}}$$

(13-52)

and the approach of the peak to the asymptote given by Eq. (13-52) for $r = 1$ is shown in Fig. (13-12).
    Equation (13-51) can be simplified (since $x_* \gg 1$) to

$$f_{x_*}(t_*) \simeq \frac{1}{\sqrt{4\pi x_*}}\ \exp\ [-\frac{(t_*-x_*)^2}{4x_*}]\ .$$

(13-53)

It was shown earlier that for sufficiently large t_* and $r = 1$,

$$f_{t_*}(x_*) \simeq \frac{1}{\sqrt{2\pi}\ \sigma_*}\ \exp\ [-\frac{1}{2}\ (\frac{t_*-x_*}{\sigma_*})^2]\ ,\ \sigma_*^2 = 2t_*\ .$$

(13-54)

The result shows that the time-concentration distribution at $x_* = x_{*_0}$ is assymmetrical with respect to t_*. A cursory glance may lead one to think that this is in contradiction with the results of the analysis leading to Eq. (13-53).

13-25

Actually, the asymmetry is small for sufficiently large t_* and the rate of spread, $d\sigma/dt$, of the contaminants is small in comparison to the mean rate of movement of the mass center of the contaminants. After a sufficiently long time, t, the average number of steps taken over the distance traversed in that time is very nearly equal to the average number of rest phases, since the contaminant progresses in an alternate sequence of steps and rest periods. Thus, for sufficiently large t_*, $\sigma_*^2 = 2t_* \simeq 2x_{*_0}$ and substitution into the above equation gives Eq. (13-53).

Nevertheless, it is interesting to determine the relative errors incurred as a result of the approximation based on the preceding argument. The relative error is defined as

$$\epsilon = \frac{f_{t_*}(x_{*_0}) - f_{x_{*_0}}(t_*)}{f_{t_*}(x_{*_0})} . \qquad (13\text{-}55)$$

In addition, define

$$\theta = (\frac{d\sigma_*}{dt_*} / \frac{d\overline{x}_*}{dt_*}) \qquad (13\text{-}56)$$

and

$$\chi = (\frac{t_* - x_{*_0}}{\sigma_*}) \qquad (13\text{-}57)$$

θ may be interpreted to be the rate of evolution or spread of the contaminants relative to the rate of movement of the mass center of the cluster of contaminants. χ is a relative measure of the approximation. From Eqs. (13-17) and (13-18) with $r = 1$

$$\sigma_*^2 = 2t_*$$

and

$$\overline{x}_* = t_* .$$

Substituting into the definitions for θ and χ,

$$t_* = \frac{1}{2\theta^2}$$

$$x_{*_0} = (2\theta\chi + 1)/2\theta^2 .$$

13-26

Upon substitution, the relative error becomes after some rearrangement,

$$\varepsilon = 1 - \frac{1}{\sqrt{2\theta\chi+1}} \exp\left[-\left(\frac{\theta\chi^3}{2\theta\chi+1}\right)\right] \quad . \qquad (13\text{-}58)$$

The graphs of the relative error, ε, against χ for different θ values are shown in Fig. (13-11). The absolute relative error, $|\varepsilon|$, can be seen to be smaller for smaller values of θ. When $|\chi| < 1$, absolute errors are less than about 2% when $\theta < 0.01$. For a given degree of approximation χ, the relative error ε diminishes when the dispersion time is very long. (Note $\theta \propto 1/\sqrt{t_*}$).

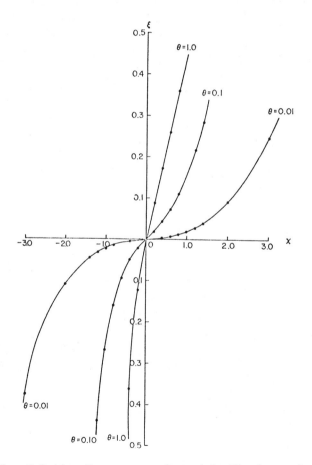

Fig. 13-11. Relative Error, ε, Caused By The Approximation $\sigma_* = 2X_*$ For Sufficiently Large $t_*(r=1)$.

The time-concentration functions

$$f_x(t) = k_{1,r}e^{-k_{1,r}x-k_{2,r}t} \sum_{n=1}^{\infty} \frac{(k_{1,r}x)^{nr-1}(k_{2,r}t)^n}{\Gamma(nr)\,n!} \;,\; r = 1,2,3$$

(13-59)

subject to the following constraint

$$q = \frac{d\bar{x}}{dt} = \frac{rk_{2,r}}{k_{1,r}} \;,\; r = 1,2,3$$

(13-60)

are almost coincident for sufficiently large values of x. The second subscript for the k's denotes the corresponding k values for the selected r values. Integration of $f_x(t)$ with respect to t over $[0,\infty)$ gives

$$\int_0^{\infty} f_x(t)dt = k_{1,r}e^{-k_{1,r}x} \sum_{n=1}^{\infty} \frac{(k_{1,r}x)^{nr-1}}{\Gamma(nr)} \int_0^{\infty} \frac{(k_{2,r}t)^n e^{-k_{2,r}t}}{n!} dt$$

$$= \frac{k_{1,r}}{k_{2,r}} e^{-k_{1,r}x} \sum_{n=1}^{\infty} \frac{(k_{1,r}x)^{nr-1}}{\Gamma(nr)}$$

$$= \begin{cases} \dfrac{k_{1,1}}{k_{2,1}} \\[2ex] \dfrac{k_{1,2}}{2k_{2,2}}\left(1 - e^{-2k_{1,2}x}\right) \\[2ex] \dfrac{k_{1,3}}{3k_{2,3}}\left[1 - e^{-\frac{3}{2}k_{1,3}x}\left(\cos\frac{\sqrt{3}\,k_{1,3}x}{2} + \sqrt{3}\,\sin\frac{\sqrt{3}\,k_{1,3}x}{2}\right)\right] \end{cases} .$$

For sufficiently large x, the application of the constraint gives

$$\int_0^{\infty} q\, f_x(t)dt = 1,\; r = 1$$

$$\approx 1,\; r > 1 .$$

(13-61)

13-28

The integrand is approximately a density function of t_* for sufficiently large x_* and it can be shown to be uniquely determined by its moments. The integrand will be shown to approach normality far downstream with $r = 2$ and 3. The method is the same as that used for the proof with $r = 1$. Using the same transformed variables

$$\phi_{\tau_*}(u) = re^{-x_*} \sum_{n=1}^{\infty} \frac{x_*^{nr-1}}{\Gamma(nr)} \int_0^{\infty} \frac{e^{-s_*\tau_* - iu\tau_*}(s_*\tau_*)^n}{n!} d(s_*\tau_*)$$

for $r = 2$ & 3

$$= re^{-x_*} \sum_{n=1}^{\infty} \frac{x_*^{nr-1}}{\Gamma(nr)} \frac{1}{(1 - \frac{iu}{s_*})^{n+1}}$$

$$\phi_{\tau_*}(u) = \begin{cases} \dfrac{2e^{-x_*}}{(1 - \frac{iu}{s_*})^{\frac{3}{2}}} \displaystyle\sum_{n=1}^{\infty} \{(\dfrac{x_*}{\sqrt{1 - \frac{iu}{s_*}}})^{2n-1} \dfrac{1}{(2n-1)!}\}, & r=2 \\[4em] \dfrac{3e^{-x_*}}{(1 - \frac{iu}{s_*})^{\frac{4}{3}}} \displaystyle\sum_{n=1}^{\infty} \{(\dfrac{x_*}{\sqrt[3]{1 - \frac{iu}{s_*}}})^{3n-1} \dfrac{1}{(3n-1)!}\}, & r=3 \end{cases}$$

$$\approx \begin{cases} \dfrac{2e^{-x_*}}{(1 - \frac{iu}{s_*})^{\frac{3}{2}}} \cdot \dfrac{1}{2} \exp(\dfrac{x_*}{\sqrt{1 - \frac{iu}{s_*}}}), & r=2 \\[4em] \dfrac{3e^{-x_*}}{(1 - \frac{iu}{s_*})^{\frac{4}{3}}} \cdot \dfrac{1}{3} \exp(\dfrac{x_*}{\sqrt[3]{1 - \frac{iu}{s_*}}}), & r=3 \end{cases} \quad (x_* \gg 1), (|\frac{iu}{s_*}| \ll 1)$$

$$= \begin{cases} (\frac{x_*+3}{2})(\frac{iu}{s_*}) + (\frac{3x_*+6}{8})(\frac{iu}{s_*})^2 + (\frac{15x_*+24}{48})(\frac{iu}{s_*})^3 + \ldots \\ \\ + \text{O.M. } (x_*^{1-\frac{s}{2}}), \quad s = 4,5, \quad r = 2 \end{cases}$$

$$= \begin{cases} (\frac{x_*+4}{3})(\frac{iu}{s_*}) + (\frac{4x_*+12}{18})(\frac{iu}{s_*})^2 + (\frac{28x_*+72}{162})(\frac{iu}{s_*})^3 + \ldots \\ \\ + \text{O.M. } (x_*^{1-\frac{s}{2}}), \quad s = 4,5, \quad r = 3 \end{cases}$$

$$\approx \begin{cases} (\frac{x_*+3}{2})(\frac{iu}{s_*}) + (\frac{3x_*+6}{8})(\frac{iu}{s_*})^2, \quad r = 2 \qquad (13\text{-}62) \\ \\ (\frac{x_*+4}{3})(\frac{iu}{s_*}) + (\frac{4x_*+12}{18})(\frac{iu}{s_*})^2, \quad r = 3 \qquad (13\text{-}63) \end{cases}$$

Application of the constraint given by Eq. (13-19) will show that for $r = 1$, 2 and 3 the time-concentration profiles are almost coincident far downstream and the profiles follow the Gaussian curve given by Eq. (13-51). It should be noted that the approach to normality is a fairly slow process.

Attenuation of Time-Concentration Peak. Since the functions $qf_x(t)$ for $r = 1$, 2 and 3 can be represented approximately by a Gaussian curve with mean $(k_{1,1}x/k_{2,1})$ and variance $(2k_{1,1}x/k_{2,1}^2)$ at a point sufficiently far downstream, that is,

$$qf_x(t) = rk_{2,r} \left\{ \sum_{n=1}^{\infty} \frac{(k_{1,r}x)^{nr-1}(k_{2,r}t)^n}{\Gamma(nr) \quad n!} \right\} \exp(-k_{1,r}x - k_{2,r}t)$$

$$\approx \frac{k_{2,1}}{\sqrt{4\pi k_{1,1}x}} \exp \left\{ -\frac{(k_{2,1}t - k_{1,1}x)^2}{4k_{1,1}x} \right\} . \qquad (13\text{-}64)$$

13-30

The asymptotes for the attenuation of the peak of the time-concentration functions are

$$\frac{f_x(t)}{k_{1,r}} \simeq \frac{k_{2,1}}{rk_{2,r}\sqrt{4\pi k_{1,1}x}} \quad , \quad r = 1, 2 \text{ and } 3 \ . \tag{13-65}$$

As can be seen in Fig. (13-12), the approach to the asymptotic values is rather slow and the time-concentration functions may be approximated by Eq. (13-64) when $k_{1,1}x$ is greater than say 40. The dimensionless peak concentrations for $r = 1,2$ and 3 are uniformly lower than their corresponding asymptotic solutions over x, and are ultimately inversely proportional to the square root of the distance from the source. From the above results, one may presume that the same general conclusions on the attenuation of the peak of the time-concentration functions also apply when r takes on non-integral values greater than unity. The approximation given in Eq. (13-64) is expected to be reasonably close in the vicinity of the peak and the approximation is expected to be poor at the "skirts" of the distribution away from the peak.

Envelope of Time-Concentration Distribution. One may observe that for fairly large times, t, the envelopes of $f_x(t)$ for $r = 1$, 2 and 3 appear to collapse into a single curve as shown in Fig. (13-13). This observation seems to be valid for Run 1M (low flow condition) and Run 2M (high transport rate) and may very well be valid for intermediate transport conditions. If this assumption holds, it suffices only to determine the form of the envelope for $r = 1$ in dimensionless terms.
Let $F_*(f_*,t_*;x_*)$ be given by

$$F_*(f_*,t_*;x_*) \equiv f_* - e^{-x_*-t_*} \sum_{n=1}^{\infty} \frac{x_*^{n-1}t_*^n}{\Gamma(n)n!} \ . \tag{13-66}$$

Equation (13-66) represents the graph of a family of curves in the dimensionless f_*-t_* plane with x_* as the parameter, wherein $t_* = k_{2,1}t$ and $x_* = k_{1,1}x$. Let $u = \sqrt{2k_{2,1}t}$ and $a = \sqrt{2k_{1,1}x}$, substituting into Eq. (13-66) gives

$$F_*(f_*,u;a) \equiv f_* - e^{-\frac{1}{2}(u^2+a^2)} \left(\frac{u}{a}\right) I_1(au). \tag{13-67}$$

Differentiating F_* partially with respect to a and equating to zero, gives, after some manipulation

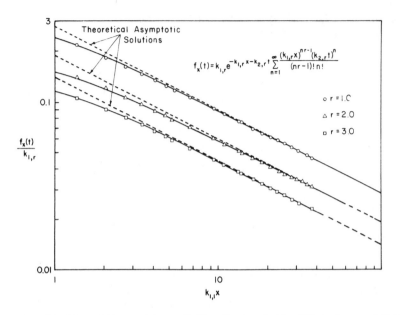

Fig. 13-12. Attenuation of the Peak of the Time-Concentration
Functions.

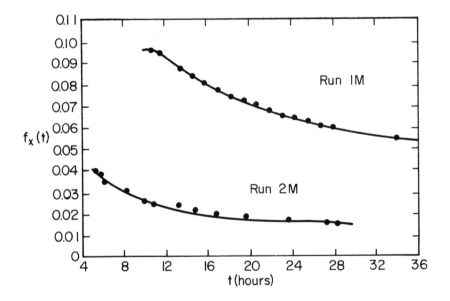

Fig. 13-13. Time-Concentration Envelope, Run 1M and 2M.

$$u \, I_2(au) = a \, I_1(au) \quad .$$

By using the following recurrence equation for modified Bessel functions

$$I_2(au) = I_0(au) - \frac{2}{au} I_1(au)$$

the preceeding equation can be reduced to give

$$u = (\frac{a^2+2}{a}) \frac{I_1(au)}{I_0(au)} \quad . \tag{13-68}$$

The problem of solving for a by numerical method can be circumvented if we settle for a reasonably accurate approximate envelope. Consider the following approximation

$$u \simeq (\frac{a^2+2}{a}) \quad (au > 10) \quad .$$

Substitution in Eq. (13-5) gives

$$f_x(t) \simeq k_{1,1} \exp \left[- \frac{1}{2} \{\frac{2(k_{1,1}^{x+1})^2}{k_{1,1}^x} + 2k_{1,1}^x\}\right]$$

$$(\frac{k_{1,1}^{x+1}}{k_{1,1}^x}) \, I_1(2k_{1,1}^{x+2}) \tag{13-69}$$

with

$$k_{2,1} t \simeq \frac{(k_{1,1}^{x+1})^2}{k_{1,1}^x} \quad . \tag{13-70}$$

Equations (13-69) and (13-70) may be used to determine the approximate envelope to the time-concentration functions for $r = 1$. The approximation is expected to be good when $2k_{1,1}^x$ is greater than about eight. The point of tangency between a time-concentration curve and the envelope to the family of curves occurs in the neighborhood of the peak. To each value of $t = t_0$, there corresponds a value of x which parameterizes the curve which is tangent to the envelope at $t = t_0$. This value of x is larger when the transport rate is higher. This means that at a given time, the approximation is better for higher rates of mass movement. For a given transport condition, the approximation to the envelope of the family of time-concentration curves as given by Eq. (13-69) and (13-70) for $r = 1$ is also an excellent approximation to the envelope function when r is different from unity when $x > 4k_{1,1}$.

13-33

<u>Critical Duration of Pollution</u>. The distribution of pollutants in a channel is governed to a large extent by the rates at which the contaminated bed-load particles are transported and dispersed. The degree of pollution (H) at a specified location over the time interval (t_1, t_2) is given to be proportional to the area under the time-concentration over (t_1, t_2). One may seek to minimize this interval to determine the critical duration of pollution.

$$(H) = \int_{t_1}^{t_2} qf_x(t)dt \qquad (13\text{-}71)$$

one seeks next to minimize $T = t_2 - t_1$. By applying Leibnitz's rule for differentiation of integrals to Eq. (13-71)

$$\frac{dt_2}{dt_1} = \frac{f_x(t_1)}{f_x(t_2)} \quad . \qquad (13\text{-}72)$$

Differentiating T with respect to t_1, and equating to zero,

$$\frac{dt_2}{dt_1} = 1 \quad . \qquad (13\text{-}73)$$

Equations (13-72) and (13-73) give

$$f_x(t_1) = f_x(t_2) \quad . \qquad (13\text{-}74)$$

For sufficiently large x, $qf_x(t)$ is approximated by Eq. (13-53). By defining

$$z = [t - E(t)] / \sqrt{E[(t - E(t))^2]}$$

$qf_x(t)$ can be represented by a standard normal and Eqs. (13-71) and (13-74) become

$$(H) = \int_{z_1}^{z_2} qf_x(z)dz$$

and

13-34

$$f_x(z_1) = f_x(z_2) \quad .$$

Consideration of symmetry gives $z_1 = -z_2$. In other words

$$\Phi\left(z_{1-\frac{\textcircled{H}}{2}}\right) = \frac{1-\textcircled{H}}{2}$$

where $\Phi(z_{1-\textcircled{H}/2})$ is the cumulative distribution function of a standard normal evaluated at the $(1 - \textcircled{H}/2)$th quantile point. The critical time limits are given by

$$t_1, t_2 = \frac{x}{q} \pm \sqrt{\frac{2k_{1,1}x}{k_{2,1}^2}}\; z_{1-\frac{\textcircled{H}}{2}} \tag{13-75}$$

according to Eq. (13-64). The critical duration is

$$t_2 - t_1 = \frac{2}{k_{2,1}}\; \sqrt{2k_{1,1}x}\; z_{1-\frac{\textcircled{H}}{2}} \tag{13-76}$$

or

$$k_{2,r}(t_2 - t_1) = 2\,\frac{k_{2,r}}{k_{2,1}}\; \sqrt{2k_{1,1}x}\; z_{1-\frac{\textcircled{H}}{2}} \quad .$$

This shows that at a considerable distance downstream, the critical duration varies directly as the square root of the distance. At points near the source, the time-concentration curve is strongly skewed. However, the determination of the critical duration is still governed by Eqs. (13-71) and (13-74). The critical time (dimensionless) limits for any degree of pollution $\textcircled{H}$ at a specified locality x_* along the channel are shown in Fig. (13-14) for $r = 1$. For example, at the location $x_* = x_{*_0}$ the critical time limits for the degree of pollution $\textcircled{H} = \textcircled{H}_0$ are given by the intercepts (t'_{1_*}, t'_{2_*}) of the horizontal line $\textcircled{H} = \textcircled{H}_0$ and the curve defined by $x_* = x_{*_0}$. The time interval $(t'_{2_*} - t'_{1_*})$ represents the critical duration.

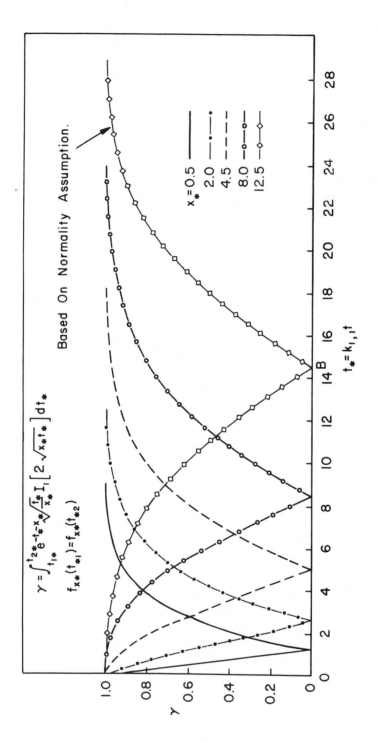

Fig. 13-14. Dimensionless Critical Time Limits For r = 1.

As with radioactive contaminants, the inverse square law is used to determine the absorption rate at a given time. Assume the subject to be at a position ξ downstream of the source of release of the contaminants and h from the line of travel of the contaminants. The rate of absorption of radiation by the subject at the time t is given by

$$\dot{R} = \alpha\zeta = \alpha^{*}\left\{\frac{e^{-k_2 t}}{\xi^2+h^2} + \int_0^{\infty} \frac{k_1 e^{-k_1 x - k_2 t} \sum\limits_{n=1}^{\infty} \frac{(k_1 x)^{nr-1}(k_2 t)^n}{\Gamma(nr)\ n!}}{(x-\xi)^2 + h^2}\ dx\right\} \qquad (13\text{-}77)$$

where α is a dimensional proportionality constant. Let

$$\left.\begin{aligned} t_* &= k_2 t \\[4pt] \zeta &= k_1^{2}\zeta_* \\[4pt] \xi_* &= k_1 \xi \\[4pt] h_* &= k_1 h \\[4pt] x_* &= k_1 x \end{aligned}\right\} \qquad (13\text{-}78)$$

then

$$\zeta_* = \frac{e^{-t_*}}{\xi_*^2+h_*^2} + \int_0^{\infty} \frac{e^{-x_*-t_*}}{(x_*-\xi_*^2)+h_*^2} \sum_{n=1}^{\infty} \frac{x_*^{nr-1} t_*^n}{\Gamma(nr)n!}\ dx \qquad (13\text{-}79)$$

If H is the radiation absorbed by the subject over the interval (t_1, t_2), then

$$\textcircled{H} = \int_{t_1}^{t_2} \dot{R}\ dt$$

$$= \int_{t_{1_*}}^{t_{2_*}} \frac{\alpha \, k_1^2}{k_2} \, \zeta_* \, dt_* \quad . \tag{13-80}$$

By letting $\textcircled{H}_* = k_2 \gamma / \alpha' k_1^2$,

$$\frac{d\gamma_*}{dt_*} = \zeta_* \quad . \tag{13-81}$$

In Figs. (13-15a) and (13-15b), as can be expected, the peak absorption rate for $\textcircled{H} = \textcircled{H}_0$ occurs at a dimensionless time, t_{0_*} , equal to $(1/r_0)$th of the dimensionless time of occurrence of the peak absorption rate for $r_0 = 1$ when ξ_* is sufficiently large. When ξ_* is large, the rate of movement of the peak of the concentration distribution function, $f_t(x)$, is nearly the same as the rate of the progression of the mass center, $\bar{x}$. Thus

$$t_{r_0} \simeq \frac{\xi}{\dfrac{d\bar{x}}{dt}} = \frac{k_{1,r_0} \, \xi}{r_0 k_{2,r_0}} = \frac{\xi_*}{r_0 k_{2,r_0}}$$

or

$$t_{*r_0} \simeq \frac{1}{r_0} \, t_{*r_0 = 1} \quad .$$

This approximation cannot be expected to hold good when ξ_* is small since the concentration distribution function is initially highly skewed and the rates of movement of the peak of $f_t(x)$ and the mass center are very different. However, one may anticipate the maximum rate of absorption to occur at approximately the same time as the passage of the peak of $f_t(x)$ at $x = \xi$, the position of the subject.

For the radiation absorbed $\tilde{\gamma}_*$, one may seek to determine the critical time limits defining the shortest duration of exposure of the subject at a given position downstream. From Eq. (13-81),

$$\textcircled{H}_* = \int_{t_{1_*}}^{t_{2_*}} \zeta_* \, dt_* \quad . \tag{13-82}$$

13-38

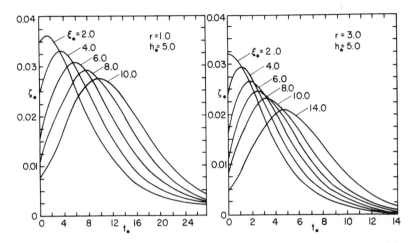

Fig. 13-15a,b. Rate of Absorption of Radiation ζ_* By Subject ξ_* Downstream and h_* From the Line of Travel of Contaminants.

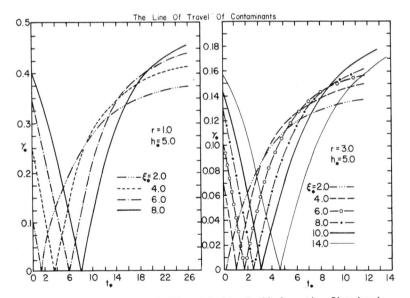

Fig. 13-16a,b. Critical Time Limits Defining the Shortest Duration of Exposure of Subject at a Point ξ_* Downstream and h_* from Line of Travel of Contaminants.

Again, by applying Liebnitz's rule for the differentiation of integrals to Eq. (13-82), the condition to be satisfied is

$$\xi_*(t_{1_*}) = \xi_*(t_{2_*}) \quad . \tag{13-83}$$

The critical time limits (t_{1_*}, t_{2_*}) for a range of absorption values $\tilde{\gamma}_*$ for different downstream positions of the subject are shown in Figs. (13-16a) and (13-16b). When the subject is at the position where $\xi_* = x_*$ and $h_* = 5$, say, and if $\overline{\textcircled{H}}_*$ is the critical level of absorption, then the intercepts between the horizontal line $\textcircled{H} = \overline{\textcircled{H}}_*$ and the curve for $\xi_* = x_{*_0}$ define the critical time limits and it is hazardous for the subject to be at the said location for a period of time extending beyond those defined by the above limits.

13.3 CONCLUDING REMARKS

The analysis has been based on the stochastic model given by Yang and Sayre (1971) and the shape factor in the Gamma distribution was allowed to take on integral values from one to three.

The concentration distribution function is initially highly skewed and becomes progressively symmetrical with time in that after a sufficient long time (about $K_2t \geq 10$), it can be approximated by a Gaussian curve. The dimensionless peak concentrations for $r = 1,2$ and 3 are uniformly higher than their respective asymptotic solutions so that after a long dispersion time, the peak varies as the inverse square root of the time. The location of the peak advances slightly faster than the mass center and they are almost coincident after a long time has elapsed. A simplified procedure of approximating the envelope of the family of distribution curves for a specified run yields a curve that is uniformly lower than the envelope. The deviation between the two curves is insignificant when $x_*/r > 5$. This technique is worthy of mention since it affords a way of deriving an envelope even for non-integral values of r.

With an instantaneous introduction of contaminants, the time concentration distributions are highly skewed near the source and become progressively more symmetrical far downstream where they can be approximately represented by a Gaussian curve. The approximate Gaussian representation does not introduce any serious error provided that the rate of spreading of the cloud of contaminants is much slower in comparison to the rate of movement of their mass center and also if the point of consideration is sufficiently far downstream. When

the normality condition is nearly approached, the peaks of
the time concentration distributions vary as the inverse square
root of the distance from the source.

An approximate envelope to the family of time concentration functions for a given mass transport rate with the shape
factor r of the step length distribution equal to one is
given. The approximation yields good results when $2K_{1,1}x > 10$

and improves progressively for higher transport rate.

For a given degree of pollution, the critical duration
increases downstream and the increase is in direct proportion
to the square root of the distance from the source where the
normality approximation is satisfactory.

With radioactive contaminants, the absorption rate is
given by the inverse square law. At a point sufficiently far
downstream, the dimensionless time of occurrence of the peak
absorption for a given r value is $(1/r)$th of the dimensionless time of occurrence of the peak for $r = 1$. This approximation is not valid for a point near the source. Owing to
mathematical complexity, the critical durations for given
absorption levels are presented graphically.

13.4 CONTINUOUS INJECTION OF CONTAMINATES AT A GIVEN LOCATION WITH UNIFORM RATE

The study of the downstream effects of a continuous injection of contaminates is extended from the case of the
instantaneous injection by means of the convolution integral.
With continuous injection at a unit rate over the time interval
$[0,t_{1_*}]$, the downstream concentration at a time $t_* \geq t_{1_*}$ is

$$C(x_*,t_*) = \int_0^{t_{1_*}} f(x_*,t_*-\tau_*)d\tau_* \qquad (13\text{-}84)$$

where $x_* = K_1 x$ and $t_* = K_2 t$.

The envelopes for each family of curves at a specified
x_* are given by the condition when the injection persists for
an infinitely long time and the time under consideration is
finite. The envelope function for $r = 1$ becomes

$$C(x_*,t_{*e}) = F_{x_*}(t_{*e}) - e^{-x_*-t_{*e}} \sqrt{\frac{t_{*e}}{x_*}}\ I_1(2\sqrt{t_{*e}x_*}) \qquad (13\text{-}85)$$

and is shown in Fig. (13-17) with $r = 2$ and 3.

13-41

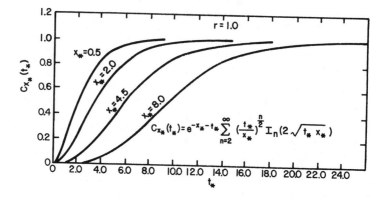

Fig. 13-17. Envelopes to the Different Families of Time-Concentration Distributions for Uniform Injection over Finite Duration, t_*.

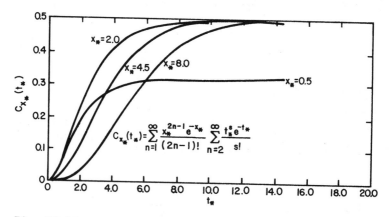

Fig. 13-18. Envelopes to the Different Families of Time-Concentration Distributions for Uniform Injection over Finite Duration, t_* (r=2).

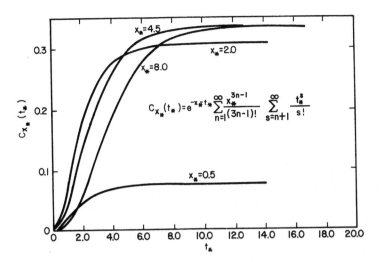

$$C_{x_*}(t_*) = e^{-x_* t_*} \sum_{n=1}^{\infty} \frac{x_*^{3n-1}}{(3n-1)!} \sum_{s=n+1}^{\infty} \frac{t_*^s}{s!}$$

Fig. 13-19. Envelopes to the Different Families of Time-Concentration Distributions for Uniform Injection Over Finite Duration, t_*. ($r=3.0$).

$$C(x_*, t_{*e}) = \sum_{n=1}^{\infty} \frac{x_*^{nr-1} e^{-x_*}}{(nr-1)!} \sum_{s=n+1}^{\infty} \frac{t_{*e}^s e^{-t_{*e}}}{s!} \qquad (13\text{-}86)$$

represents the envelope functions for the time concentration function and is shown in Figs. (13-18) and (13-19). In Fig. (13-17) the envelope functions approach their asymptotic value of 1.0. This can be shown analytically by letting $t_* \to \infty$. In Figs. (13-18) and (13-19) the envelope functions approach different asymptotic values depending on the values of x_* and r. The asymptotes of these envelope functions are obtained by letting $t_{*e} \to \infty$ in Eq. (13-86). We have

$$C(t_*, t_{*e}) = \sum_{n=1}^{\infty} \frac{x_*^{nr-1} e^{-x_*}}{(nr-1)!} \sum_{x=n+1}^{\infty} \frac{t_{*e}^s e^{-t_{*e}}}{s!}$$

$$= \sum_{n=1}^{\infty} \frac{x_*^{nr-1} e^{-x_*}}{(nr-1)!} \int_0^{t_{*e}} \frac{s^n e^{-s}}{n!} \, ds \qquad (13\text{-}87)$$

$$\lim_{t_{*e} \to \infty} C(t_*, t_{*e}) = \sum_{n=1}^{\infty} \frac{x_*^{nr-1} e^{-x_*}}{(nr-1)!}$$

13-43

$$= \begin{cases} 1 & , \; r = 1 \\[2mm] \frac{1}{2} (1 - e^{-x_*}) & , \; r = 2 \\[2mm] \frac{1}{3} [1 - e^{-\frac{3}{2} x_*} (\cos \frac{\sqrt{3} \, x_*}{2} + \sqrt{3} \sin \frac{\sqrt{3} \, x_*}{2}) & \end{cases} \qquad (13\text{-}88)$$

are shown in Fig. (13-20). It is interesting to note that the asymptotes for a given r attain a limiting value of $1/r$ far downstream. Thus, at a position far downstream one would not expect the concentration to exceed $1/r$th of the rate of injection even if the injection persists uniformly over a long time.

13.5 SUMMARY FOR ENGINEERING APPLICATION

The exact solution to the dispersion of contaminated bed-load particles required the knowledge of K_1, K_2 and r in the distributions of the step lengths and rest periods. Since the variations of K_1, K_2 and r with various flow conditions have still not been established, engineering solutions of this problem will be discussed in the following two cases, i.e., Case 1: if some measurements can be made under the design flow conditions, and Case 2: how to estimate the dispersion of contaminated bed-load particles when no measurements are available. In both cases, the solutions are limited to i) cohesionless sediment, ii) sediment size almost uniform, iii) contaminants must be firmly attached to sediment bed particles, iv) seepage effect is negligible, v) sediment bed material load concentration is less than 870 ppm by weight and vi) two-dimensional flows.

Case 1 - If Some Measurements Can be Made in Design Flow Conditions. a) For instantaneous injections of contaminated concentrations perhaps the easiest measurements to be made are: i) $d\bar{x}/dt$ (movement of mass center), ii) $d\sigma^2/dt$ (the rate of spread), and iii) location of peak concentrations, as performed by Yang and Sayre (1971) with suitable tracers. From these three items one can calculate K_1, K_2 and r and plot curves: i) as shown in Figs. (13-1) and (13-2) for the decay of peak concentrations, ii) envelopes of concentrations as shown by Fig. (13-6), iii) iso-concentration contours as shown in Figs. (13-7) and (13-8). Since the envelopes of concentration (as shown by Fig. (13-6) are independent of the values of r, these curves can be obtained when only $d\bar{x}/dt$ and $d\sigma^2/dt$ are known. The decay of concentration at the location of contaminant injection is always exponential with time.

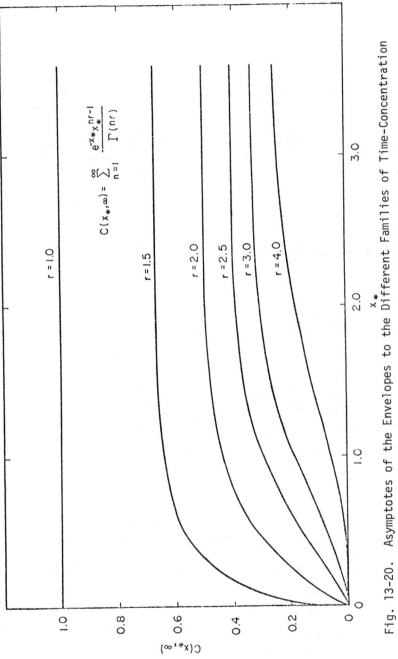

$$C(x_*, \infty) = \sum_{n=1}^{\infty} \frac{e^{-x_*} x_*^{nr-1}}{\Gamma(nr)}$$

Fig. 13-20. Asymptotes of the Envelopes to the Different Families of Time-Concentration Distributions for Uniform Injection Over Infinite Duration.

b) For continuous injection over finite durations of contaminated concentrations, the envelopes of the contaminated concentration at different x and t, such as given in Figs. (13-17), (13-18) and (13-19) for r = 1,2, and 3 respectively, can be obtained if K_1, K_2 and r are determined from the measurements of dx/dt, d /dt and a plot of asymptotic solution (over a long period of time) of concentration distribution for finite duration of continuous injection. The last plot, as shown in Fig. (13-20), gives a good determination of the value of r.

Case 2 - If No Measurement Can Be Made in Design Flow Conditions. The approach is to study the data and curves presented by Grigg (1970). "Hopefully" an order of magnitude estimate can be made there for K_1, K_2 and r for various flow conditions. The obvious conclusion here is that a much more comprehensive data collection program is urgently needed to study the variation of K_1, K_2 and r with flow conditions for the complete solution of the dispersion of contaminated bed-load sediment particles.

13.6 NOTATION

a	$\sqrt{2k_1 x}$
C	concentrated
d	depth of zone of particle movement
e	2.71828
$f_t(x)$	concentration distribution function parameterized by time t
$f_x(t)$	time concentration function parameterized by downstream location x
$f_x(t)$	mode of time concentration function for location x
h	x distance between the contaminant and the subject concerned
$I_{(0,\infty)}(\cdot)$	Indicator function defined by

$$I_{(0,\infty)}(\cdot) = \begin{cases} 1 & 0 \leq \cdot < \infty \\ 0 & \text{otherwise} \end{cases}$$

$I_m(\cdot)$	modified Bessel function of the first kind of order m
K_1	reciprocal of the mean step length of a particle
K_2	reciprocal of the mean rest period of a particle
log	logarithm to base 10
M_j	jth central moment of the time concentrated function
N(t)	number of steps taken by the particle during the interval (o,t)
n	an integer notation

q	$d\bar{x}/dt$
q_s	sediment transport rate per unit width
R	rate of absorption of radiation
$r, r_o, (r_o \geq 1)$	shape parameter in the two parameter Gamma distribution for step length of particle
s_*^2	second central moment of the time concentration function
s	variable
t	time
t_*	dimensionless time scale defined by $t_* = K_2 t$
u	$\sqrt{2K_2 t}$
u'	variable
x	downstream coordinate
X_t	position of particle at time t
X_n	position of particle after n steps
$\bar{x}$	mass center of concentration distribution function
x_*	dimensionless length scale defined by $x_* = K_1 x$
x_e	envelope curve coordinates in the x-direction
x_p	downstream position of the mode of $f_t(x)$
y_p	$2\sqrt{K_1 K_2 x_t}$
z	variable
α	porosity of sand bed
$\propto$	proportionality constant
Δ	residual
Δt	increment in time
Δx	increment in x
γ_s	specific weight of sediment
$\Gamma(\cdot)$	complete gamma function with real argument
σ^2	second moment about $\bar{x}$ of the concentration distribution function
σ_*	$K_1 \sigma$
χ	$\dfrac{t_* - x_{*o}}{\sigma_*}$
ε	relative error
Ⓗ	degree of pollution
ξ_*	x_*/σ_*
$\phi(u)$	characteristic function of $\cdot$
τ_*	t_*/s_*

REFERENCES

Einstein, H. A., 1937, "Bed Load Transport as a Probability Problem," Dr. Sc. Thesis, Federal Institute of Technology, Zurich, Switzerland. See also Sedimentation, 1972 edited by published by H.W. Shen, P. O. Box 606, Fort Collins, Colo., for an English Translation by W. W. Sayre.

Hubbell, D. W., and Sayre, W. W., 1964, "Sand Transport Studies with Radioactive Tracers," Journal of the Hydraulics Division, ASCE, Vol. 90, No. HY3, pp. 39-68.

Parzen, E., 1962, "Stochastic Processes," Holden Day, San Francisco.

Sayre, W. W., and Hubbell, D. W., 1965, "Transport and Dispersion of Labelled Bed Material, North Loup River, Nebraska," U.S. Geological Survey Professional Paper 433-C.

Shen, H. W., and Todorovic, P., 1971, "A General Stochastic Sediment Transport Model," paper presented at the International Symposium on Stochastic Hydraulics held at Pittsburgh, Pennsylvania, May 31, June 2, 1971.

Yang, C. T., and Sayre, W. W., 1971, "Stochastic Model of Sand Dispersion," Journal of the Hydraulics Division, ASCE, Vol. 97, No. HY2, February.

Chapter 14

BEHAVIOR OF COHESIVE MATERIAL
FROM A SOIL ENGINEER'S VIEWPOINT

by

F. Dwayne Nielson, Associate Professor of Civil Engineering,
Colorado State University, Fort Collins,
Colorado

Chapter 14

BEHAVIOR OF COHESIVE MATERIAL
FROM A SOIL ENGINEER'S VIEWPOINT

14.1. INTRODUCTION

Erosion of cohesive soils has been the subject of extensive study by hydraulic engineers. Many of the early studies
tried to relate the erosive properties of clay to the same
variables that erosion of cohesionless materials have been
related to. These early studies have yielded results that may
be considered contradictory to each other. Many researchers
have investigated a given soil type and made only limited
analysis of the soil properties. Their results indicate that
erosion of cohesive soils is directly related to one or two
soil properties. Other investigators have found no correlation with the same variables. As a result confusion has
occurred because of the apparent contradiction of results.

The erosive characteristics of cohesive soils are controlled by electrical surface phenomena while granular soil is
controlled by gravity forces. Therefore, one would not expect
the same variables to be related to erosion resistance in the
same manner for the two soil types. In granular soils one
would expect such items as specific gravity, grain size, and
density to be the controlling variables, but in cohesive soil
there are many more variables to consider. Electrical surface
charge on the clay particle has a major effect on the performance of the cohesive soil mass. Cations in the pore fluid also
have a significant effect on the erosive characteristic of the
soil. In general, the nature of erosion resistance in cohesive
soil is much more complex than in granular soils. This paper
will express some views of a soil engineer on variables that
need to be considered when making erosion studies on cohesive
soils. Many other variables than the ones discussed may be
important, but only the more obvious ones are included here.

14.2. SOIL TYPES

The number of soils encountered in nature is very large.
As a result of the various soil conditions encountered, the
problem of predicting erosion in cohesive soil is indeed very
complex and not completely understood. However, research has
identified many variables which must be evaluated, and has
shown clearly that soil properties and the characteristics of
the eroding fluid has a significant effect on soils resistance
to erosion. In order to give some idea of the number of different soils involved, Table 14-1 gives a listing of some of
the basic soil types. In addition to these, there are many
soils that are combinations of those in Table 14-1. These
minerals may also be in various stages of weathering. Each
soil may have different resistances to erosion, depending on
many different environmental factors.

TABLE 14-1.   NOMENCLATURE OF CLAY MINERALS

1. Crystalline Minerals
    A. Carbonates
    B. Oxides
    C. Silicates
        1. Chain Structures
            a. Palygorskite
            b. Sepiolite
        2. Layer Structures
            a. 2:1 Family (Triphormic)
            1) Smeotites (to replace montmorin, montmorillonoid, montmorillonite group)
                a) Dioctahedral
                    Beidellite
                    Montronite
                    Yolkonskoite
                    Montmorillonite
                b) Trioctahedral
                    Saponite
                    Sauconite
                    Hectorite
                    Stevensite
            2) Vermicurites
                a) Dioctahedral
                b) Trioctahedral
                    Jefferisite
                    Mi-vermiculite
            3) Micas
                a) Dioctahedral
                    Muscovite   Illite
                    Glauconite
                    Paragonite
                b) Trioctahedral
                    Phlogopite
                    Bietite   Ledekite
                    Lepedomelane
            4) Brittle Micas
                a) Dioctahedral
                    Margarite
                b) Trioctahedral
            5) Tale
            6) Pyrophyliite
            7) Interstratified minerals
            8) Chlorites
                a) Both octahedral sheets dioctahedral
                b) Leptochlorites (cookeite)
                c) Orthochlorites
                    Unoxidized chlorites
                    Oxidized chlorites
            b. 1:1 Family (diphormic)
            1) Dioctahedral

14-2

                                    a) Kandities (replaces "Kaolin group")
                                       Necrite
                                       Dickite
                                       Kaolinite
                                       Halloysite
                                 2) Trioctahedral
                                    a) Sepentines
                                       Antigorite
                                       Chrysotile
                                    b) ----------
                                       Amesite
                                       Cronstedtite
                                       Berthlerine
2. Amorphous Minerals
   A. Oxides
      1. Opaline Silica
      2. Limonite
      3. Kilechite
      4. Wad
   B. Silicates
      1. Allophane
      2. Hisingerite
   C. Phosphates
      1. Evansite
      2. Azovskite

The majority of cohesive soils can be classified as layer silicates. The crystal structures of these particles are unique in that the clay particles formed are very thin, flat, plate-like particles. The high ratio of surface area to volume and an unbalanced electrical charge give them properties which are unique. A review of the crystal structure of three different layer silicates will be presented here. They are a smectite (montmorillonite), a kandite (kaolinite), and a chlorite. A more detailed description of these minerals can be found in Grim (1953), Partheniades (1971), Van Olphen (1963), and Evans (1964).

Kaolinite. The structure of kaolinite is composed of a single silica tetrahedral sheet and a single alumina octahedral sheet combined into a unit so that the tips of the silica tetrahedrons and one of the layers of the octahedral sheet form a common layer as shown in Fig. 14-1.

The electrical charges within the structural unit are balanced. Analysis of many samples of kaolinite minerals has shown that there is very little substitution within the lattice. The cation exchange capacity (CEC) that kaolinite does have results from broken bonds around the edges of the clay particle. The resulting CEC of kaolinite is about 10 meg/100 grams of soil which is low in comparison with other soils. The bonding between layers of kaolinite is a hydrogen bond which is much weaker than the bonding which occurs within the tetrahedron and octahedron, but is considerably stronger than the interlayer

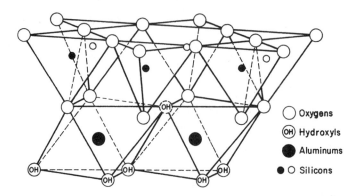

○	Oxygens
(OH)	Hydroxyls
●	Aluminums
● ○	Silicons

Fig. 14-1. Diagrammatic Sketch of the Structure
of the Kaolinite Layer.

bonding of some of the expanding clay minerals. As a result of
the interlayer bond, kaolinite particles are considerably larger
than some of the clays with weak interlayer bonds.
  Montmorillonite. The generally accepted structure of montmorillonite is composed of units made up of two silica tetrahedral sheets with a central alumina octahedral sheet. The
layers are continuous in the a and b directions and are
stacked one above the other in the c direction as shown in
Fig. 14-2. In the stacking of the montmorillonite units, O^{--}
layers of each unit are adjacent to the O^{--} layer of the
neighboring units with the consequence that there is a very
weak bond and an excellent cleavage between layers. Water and
other polar molecules can enter between the unit layers, causing
the lattice to expand in the c direction. Exchangeable cations
are found between the silicate layers, and the c-axis spacing
depends on the size of the interlayer cation. The thinkness of
the water layers between the silica units also depends on the
nature of the exchangeable cation at a given water vapor pressure.
    In order for the structure to be electrically neutral the
octahedral units must contain aluminum ions. In montmorillonite,
part of the aluminum ions are replaced by magnesium ions causing
an excess negative charge in the crystal which must be satisfied by external exchangeable ions. The excess negative charge
is responsible for many of the observed properties of montmorillonite. The erodibility of montmorillonite will depend on the
negative charge and the concentration and type of the cations
in solution which satisfy the negative surface charges.
  Chlorite Minerals. The structure of the chlorites consists
of alternate mica-like and brucite-like layers as shown in Fig.
14-3. The layers are continuous in the a and b directions

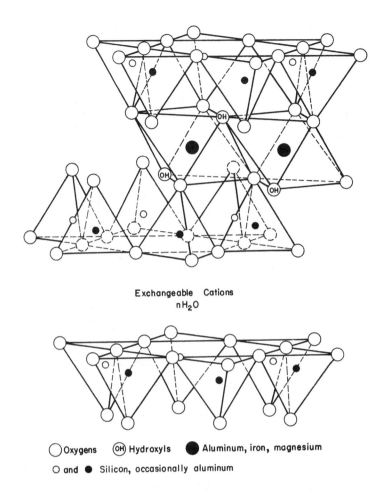

Exchangeable   Cations
nH_2O

○ Oxygens   ⊛ Hydroxyls   ● Aluminum, iron, magnesium

○ and ● Silicon, occasionally aluminum

Fig. 14-2.   Diagrammatic Sketch of the Structure
of Montmorillonite.

and are stacked in the c direction with basal cleavage between
the layers. Various members of the chlorite group differ from
each other in the kind and amount of substitution within the
brucite layer and the tetrahedral and octahedral positions of
the mica layer.

14.3 PHYSICO-CHEMICAL PROPERTIES

Orientation of Clay Minerals. Orientation of clay minerals
have been described as dispersed, flocculated, and packets.
These are usually depicted as shown in Fig. 14-4. Particle
orientation can be a very important factor in determining the
erodibility of cohesive soil. Particle orientation (fabric) may
cause enough change in the erodibility of cohesive soil so that

laboratory studies are not feasible because of changes in soil
properties caused by sample preparation. Unfortunately, information on this factor is not available. However, the effects
of fabric change might be inferred by results obtained by
Partheniades (1965), in which he prepared cohesive samples for
the laboratory by two different methods. Shear strength varied
greatly between the two samples. One sample was "compacted"
while the other was "sedimented" into place. The sedimented
sample should have a much more flocculated fabric than the

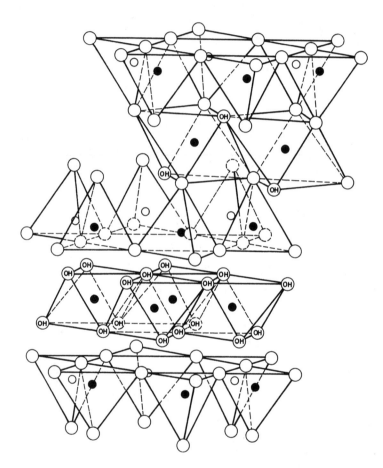

Fig. 14-3. Diagrammatic Sketch of the Structure
of Chlorite.

Flocculated

Dispersed

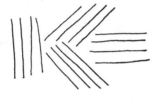

Packet

Fig. 14-4. Orientation of Clay Particles.

compacted sample. The change in erodibility due to shear
strength appears to be of the same magnitude and opposite
sign to that caused the facric change.
An examination of Electron Micrographs of different soil
fabrics may be of great value in explaining the erodibility
difference. Fig. 14-5 shows an electron micrograph of kaolinite
with a flocculated structure with some packets, while Fig. 14-6
shows a kaolinite sample with a dispersed fabric. It is not
hard to visualize that the erodibility of these two soils would
be different even though their density, void ratio, grain size
and atterberg limits are the same.
<u>Double Layer Theory.</u> If it is assumed that the clay particle
is a uniformly charged plate, infinite in two dimensions, the
relation between the potential ψ , distance from the plate x ,
and the concentration of charges or ions ρ is given by the
Poisson equation

14-7

Fig. 14-5. Electron Micrograph of Kaolinite Showing a
Flocculated Soil Fabric (Made by Prof. R.L. Sloane)

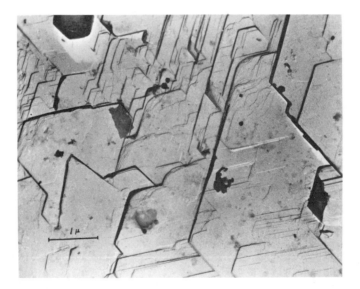

Fig. 14-6. Electron Micrograph of Kaolinite Showing a
Dispersed Soil Fabric.

$$\frac{d^2 \psi}{d x^2} = - \frac{4\pi \rho}{D} \qquad (14\text{-}1)$$

where D = dielectric constant of the solution.
    The distribution of ions in the electwic field is gi-en
by Boltzmann equation:

$$n_+ = n_0 \exp [-(ze\psi/kt)] \qquad \text{for cations} \quad (14\text{-}2$$

and

$$n_- = n_0 \exp (ze\psi/kt) \qquad \text{for anions} \quad (14\text{-}3)$$

where
    k = Boltzmann constant
    T = absolute temperature

Also

$$\rho = \Sigma\, eZ_+ n_+ + \Sigma\, eZ_- n_- \qquad (14\text{-}4)$$

where
    e = electronic charge
    Z = valence of ion
    Assuming that the suspension contains a single symmetrical
electrolyte, the Boltzmann values for n_+ and n_- can be substituted into the equation for ρ , and this substituted into
the Poisson equation.
    By defining, $y = - \frac{e\psi |Z_i|}{kT}$ a dimensionless potential,
the Poisson equation becomes:

$$\frac{d^2 y}{dx^2} - = \frac{4\pi e^2 n_0 Z_i^2}{D\, k\, T} (e^y - e^{-y}) \qquad (14\text{-}5)$$

$$= \frac{8\pi e^2 n_0 Z_i^2}{D\, k\, T} \sinh y \qquad (14\text{-}5)$$

where
    Z_i is the absolute value of the valence of the ion.
The solution of this equation is

$$y = 2 \ln \frac{e^{Kx} + a}{e^{Kx} - a} \qquad (14\text{-}6)$$

where

$$a = \text{Tanh} \left(\frac{y_0}{4}\right) = \text{Tanh} \left(\frac{-e\, \psi_0\, Z_i}{4\, kT}\right) \qquad (14\text{-}7)$$

and

14-9

$$K = \sqrt{\frac{8\pi Z_i^2 e^2 n_o}{D \, k \, T}} \qquad (14\text{-}8)$$

Knowing y as a function of x, one may return to the Boltzmann equation and find the concentration as a function of x as follows:

$$n_i = n_o \left[\frac{1 - ae^{-Kx}}{1 + ae^{-Kx}} \right]^{2 \, Z_i / |Z_i|} \qquad (14\text{-}9)$$

The distribution of the electric potential and the concentration have now been found (See Babcock, 1963).

Equation 14-9 shows that the distribution of cations vs distance away from the clay particle is a function of the following variables:

a. Concentration of the ions in the bulk solution at a large distance away from the clay particle, similar to what may be considered the eroding fluid.

b. Valence of cations in solution

c. Surface potential on clay particle

d. Temperature

Since the properties of clay depend on the distribution of the cations around the clay particle, it is to be expected that these same variables would have a significant effect on the erosion of cohesive soils.

Effects of Cation Concentration. Cation type and concentration in the pore fluid (water) seems to have a significant effect on the erodibility of cohesive soils. Figure 14-7 shows the distribution of ions around a single clay particle. As the concentration of ions in the bulk fluid increases, the double layer around the clay particle is compressed.

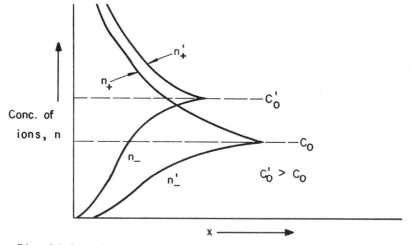

Fig. 14-7. Distribution of Ions in the Double Layer for Two Salt Concentrations in the Equilibrium Solution.

14-10

Because of the various assumptions, Eq. 14-9 is limited to very dilute clay suspensions of low surface charge densities. The equation does show, however, that the lower the concentration and valence of the dissolved salts, the larger the ratio of cation/anion at any distance "x" away from the clay particle and that the valence of the cation has an effect on the thickness of the diffused double layer. As the valence of the cation increases, the double layer is collapsed as shown in Fig. 14-8.

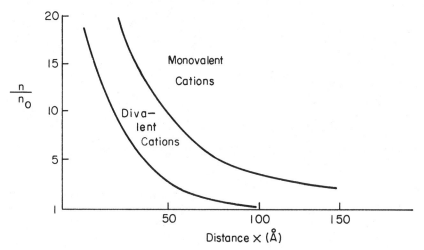

Fig. 14-8. The Influence of Cationic Charge on Distribution in the Double Layer at Constant Salt Concentration.

The previous discussion on electric double layer probably will not be applicable to soil in an erosive environment, however, it should give an indication of the variables which will have important influence.

Liou (1970) has performed tests to determine the effects that electrolyte concentration has on the erosion resistance of clays. Figures 14-9 and 14-10 show some of the results obtained. One might speculate about the reasons for the change in erosion resistance due to the change in the electrolyte concentration. If it is assumed that the clay particles on the interface between the soil and water have a fully developed double layer, the clay with the lower electrolyte concentration (0.1 N $CaCl_2$) should have a thicker double layer. The viscosity of the water in the double layer is usually thought to be higher than "free water." Thus, it would appear that the shear force exerted by the water on the clay particle might be greater on low salt concentration soils than on a particle with a collapsed double layer. This would cause the particle with the expanded double layer to be pulled away from the soil mass under lower stream velocity than one with a collapsed double layer.

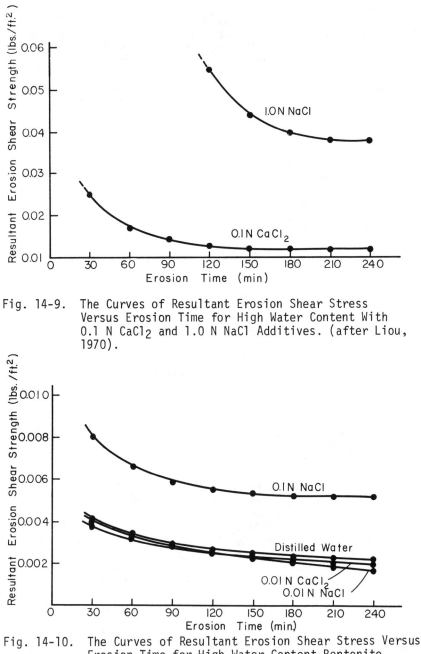

Fig. 14-9.   The Curves of Resultant Erosion Shear Stress
Versus Erosion Time for High Water Content With
0.1 N CaCl$_2$ and 1.0 N NaCl Additives. (after Liou,
1970).

Fig. 14-10.   The Curves of Resultant Erosion Shear Stress Versus
Erosion Time for High Water Content Bentonite
Samples Without Chemical Additives and With 0.1,
0.01 N NaCl and 0.01 N CaCl$_2$ Additives. (after
Liou, 1970).

14-12

Effects of Temperature. Equation 14-9 shows that temperature
has an effect on the distribution of cations in the double
layer surrounding the clay particle. As the temperature increases the thickness of the double layer increases. The effect
of increasing the double layer seems to allow erosion to take
place at lower stream velocities. The viscosity of the eroding
fluid also decreases with an increase in temperature. If the
viscosity of the fluid in the double layer also decreases, it
probably would cause a reduction of the shear force exerted on
the soil particle.

Liou (1970) has also performed erosion studies to determine the effects that temperature has on the erosion resistance
of bentonite. Figure 14-11 shows the results of his study. As
can be seen, temperature has a significant effect on erosion
resistance.

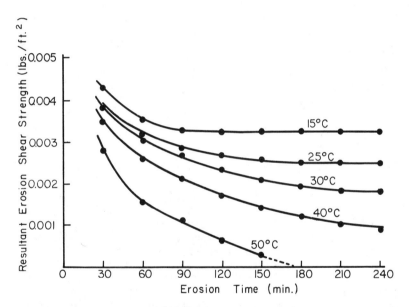

Fig. 14-11. The Curves of Resultant Erosion Shear Stress
Versus Erosion Time for Bentonite Sample at
Different Eroding Water Temperatures (after
Liou, 1971).

Effects of pH. A charged edge of the clay particle often
exists from broken bonds occurring along the edges perpendicular
to the basal plane. The amount of broken bond surface is small
relative to the basal plane surface because particle dimensions
along the a and b axes are 10 to 20 times that parallel to
the c axis.

The broken bond surface may develop either positive or
negative exchange sites, depending on the pH of the environ-

ment and location of the broken bond. Figure 14-12 shows the
effects that pH have on the development of the charge.

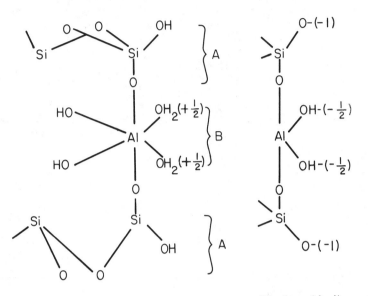

Acid Media   Alkaline Media

Fig. 14-12.   Effects of pH on Charge at Broken Edges

    The site in Region A (Fig. 14-12) would be neutral in an
acid environment but H+ would dissociate (proton donor) at
a higher pH and it would then be a negative site.
    In Region B, if it is assumed that octahedral coordination
is maintained, then the two broken bond sites are negative when
occupied with OH ions (alkaline media) or are positive when
occupied with OH_2 (acid media). If it is assumed that 5
coordination is attained, then the site is positive in acid
media, neutral at intermediate acidity and negative in alkaline
media.
    The charges on the clay edge has positive sites in acid
media that change to negative sites in alkaline media. The
isoelectric pH (neutral charge) depends upon a number of factors,
such as type of clay and other anions in the system.
    The following evidence demonstrates that positive edge
sites do exist and that they are a function of pH: a) that a
negative gold sol will be adsorbed on crystal edges but not on
faces has been shown by electron microscopy; b) adsorption of
polyphosphates on edges prevents the adsorption of the gold
sol and it also increases the cation exchange capacity; and
c) anion adsorption decreases with increasing pH.
    Because of greater accessibility (less interference from
Si groups) the positive sites would be expected to be more
active on kaolinite than on montmorillonite.

14-14

Liou (1970) has performed erosion studies (Fig. 14-13) to determine what effect pH has on the erodibility of kaolinite. The pH was adjusted with NaOH to a value of 5.6, 6.5, and 8.2 at 25°C. pH is kaolin clay proved to be a critical factor controlling its erodibility. At low pH, kaolin clay particles flocculate due to electro static attraction between oppositely charged surfaces, and these forces between particles give high resistance to erosion. At high pH, by adding NaOH solution to kaolin clay, the particles will disperse each other because of the positive charges on the edge of the clay particle will be destroyed. The destruction of the positive charge eliminates the edge to face bonding between the particles. It may also cause the diffused double layer to expand slightly on the free surface between the soil and water, causing essentially the same effect as a reduction in cation concentration.

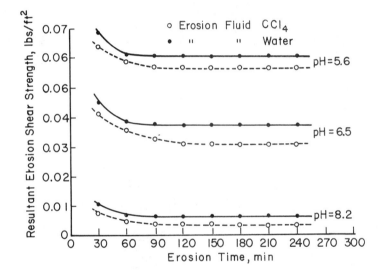

Fig. 14-13. The Curves of Resultant Erosion Shear Stress Versus Erosion Time for Kaolin Clay Samples With pH 5.6, 6.5, and 8.2. (after Liou, 1970).

Effects of Water Content. The ion distribution when soil particles are close together is of considerable interest in erosive studies. In soils at low moisture contents the particles are sufficiently close to cause the diffuse double layers to overlap.

When the interparticle separation is less than about 15 A° , the diffuse double layer described by Gouy-Chapman breaks down and the exchangeable cations are essentially uniformly distributed between the layers. The interparticle spacing is difficult to determine, but it can be estimated from

$$t = \frac{\%\text{water by weight}}{S \quad \gamma_w} \tag{14-10}$$

if the thickness, t , of the water layer is assumed to be uniform on all soil surfaces; where S is specific surface and γ_w is density of the water. The distance between adjacent particles surfaces is twice the thickness of the water layer.

Water content of a saturated soil is an important factor in the performance of cohesive soil subjected to erosion. It changes the distribution of cations surrounding a clay particle as well as governs the distance between particles.

Figure 14-14 shows some test results by Liou (1970) in which the erodibility of bentonite was investigated at various moisture contents. As the water content increased (indicating larger spacing between soil particles) the resistance to erosion decreased considerably.

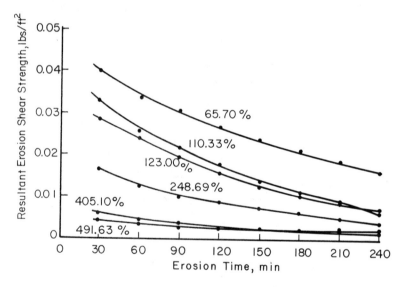

Fig. 14-14. The Curves of Resultant Erosion Shear Stress Versus Erosion Time for Bentonite Samples With Out Chemical Additives at Different Water Contents (after Liou, 1970).

Organic Content. Organic content of the soil should have a significant influence on the erodibility of the soil although information concerning its effect is very limited. It would

14-16

be expected that the organic matter would have more effect in materials where broken edges are of major importance, such as kaolinite. Organic matter will reduce the amount of phosphate adsorption on a clay maneral. This apparently is caused by the organic molecule covering some of the positive sites on the edge of the clay particle where the anions are adsorbed. If this is the case, the resulting effect might be somewhat the same as pH which controls the amount of positive sites available on the clay surface.

Organic matter will also change the Atterberg limits of a clay soil. Since both the Atterberg Limits and pH have direct relationships with erodibility, one would expect that organic matter content would also have a direct effect.

14.4. MECHANICAL PROPERTIES OF COHESIVE SEDIMENTS

Shear Strength. The classical Coulomb's equation for shear strergth of soil is

$$\tau = C + \overline{\sigma} \, Tan\phi \qquad (14\text{-}11)$$

where τ is shear strength of the soil, C is the cohesion strength, $\overline{\sigma}$ is the effective normal stress and ϕ is the angle of internal friction. Shear strength is usually measured by a triaxial shear test, direct shear test, vane shear or an unconfined compression test. The shear strength of a soil is a measure of the ability of the particles to resist movement between each other within the soil mass. Since erosion is normally a surface phenomena, shear strength may not correlate very well with resistance to erosion. However, the physico-chemical variables previously mentioned also have a significant effect on the shear strength of soil. In a given soil with a constant cation concentration and type, and no change in soil fabric, the erosion resistance of clay should be approximately related to shear strength. However if the cation type and concentration and soil fabric change, deviation can be expected.

Dunn (1959) found that the critical shear stress increased with vane shear strength. Dunn's testing procedure for soil preparation was the same for all samples. He describes his sample preparation as follows:

"A sample of soil which had been oven dried and passed through a No. 10 U.S. Standard Sieve was thoroughly mixed with water and puddled into a metal container. The moisture content was above both saturation and the liquid limit, but was not high enough to allow segregation of the soil particles. The soil was consolidated between porous plates for three days. The load and top porous plate were then removed and the lucite cylinder was clamped into position and filled with water. The soil was allowed to come to equilibrium under zero load for two days. This time was considered sufficient to reduce excess

hydrostatic pressures in the soil to a negligible
value. The jet was then positioned above the soil
sample and the head of water on the nozzle was
slowly increased."
The results of Dunn's (1959) study are shown in Fig. 14-15.

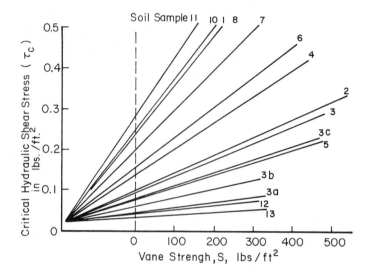

Fig. 14-15. (after Dunn, 1959).

Figure 14-15 shows that erosion resistance of a soil is dependent on more than just the vane shear strength. Dunn (1959)
indicated that the slope of each line is a function of soil
type.

      Partheniades (1965) reported erosion studies made in
flumes in the laboratory. Water used was at ocean salinity.
Soils used were San Francisco Bay Muds. In his studies he
reports that "minimum scouring shear stresses and erosion rates
are independent of the strength of the bed material, provided
that the flow does not induce stresses of an order higher than
the order of the macroscopic strength of the bed."

      The method of soil preparation may have been responsible
for the inconsistency of reported results between Dunn's and
Partheniades findings. Dunn prepared all his samples by con-
solidating them in essentially the same manner. Soil fabric,
bonding between particles and void ratio should have been
related to preparation procedures. Partheniades prepared his
soil bed in two different ways, even though they were the same
soil. He describes them as follows. "Two types of beds were
tested. The first 0.1 ft. thick bed was made of natural
material at field moisture. The second was a flocculated deposited loose bed formed by deposition of the material of the

first bed after being put into suspension in the water of the flume. Its strength varied from 1/136 to 1/12 of the strength of the dense bed."

The consolidation procedure used by Dunn would tend to orient the clay particles into a dispersed structure. Yong and Warkentin (1966) have shown that consolidation changes clay fabric from a more random fabric to a dispersed (parallel) fabric. Partheniades did not indicate how his "dense" soil beds were prepared but at moistures contents he reported a dispersed soil fabric can be expected, while his sedimented beds should have had a flocculated (structure) fabric.

ASCE Task Committee (1968) presented relationships between vane shear strength and critical shear stress as shown in Fig. 14-16. Data obtained from San Saba Clay displayed a great amount of scatter and when fitted with a least squares regression, the resulting relation showed an opposite trend found for the other soils. No explanation has been offered for the reversed behavior of this particular soil.

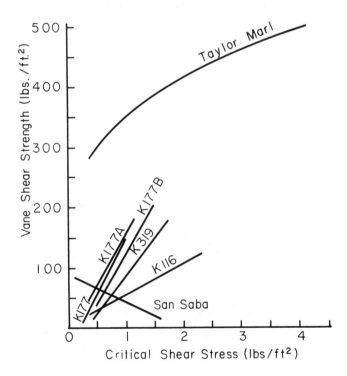

Fig. 14-16. Vane Shear Strength vs Critical Shear Stress after ASCE Task Committee on Erosion of Cohesive Materials (1968).

Compression Strength. The relationship between compression
strength and vane shear strength should be related to erosion
in the same manner. Coulomb's law related the two.

$$\tau = C + \bar{\sigma}\ \text{Tan}\phi \qquad (14\text{-}12)$$

The unconfined compression in saturated undrained cohesive soil
is essentially a measure of the cohesion, C . At the surface
of the clay soil where erosion takes place the effective stress,
$\bar{\sigma}$, is considered to be zero. Thus, the two tests should correlate to erosion resistance with approximately the same degree
of accuracy.

Compression strength of soil was found to have no effect
on erosion by Bergharger and Ladd (1964). However, a positive
relation between compression strength and erodibility was
determined by Flaxman (1963) as shown in Fig. 14-17. Sample
preparation method may have been the reason for the difference
between Flaxman and Bergharger and Ladd's findings.

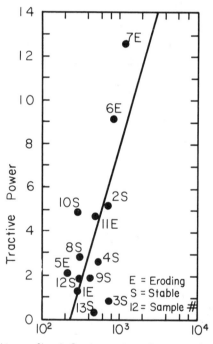

Fig. 14-17.   Relationship Between Unconfined Compressive
              Strength and Tractive Power (after Flaxman, 1963).

Atterberg Limits. Many studies trying to correlate the
Atterberg limits with erosion resistance of cohesive soils have

14-20

been made with varying degrees of success. The Atterberg limits are determined on remolded soil in the laboratory and, therefore, do not reflect the effects of such variables as void ratio (density), past loading history of the soil (pre-consolidation), degree of compaction, and particle orientation. It is therefore questionable if erodibility of cohesive soils can be directly correlated with Atterberg limits for all soils without taking into account other variables. However, Smerdon and Beasley (1959) found that the critical tractive force increased with plasticity as shown in Fig. 14-18.

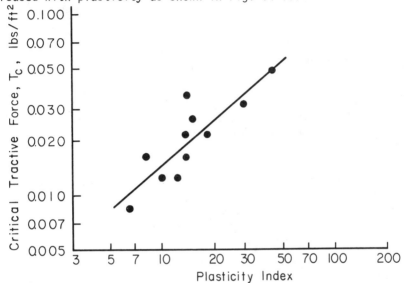

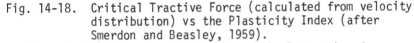

Fig. 14-18. Critical Tractive Force (calculated from velocity distribution) vs the Plasticity Index (after Smerdon and Beasley, 1959).

Dunn (1959) also found that the critical tractive force of cohesive soil was a function of the vane shear strength, and plasticity index.

The Bureau of Reclamation (See Gibbs, 1962) has correlated erosion resistance with the Atterberg limits of various canal linings. Their findings are shown in Fig. 14-19, and their suggested soil selection chart for canal lining is shown in Fig. 14-20.

Rektorik and Smerdon (1964) found no apparent correlation between the critical shearing force of the soils at the liquid limit moisture content and plasticity index.

Particle Size. Particle size has been an attractive area of research in cohesive soils because of the good correlation that has been obtained between erodibility and particle size of coarse grain soils. Particle size has an influence in the erodibility of cohesive soils but other variables also become important.

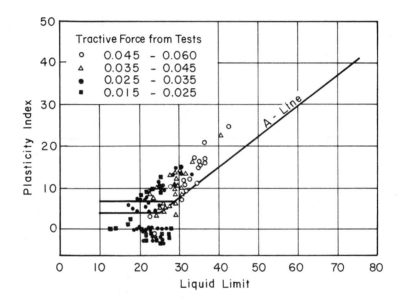

Fig. 14-19. Plasticity Characteristics With Laboratory
Tractive Force Values Adjusted Because of High
and Low Density. Samples With Densities Below
80 PCF Were Raised in Value and Samples With
Densities Above 100 PCF Were Lowered in Value
(after Gibbs, 1962).

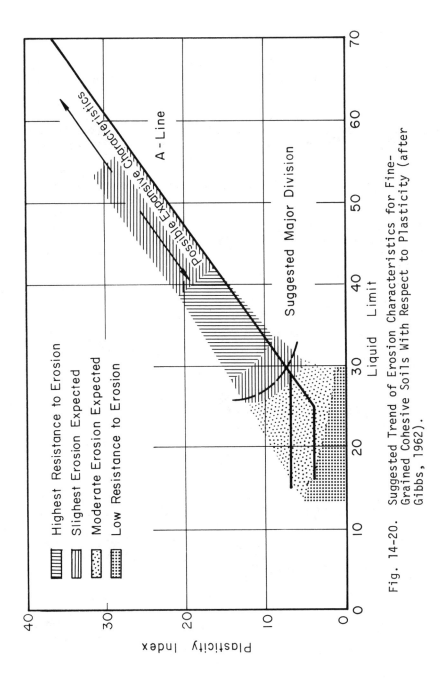

Fig. 14-20. Suggested Trend of Erosion Characteristics for Fine-Grained Cohesive Soils With Respect to Plasticity (after Gibbs, 1962).

14-23

Smeardon and Beasley (1959) tested 11 soils to determine the effects on particle size on erosion characteristics. All 11 soils were gathered in the state of Missouri. Although no mineralogical analysis is given, it is suspected that most of the soils were of one major clay group. If this were the case, one would expect some relation between erodibility and grain size as long as they were placed in the flume used for the erosion experiment in a consistent manner. According to their article all soils were placed in the same manner which reduces to a minimum the influence of such soil variables as fabric. No effects of salt in pore fluid or temperature sould be encountered in their experiment. Figures 14-21 and 14-22 shows some of the relationships they obtained between critical tractive stress and particle size.

Sundborg (1956) presented two sets of curves, which were obtained by Forbes and Julstrom, to relate critical erosion velocity and grain diameter. These curves are given in Fig. 14-23, which shows that there is at least a ten-fold increase in velocity between an unconsolidated clay (10^{-3}mm dia.) and a consolidated clay. Part of this difference could be due to void ratio, but a significant part of the difference may be due to change in soil fabric.

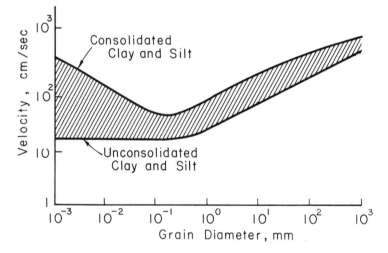

Fig. 14-23. Curves Shwoing the Relation Between Particle Size and Critical Erosion Velocity, (after Sundborg, 1956).

14.5. CONCLUSIONS

Erosion of cohesive soil is a very complex problem and much additional research must be done before a general solution can be achieved. It is the opinion of the writer, and it is highly open to discussion, that the following variables as a

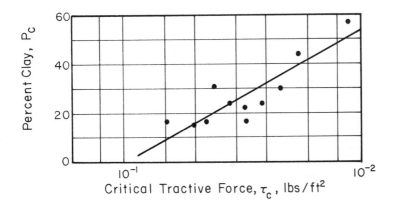

Fig. 14-21. Critical Tractive Force Determined by Equation (1) or (14) Versus Percent Clay (after Smerdon and Beasley, 1959).

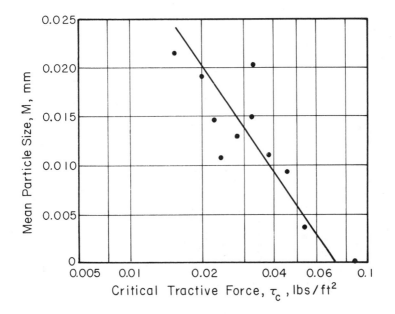

Fig. 14-22. Critical Traction Force vs Mean Particle Size (after Smerdon and Beasley, 1969).

minimum must be included in any research on cohesive soil.

1. Soil type
2. Soil Fabric
3. Cation exchange capacity or some directly related measurement of the electric charge on the clay particles.
4. Cation type and concentration in the pore fluid and as exchangable cations
5. Temperature
6. pH
7. Water content of the soil
8. Organic matter in the soil
9. Soil density (void ratio)
10. Shear strength
11. Atterberg limits
12. Particle size

Any research that is done on soil which does not include these variables may confuse the situation more than it will help. As one final comment "God help the researcher that tries to include all of the above mentioned variables. He will need all the help he can get."

REFERENCES

ASCE Task Force Committee on Erosion of Cohesive Materials, 1968, Erosion on Cohesive Sediments; Proc. Paper 6044, J. of Hydr. Division, ASCE, July.

Babcock, K.L., 1963, Chemical Properties of soil Colloids; Hilgardia, Vol. 34, No. 11, August.

Berghager, D., and Ladd, C.C., 1964, Erosion of Cohesive Soils; Research Report R64-1, Massachusetts Institute of Technology Department of Civil Engineering, January.

Dunn, I.S., 1959, Tractive Resistance of Cohesive Channels; Journal of Soil Mechanics and Foundation Division, ASCE, Vol. 85, No. SM3 Proc. Paper 2062, June.

Evans, R.C., 1964, An Introduction to Crystal Chemistry; 2nd Edition, Cambridge University Press.

Flaxman, E.M., 1963, Channel Stability in Undistrubed Cohesive Soils; Journal of Hydraulics Division, ASCE, March.

Gibbs, H.J., 1962, A Study of Erosion and Tractive Force Characteristics in Relation to Soil Mechanics Properties-Earth Research Program; Soils Engineering Report No. EM-643, U.S. Department of the Interior-Bureau of Reclamation Denver, Colo.

Grim, Ralph E., 1953, Clay Mineralogy, McGraw Hill Book Company, New York.

Liou, Y.D., 1970, Hydraulic Erodibility of Two Pure Clay Systems, Ph.D. Thesis, Colorado State University, Report No. CED 70-71YDL5, Fort Collins, Colo.

Partheniades, E., 1965, Erosion and Deposition of Cohesive Soils, Journal of Hydraulics Division, ASCE, January.

Partheniades, E., (1971) Erosion and Deposition of Cohesive Materials; Chapter 25, River Mechanics Vol. II, Edited and Published by H.W. Shen.

Rektorik, R.J. and Smerdon, Ernest T., 1964, Critical Shearing Forces in Cohesive Soils from a Rotating Shear Apparatus; Paper presented at the 1964 Annual meeting American Society of Agricultural Engineers, Ft. Collins, Colo.

Smerdon, E.T. and Beasley, R.P., 1959, The tractive Force Theory Applied to Stability of Open Channels in Cohesive Soils; Research Bull. 715, University of Missouri College of Agriculture, Agr. Exp. Sta., October.

Sundborg, A., 1956, The River Klarelven, A Study of Fluvial Processes; Meddeland en Fran Uppsala University Sweden, Geografiska, Institute Ser. A. No. 115.

Van Olphen, H., 1963, An Introduction of Clay Colloid Chemistry; Interscience Publication.

Yong, R.N., and Warkentin, Benno P., 1966, Introduction to Soil Behavior; Macmillian Company, New York.

Chapter 15

UPSLOPE EROSION ANALYSIS

by

W.H. Wischmeier, Research Statistician, Agricultural
Research Service, U.S. Dept. of
Agriculture, and Associate Professor
of Agricultural Engineering, Purdue
University, Lafayette, Indiana

Chapter 15

UPSLOPE EROSION ANALYSIS[1]

15.1 INTRODUCTION

Much of the sediment transported to rivers and reservoirs is eroded from upslope areas such as farmland and construction sites. Accelerated upland erosion damages the land where it occurs, pollutes surface waters, and often causes serious problems where it is deposited. The rate of erosion on a particular land area is determined by complex interrelations of many factors. These include factors that influence the erosive forces of rainfall and runoff and others that influence the resistance of the soil to detachment or transport by the erosive agents.

Cook (1936) recognized a clear understanding of fundamental factors involved in the erosion process and the development of practical methods for changing them as the means for attaining soil conservation. Under his planning and guidance, Laws and Parsons (1941 and 1943) began to investigate the velocities and size distribution of raindrops in relation to rain intensity. Their studies signaled the beginning of the concept that erosion is a work process for which energy is supplied by the falling raindrops and flowing runoff. That concept and other basic principles summarized by Meyer (1970) contributed substantially to the interpretation of the results of 40 years of upslope erosion studies.

Achieving a full understanding of the erosion and sedimentation process will require closely coordinated research by teams of specialists in the various related disciplines. Such an effort is now underway in the U. S. Agricultural Research Service. A suitable framework has been developed for combining basic concepts, principles and relationships in a fundamentally sound mathematical erosion model (Meyer and Wischmeier, 1969). Research is underway to develop additional basic concepts and relationships needed to make such a model fully operational.

Details of the basic model and principles underlying the erosion process were presented by Meyer (1970) at the first River Mechanics Institute. This report will supplement his presentation with a resume of existing upslope erosion data and their analyses, and an in-depth discussion of the now widely used universal soil-loss equation (Wischmeier and Smith, 1960). This equation is a less refined but highly useful

---

[1] Contribution from the Corn Belt Branch, Soil and Water Conservation Research Division, Agricultural Research Service, USDA, in cooperation with the Purdue Agricultural Experiment Station, Lafayette, Indiana.

erosion model that was empirically derived from the upslope
erosion data of the past 40 years. My objectives will be to:
(1) analyze the universal soil-loss equation and its functions
in erosion-control planning, and (2) elaborate on important
derivational and interpretational details that reflect its
strengths, weaknesses and confidence levels.

15.2 UPSLOPE EROSION DATA

Nature and Scope. Attempts to measure runoff and erosion
from field plots date back to 1915. In general, the purpose
of the first stations was to demonstrate and evaluate the
enormous damage to the soil by the erosion process (Middleton
et. al., 1932). The U.S. Department of Agriculture became a
partner in erosion research about 1930, when establishment of
the first 10 Federal-State cooperative stations was begun.
Within the next 25 years, erosion plot studies were established
at 32 additional locations. Precise measurements of precipitation, runoff and soil loss at the 42 stations in 23 states were
continuous for periods of from 5 to 30 or more years. The
studies were designed to measure the relation of factors such
as length and percent of slope, type of vegetal cover, crop
sequence and management practices to runoff and erosion from
fractional-acre plots and small segments of natural watersheds.
    The field plots were rectangular to facilitate normal row
spacing for cultivated crops. Confounding of factor effects
was reduced by selecting the plot sites for homogeneity of
slope shape, steepness, soil and rainfall within each plot
series. The small-watershed studies had the advantage of
more-natural drainage patterns, but the disadvantage of factor-
effect confounding by heterogeneity of soil and hydrologic
characteristics. Some of the stations also conducted indoor-
laboratory studies. These were more controlled and helped
to interpret the results of the field studies.
    In 1956 a portable rainfall simulator was constructed
that has the capability of simulating the drop size distribution and terminal velocities of natural rainfall and
applying the simulated rain to several 75-foot plots
simultaneously (Meyer and McCune, 1958). This development
has added substantially to the information on upland erosion.
    Runoff and Soil-Loss Data Center. In 1954 the Soil and
Water Conservation Research Division of the Agricultural
Research Service established a national runoff and soil loss
data center at Purdue University. The basic data from more
than 10,000 plot-years of erosion studies were assembled at
this center from the 42 stations, standardized in units, and
transferred in detail to punched cards for consolidation and
analysis (Wischmeier, 1955). Subsequent data from continuing
studies are added annually. The large amount of basic data
used in analyses at the data center, and the wide geographic
distribution of data sources, made possible the empirical

derivation of mathematical expressions for factor relationships whose basic and theoretical validity has been substantiated by subsequent fundamental research.

Problems in Analysis of Plot and Watershed Data. Erosion
studies under natural conditions are much more difficult to
control than laboratory experiments. Factor interactions play
important roles in determining the amount of soil eroded from
a given area. Some of the uncontrolled parameters that inter-
act with controlled parameters vary randomly over time. Others,
such as rainfall distribution and storm characteristics, tend
to follow a particular long-term trend at a given location but
vary unpredictably in the short run. The effect of any one
soil, weather, or management parameter on soil loss is generally
influenced by the particular way in which other variables
happen to be combined at the particular time and place of the
observation. Consequently, tremendous within-treatment variation is characteristic of erosion data.

In single-location experiments, the effects of several
important physical parameters - soil, percent slope, rainfall
distribution and storm characteristics - are often completely
confounded. The results can be safely extrapolated to another
location or another time period only when the data can be
analyzed in a design that is sufficiently comprehensive to
make separation of these effects possible.

The use of rainfall simulators (Meyer, 1960) eliminates
rainfall as an uncontrolled variable in the experiment and has
other important advantages. However, the constant-intensity
simulated storms do not measure the effects of the wide intensity variations that are usually characteristic of natural
rain and do not eliminate the soil-loss variability that is
due to short-term variations in antecedent soil-surface and
crop conditions.

Statistical determination of significant differences in
treatment effects at a preselected confidence level is a
helpful initial step but falls short of the needs of overall
soil-loss data analysis. The knowledge that one cropping
system or practice is more effective than another is not
sufficient information to determine the adequacy of either
treatment in a given situation or to compute gross sediment
yields.

The use of multiple-regression analyses to evaluate both
primary and interaction effects and to determine expressions
for factor relationships was the most successful technique for
gleaning additional information from the assembled data. This
technique also provided a means for valid extrapolation of
results to other locations and other time periods.

15.3 THE UNIVERSAL SOIL-LOSS EQUATION

Design Criteria. The universal soil-loss equation was
designed to meet the need for a convenient working tool for
conservationists, technicians and planners. Their primary

need was a relatively simple technique for predicting the most likely soil-loss rates for specific situations. Therefore, refinements needed only for short-run predictions were sacrifices in the interests of conciseness and simplicity.

Concepts developed by many other researchers since 1930, and analyses of the assembled data, led to the conclusion that all important parameters for upslope soil-loss prediction could be grouped under six major factors. Predetermined criteria required that each of the factors: (1) could be represented by a single number, (2) could be predicted from meteorological soils, or erosion-research data on a locational basis, and (3) must be free from any geographically oriented base. Since no satisfactory runoff-prediction equation was available, the decision was made not to distinguish between predictions of runoff and its soil content in the model. (This decision hastened the availability of the soil-loss equation and facilitated simplicity. Work on a runoff equation for cropland is now underway.)

The most accurate type of mathematical expression for the relationship of each of the six major factors to soil loss was determined from exploratory statistical analyses of the assembled data. The effects of slope length and steepness, crop sequence, and soil- and crop-management practices were most accurately described in the form of percentage increases or decreases in soil loss. Therefore, a multiplicative model was selected for the equation which utilizes four dimensionless factors to modify a basic soil loss that is described by dimensional rainfall and soil factors.

A "unit plot" to serve as a common reference point for evaluation of the equation's factors was arbitrarily defined as follows: a cropland plot 72.6 feet long, on a 9% uniform slope, and continuously in bare fallow that is tilled to break surface crusts. These dimensions were selected because most of the plots in U. S. erosion studies from 1930 to about 1960 were 72.6 feet long and on slopes near 9%. Continuous fallow was selected as a common base for two reasons: (1) No cropping system is common to all agricultural areas, and (2) Soil loss from any other plot condition would be influenced by residual and current crop-and-management effects that vary from one location to another. Complete isolation of soil effect was essential.

The equation. The universal soil-loss equation is

$$A = R\ K\ L\ S\ C\ P$$

where A is the computed soil loss in the dimensions selected for K and for the time period selected for R.

R is the rainfall factor, usually expressed in units of the rainfall-erosivity index, EI, and evaluated from the iso-erodent map, figure 1. (Two exceptions to use of EI for R will be pointed out later.)

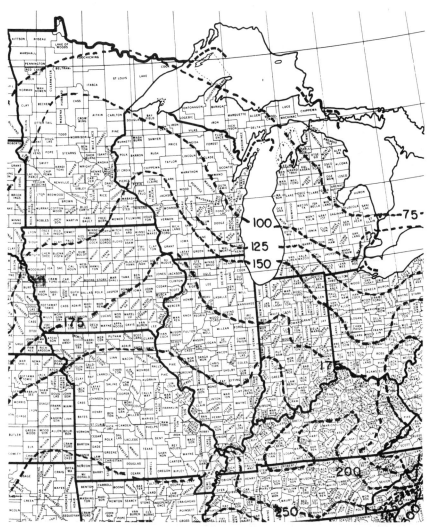

Figure 15-1   Section of iso-erodent map showing average annual
values of factor R as determined by the rainfall
parameter EI (from Wischmeier and Smith, 1965).

K is the soil-erodibility factor, commonly expressed in
tons per acre per EI unit and evaluated from the
erodibility nomograph, figure 2.
L is a dimensionless slope-length factor, evaluated from
the slope-effect chart, figure 3.
S is the slope-steepness factor, evaluated in combination
with L from figure 3.
C is the cropping and management factor, evaluated by a
technique utilizing EI-distribution curves and a soil-
loss-ratio table.

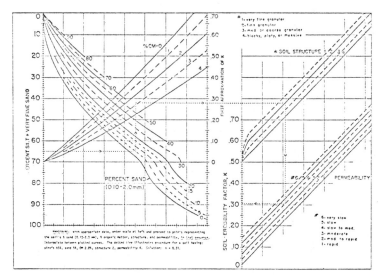

Figure 15-2   Soil-erodibility nomograph used to determine
factor K for specific topsoils or subsoil
horizons.   Solutions are in tons per acre.
(from Wischmeier, et al., 1971).

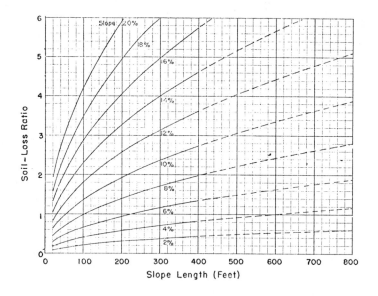

Figure 15-3   Slope-effect chart used to determine combined
value of factors L and S as computed by: LS =
$\lambda^{0.5}(0.00076\ s^2 + 0.0053\ s + 0.0076)$, where λ =
slope length in feet and s = steepness in per-
cent. (from Wischmeier and Smith, 1965).

15-6

P is the factor for supplemental practices such as contouring, terraces, and stripcropping and is evaluaed from table 1.

TABLE 15-1   VALUES OF PRACTICE FACTOR, P

Land slope (percent)	Farming on contour	Contour stripcrop	Terracing 1/	Terracing 2/
2 to 7	0.50	0.25	0.50	0.10
8 to 12	.60	.30	.60	.12
13 to 18	.80	.40	.80	.16
19 to 24	.90	.45	.90	.18

1/ For erosion-control planning on farmland.

2/ For prediction of contribution to off-field sediment load.

In general terms, the first four factors have fixed values at a given site, at least in the short run, and together they determine the basic soil-loss potential for that site. The last two factors are readily changed by land-use and management decisions and very substantially affect the relation of actual soil loss to the basic potential computed by R, K, L and S. (The values of L, S and K can also be changed, but less readily: L, by terraces or diversions; S, by topographic modification;   K by long-term management or use of chemical soil stabilizers.)

The universal soil-loss equation resembles its predecessors in form, but the factors assume new meanings and predictive accuracy. Major improvements incorporated in the equation include:

1. More complete separation of factor effects so that results of a change in any factor can be more accurately predicted.

2. A new rainfall-erosivity index that provides a more accurate rainfall factor.

3. A quantitative soil factor that is directly evaluated without reference to any particular soil or geographic region.

4. A new technique for predicting a soil's inherent erodibility without erosion measurements.

5. A method of accounting for interactions between cropping and management parameters.

6. A method of evaluating the cropping-management factor on the basis of local climate and specific crop cultural conditions.

Application. For conservation planning on farmland the equation is used in conjunction with soil-loss tolerance limits. These limits define the average annual rates of soil loss that can be tolerated without reducing crop-production potential and range from 1 to 5 tons per acre (Wischmeier and Smith, 1965). Greater emphasis on downslope damage by sediment may require modification of these rates for some situations. Erosion rates predicted by the equation are compared with the appropriate tolerance limit, T. It is desirable to obtain, for each field, a list of the various cropping and management alternatives that would hold the erosion rate on the field below the applicable tolerance limit, so that the system best suited to the particular farm enterprise can be selected. The factor C accounts for all effects of cropping and management. Therefore, the desired list of suitable alternatives can be obtained by solving the soil-loss equation for C when A = T and comparing this value with the list of cropping-system C values applicable to that location. For this purpose it is convenient to rewrite the equation as C_{max} = T/RKLSP. Any of the systems for which the table lists a C value smaller than the computed C_{max} should hold soil loss from the field within the tolerance limit. Tables of C values for specific rainfall regions, derived by the technique discussed in the next section, are available from the Soil Conservation Service.

To illustrate, we will assume a situation in Monona County, Iowa. From figure 1, R = 160 in Monona County. The present plowed depth of the Monona silt loam soil on this field is comprised of 74% silt, 23% clay, 2.2% organic matter, and no sand fraction. The soil has a medium subangular blocky structure and is moderately permeable. For this description the erodibility nomograph (figure 2) computes a K value of 0.42. The field has a 10% slope with an average length of 300 feet. For this combination the slope-effect chart (figure 3) gives an LS value of 2.37. For contouring on 10% slope, P = 0.6 (table 1). An annual soil loss of 5 T/A is considered tolerable on this deep loess soil. Combining these values,

$$C_{max} = 5/(160 \times 0.42 \times 2.37 \times 0.6) = 5/96 = 0.052$$

Any cropping system listed in the C value table for this geographic region that has a C value smaller than 0.052 would provide acceptable erosion control for the field. A C_{max} as small as 0.052 is quite restrictive and shows that a 300-foot length is excessive on this soil and slope for any system that includes more than one cultivated crop in 4 years. A system of terraces, or even one diversion halfway downslope, would reduce the concentration of runoff by reducing the effective slope length. Terraces at 75-foot intervals would reduce LS to 1.19 and double the computed C_{max}. The table of rotation C values would show that with C_{max} = 0.104, the list of acceptable systems would include continuous cropping to corn if it were no-till planted with at least 2 tons of shredded cornstalk residue remaining on the surface after planting. With the conventional plow-disk-plant system, however, sod crops in rotation with the corn would still be needed.

The maximum slope lengths on which specific crop and management systems would provide adequate erosion control on a given field are determined by solving the equation L_{max} = T/RKSCP. Other factors can be similarly maximized for given situations.

When planning construction projects which require re-shaping of the soil surface, the erodibility nomograph (figure 2) is used to predict the erodibilities of subsoil horizons that may be exposed during construction, and the complete equation serves to predict sediment loads that would be delivered to sediment basins under various alternative plans for the construction period.

Use of the soil-loss equation for computation of upslope-area contributions to watershed sediment yields will be discussed later.

For a better understanding of how the equation functions and of likely variability in confidence limits on its quantitative predictions, each of the factors will be considered in more detail.

15.4 INTERPRETATION AND EVALUATION OF THE EQUATION'S FACTORS

Rainfall Factor, R. The function of R is to quantify the interrelated erosive forces of rainfall and runoff. The parameter used to evaluate R must be predictable on a probability basis from meteorological data. It must be definable for specific storms, seasons, and specific periods of time as well as on an annual basis, and its seasonal or annual evaluation must be influenced by all significant rains rather than only by annual maxima. These requirements are not satisfied by the rainfall factor used by Musgrave (1947).

The parameter EI meets all the requirements listed above, and for nonorographic rainfall it is the best rainfall-erosivity index presently known (Wischmeier, 1959). For a given storm, EI is defined as the product: kinetic energy of the storm in foot-tons per acre-inch, times maximum 30-minute intensity, times 10^{-2}. Individual-storm values of this interaction term are nearly always less than 100 and are highly correlated with soil loss. Since the relationship is linear, individual-storm values of EI can be summed to obtain seasonal or annual values of the parameter. Frequency distributions of annual, seasonal, or annual-maximum-storm EI values follow the log-normal type of curve that is typical of many hydrologic data.

An iso-erodent map developed from Weather Bureau data (Wischmeier, 1962) provides average annual values of EI (and factor R) for nearly all locations in the 37 states east of the Rocky Mountains (figure 1). Iso-erodents are lines joining

points of equally erosive rainfall. Linear interpolation
between the iso-erodents is recommended. To develop the map,
storm-EI values were computed directly from recording-raingage
records covering a 22-year period at each of more than 200
locations distributed over the entire 37-state area. Annual
EI values for about 2,000 additional locations were then
derived by an approximation method (Wischmeier and Smith, 1962).
The regionalized relationships used for approximations of annual
EI from Weather Bureau isopluvial maps were those shown in
figure 4. Statistical confidence limits on the EI values of
the iso-erodent map cannot be computed because direct physical
measurements of EI are not available. However, tests of
their reasonableness in more than a decade of widespread
application have indicated a high level of confidence in their
validity.

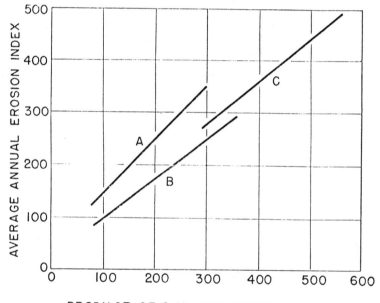

PRODUCT OF 2-YR.I-HR., 2-YR.24-HR., AND
AVERAGE-ANNUAL RAINFALL AMOUNTS

Figure 15-4   Approximate relation of average annual EI to the
product of three rainfall parameters available
from Weather Bureau isopluvial maps: Curve A,
sub-humid and semi-arid western plains; Curve B,
Northeastern States; Curve C, lower Mississippi
Valley and Gulf coastal states. (from Wischmeier
and Smith, 1962).

15-10

Specific-probability values for annual and maximum-storm EI were published by Wischmeier and Smith (1965) for more than 200 widely distributed locations. These values are used for R if specific return-period soil-loss rates are desired. Curves showing the monthly distribution of EI in each of 33 rainfall regions were included in the same publication.

To obtain rainfall-energy data for testing its correlation with runoff and soil loss, Wischmeier and Smith (1958) derived the rainfall energy-intensity relationship: $KE = 916 + 331 \log_{10} I$, where KE is kinetic energy in foot-tons per acre-inch and I is intensity in inches per hour. Drop size measurements of non-orographic rain made in the United States and several other countries have all shown fair to good agreement with respect to the relation of median drop diameter to intensity (Smith and Wischmeier, 1962). The terminal velocities of drops falling freely through the atmosphere are proportional to drop size, and for equal mass the kinetic energy is proportional to velocity squared. Therefore, the kinetic energy per unit of rainfall increases as intensity increases. Computed kinetic energies for derivation of the relationship were based on detailed drop size distribution data by Laws and Parsons (1943) and on terminal velocities for various sized drops as measured by Laws (1941) and Gunn and Kinzer (1949). The relation of median drop diameter to intensity has, however, been shown to be different for low-intensity rain in which drops are formed at low altitude and and warm cloud conditions.

The EI parameter to represent R was selected by process of elimination in exploratory regression analyses using soil-loss data from fallowed plots as the dependent variable. The coefficient of determination (R^2) was used as the measure of the capability of a parameter or set of parameters to predict erosive potential. Neither rainfall energy nor any of the commonly used rainfall parameters showed acceptable prediction accuracy. The studies showed that whether the primary parameter be rain amount, energy, momentum, or VD (drop velocity times diameter), a product-term that reflected the interaction of the parameter with some maximum prolonged intensity had much greater predictive capability. The consistently most informative index was the parameter EI (table 2).

Rainstorm-energy times maximum 15-minute intensity and energy times 60-minute intensity were also tested as erosivity indices. Average 60-minute intensities tended to overly dilute the high intensities, and 15-minute periods were too short for a good indication of runoff. Overall, both EI_{15} and EI_{60} were significantly poorer predictors than EI_{30}.

The E component of EI quantifies the storm's available kinetic energy but provides no information on its distribution over time or on the amount of associated runoff available to transport the detached soil material. Apparently the product

15-11

TABLE 15-2 EXAMPLES OF PERCENTAGES OF TOTAL SOIL-LOSS VARIATION ACCOUNTED FOR BY CERTAIN RAINFALL PARAMETERS.[1]

| | Soil type and no. of storms in analysis | | | | | |
| Rainstorm parameter(s)[2] | Shelby loam | | Marshall si c l (92) | Fayette si l (115) | Cecil s. l. | |
	topsoil (136)	subsoil (136)			Rep 1 (81)	Rep 2 (81)
I	56	42	55	82	76	72
E	82	77	57	70	70	72
M	74	69	50	62	65	67
VD	78	70	63	79	62	68
E & I	83	77	68	86	84	83
M & I	78	69	68	86	83	81
VD & I	79	70	69	87	83	84
EI	89	82	74	90	97	95
MI	87	79	74	90	96	93
VDI	86	75	74	90	85	90

1/ Determined by coefficient of determination, R^2, in regression analyses with soil loss from bare fallow as the dependent variable.

2/ Definitions: I = maximum 30-minute intensity; E = kinetic energy of the rain; M = momentum; VD = drop velocity times diameter; the symbol "&" between parameters indicates their combination in an additive model; EI, MI and VDI are interaction terms derived as products of the parameters.

term, EI, successfully provides this additional information. The data used in the tests were from 72.6-foot plots. Runoff concentration, velocity, and erosive potential vary with slope length and steepness, but this variation is accounted for by factors L and S in the equation.

Maximum 30-minute intensity is defined as twice the greatest amount of rain falling in any 30 consecutive minutes. The storm energy is computed from recording raingage records used in conjunction with table 3 or the energy-intensity equation. The amount and intensity of rain are computed for each storm segment (between successive inflection points on the recorder chart). The energy in foot-tons per acre-inch of rain is read from table 3 for each intensity increment and multiplied by the number of inches of rain in that segment. The products are summed to obtain total energy for the entire storm. Rains of less than 0.5 inch were omitted from EI calculations as insignificant. In general, the best correlations of soil loss with EI values were obtained when rains separated by less than 6 hours were treated as a single storm (Wischmeier, 1959).

Two exceptions to the use of the EI parameter for R need to be noted. One applies to rainfall in which the drops are formed at low altitude and in warm clouds, as on the leeward side of a mountain. This type of rain is characterized by small drops and very low intensities. Therefore, the

TABLE 15-3 KINETIC ENERGY OF NATURAL RAINFALL (FOOT TONS
PER ACRE INCH)*

Inten-sity	Intensity, inches/hr									
	0.00	0.01	0.02	0.03	0.04	0.05	0.06	0.07	0.08	0.09
in/hr										
0	0	254	354	412	453	485	512	534	553	570
0.1	585	599	611	623	633	643	653	661	669	677
0.2	685	692	698	705	711	717	722	728	733	738
0.3	743	748	752	757	761	765	769	773	777	781
0.4	784	788	791	795	798	801	804	897	810	814
0.5	816	819	822	825	827	830	833	835	838	840
0.6	843	845	847	850	852	854	856	858	861	863
0.7	865	867	869	871	873	875	877	878	880	882
0.8	884	886	887	889	891	893	894	896	898	899
0.9	901	902	904	906	907	909	910	912	913	915
	0	0.1	0.2	0.3	0.4	0.5	0.6	0.7	0.8	0.9
1	916	930	942	954	964	974	984	992	1000	1008
2	1016	1023	1029	1036	1042	1048	1053	1059	1064	1069
3	1074	1079	1083	1088	1092	1096	1100	1104	1108	1112
4	1115	1119	1122	1126	1129	1132	1135	1138	1141	1144
5	1147	1150	1153	1156	1158	1161	1164	1166	1169	1171
6	1174	1176	1178	1181	1183	1185	1187	1189	1192	1194
7	1196	1198	1200	1202	1204	1206	1208	1209	1211	1213
8	1215	1217	1218	1220	1222	1224	1225	1227	1229	1230
9	1232	1233	1235	1237	1238	1240	1241	1243	1244	1246

*Computed by the equation, $E = 916 + \log_{10} I$.

kinetic energy per inch of rain is extremely low and annual EI
values may be less than 10. The Palouse region of Washington
and western Idaho is an example. There, the low EI correctly
predicts relatively little rainfall-induced erosion from
moderate slopes, but small rains accompanying early-spring
thaws produce substantial runoff, and runoff-induced erosion
from the long and steep slopes is a serious problem. Since
most of the runoff water is from thaw or snowmelt, the EI
for the rain immediately associated with the runoff does not
predict its erosive potential. For such situations, a runoff
predictor other than EI is needed for the equation's factor
R.
     The second exception is the hurricane-associated storms
on the flat coastal plains of the Gulf of Mexico. Because of
the flat slopes, runoff velocities are too slow to be highly
erosive, and the prolonged high intensities quickly cover
the soil surface with a film of water sufficiently deep to
shield it from the raindrop impact. The extremely high 30-
minute intensities compute EI values that substantially over-
predict observed soil losses for these conditions. Derivation
of "effective" EI values that reflect the effects of the
deep, low-velocity surface-water cushions may offer a solution
to this localized problem.

15-13

Soil-Erodibility Factor, K . Some soils erode much more
readily than others under similar conditions. The equation's
factor K reflects these differences and together with R
provides a quantitative soil-loss base for the equation. It
combines in a single factor the effects of soil characteristics
on water-intake capacity and on the soil's susceptibility to
detachment and transport by rainfall and runoff.

K is defined as the average increase in soil loss for
each additional unit of EI when L , S , C and P equal
1.0. This is the term b in the linear model y = bx+a for
data obtained under the conditions previously outlined as
criteria for a "unity plot". This definition also facilitates
computation of confidence limits on K values computed from
short-term data. K is usually expressed in tons per acre per
EI unit, and observed values have ranged from 0.02 to 0.69
(Olson and Wischmeier, 1963). The factor could readily be
expressed in metric units.

The experimental designs on many of the early erosion-
research stations included plots that were continuously fallowed
and tilled similarly to those in corn (maize). These plots met
all the criteria for the previously defined unit plot except
that in some cases adjustment of the data to 9% slope was
required. Location differences in soil loss per unit of EI ,
after the slope adjustment, were assumed to be valid measurements of differences in the inherent erodibilities of the soils.
Where long-term studies did not include fallow plots, adjustments for crop effects were based on relationships established
from other data.

K was directly evaluated in this manner for 23 benchmark
soils (Wischmeier and Smith, 1965). Values for some additional
soils were derived from more recent plot studies under natural
and simulated rain. For soils that do not occur naturally on
slopes that are near 9%, expressing K quantitatively in terms
of a 9% slope introduces a potential slope-effect adjustment
error. In practice, however, such errors would be largely offset by equivalent adjustments in the opposite direction when
the equation is used on those soils.

Values of K for other topsoils and for specific subsoil
horizons can now be computed without erosion measurements.
Wischmeier and Mannering (1969) determined relationships of
various soil properties to its erodibility and derived a soil-
erodibility equation that is applicable for a broad range of
medium-textured soils. The equation is, however, too complex
to serve as a working tool for field technicians. Wischmeier,
et al. (1971) found that very fine sand (0.05-0.10 mm) should
be included in the silt fraction in mechanical analyses. They
defined a statistical parameter that is a measure of the interrelations of a soil's various particle-size groups. The parameter is: % silt times (100 - % clay). These findings greatly
increased the prediction capability of mechanical-analysis
data, and they were able to predict erodibility from information on only three soil characteristics in addition to the

new particle-size parameter: percent organic matter, soil structure, and profile permeability.

The soil erodibility nomograph (Fig.15-5) graphically computes K on the basis of the findings by Wischmeier, et al. (1971). The 55 soils from which the nomograph relationships were derived encompassed a wide range of soil types, textures and organic-matter levels. Erosion data were obtained by applying simulated rain on field plats at an intensity of 2.5 inches per hour. The storm-size and antecedent-moisture variabilities associated with annual rainfall were brought into the observed K values by computing soil loss per EI unit for combinations of thirteen 2.5-inch rains on moderately dry soil, four 1.25-inch rains on wet soil, and three 2.5-inch rains on wet soil.

For the 55 soils in the sample, the error variance indicates that two out of three nomograph solutions should be within ±0.02, or 6.4%, of the true values and 95% of them should be within ±0.04. Measured K values for the 55 soils ranged from 0.03 to 0.69. When checked against established K values for 13 soils not included in its derivation, the nomograph predicted 11 of them within ±0.02 and all within ±0.04. For three denuded subsoils on which soil loss data were available, the accuracy of predictions was at comparable level.

Slope-Length Factor, L. This factor adjusts the plot data to field slope lengths. It is defined as the ratio of soil loss from a particular slope length to that from a 72.6-foot length when all other conditions are the same. For slopes of from 1 to 10 percent, the ratio $(\lambda/72.6)^{0.5}$, where λ = slope length in feet, is commonly used for L. An exponent of 0.6 is recommended for steeper slopes, and 0.3 for long slopes with less than 0.5% gradient (Wischmeier and Smith, 1965).

For field application, slope length has been defined as the distance from the point of origin of overland flow to the point where either the slope decreases to the extend that deposition begins, or the runoff water enters a well-defined channel (Smith and Wischmeier, 1957).

The effect of slope length on runoff per unit area is of questionable significance (Wischmeier, 1966). In 21 slope-length studies, total growing-season runoff per unit area was greatest on the short slopes at 18 of the locations and greatest on the longer slopes at two. Total dormant-season runoff at 11 of the locations was greater on the longer slopes, but at the other 10 it was either equal or greater on the short slopes. The texture range of the 21 soils was from fine sandy loam to clay loam. The differences in runoff relative to slope length were quite small, and many of them were not significant at the 95% confidence level.

The effect of slope length on soil loss is, therefore, primarily a result of increased erosive potential due to greater accumulation of runoff on the longer slopes. Runoff velocity increases as the runoff rate increases or the flow

15-15

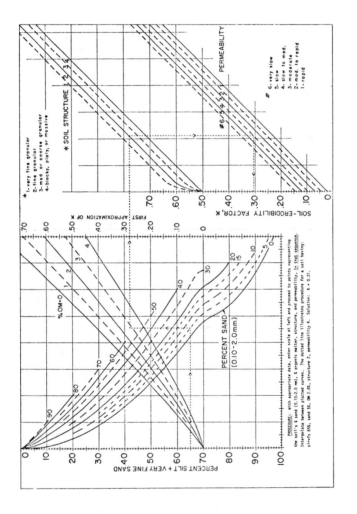

Fig. 15-5 Soil erodibility nomograph used to determine factor K for specific topsoils or subsoil horizons. Solutions are in tons per acre. (From Wischmeier, et al., 1971).

concentrates, and both detachment capacity and transport capacity of the runoff increase geometrically with increased velocity. The factor L accounts for this effect.

Zingg (1940) concluded that average soil loss per unit area increases in proportion to the 0.6 power of slope length. This form of expression for the relationship is compatible with the results of subsequent studies, but the magnitude of the length-exponent is not the same for all situations. The Musgrave Committee (1947) considered other data and recommended a value of 0.35 for the exponent. Analysis of the data from 11 slope-length studies conducted prior to 1956 showed a range from about 0.3 to 0.7 in its apparent locational values, with 0.45 as both the median and the mean. Leaders in erosion research and application programs, meeting in a nationwide soil-loss prediction workshop at Purdue University in 1956, agreed on general use of 0.5 for the exponent until its variations can be related to predictable parameters.

The length-exponent is believed to be related to the importance of runoff-induced erosion relative to rainfall-induced erosion. The plots used in field measurements of slope-length effect were in intertilled crops with conventional seedbed preparation and tillage parallel to the slope direction. In the two studies where length effect was least, runoff volume per unit area decreased significantly with slope length. Where the highest two values of the exponent were observed, runoff per unit area increased significantly with slope length. If the effect of slope length on runoff is generally insignificant, as previously indicated, $L = (\lambda/72.6)^{0.5}$ should be reasonably accurate for most of the tilled land areas other than textural extremes. There are, however, indications that the exponent is related to slope steepness, particle size, storm characteristics and residue management. Evaluation of these interaction effects in adequate research should define predictable variations in the length exponent and improve confidence limits.

Slope-Steepness Factor, S . The factor S accounts for the increase in erosive potential of rainfall and runoff as slope steepens. It is defined as the ratio of soil loss from a given slope to that from a 9% slope when all other factors are the same.

In the assembled plot data, runoff from cropland has tended to increase significantly as slope steepens. For row-crop land the increase was curvilinear, increasing at an increasing rate. It was approximately linear for small grain and insignificant for good meadow sod (Wischmeier, 1966).

Because runoff increases in velocity as well as amount when slope steepens, soil loss increases more rapidly than runoff. The combined data from plot studies under natural and simulated rain, when adjusted to a common soil and crop base, gave a very good least-squares fit to the parabolic equation $A = 0.043 s^2 + 0.30 s + 0.43$, where A is soil loss and s is percent slope (Smith and Wischmeier, 1957). This is an

15-17

evaluation of A for a specific soil, rainfall pattern and
cropping system, but the dimensionless factor S of the erosion equation can be derived by dividing it by the value of A
for s = 9% . Thus, S = (0.043 s^2 + 0.30 s + 0.43)/6.613 .
When this equation is combined with the slope-length formula,

$$LS = \sqrt{\lambda}(0.00076 \ s^2 + 0.0053 \ s + 0.0076) \ .$$

In practice, appropriate LS values can be conveniently
obtained from the slope-effect chart derived by this formula
(figure 3).

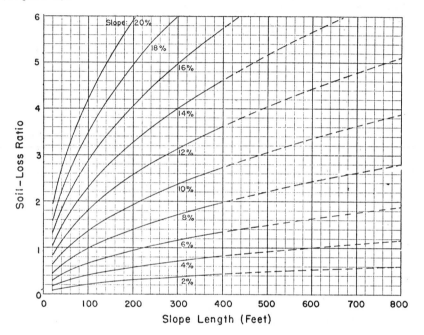

Fig. 15-6 Slope-effect chart used to determine combined
            value of factors L and S as computed by:
            $LS = \lambda^{0.5}(0.00076 \ s^2 + 0.0053 \ s + 0.0076)$,
            where λ = slope-length in feet and s =
            steepness in percent (from Wischmeier
            and Smith, 1965).

     The slope formula and Fig.15-6 assume uniform gradients.
Concave or convex slopes must be subdivided for prediction of
sediment loads. For the upper segment, dimensions for entering
the LS chart are obtained from that segment alone. For the
lower segment, however, the steepness of the segment is used
with the overall slope-length. A change in land use along a

15-18

slope does not terminate the effective slope-length unless the runoff from the upper field is diverted.

The parabolic equation for effect of slope steepness is applicable to tilled land with slopes in the 2 to 20 percent range. There are indications that a heavy mulch cover on randomly oriented, close-growing vegetation may significantly reduce the slope-gradient effect, but this has not been fully tested. Also, it is intuitively apparent that the parabolic relationship cannot be extrapolated indefinitely beyond the range of the data. The slope effect for short, very steep slopes such as roadside banks has not been determined. For steep slopes of undisturbed soil such as on western rangeland, extrapolation of the relation $S = (s/9)^{1.4}$ is presently recommended but has not been adequately tested.

Cropping-Management Factor, C . The factor C is the ratio of soil loss from land cropped under specified conditions to the corresponding loss from tilled, continuous fallow. For cropland, values of C range from near-zero to 1.0. The specific value depends on the particular combination of cover, crop sequence and management techniques, and it also depends on the particular stage of development of the vegetal cover at the time of the rain. The correspondence of expected periods of highly erosive rainfall with periods of good or poor soil cover differs appreciably between climatic areas. Therefore, the value of C for a particular cropping-and-management system will not be the same for all parts of the country.

A procedure was developed for deriving locational values of C on the basis of rainstorm-timing probabilities and research data that reflect the erosion-reducing effectiveness of crops and management during successive periods within a rotation cycle. The data needed for this procedure were provided in Agriculture Handbook 282 (Wischmeier and Smith, 1965) in the form of 33 regional EI -distribution curves and a comprehensive soil-loss-ratio table.

For derivation of the soil-loss-ratio table, the normal crop year was divided into five crop stages: rough fallow, seedling, establishment, growing and maturing crop, and residue or stubble. The ratio of soil loss from cropped plots to corresponding loss from continuous fallow when all other factors are the same was determined for various specific combinations of crop, sequence, and management and for each crop stage. About 10,000 plot-years of basic erosion data were used for these determinations. Individual lines in the table reflect specific combinations of cropping and management variables and thus quantify interaction effects as well as primary effects. Soil-loss ratios for recently introduced practices that retain appreciable amounts of residue on the soil surface after rowcrop planting were not included in the published table but are now being derived from current data.

To compute C for a particular cropping system at a given location, the entire rotation cycle is divided into successive

cropstage periods as defined for the soil-loss-ratio table.
Probable calendar dates for the events that begin each of the
successive periods are selected on the basis of local climate
and farm practices. Entering the appropriate EI -distribution
curve with these dates, the percentage of the annual EI that
normally occurs during each of the crop stages is determined.
These percentages are multiplied by the corresponding soil-loss
ratios from the published table. The partial products are
summed over the rotation cycle, and the total is divided by
the number of years in the cycle. The procedure is demonstrated
in detail in Agriculture Handbook 282.

Practice Factor, P . This factor is similar to C except
that P accounts for additional effects of practices that are
superimposed upon C , such as contour farming, terrace
systems, diversions, or contour stripcropping. These practices
reduce the erosive potential of runoff by their influence on
drainage pattern, runoff concentration and runoff velocity.
Values of P for these practices, related only to slope steepness, are listed in table 1. The values are based on rather
limited data but are involved in soil-loss prediction much less
frequently than the other five factors.

Slope-length limits for effectiveness of contouring and of
no-plow seeding methods for row crops are known to exist but
have not been defined for specific situations. Research is now
getting underway seeking to relate breakdown-points for the
practices to concentration, rate and velocity of runoff.

15.5 CONFIDENCE IN THE EQUATION'S PREDICTIONS

As previously indicated, some of the major terms in the
soil-loss equation are themselves functions of several significant parameters and must be derived by separate formulas and
subroutines. Therefore, the complete equation could not be
derived as a single least-squares fit to the 10,000 plot-years
of basic data, and overall statistical confidence limits could
not be computed by the usual analysis of variance technique.
We did, however, obtain an indication of confidence limits by
using the equation and the published iso-erodent map, EI-
distribution curves, slope-effect chart and soil-loss-ratio
table to predict long-run average annual soil losses on 189
plots for which we had a total of about 2300 plot-years of
soil-loss records. The 189 individual-plot predictions
deviated from the corresponding measured soil losses by an
average of 1.4 tons per acre per year, which is about 12% of the
11.3-ton overall-average soil loss for the sample. About 84%
of the deviations were within 2 tons per year, but the variance
indicates that about 5% of such predictions may be in error by
as much as 4.6 tons, or 40% of the sample-average soil loss.

There is strong evidence of 20- to 22-year cycles in rainfall pattern (Newman, 1970). The iso-erodent map and EI -
distribution curves were derived from 22-year location

rainfall records, which represent full cycles and therefore predict long-time average losses. Thus the predicted values in the foregoing comparison are long-time averages while the actual data with which they were compared represent specific time periods, some as short as 5 years. Since cyclical changes in rainfall pattern tend to be widespread geographically and most of the short-term locational studies in the sample were approximately concurrent, the effects of deviations from long-time average rainfall and seasonal distribution of erosive rainstorms would not have averaged out. For the 2300 plot-years in the sample, the equation overpredicted by an average of 0.4 ton per acre per year. Of the 88 deviations of 1 ton or more, 59 were from comparisons representing less than half of the normal rainfall cycle.

Confidence bands on predictions by the equation will be the narrowest for silt, silt loam and loam soils and for uniform slopes of from 5 to 12 percent, lengths not exceeding 400 feet, and consistent cropping systems that are directly represented by lines in the soil-loss-ratio table. Beyond these limits significant extrapolation errors become more likely, but the predictions are believed to have sufficient accuracy for most applications over a much wider range of conditions. The equation's accuracy for predicting long-term average soil loss for a given situation is limited by lack of available data to evaluate its individual terms rather than by the model itself. Therefore the overall prediction accuracy attainable is continuously improving as research provides data for accurate evaluation of the factors over a wider range of conditions.

15.6 SEDIMENT YIELD PREDICTION

The equation is designed to predict average annual soil losses by sheet and rill erosion on upslope areas such as farmland and construction sites. It can be helpful for prediction of contributions from these sources to downstream sediment loads, but its capabilities and limitations for this use must be recognized. It is an erosion equation and is not designed to predict deposition. Its predictions do not include sediment contributions from gully erosion, and it does not include factors to account for sediment losses or gains between the field and the stream or reservoir. These items must be evaluated separately.

For conservation planning, soil washed to a terrace channel is considered lost for future crop production on the inter-terrace strip, and terracing is credited only for shortening the slope length. Research data have shown that as much as 90% of the soil washed to the channel may be deposited in the channel and grassed outlet and not leave the farm (Zingg, 1940). Therefore, the factor P assumes different values for prediction of off-field sediment loads than for erosion-control planning on farmland (table 1).

15-21

With the modern parallel, grass-backslope terrace systems which outlet through tile drains, little more than the colloidal material remains in suspension long enough to be carried off the field. However, there may still be substantial movement of soil toward the tile inlet. When sediment-laden runoff water moves across a strip of relatively flat land on its way to the nearest established waterway, substantial amounts of sediment may be deposited enroute, even when the strip has no vegetal cover. If there is close-growing vegetation on the strip, most of the sediment may be filtered out. Alternating strips of corn and meadow, in rotation, on the contour is given a conservative P value equal to 0.5 of the factor for contouring alone (table 1). Analytically, it seems apparent that this factor would be reduced to less than half that value if the sod strip were always at the foot of the slope.

Sediment load prediction may involve upslope source areas other than farmland and construction sites. To allow objective approximation of the equation's factor C for situations such as permanent pasture, rangeland and woodland, where the soil surface is not disturbed by tillage, the factor was subdivided into three types of effects: those above, at, and beneath the soil surface. Relationship curves for the three effects were derived from a combination of basic concepts and research data for analogous situations that had been represented in plot studies. By this technique, a table of approximate C values for various qualities of woodland, rangeland and idle land was derived (Wischmeier, 1971). Confidence limits for these C values are substantially broader than for the soil-loss ratios in Agriculture Handbook No. 282. However, the approach demonstrates a technique for obtaining reasonable accurate guides for quantifying sediment yields in areas where research data are not available.

The use of return-period values of EI for R can provide an indication of the probable range in annual soil losses from a given field. However, the equation cannot predict a future specific-year loss because major short-run variations in rainfall can presently not be predicted. For estimation of soil loss from a past specific storm, the actual storm- EI is used for R and the soil-loss ratio for the cropstage period in which the rain occurred is used in lieu of the rotation C . For short-term computations, this procedure should be repeated for each significant rainstorm rather than using the long-term EI -distribution curve.

15.7 CONCLUSION

The large amount of existing upslope erosion data can be most effectively utilized by application agencies in the form of prediction equations. The universal soil-loss equation is an empirical erosion model derived from more than 10,000 plot-years of basic soil-loss and related data. More than a decade of widespread use has proved the value of this equation as a working tool for conservation planners and technicians.

The equation computes sheet and rill erosion as a function of rainfall erosivity, soil erodibility, length and percent of lant slope, cropping and management, and supplemental conservation practices. The existing data have provided tables and graphs for locational evaluation of the equation's six factors anywhere within the 37 states east of the Rocky Mountains. To keep the equation simple as a working tool, factors were not included to account for effects of short-term variations in weather and surface conditions. For predictions of long-term average soil losses from specific upslope areas, its accuracy within the 37 states appears to be well within the needs for erosion-control planning.

The name "universal" soil-loss equation originated as a means of distinguishing this prediction model from the highly regionalized models that preceded it. None of its factors utilizes a reference point that has direct geographic orientation. In the sense of the intended functions of the equation's six factors, the model should have universal validity. However, its application is limited to states and countries where information is available for local evaluations of the equation's individual factors. There are exceptions to the validity of the EI parameter as a measure of the combined erosive forces of rainfall and runoff. For some situations, a more accurate predictor of runoff-erosion potential needs to be substituted as the value of R . The indicated nature of effects of topographic, cover, and management variables is probably universal, but it has not been shown that the specific ratios for L , S and C that were derived on the U. S. mainland are necessarily accurate on vastly different soils, such as those of volcanic origin for example. Slope effect in situations where gradients appreciably exceed 20 percent is still a serious void in research information.

The relationships, graphs and tables presented for evaluation of the equation's factors cannot be simply transported verbatim to states or countries where the type of rainfall or the soil genesis is vastly different. However, a relatively small amount of well designed local research should enable many countries to adapt the soil-loss equation and basic relationships to their situations.

15.8 CONVERSION TO METRIC SYSTEM

The rainfall intensity-energy equation in the metric system is: $E = 210.3 + 89 \log_{10} I$, where E is kinetic energy in metric-ton meters per hectare per centimeter of rain, and I is rainfall intensity in cm/hr. For direct conversion of table 3 to metric-ton meters per hectare per centimeter, multiply by 0.269. A logical counterpart to the English-system EI is the product: storm energy in metric-ton meters per hectare times the maximum 30-minute intensity in cm/hr. The magnitude of this product would be 1.735 times that of the EI as defined in English units. The factor for direct conversion of K to metric-tons per hectare per metric EI unit is 0.2572.

For practical purposes, it would be expedient to redefine the unit-plot as having a length of 25 meters and a slope of 10 percent, to derive K on the basis of those dimensions, and to recompute the slope-effect chart. The translated values would be: $L = \lambda^{0.5}/5$, where λ is slope length in meters; and $S = (0.043\ s^2 + 0.30\ s + 0.43)/7.73$, where s = percent slope. Combining the two, $LS = \sqrt{\lambda}(0.00111\ s^2 + 0.00776\ s + 0.0111)$.

15.9 NOTATIONS

A	Computed soil loss per unit area
C	Cropping-management factor
C_{max}	Maximum-tolerable C value
E	Total kinetic energy of rainstorm
EI	Energy-intensity erosion index
I_{30}	Maximum 30-minute rain intensity
K	Soil-erodibility factor
L	Factor for slope-length effect
L_{max}	Maximum-tolerable slope-length factor
P	Erosion-control-practice factor
S	Factor for slope-steepness effect
s	Land slope (%)
T	Soil-loss tolerance
λ	Slope length (feet)

REFERENCES

Cook, H. L., 1936, The nature and controlling variables of the water erosion process; Soil Sci. Soc. Amer. Proc., V. 1, p. 487-494.

Gunn, R., and Kinzer, G. D., 1949, The terminal velocity of fall for water droplets; J. Met., V. 6, p. 243-248.

Laws, J. O., 1941, Measurement of fall velocity of water drops and rain drops; Trans. Amer. Geophys. Union, V. 2, p. 709-721.

Laws, J. O., and Parsons, D. A., 1943, The relation of rain drop size to intensity; Trans. Amer. Geophys. Union. V. 24, p. 452-459.

Meyer, L. D., 1960, Use of the rainulator for runoff plot research; Soil. Sci. Soc. Amer. Proc., V. 24, No. 4, p. 319-322.

Meyer, L. D., 1970, Soil erosion by water on upland areas; River Mechanics, Vol. II, Chapt. 27, H. W. Shen, Fort Collins, Colo.

Meyer, L. E., and McCune, D. L., 1958, Rainfall simular for runoff plots; Agr. Engr., V. 39, No. 10, p. 644-648.

Meyer, L. D., and Wischmeier, W. H., 1969, Mathematical simulation of the process of soil erosion by water; Agr. Engr., V. 12, No. 6, p. 754-758, 762.

Middleton, H. E., Slater, C. S., and Byers, H. G., 1932, Physical and chemical characteristics of the soils from the erosion experiment stations; U.S.D.A. Tech. Bull. 316, 51 p.

Musgrave, G. W., 1947, The quantitative evaluation of factors in water erosion, a first approximation; Jour. Soil Water Conserv., V. 2, p. 133-138.

Newman, J. E., 1970, Climate in the 1970's; Crops and Soils, V. 22, p. 9-12.

Olson, T. C., and Wischmeier, W. H., 1963, Soil erodibility evaluations for soils on the runoff and erosion stations; Soil Sci. Soc. Amer. Proc., V. 27, p. 590-592.

Smith, D. D., and Wischmeier, W. H., 1957, Factors affecting sheet and rill erosion; Amer. Geophys. Union Trans., V. 38, p. 889-896.

Smith, D. D., and Wischmeier, W. H., 1962, Rainfall erosion; Advances in Agronomy; V. 14, p. 109-148, Academic Press, Inc., New York, N. Y.

Wischmeier, W. H., 1955, Punched cards record runoff and soil-loss data; Agr. Engr., V. 36, No. 10, p. 664-666.

Wischmeier, W. H., 1959, A rainfall erosion index for a universal soil-loss equation; Soil Sci. Soc. Amer. Proc., V. 23, p. 246-249.

Wischmeier, W. H., 1962, Rainfall erosion potential - geographic and locational differences of distribution; Agr. Engr., V. 43, No. 4, p. 212-215.

Wischmeier, W. H., 1966, Relation of field-plot runoff to management and physical factors; Soil. Sci. Soc. Amer. Proc., V. 30, p. 272-277.

Wischmeier, W. H., 1971, Approximating the erosion equation's factor C for undisturbed land areas; Proc. SCS Workshop, Chicago, Nov. 22-24 (mimeo).

Wischmeier, W. H., Johnson, C. B., and Cross, B. V., 1971, A soil-erodibility nomograph for farmland and construction sites; Jour. Soil Water Conserv., V. 26, No. 5, p. 189-193.

Wischmeier, W. H., and Mannering, J. V., 1969, Relation of soil properties to its erodibility; Soil Sci. Soc. Amer. Proc., V. 33, p. 131-137.

Wischmeier, W. H., and Smith, D. D., 1958, Rainfall energy and its relationship to soil loss; Trans. Amer. Geophys. Union, V. 39, p. 285-291.

Wischmeier, W. H., and Smith, D. D., 1960, A universal soil-loss estimating equation to guide conservation farm planning; Trans. 7th Cong. of Internat'l. Soil Sci. Soc., V. I, p. 418-425.

Wischmeier, W. H., and Smith, D. D., 1962, Soil-loss estimation as a tool in soil and water management planning; Internat'l. Assoc. Sci. Hydrology, Publ. No. 59, p. 148-159.

Wischmeier, W. H., and Smith, D. D., 1965, Predicting rainfall-erosion losses from cropland; U.S.D.A. Agr. Handbook No. 282, 47 p., U. S. Govt. Printing Office, Wash., D. C.

Zingg, A. W., 1940, Degree and length of land slope as it affects soil loss in runoff; Agr. Engr., V. 21, p. 59-64.

Chapter 16

APPLICATION OF REMOTE SENSING TO RIVER MECHANICS

By

M. M. Skinner, Assistant Professor of Civil Engineering
Colorado State University, Fort Collins,
Colorado

And

J. F. Ruff,   Assistant Professor of Civil Engineering
Colorado State University, Fort Collins,
Colorado

Chapter 16

APPLICATION OF REMOTE SENSING TO RIVER MECHANICS

16.1 INTRODUCTION

This paper summarizes the potential applications of
multiband photography, precision mapping camera photography, and
thermal infrared imagery obtained with a line scanner for
evaluating certain characteristics related to river mechanics.
These three remote sensing systems provide a record of the
intensity of electromagnetic energy being reflected or emitted
from a terrestrial scene. There is a variety of film-filter
combinations available for photographic work over the wavelengths from approximately 0.3 micrometers to 0.9 micrometer*;
optical-mechanical line scanners with appropriate detectors can
be used for obtaining imagery in a variety of wavelength bands.
Cameras and line scanners are discussed. In order to provide a
common understanding of the limitations and capabilities of these
three remote sensing systems, a brief discussion of the fundamentals of electromagnetic radiation and radiation transmission
through the atmosphere and water is presented.

16.2 FUNDAMENTALS OF ELECTROMAGNETIC RADIATION

Radiation, which is one of the three principal processes
whereby energy is transferred, is encountered in our every day
experiences in many different forms: visible light, heat from
a campfire, radio waves, x-rays, and radar signals, to name a
few. All these forms of energy are inherently similar in nature
and are grouped under the single classification of electromagnetic radiation. They are commonly ordered on the electromagnetic spectrum according to wavelength or frequency. For
example, where the spectrum is arranged in order of increasing
frequency the following order is given: 1) audio-frequencies
(power and telephone), 2) radio waves, 3) microwaves, 4) infrared,
5) visible light, 6) ultraviolet, 7) x-rays, and 8) gamma rays.

All forms of electromagnetic radiation travel in a straight
path at the speed of light; obey similar laws of reflection,
refraction, diffraction, and polarization; can be focused and
imaged; and do not depend on the presence of matter for
propogation. The product of the wavelength (the mean distance
between two maxima of the periodic fluctuations; commonly
expressed in Angstroms, microns or micrometers, meters, or kilo-
meters) and the frequency (time rate of recurrence of the
fluctuations; commonly expressed in cycles per second or hertz,
or radians per second) is a constant --- the speed of light.

---

* micrometer, 10^{-6} meters, will be abbreviated μm in the
  remainder of this paper

Wavelengths of importance in transferring the electro-magnetic energy from the sun to the earth range from about 0.1μm to 4.0μm. Radiant energy with these wavelengths are commonly referred to as short-wave radiation or solar radiation. About 10 percent of the total energy in the solar stream is in the ultraviolet region from 0.1μm to 0.4μm: the remainder is nearly evenly distributed between visible light (0.4μm to 0.7μm) and in-frared radiation (0.7μm to 4.0μm). Emitted radiation from the earth's surface, in turn, is in the infrared region from 4.0μm to about 100μm, commonly referred to as long-wave radiation or terrestrial radiation. Absorption of radiation results in the transformation of the energy to longer wavelengths when reemitted.

Of the total amount of radiant energy reaching the surface of the earth, part can be reflected, part absorbed, and part transmitted (if the receiving object is partially transparent to the particular incident radiation wavelengths). Alternately;

$$1 = \rho + \alpha + \tau \qquad\qquad (16\text{-}1)$$

where:

ρ = radiant reflectance.... ratio of reflected radiant flux to incident radiant flux,

α = radiant absorptance.... ratio of absorbed radiant flux to incident radiant flux,

and

τ = radiant transmittance....ratio of transmitted radiant flux to incident radiant flux,

also;ε = radiant emissivity...ratio of radiant emittance of a source to that of a blackbody at the same temperature.

The reflected energy in the 0.4μm to 0.7μm wavelength region allows one to perceive the presence of objects in both spatial (shape) and spectral (color) format (human vision and photography). The color of an object is determined by the relative amounts of the primary colors (blue, green, red) reflected from the surface of the object. Reflected energy in wavelengths, within as well as outside the visible band, can be detected and imaged with electro-mechanical scanners employing appropriate detectors. Specially sensitized films are also available for recording scenes with reflected energy outside the visible region in the ultra-violet, 0.3μm to 0.4μm and in the photographic infrared, 0.7μm to 0.9μm.

All objects having temperatures greater than absolute zero (-273°C) emit electromagnetic energy in proportion to their respective emissivity and absolute temperature (°Kelvin) to the fourth power. This energy can be recorded indirectly with a radiometer or may be transduced with a special detector and imaged through the use of an electro-mechanical scanner. Consequently, terrestrial objects (since they have a temperature greater than absolute zero) can be mapped with infrared imaging systems, even in total visual darkness.

16.3 ELECTROMAGNETIC RADIATION TRANSMISSION

Radiant energy transmission is a very important factor
for consideration in practical remote sensing studies of the
natural terrain. Optimum transmission of light in water and
the transmission of ultraviolet, visible, and infrared
electromagnetic energy through the atmosphere need be considered.

Radiant energy is attenuated in a path of fluid (water or
the atmosphere) by a general process called extinction. The
transmittance can be expressed:

$$\tau = e^{-\sigma x} \tag{16-2}$$

where

σ is the extinction coefficient,

and x is the path length.

The extinction coefficient, σ , is a consequence of both
absorption and scattering. The absorption coefficient, a ,
and the scattering coefficient, γ , can be combined to account
for the extinction process:

$$\sigma = a + \gamma \tag{16-3}$$

Both a and γ vary with wavelength. The attenuation of visible
light in distilled water is a minimum for the blue-green (0.48μm)
portion of the spectrum and the longer wavelength energy in the
red portion (0.6μm to 0.7μm) suffers severe attenuation as shown
in Fig. 16-1. As water becomes more turbid, studies have shown

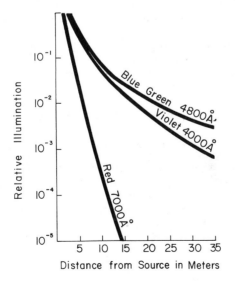

Fig. 16-1. The relative illumination versus distance in distilled
water from a monochromatic source.

that the wavelength of minimum attenuation in water shifts
slightly to longer wavelengths. The scattering of light back
towards the observer in clear water and particularly in turbid
water conditions reduces the visibility in the water.

The transmission of the atmosphere is strongly dependent
upon the wavelength of the radiant energy. Of particular
interest are the "windows" in the atmosphere for wavelengths in
the visible (0.4μm to 0.7μm), photographic infrared (0.7μm
to 0.9μm), and in the thermal infrared (3.5μm to 5.5μm) and
(8μm to 14μm).

For consideration in photographic processes, scattering
of light is attributed to three size classifications of suspended
particles:

1) Rayleigh scattering, where the particles are considerably
smaller than a wavelength of light,

2) Mie scattering, where the particles range in size from
approximately 1/10 of a wavelength to 10 wavelengths, and

3) non-selective scattering for particles larger than
10 wavelengths.

Air molecules are the predominant particle size in the
case of Rayleigh scattering. Rayleigh scattering is inversely
proportional to the fourth power of the wavelength, so blue
light is scattered almost six (6) times as strongly as red light.
This type of scattering makes the sky appear blue. Rayleigh
scattering is paramount on clear, bright days; whereas Mie
scattering predominates as the particles in the atmosphere
increase in size and visibility decreases. Again the scattered
light tends to be in the blue part of the spectrum and minus-
blue filters on aerial cameras can materially enhance the
contrast of the terrain scene. For example, non-selective scattering scatters all light wavelengths and clouds appear white.
Although water vapor is the most common cause of non-selective
scattering, smoke and dust particles can be important, too.
Color infrared or black and white infrared film (with a minus-
blue filter) can produce a good, sharp photograph even under
hazy-sky conditions.

16.4 REFLECTED AND EMITTED ELECTROMAGNETIC RADIATION

Since a river system analyses can be dependent upon water
temperature effects; or imagery is required under reduced
visible-light conditions or even in total darkness; or interpretation is enhanced by the emission characteristics of a
particular scene, a section is devoted to both reflected energy
and emitted energy. Only a very basic discussion will be
presented, but hopefully in sufficient detail to give the reader
adequate understanding of what can be photographed (reflected
energy) or recorded on thermal infrared imagery (emitted energy);
and to assist the user in interpretation of such imagery related
to river mechanics.

Radiant reflectance from a particular material surface is
a function of the wavelength of the incident radiation, the

character of the reflecting surface and the material itself,
and on the illuminating and viewing angles. For opaque materials
the sum of the radiant absorptance and the radiant reflectance
must be 1.0; radiant absorptance varies between 0 for a perfect
reflector and 1 for a perfect absorber - a blackbody. Reflectance,
absorptance,and transmittance are, however, wavelength dependent.
For example, reflectance curves are available for a variety of
natural terrain features and should be utilized in planning for a
particular remote sensing mission; proper choice of wavelength
bands can be predetermined in many cases for enhancing certain
features with multiband photography.

Reflectance can be described for monochromatic radiation
(narrow-band width on the electromagnetic spectrum) or for all-
wave radiation; or it can be defined for a wider band such as
visible light (0.4μm to 0.7μm), solar radiation (0.1μm to
0.4μm) or some other restricted wide-band radiation. A
commonly used term, albedo, may refer to the reflectance of the
entire solar radiation band or to the visible portion; usage
varies and caution should be exercised in interpreting the
literature on reflectance where specific band widths are not
specified.

For detecting and imaging the terrestrial environment, two
types of reflectance are important, specular and Lambertian.
The simplest type of reflection is the specular or mirror
reflection, where the angle of incidence and the angle of
reflection are equal. Water and other smooth surfaces, such as
aluminum roofs, can produce undesirable specular reflections
or "hot spots" on aerial photography. Generally, this
undesirable phenomenon can be minimized by proper planning of
the photographic mission.

Most terrain features, however, reflect more or less
diffusely. If the reflectance is uniformly diffuse, that is,
the reflected radiant flux is the same in all directions, then
that surface is said to be a Lambert surface. For a flat
Lambert surface, radiant energy (either reflected or emitted
energy) is traveling in all directions, not just perpendicular
to the surface. According to Lambert's cosine law, the radiant
intensity traveling in any direction from a perfectly diffuse
radiating surface varies as the cosine of the angle between
the perpendicular to the surface and the direction of the
reflected radiation.

A blackbody emits energy at all wavelengths in accordance
with Planck's law. The total radiant emittance, W , from a
particular blackbody increases rapidly with the temperature;
and the peak emittance value shifts to shorter wavelengths with
increasing temperature as shown in Fig. 16-2. The total flux
radiated into a hemisphere above a blackbody which is one square
centimeter in area can be found by integrating Planck's law from

Fig. 16-2. Blackbody spectral emittance at various temperatures.

zero to infinity. This is known as the Stefan-Boltzmann law:

$$W = \sigma T^4 \qquad (16\text{-}4)$$

where
  W = radiant emittance, watts cm^{-2}
  σ = Stefan-Boltzmann constant $(5.6697\pm 0.0029) \times 10^{-12}$
    watts $cm^{-2}{}^\circ K^{-4}$

  T = temperature, degrees Kelvin

Differentiating Planck's law and solving for the maximum value produces Wien's displacement law:

$$\lambda_m = \frac{a}{T} \qquad (16\text{-}5)$$

where
  λ_m = wavelength of maximum spectral radiant emittance
  a = $2897.8 \pm 0.4\mu m^\circ K$

  T = temperature, degrees Kelvin

Practical applications of both the Stefan-Boltzmann law and the Wien's displacement law allow for the selection of the proper detector, depending on the detector sensitivity characteristics and the temperature of the scene.

At a given temperature, the ratio of radiant emittance to the radiant absorptance is a constant for all materials and is equal to the radiant emittance of a blackbody at that temperature. This relationship is known as Kirchhoff's law:

$$\frac{W'}{\alpha} = W \qquad (16\text{-}6)$$

where

W' = radiant emittance of the material
α = radiant absorptance of the material, and
W = radiant emittance of a blackbody at the same temperature.

Kirchhoff's law illustrates that "good absorbers" are "good emitters"; more explicitly, rearranging Kirchhoff's law yields:

$$W' = \alpha W \qquad (16\text{-}7)$$

and by substituting

$$W' = \varepsilon\sigma T^4 \qquad (16\text{-}8)$$

and

$$W = \sigma T^4 \qquad (16\text{-}9)$$

or

$$\varepsilon\sigma T^4 = \alpha\sigma T^4 \qquad (16\text{-}10)$$

it follows that

$$\varepsilon = \alpha \; . \qquad (16\text{-}11)$$

Therefore, the emissivity of any material at a given temperature is equal to its absorptance at that temperature.

For opaque materials:

$$\alpha + \rho = 1 \text{ and } \varepsilon + \rho = 1 \text{ or } \varepsilon = 1 - \rho \; . \qquad (16\text{-}12)$$

This relationship allows one to calculate the emissivity of an opaque material by measuring its reflectivity.

16.5 CAMERAS

Multiband photography in this paper refers to the process whereby the same scene is photographed simultaneously through two or more film-filter combinations. Commonly, four bands are used to represent the blue, green, red, and photographic infrared portions of the spectrum. The resulting black and white photography generally obtained on black and white infrared film, which has a wide spectral response, may be viewed on a light table or combinations of any of the four channels can be combined with a selected color coding for each channel. A multiband photograph is shown in Fig. 16-3.

Precision mapping cameras provide a 9" x 9" film format of minimum distortion and very high resolution. The Wild RC-8 camera is shown in Fig. 16-4. Photographs taken with such a camera can be used for manual and automated interpretation, compiling contour maps, and for the very accurate determination of the spatial location of selected points.

The authors have been involved in the use of basically five different types of film: 1) color, 2) color infrared, 3) minus-blue, 4) black and white, and 5) black and white infrared. The basic characteristics of these five films are discussed in the following paragraphs.

Color film has three layers of emulsion sensitized to respond to the wavelengths corresponding to blue, green, and red. Through a subtractive color process the film recreates the "true" color of the scene in a tristimulus mode. Kodak aerocolor negative film 2445 (Estar base), aerial exposure index of 32, can be processed to a color diapositive, paper print, or transparency; or to a black and white diapositive plate or paper print.

Color infrared film also has three layers of emulsion, but they are sensitized to respond to the wavelengths corresponding to green, red, and photographic infrared. Through a subtractive color process this film produces a "false" color image of the scene in which green appears blue, reds appear green and photographic infrared appears red. The color infrared film, Kodak aerochrome infrared film 2443, (Estar base), aerial exposure index of 10 (including filter), requires a minus-blue filter (preferably a Kodak Wratten No. 12). The film is normally processed to a positive transparency for direct viewing on a light table; the direct contact print process from the positive transparency can be used. Color infrared film, processed to a positive transparency and viewed on a light table with a magnifying glass provides a most useful media for river studies. This procedure will be discussed later in this paper.

Minus-blue film is similar to the regular color Anscochrome film, but does not have the blue sensitive top layer of emulsion. The film was developed for the United States Naval Oceanographic Office for use in mapping submerged offshore features. Water depth penetrations on the order of one hundred and fifty (150) feet have been reported using this film. Reportedly, the new Anscochrome minus-blue film has several distinct advantages over conventional color or color infrared aerial films:

1) for clear water penetration, exposures should be increased 2-3 times over that for the terrain; the terrain and shallow-water areas will still retain sufficient detail for interpretation, however,

2) effective film speed is approximately four (4) times

16-8

BLUE (0.40μm - 0.47 μm) INFRARED (0.74μm - 0.80 μm)

GREEN (0.47μm - 0.59μm)   RED (0.59μm - 0.69μm)

Fig. 16-3. Multiband photography

Fig. 16-4. Wild RC-8 precision mapping camera

16-9

that of Anscochrome D-500 exposed through a yellow filter, no
filter is required for the minus-blue film:
    3) improved image contrast, and
    4) processing and drying times are approximately 20% less
than the conventional three-layer film.
    Kodak Tri-X Aerographic Film 2403 (Estar base), is a black
and white (panchromatic) negative film having an aerial exposure
index of 250. The film is particularly useful for mapping and
other photogrammetric applications under minimum light levels.
The authors generally use prints from this film for constructing
mosaics for planning and coordinating color infrared photography
and thermal infrared imagery flights.
    A fifth film type that can be used in certain cases in
lieu of color infrared film for river studies is black and white
infrared film. Kodak infrared aerographic film 2424 (Estar
base) has an aerial exposure index of 100 (without a filter); but
is generally used with either a yellow, red, or deep red filter.
The film is sensitive over a broad range of wavelengths from
(0.4μm to 0.9μm) and consequently can be used with a variety of
interference filters in conjunction with infrared blocking filters
to produce photography in discrete bands of blue, green, red, and
and photographic infrared.
    All five (5) of the film types discussed previously can be
processed to prints and viewed in stereo pairs with a mirror
stereoscope. Considerable information can also be derived from
individual prints. Individual frames of color infrared film,
processed to a positive transparency and viewed on a light table
with some form of magnifying glass (preferably a large size
reading glass, five (5) inches in diameter or greater) provide
a useful format for river system analyses. A psuedo-stereo
effect is produced that allows the interpreter to judge the
relative depths of clear water stretches and to study the
intricate detail of the submerged bars and other bed forms.
This psuedo-stereo effect has not been apparent on any other
type of film transparency or print.

16.6 LINE SCANNERS

    In order to image emitted infrared radiation (commonly
called thermal infrared) electro-mechanical line scanners with
special detectors have to be utilized. Film emulsions could
undoubtedly be developed which were sensitive to thermal infrared energy, but the entire camera system would have to be cooled
to absolute zero temperature in order to keep the camera system
itself from emitting thermal infrared energy and consequently
exposing the film. In addition, the required transmission characteristics of a lens for focusing the thermal infrared radiation
onto a specially sensitized film would require a lens of special
material. Thermal infrared line scanners, employing reflective
optics, and cooled detectors have been developed and are now being
used routinely for mapping terrain features. The output from

such a scanner can be in the form of black and white film and/or
magnetic tape. A schematic of a scanner is shown in Fig. 16-5.

Typical spatial resolution for line scanners are on the
order of 3.0 milliradians (3.0 foot diameter spot size on the
temperature resolution can be on the order of 1.0° Centigrade.
Interpretation of the thermal infrared line scanner imagery
can be accomplished from black and white film prints; or the
imagery can be color enhanced to show discrete film-density
levels corresponding to radiometric temperature differences in
the scene; or digital and/or analog computer processes can be
employed to print out an iso-thermal map.

SIMPLIFIED SCANNER OPERATION DIAGRAM

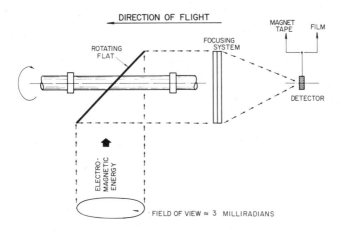

Fig. 16-5. Schematic of a thermal infrared line scanner with
both film and magnetic tape output.

16.7 POTENTIAL APPLICATIONS

Multiband photography, precision mapping camera photography, and thermal infrared imagery each can provide valuable information about a river system. The photographic processes require good light conditions, preferably without clouds (very high, thin clouds are acceptable). Thermal infrared imagery, on the other hand, can be collected either day or night; intervening cloud cover, fog, or high concentrations of water in the path length between the scanner and the ground are detrimental.

Of the three systems discussed the precision mapping camera with color infrared film has proved to be the most useful single sensor system for river studies. However, the thermal properties of the surface of the water, the ground, or the ground cover, can only be determined using a thermal infrared line scanner. The authors recommend that at least two systems be flown simultaneously; an outstanding combination is a precision mapping camera with color infrared film and a thermal infrared line scanner operating in the 8μm to 14μm band.

One of the most useful applications of the color infrared film is the evaluation of sediment transport processes in streams. Small differences in suspended material concentration in water provide a distinctive tone change on the color infrared film. This tone varies from very dark blue for relatively clear water, to very light blue for waters containing high concentrations of suspended material; green colors are produced in some cases on the false color film where the true color of the water approaches a red tone. This distinctive tone change can be used to monitor the source of sediment, the transport process, and the deposition locations along a river system. In those cases where color infrared photography is obtained for long reaches of a river, sediment sources and sinks can be readily identified. Fig. 16-6 illustrates the use of color infrared photography for monitoring sediment sources and transport. (Note this is a black and white reproduction of a color infrared photograph).

Likewise, the tone differences induced by the suspended material in water can be used to identify mixing processes, circulation patterns, position of the thalweg, and the general characteristics of a river. Fig. 16-7 shows the circulation cells along the shear zone where chute and bend flows combine. In addition, the color infrared film enhances the presence of foam and debris at the surface of the water which can be useful for identifying discrete flow paths. Fig. 16-8 shows foam lines that coincide with the deepest locations in the channel cross-section. Foam and debris at the surface can be used to identify small scale localized flow phenomena.

Fig. 16-6. High sediment concentrations in a tributary flow.

Fig. 16-7. Circulation patterns in the Mississippi River at the confluence of chute and bend flows.

Fig. 16-8. Foam lines in a bendway of the Mississippi River.

A thermal infrared line scanner operating in the 3.5μm to 5.5μm band can be used for a dual purpose, since a portion of the sun's reflected energy as well as the objects emitted energy can occur in this wave band. The authors have been able to identify wakes behind boats and other flow patterns manifested by suspended material concentration differences (recorded by reflected energy) and temperature gradients (recorded by emitted energy). Line scanners operating in the 3.5μm to 5.5μm band during daylight hours, however, can produce undesirable hot spots in the imagery caused by specular reflection of sunlight off the water surface. If pure thermal information is required during daylight hours, the 8μm to 14μm band should be used; however, with care and interpretation, the presence of both the reflected and the emitted portions of the spectrum in the 3.5μm to 5.5μm band can be quite useful.

The thermal infrared line scanner operating in the 3.5μm to 5.5μm band or the 8μm to 14μm band can be used to image thermal differences at the surface of water bodies. The interpreter must keep in mind that the thermal infrared scanners are recording the emitted energy from the top layer of the water surface and that no appreciable penetration is occurring. However, the surface temperature distribution alone can be quite helpful and in some cases interpretation can be inferred about the thermal distribution below the surface. On the other hand, the surface temperature pattern can be quite misleading in the case where a thin film of hot water is spreading out over the surface of a cooler water body.

One of the most important findings to date about either mixing processes of sediment-laden water or mixing processes of thermal effluents into rivers is that the mixing process is very slow in the lateral direction. A point source of either sediment or thermally enriched waters can persist as a distinct narrow band for considerable distances downstream with very little lateral mixing. The identification of these zones along a stream can be very useful for defining the proper sampling locations for identifying the true characteristics of a river.

In the case of clear waters, such as mountain streams found in the Rocky Mountain areas, color infrared photography and minus-blue photography can be used to achieve depth penetration. As mentioned earlier, the minus-blue film has been used to penetrate up to 150' deep in relatively clear water in order to map bottom features. The authors have used color infrared film to obtain penetrations in clear water up to about 8'. The value of the use of color infrared film, however, is that on the positive transparency (viewed on a light table with a reading glass) it provides the proper impression of the depth variation in a river cross-section or longitudinal section. Depending on the scale of the photograph, the bedforms are often visible, the locations of the pools and crossings are enhanced, and in general one can do a very good qualitative inventory of the depth characteristics of clear water. However, in order to get detail in deeper portions of a clear stream, the film exposure may need to be increased two to three times.

Pollution detection, monitoring, and evaluation can be achieved using any one of the three remote sensing systems, but preferably in combination involving at least the thermal infrared imagery. The pollutants can be enhanced by selecting the proper film-filter combination or in some cases the presence of the pollution can be inferred by the effect on bordering vegetation along the banks.

Color infrared film, as well as color film in some cases, can be used very effectively for identifying vegetation types and extent along the river banks, on point bars, and islands. Color infrared film, again, is the most useful since the highly reflectant green vegetation produces a brilliant red color. Additionally, plants stressed by some factor can be readily identified by a reduced reflectance characteristic. Soil moisture in conjunction with plant life can be very useful for identifying the stability of banks and levees.

Accurate land classification can be facilitated over the entire floodplain, particularly using color infrared film. Those areas susceptible to high water table and resulting salinity problems can be identified and remedial measures taken before conditions become irreparable. Underwater plants can be identified using the proper film-filter combination. This is particularly important in those areas where water weeds might be impeding the flow in channels; or in cases where the presence of some underwater or surface bio-mass can be used to indicate the quality of the water.

Remote sensing systems operated from an aircraft platform can be used to record the total system operation of a river or water-supply complex. The operation of spillways, water intake structures, canals, and headgates can be effectively monitored using high resolution films and thermal infrared imagery. Sequential flights over a total water resource supply system can provide management with up to date information about the performance and maintenance requirements of the system.

Critical dimensional characteristics of the terrestrial scene can be obtained from precision mapping camera photography reduced in an appropriate measuring device such as a comparator. For example, elevation differences of well marked points on the order of 0.5' can be determined quite readily using a comparator with 1:3000 scale photography. This ability to extract accurate spatial information about the scene can substitute almost entirely in some cases for onsite ground surveys. However, some ground control targets or points of known spatial position are needed.

Photography and imagery can be used for the broad classification of river pattern--meander, straight, and braided. Figure 16-9 shows a typical meander pattern with cut-offs and resultant ox-bow lakes. A braided stream and contiguous flood

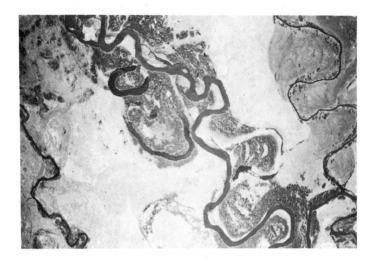

Fig. 16-9.   Meander pattern of the Beaverhead River near Dillon, Montana.

plain is illustrated in Figure 16-10.   Figure 16-11 shows typical bank instability related to a bridge crossing of a braided stream.

Remote sensing systems can be used to record and evaluate the damages associated with flooding.   The use of photography and imagery can be implemented for assisting in clean-up operations as well as identifying the characteristics of the flood waves and the lateral extent of the flooding.

Fig. 16-10. Black and white reproduction of a color
infrared transparency illustrating a braided stream and the
flood plain.

Fig. 16-11. Example of bank instability at a
bridge crossing of a braided stream.

Geophysical exploration for water resources lying adjacent
or beneath the river can be supplemented using certain remote
sensing systems. Thermal infrared imagery can be used to map
the lateral extent of the near-surface, ground-water reservoir
which exists in conjunction with the surface flow. The aerial
extent of the near-surface ground-water reservoir is indicated
by the darker tone in the flood-plain as shown in Figure 16-12.

Fig. 16-12. Thermal infrared imagery of the
Beaverhead Valley near Dillon, Montana(8μm to 14μm).

16-19

Seepage below canals and impoundments can be identified using
the color infrared film and/or thermal infrared imagery, see
Figure 16-13. The lighter tones indicate warmer regions.
Point A represents seepage under the dam; point B represents
a relatively large spring discharging into the cooler river
water. A 3°F temperature difference was measured between point
A and the river.

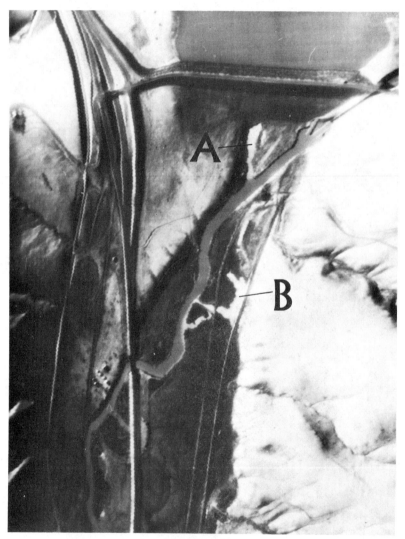

Fig. 16-13. Clark Canyon Dam on the Beaverhead
River near Dillon, Montana(8μm to 14μm).

Thermal effluents can be detected as demonstrated in Fig. 16-14. Near the outlet the temperature difference between the river water and effluent was 3°F.

Fig. 16-14. Thermal effluent from a power plant discharging into the Missouri River (8μm to 14μm).

16.8 CONCLUSIONS

Three relatively simple remote sensing systems can be operated individually or preferably in combination from a light twin engine aircraft to collect valuable information related to river mechanics. The data is collected in the form of a photograph or an image (the imagery can also be recorded on a magnetic tape format) which can provide an unique, quasi-synoptic record of flow phenomena over relatively large areas. The invisible portions of the spectrum can be utilized in order to enhance certain phenomena; particularly the thermal infrared wavelengths are of value for mapping the radiometric temperature patterns at the surface.

The potential applications listed in this paper represent the characteristics related to river mechanics that the authors have actually experienced in their course of interpreting the photography and imagery from a variety of different river systems. This list of characteristics is not exhaustive in view of the authors experiences and certainly other characteristics related to river mechanics will hopefully be interpreted by other practicing river engineers as broader application of remote sensing develops.

It is important to note that personnel acquainted with practical river mechanics can use photography and imagery effectively without too much prior experience in interpreting such photography and imagery; and oftentimes without having much information about the particular scene. However, the fullest utilization of the photography and imagery can be developed by a person trained in both river mechanics and the variety of interpretation processes. Interpretation is most effective when done in conjunction with adequate ground truth information. The authors encourage the implementation of photography and imagery as a part of the set of basic tools available to the engineer.

Chapter 17

SUSPENDED-SEDIMENT SAMPLING VARIABILITY

by

James P. Bennett, Research Hydrologist, U. S.
Geological Survey, Fort Collins,
Colorado

and

Carl F. Nordin, Research Hydrologist, U. S.
Geological Survey, Fort Collins,
Colorado

Chapter 17

SUSPENDED-SEDIMENT SAMPLING VARIABILITY[1]

17.1 INTRODUCTION

A knowledge of the possible variations to be encountered in sampling is necessary for intelligent interpretation of any suspended-sediment data. Unfortunately, there is presently a scarcity of both analytical and experimental information concerning this subject. Analytical information is scarce primarily because the general differential equation governing the distribution of suspended sediment (Eq. 12-36, Nordin and McQuivey, 1971) is impossible to solve in closed form except in a very few highly restricted cases of limited practical interest. Experimental information is scarce because sediment samples are expensive, difficult, and time consuming to collect and analyze.

In the following, two analytic solutions to simplified versions of Eq. 12-36 of Nordin and McQuivey (1971) are presented. In addition, a new numerical solution to the steady-state two-dimensional version of this equation is presented. These solutions are used to illustrate a number of important factors concerning suspended-sediment sampling variability. Also presented are several sets of experimental data which illustrate the variations that can occur in sampling at a point, in a vertical and in a cross section. The influence of bed form on this sampling variability is also discussed.

17.2 SOME CLOSED-FORM SOLUTIONS

In order to evaluate analytically the expected variations in sediment sampling, it is necessary to solve the convective-dispersion differential equation governing suspended-sediment transport for boundary conditions varying in space and time. In this manner, the response of the suspended-sediment transport-open-channel flow system to various types of perturbations may be investigated. The earliest work along these lines was presented by Kalinske (1940) who solved

$$\overline{U} \frac{\partial C}{\partial x} = \omega \frac{\partial C}{\partial y} + \varepsilon_s \frac{\partial^2 C}{\partial y^2} \quad , \quad (17\text{-}1)$$

with the boundary conditions

$$C = 0 \quad \text{at} \quad x = 0 \quad , \text{ all } y \qquad (17\text{-}2a)$$

$$C = 0 \quad \text{at} \quad y = \infty \quad , \text{ all } x \qquad (17\text{-}2b)$$

$$C = C_a \quad \text{at} \quad y = a = 0 \, , \, x > 0 \qquad (17\text{-}2c)$$

---
[1]Publication authorized by the Director, U.S. Geological Survey.

to obtain

$$\frac{C}{C_a} = \exp\left(-\frac{\omega y}{\varepsilon_s}\right) - \frac{2}{\pi}\int_0^\infty \frac{n}{-B}\exp\left[\frac{B\varepsilon_s x}{\bar{U}} - \frac{\omega y}{2\varepsilon_s}\right]\sin ny\, dn \quad (17\text{-}3)$$

where $B = -[n^2 + (\omega^2/4\varepsilon_s^2)]$, ε_s is the mass transfer coefficient in the y direction, x is distance in the mean flow direction, y is measured upward from the bed, C is concentration, and ω is the particle fall velocity. (The notation used throughout this paper is summarized in Section 17.6.) In Eq. (17-1), it is assumed that the velocity $\bar{U}$ and diffusion coefficient ε_s are uniformly distributed throughout the flow field. The assumption of uniform velocity severely restricts the applicability of Eq. (17-3) in the analysis of suspended-sediment sampling variability. Mei (1969) presents an analytic solution to Eq. (17-1), with boundary condition Eq. (17-2b) replaced by the condition of zero transport, $\varepsilon_s(\partial C/\partial y) + \omega C = 0$, at $y = D$, the water surface. Mei's solution suffers from the same disadvantage as Kalinske's, and because it is so complicated, it will not be presented here.

Dobbins (1944) has presented a solution to

$$\frac{\partial C}{\partial t} = \omega\frac{\partial C}{\partial y} + \varepsilon_s\frac{\partial^2 C}{\partial y^2} \quad . \qquad (17\text{-}4)$$

Mathematically, Eq. (17-4) is exactly the same as Eq. (17-1) if t is interchangeable with $x/\bar{U}$. The boundary conditions for Dobbins' solution are

$$\varepsilon_s\frac{\partial C}{\partial y} + \omega C = 0 \quad \text{at} \quad y = 0 \quad \text{and at} \quad y = D , \quad t > 0 \quad (17\text{-}5a)$$

$$C = f(y) \quad \text{at} \quad t = 0 \quad . \qquad (17\text{-}5b)$$

The expression $f(y)$ is the equilibrium profile corresponding to some concentration C_0 at $y = 0$ when $t = 0$. Dobbins' (1944) solution may be written

$$\frac{C}{C_a} = \exp\left(-\frac{\omega y}{\varepsilon_s}\right)$$

$$+ \frac{C_0 - C_a}{C_a}\exp\left(-\frac{\omega y}{2\varepsilon_s}\right)\sum_{n=1}^\infty \frac{2\alpha_n^2\omega\exp(-\varepsilon_s At)}{\varepsilon_s A[AD + (\omega/\varepsilon_s)]}Y_n \quad , \qquad (17\text{-}6)$$

where C_a = the concentration at $y = 0$ for $t > 0$, and

$$A = \alpha_n^2 + \frac{\omega^2}{4\epsilon_s^2}$$

$$Y_n = \cos \alpha_n y + \frac{\omega}{2\epsilon_s \alpha_n} \sin \alpha_n y \quad ,$$

and α_n are the successive roots of

$$2 \cot D = \frac{D\alpha}{\omega D/2\epsilon_s} - \frac{\omega D/2\epsilon_s}{D\alpha} \quad .$$

Dobbins (1944) collected suspended-sediment data from a stirred tank in which it was possible to produce an essentially uniform turbulence field with $\bar{U} = 0$. Figure 17-1 shows the results of one such study in which $\omega/\epsilon_s = 0.915$ ft^{-1} , $D = 1.37$ ft , and $C_a = 0$, corresponding to no pickup of particles from the bed. Figure 17-2 shows the results of a similar experiment in which $\omega/\epsilon_s = 1.95$ ft^{-1} , $D = 1.48$ ft , and $C_a/C_0 = 0.3$, corresponding to a constant rate of pickup of particles from the bed. If it is assumed that the conditions of Fig. 17-1 are representative of an open-channel flow with a logarithmic velocity profile, a slope of 0.001, a dimensionless Chezy discharge coefficient, $c/\sqrt{g} = 10$, von Karman's $\kappa = 0.4$, ϵ_s = the depth averaged value for the flow, and $D = 1.37$ ft , then the fall velocity, ω , for this figure is 0.013 ft per second, corresponding to a particle diameter, d , of 0.062 mm. Similarly, for the conditions of Fig. 17-2, with $D = 1.48$, ω is 0.042 ft per second, corresponding to a d of 0.14 mm. This means that if the conditions of Fig. 17-1 were applicable to an open channel flowing as assumed above, it would take a reach of length 750 feet for a transition from the $t = 0$ concentration profile to the $t = 360$ second profile of that figure. Similarly, for the conditions of Fig. 17-2, an 800 ft reach would be required for a transition from the $t = 0$ to the $t = 360$ second profile. From these hypothetical situations, it appears that the response of the system to drastic changes in boundary conditions can be rather slow, at least for fine sediments. Thus, in sampling situations where the bed material is fine and where bottom concentrations are likely to be changing markedly with longitudinal position, care should be exercised in selecting the sampling verticals so that the sediment samples are truly representative of the hydraulic conditions at that particular vertical.

17.3 NUMERICAL SOLUTIONS

The material in the above paragraphs fairly well exhausts the knowledge that can be gained concerning suspended-sediment sampling variability using currently available closed-form

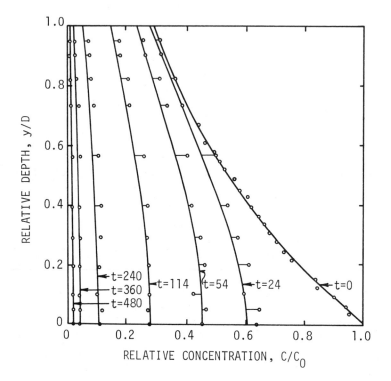

Fig. 17-1. Concentration changes with time, t , in
seconds, for values of ω/ε_s = 0.915 ft^{-1},
D = 1.37 ft, and C_a = 0 (after Dobbins,
1944). The solid lines represent Eq.
(17-6); the points are the experimental
values.

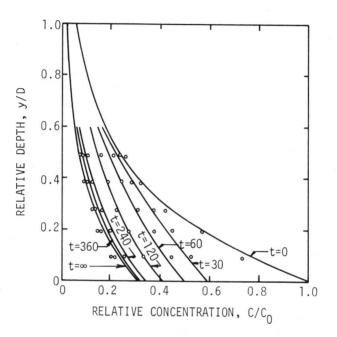

Fig. 17-2. Concentration changes with time, t, in seconds, for values of $\omega/t_s = 1.95$ ft^{-1}, $D = 1.48$ ft, $C_a/C_0 = 0.3$ (after Dobbins, 1944). The solid lines represent Eq. (17-6); the points are the experimental values.

solutions to the convective dispersion equation for suspended sediment. Further information obtained from solutions to this differential equation must come from numerical solutions. In this section, we discuss briefly a series of numerical solutions which were obtained to

$$U(y) \frac{\partial C}{\partial x} - \omega \frac{\partial C}{\partial y} = \frac{\kappa DU_*}{6} \left(\frac{\partial^2 C}{\partial y^2} + T \frac{\partial^2 C}{\partial x^2} \right) \qquad (17\text{-}7)$$

with boundary conditions

$$C(0,y) = C_a \exp \left[- \frac{6\omega}{\kappa U_* D} (y - a) \right] \qquad (17\text{-}8a)$$

$$C(x,a) = C_a \left(1 + h \sin \frac{2\pi x}{\lambda} \right) \qquad (17\text{-}8b)$$

$$\omega C + \frac{\partial C}{\partial y} = 0 \qquad x \geq 0 , \quad y = D , \qquad (17\text{-}8c)$$

and a velocity distribution given by

$$U(y) = \frac{U_*}{\kappa} \ln \frac{y}{\delta} \qquad (17\text{-}9)$$

where U_* is the shear velocity, $U_* = (gDS)^{\frac{1}{2}}$, and δ is a characteristic roughness height.

In solving Eq. (17-7), we have assumed (a) a logarithmic velocity profile, (b) the vertical mass transfer coefficient, $\varepsilon_s = \kappa DU_*/6$, is a constant equal to the average over the depth of the value given in Eq. 12-47 of Nordin and McQuivey (1971), (c) the mass transfer coefficient in the x direction is some constant value T times ε_s, (d) the concentration profile at $x = 0$, given by Eq. (17-8a), is the equilibrium profile for a concentration, C_a, at $y = a$, and for constant ε_s as in assumption b, (e) transfer through the water surface is zero as indicated by Eq. (17-8c), and (f) for $x > 0$ the concentration at $y = a$ has an average value of C_a and fluctuates sinusoidally around this value with an amplitude of $2h$ and a wave length in the x direction of λ, as indicated in Eq. (17-8b). The assumption of constant values of mass transfer coefficients in the x and y directions was made mostly for convenience in the numerical solution. It is not a severe restriction on the generality of the solution, and should have only a minor effect on the resulting calculated concentration profiles. The present state of knowledge does not afford a precise estimate of the value of the parameter T; however, there is good reason to

believe that values of the horizontal and vertical mass transfer coefficients are of the same order of magnitude, so T
probably is close to unity. The sinusoidal form of Eq. (17-8b)
for the sediment concentration at the lower edge of the flow
field was assumed for convenience in the numerical solution of
the differential equation. It is, however, a realistic assumption for the concentration near the bottom of an alluvial
channel flowing over bed forms such as ripples, dunes, or
antidunes because the concentration at this level must be
derived from the transport in contact with the bed, and as
demonstrated by Simons and others (1965), bed-load transport
must be proportional to the local elevation of the bed above
its lowest point. Since the shapes of many bed forms closely
approximate sinusoids, the concentration near the bed might
reasonably be very closely approximated by an equation such as
Eq. (17-8). The near-bottom concentration can certainly be
approximated by a Fourier series, which consists of a sum of a
number of terms such as Eq. (17-8b). Since Eq. (17-7) is
linear, the sum of a series of solutions for boundary conditions
such as Eq. (17-8b) would equal the solution for the boundary
condition consisting of the Fourier series, thus examination of
the solution of Eq. (17-7) for the boundary conditions of Eq.
(17-8) would be very pertinent to an investigation of suspended-
sediment sampling variability.

Equation (17-7) can be put in a form more convenient for
analysis by dividing by ε_S and non-dimensionalizing x and
y using the depth, D ,

$$R(y) \frac{\partial C}{\partial x'} - Z \frac{\partial C}{\partial y'} = \frac{\partial^2 C}{\partial y'^2} + T \frac{\partial^2 C}{\partial x'^2} \qquad (17\text{-}10)$$

The parameter R is a diffusion Reynolds number, and its depth-
averaged value, $\bar{R}$, is $15\, c/\sqrt{g}$ where c is the Chezy discharge coefficient, and g is the gravitational constant. The
parameter Z is the sediment mobility parameter, and it is
equal to $15\, \omega/U_*$. In the following, the primes on x and y
will be dropped, but it should be kept in mind that x and y
are now non-dimensionalized by the depth D , so that $0 \leq y \leq 1$
and all values of x are quoted in multiples of D .

To solve Eq. (17-10) with the boundary conditions of Eq.
(17-8) (suitably transformed), the writers chose a numerical
procedure known as Galerkin's method using piecewise polynomials
as basis functions. This method was chosen because it has
proven extremely effective and accurate in solving problems of
the convective dispersion type (see Price and others, 1968).
In particular, it is free of the problems of instability and
numerical dispersion which plague the finite difference solutions to the convective dispersion equation. Furthermore, the
method lends itself extremely well to matrix formulation, it is
easy to program, and a surprisingly small amount of computer

time is required for solution. Essentially, the Galerkin method solves Eq. (17-10) by transforming the second-order partial differential Eq. (17-10) into a system of second-order ordinary differential equations. The resulting system of ordinary differential equations was solved using an implicit finite difference technique, but the Runge-Kutta method could probably be used almost as easily and probably more accurately.

Equation (17-10) was solved for values of $\bar{R}$ of 135 and 270, the former corresponding to a $c/\sqrt{g}$ value near the lower edge of ripple-dune range of bed forms, the latter to $c/\sqrt{g}$ values near the upper edge of the dune range, and to antidunes. Sediments with fall velocities corresponding to d's of 0.062 mm, 0.2 mm, and 0.4 mm were used in calculating representative Z values. Values of the parameter T were 1.0 and 5.0, h was 0.75, and λ was always $4D$. The calculations were performed for a distance in x corresponding to 4 cycles of the sine function, that is, for a distance of 16 stream depths. Recall that boundary condition Eq. (17-8a) states the starting condition to be the equilibrium concentration profile for a sediment concentration of C_a at elevation $y = a$.

The results of the calculations are presented for a distance corresponding to the last cycle in concentration at elevation a. Figure 17-3 gives concentration profiles for four values of Z at various locations in x. An examination of the numerical results showed that values of T had negligible effects on the relative concentration profiles, so the plotted results apply for both $T = 1$ and $T = 5$. In addition, when drawn to the scale of Fig. 17-3, concentration profiles for $\bar{R} = 135$ could not be distinguished from concentration profiles for $\bar{R} = 270$, although some minor variations are apparent in the numerical tabulations. The shapes of the relative concentration profiles are almost entirely determined by the parameter Z and by the position, x/λ.

Figure 17-4 shows selected values of the variation with distance of the relative suspended load discharge calculated from the concentration profiles of Fig. 17-3 and the velocity profile, Eq. (17-9). Values of the ratio $q_s/(q_s)_e$ were computed for all values of $\bar{R}$, Z, and T noted above, but for clarity, only three curves are shown on Fig. 17-4. Maximum deviations occur for $Z = 15$, $\bar{R} = 270$; minimum deviations for $Z = 0.55$, $\bar{R} = 135$. All other values of the ratio $q_s/(q_s)_e$ fall between these two curves. The suspended load discharge was computed using

$$q_s = \frac{1}{(q_s)_e} \int_{a/D}^{1} U\, C\, dy \quad , \qquad (17\text{-}11)$$

where $(q_s)_e$ is the sediment discharge for the equilibrium concentration profile. The values of $(q_s)_e$ for various values of Z and $\bar{R}$ are given in Table 17-1.

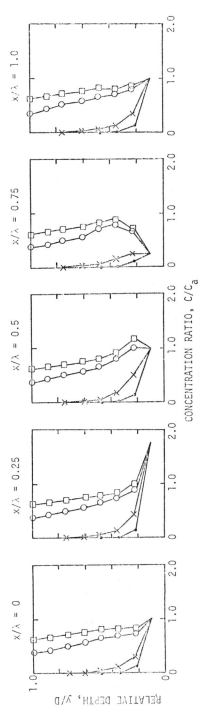

Fig. 17-3. Concentration ratio, C/C_a, plotted against relative depth, y/D, for various relative longitudinal positions, x/λ. Values of Z are as follows: □ – 0.55, ○ – 1.1, x – 7.5, • – 15.

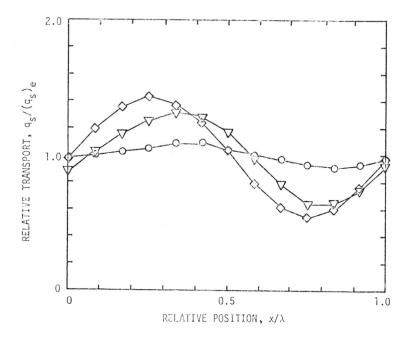

Fig. 17-4. Variation of sediment discharge with longitudinal position. $\circ$ - Z = 0.55, $\overline{R}$ = 135; $\triangledown$ - Z = 15, $\overline{R}$ = 135; $\diamond$ - Z = 15, $\overline{R}$ = 270.

Table 17-1. Sediment discharge for the equilibrium
concentration profile.

$\overline{R}$	$\overline{Z}$	$(q_s)_e$
135	0.55	8,390
	1.1	1,311
	7.5	834
	15	80
270	0.55	15,570
	1.1	1,550
	15	167

The results shown in Fig. 17 3, Fig. 17-4, and Table 1
indicate that variations in the values of $\overline{R}$ over the range
found in dune bed flow do not significantly affect the shape of
the concentration profile or the longitudinal variation of the
relative suspended-load transport. However, the value of $\overline{R}$
does significantly influence the amount of material transported;
doubling $\overline{R}$ approximately doubles $(q_s)_e$.
The suspended-load transport varies longitudinally from
less than ±10 percent of the mean for the smaller Z values to
more than ±40 percent for $Z = 15$. This is because for the
larger Z values, there is very little material suspended
above the zone where the local value of the bottom concentration has significant influence on the concentration profile.
If natural longitudinal variations in suspended load can be
expected to be less than ±10 percent, as would be the case for
very fine sands, the location of sampling verticals is of little
concern. On the other hand, if these variations are on the
order of ±40 percent, the location of the sampling verticals
may be very important.
Figure 17-3 does not show enough detail to give a really
good picture of the vertical mass transfer process where the
lower boundary condition varies with distance. To alleviate
this lack of detail, 13 concentration profiles from longitudinal
positions in the 4th cycle varying from $x/\lambda = 0$ to $x/\lambda = 1$
are plotted in Fig. 17-5. In this figure it is possible to
trace the upward movement and falling out of the cloud of sediment picked up in the first half of the cycle, and to trace the
influence of the low concentration zone in the second half of
the cycle. It was mentioned previously that in Fig. 17-3 there
was no noticeable influence of $\overline{R}$ on the concentration profile.
On a figure of the scale of Fig. 17-5, the influence of $\overline{R}$
would be apparent, for example at $y/D = 0.26$, in Fig. 17-5,
the C/C_a range for the various profiles is from 0.64 to 1.12

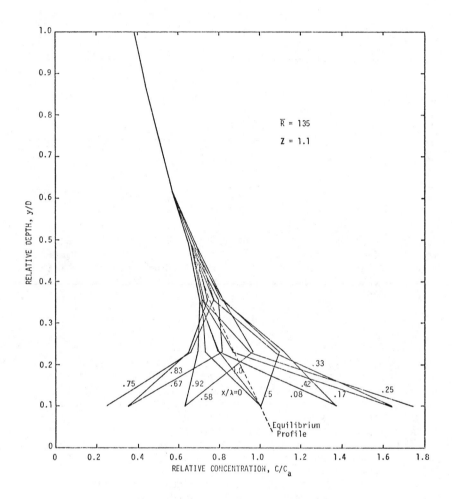

Fig. 17-5. Variation of calculated concentration
profiles with longitudinal position.

while for $\bar{R}$ = 270 , at this elevation, it ranges from 0.76 to 1.02. The diffusion Reynolds number does then, it appears, have a certain small influence in damping the fluctuations of the concentration profile.

17.4 EXPERIMENTAL EVIDENCE

To this point the discussion has been based on the results of calculations performed using a simplified mathematical model with some assumed boundary conditions. From this it might be concluded tentatively that the longitudinal variation of the sampled suspended load will be small for streams with bed sediments with small values of the sediment mobility parameter, and large for those with larger values of this parameter. We turn next to experimental information to see if this conclusion can be verified.

As an index of the minimum probable sampling variability, two series of samples were collected from a particular point in a flow field which should have yielded as reproducible results as can be expected when dealing with the sediment-transport phenomenon. The flow field was a flat-bed flow in a recirculating flume; the flow depth was 1.2 feet, the average velocity was 3.0 ft/sec, the bed material median diameter was 0.25 mm, and the samples were collected 1.0 ft below the water surface at the flume centerline. The first series consisted of 16 individual one-pint samples collected using a U.S. DH-48 sampler modified for point sampling. Each sample was taken over a time interval of about 14 seconds, so that the length of flow filament sampled was about 52 feet. The mean sediment concentration for these samples was 448 mg/ℓ and the standard deviation was 39 mg/ℓ. The second series consisted of 8 individual one-gallon samples, siphoned from the stream at mean-stream velocity over a time period of about 54 seconds, so that the length of filament sampled was on the order of 162 feet. The mean sediment concentration of these samples was 438 mg/ℓ, and the standard deviation was 28 mg/ℓ. The longer sampling period reduced the standard deviation slightly, but in both cases, the standard deviation of the sample concentration is on the order of 10 percent of the mean. In light of what is presently known of the sediment-transport phenomenon, it is felt that a standard deviation of point samples on the order of 10 percent of the mean is the best obtainable while limiting samples to a reasonable volume.

The statistics cited in the paragraph above were for concentration at a single point in a flat bed flow, while the numbers plotted on Fig. 17-4 were depth-integrated concentrations, or suspended loads, for flow conditions which approximate dune or antidune bed forms. Figure 17-6 (taken from Guy, 1970) is a plot of frequency distributions of depth-averaged concentrations collected consecutively at a single vertical for both a flat-bed and a dune-bed flow on the Middle Loup River, near Dunning, Nebraska. Near Dunning, the bed material of the

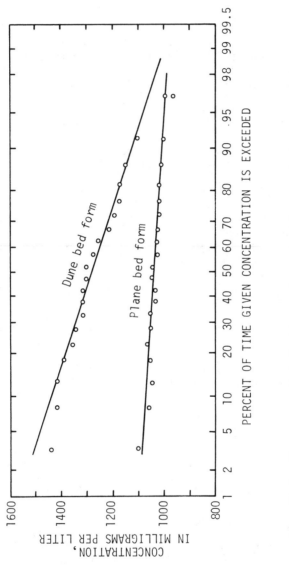

Fig. 17-6. Frequency distributions of consecutive sampled concentrations at single verticals of the Middle Loup River at Dunning, Nebr.

Middle Loup has a median diameter, d_{50}, of approximately 0.4 mm, and its depth-integrated suspended load averages about 20 percent finer than 0.0625 mm. From Fig. 17-6, for the flat-bed flow, the mean value of the depth-averaged concentration at the vertical in question is 1045 mg/ℓ and the standard deviation is about 30 mg/ℓ, while for the dune-bed flow, the mean is about 1280 mg/ℓ and the standard deviation is about 130 mg/ℓ. The standard deviation in the first case is about 3 percent of the mean; in the second case, it is about 10 percent of the mean. If the standard deviations of the depth-averaged suspended loads at a particular vertical are never larger than this, special effort in selecting sampling verticals should not be required.

Having discussed the variability of suspended-sediment sampling at a point, and in the depth-integrated sense at a vertical, we consider next the cross-sectional variability of suspended-sediment sampling. Typical cross-sectional profiles of velocity, depth, and depth-integrated suspended load for a sand-bed stream are presented on Fig. 17-7, which was taken from Hubbell and Matejka (1959). The data were collected at three different times during a one-year period from two cross sections on the Middle Loup River near Dunning, Nebraska. In some cases the variation in depth-averaged concentration between two points in the cross section on the same day can be greater than 100 percent. Furthermore, the verticals containing the maximum and minimum concentrations change position in the cross section with time, so that it is impossible to tell which, if any, single vertical in the cross section is representative of the whole. It must be concluded that for sand-bed streams it is impossible to pick a single unique vertical in a cross section which will always be representative of the entire cross section for suspended-sediment sampling.

Further evidence of the cross-sectional variation which can be expected from suspended-sediment samples in shown in Fig. 17-8. Contour lines of equal suspended-sediment concentration for two different size ranges are plotted using data for a series of point-integrated samples from the Rio Grande conveyance channel near Bernardo, New Mexico, reported by Culbertson and others (1971). The channel has a median bed material size, d_{50} = 0.25 mm. The material finer than 0.0625 mm was essentially uniformly distributed in the cross section. For the coarser material, the elevations of the various contours above the streambed vary considerably with lateral position in the cross section. From these two examples, it appears that in order to obtain a representative measure of the total suspended-load transport through a cross section of a shallow sand-channel stream, a number of verticals in the cross section must be sampled.

As a final illustration of sampling variability, we present Fig. 17-9, a typical time series of concentration of total-load samples collected under equilibrium flow conditions in a laboratory flume. The samples were collected using a

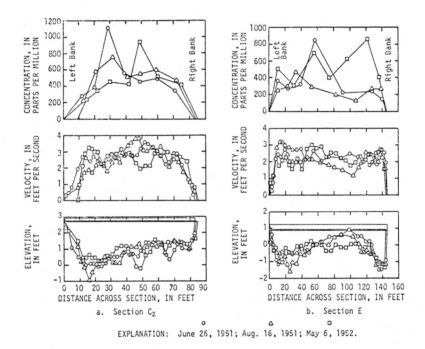

EXPLANATION: June 26, 1951; Aug. 16, 1951; May 6, 1952.

Fig. 17-7. Lateral variation of measured suspended-sediment
concentration, stream velocity, and bed and water
surface elevations.

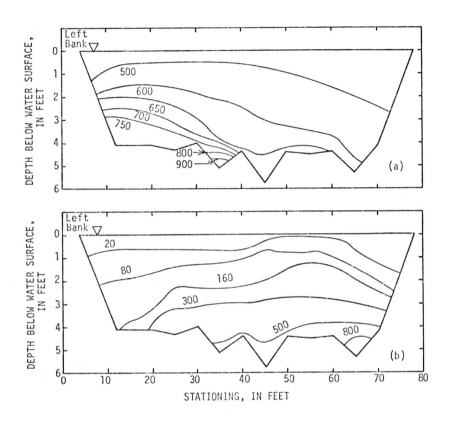

Fig. 17-8. Cross-sectional variability of suspended material
in two different size ranges, Rio Grande, near
Bernardo, New Mexico. (a) Contours in mg/ℓ for
material between 0.0625 and 0.125 mm; (b) Contours
in mg/ℓ for material between 0.25 and 0.5 mm.

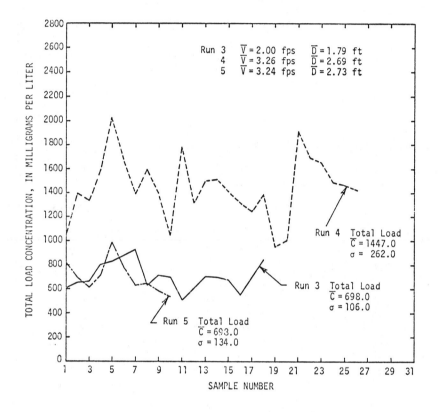

Fig. 17-9. Variation with time of total load from a series of flume runs.

traversing slot which sampled the entire depth of the nappe falling from the lower end of an 8-foot-wide flume. The slot was moved across the entire width of the flume during sampling, obtaining a cross-sectional average total load. The sand in the flume has a median diameter of 0.25 mm. In the case of run 5 for which the bed form was alternating dunes and flat bed, the standard deviation of the concentrations was 26 percent of the mean. For other runs in the series, the standard deviation was as high as 44 percent for breaking antidunes and as low as 7 percent for a run during which the bed was entirely flat. Figure 17-10 shows a running average of the concentrations given in Fig. 17-9. This figure gives an indication of the number of samples required to obtain a stable estimate of the total-load concentration from a time series of individual samples. The time interval between samples was approximately 15 minutes for runs 3 and 5, and about 20 minutes for run 4. In all cases, 7 to 9 cross-sectional average measurements are required to obtain an average concentration asymptotic to the long-term average value of the total-load concentration.

17.5 CONCLUSIONS

From the foregoing discussion, the following conclusions may be drawn. First, the closed-form and numerical solutions to Eq. 17-7 provide reasonable indication of the variation of sediment concentration that can be expected due to boundary conditions that vary in space and time. For example, Fig. 17-4 suggests that the local transport rate along a dune bed might vary up to 40 percent for sand sizes of 0.4 mm ($Z = 15$) and only a few percent for finer sizes. Second, for most cases of practical interest, the standard deviation of the depth-integrated average concentration of suspended load in a particular vertical will not often be larger than 10 percent of the mean concentration in the vertical. This means that any properly collected depth-integrated sample in a particular vertical probably will well represent the mean suspended load through that vertical. Third, the variation between various verticals in a cross section, shown in Fig. 17-7 and Fig. 17-8, may be much larger than 100 percent, requiring that a number of verticals be sampled to obtain a good estimate of the total suspended load transported through a particular cross section. Finally, from the experimental evidence shown in Fig. 17-10, one would conclude that from 7 to 9 cross sections may have to be sampled to obtain a stable estimate of the total material being transported by a shallow sand-channel stream.

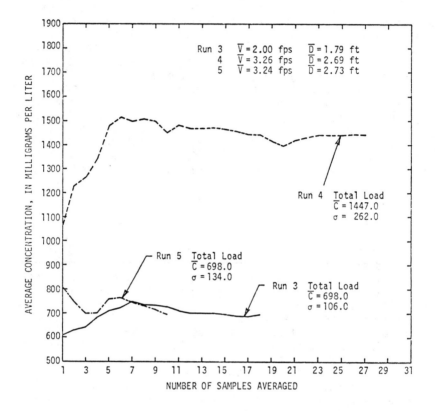

Fig. 17-10. Running average of total load from a series of flume runs.

17.6 NOTATIONS

A	A parameter in Eq. (17-6)
a	A distance from the bed
B	A variable in Eq. (17-3)
C	Sediment concentration
c	Chezy discharge coefficient
C_0	Sediment concentration at $y = 0$ for $t = 0$
C_a	Sediment concentration at $y = 0$ for $t > 0$
D	Flow depth
d	Particle diameter
g	Acceleration due to gravity
n	A variable of integration or an index
q_s	Sediment discharge per unit time per unit width of channel
$(q_s)_e$	Sediment discharge for an equilibrium concentration profile
R	A diffusion Reynolds number
$\bar{R}$	Depth-averaged value of R
S	Slope of the energy gradient
T	The ratio of mass transfer coefficient in the x direction to the mass transfer coefficient in the y direction
t	Time
U	Flow velocity
U_*	Shear velocity, $(gDS)^{\frac{1}{2}}$
x	Distance in the mean flow direction
x'	A dimensionless distance, x/D
y	Vertical distance measured upward from the bed
y'	A dimensionless distance, y/D
Y_n	A parameter in Eq. (17-6)
Z	A sediment mobility parameter, $15\,\omega/U_*$
α_n	A parameter in Eq. (17-6)
δ	A height of roughness element
ε_s	Mass (sediment) transfer coefficient in the y direction
κ	von Karman's constant
λ	A wave length
ω	Fall velocity of a sediment particle

REFERENCES

Culbertson, J. K., Scott, C. H., and Bennett, J. P., 1971, Summary of alluvial-channel data from Rio Grande conveyance channel, New Mexico, 1965-69; U.S. Geological Survey Open-File Report, Fort Collins, Colo.

Dobbins, W. E., 1944, Effect of turbulence on sedimentation; Trans. Am. Soc. Civil Engineers, Vol. 109.

Guy, H. P., 1970, Fluvial sediment concepts; U.S. Geological Survey Techniques of Water-Resources Investigations, Bk. 3, Ch. C1.

Hubbell, D. W., and Matejka, D. Q., 1959, Investigations of sediment transportation, Middle Loup River at Dunning, Nebraska; U.S. Geological Survey Water-Supply Paper 1476.

Kalinske, A. A., 1940, Suspended-material transportation under non-equilibrium conditions: Trans. Am. Geophys. Union, Pt. II.

Mei, Chiang C., 1969, Non-uniform diffusion of suspended sediment; Proc. Am. Soc. Civil Engineers, Vol. 95, No. HY1.

Nordin, C. F., and McQuivey, R. S., 1971, Suspended load; River Mechanics Inst. Proc., Colorado State Univ., Chap. 12, Vol. 1.

Price, H. S., Cavendish, J. C., and Varga, R. S., 1968, Numerical methods of higher-order accuracy for diffusion-convection equations; Society of Petroleum Engineers Jour., Sept.

Simons, D. B., Richardson, E. V., and Nordin, C. F., Jr., 1965, Bedload equation for ripples and dunes; U.S. Geological Survey Prof. Paper 462-H.

Chapter 18

FISH FACILITIES AT RIVER DEVELOPMENT PROJECTS

by

Khalid Mahmood, Assistant Professor
                 Civil Engineering Department
                 Colorado State University
                 Fort Collins, Colorado

Chapter 18

FISH FACILITIES AT RIVER DEVELOPMENT PROJECTS

18.1 INTRODUCTION

To meet their biological needs of procreation and
survival, the fish select their habitats for certain stream
characterisitics like the flood hydrographs, variations of
sediment content, water temperatures, availability of dissolved oxygen, food, spawning areas etc. In natural streams,
the fish move about, almost instinctively, migrating from one
stretch to another for known suitable environments. River
development projects alter the regimen of the streams. Dams
constructed on rivers, change their water level, flow and
temperature characteristics. Irrigation or trans-valley flow
diversions, reduce the stream flows with accompanying changes
in the sediment content, velocities and depths. One of the
consequences of river development is the effect on the fish
life supported by the streams.

The impact of river development has been acutely felt on
certain fish that migrate over long distances, between sea and
the inland streams. Such fish are called anadromous, when they
are hatched in sweet water streams but spend their adult life
in sea. They return to the inland streams for spawning. Salmon
and shad are two important anadromous fishes. The economic
importance of these fish, has resulted, in the past, in a conflict between the river development and the fishery interests.
A great deal of knowledge has been accumulated over the last
few decades about the relation between the biological needs of
the fish and the affects of river development. An impressive
array of ingenious devices and methods to mitigate and counter
balance the adverse effects on fish have also been evolved over
the same period. These consist of improved types of facilities
for the migration of adult and juvenile fish; screening from
powerhouses and spillways where the juveniles are likely to
encounter fatal conditions; artifical propagation of fish and
improvement of channel conditions for spawning. Most of this
development has taken place on the Pacific Northwest, mainly
because the Columbia river is rich in fishery, water and power
resources.

The object of this chapter is to outline some of the
specific consequences of river development for the fish and to
present a summary of the engineering solutions. This is drawn
largely from the progress made in this country. Some examples
from other countries are included to show the world wide nature
of this problem.

The Conflict. The conflict between the fishery and river
development is caused by the following factors.

(1) Structures like dams and barrages create a barrier in
the migatory path of fish. Any structure creating a fall of a

few feet or more in the water surface is a barrier to the upstream migration of the fish. If the migration is a vital need of the fish, as in the case of salmon, the barrier may ultimately eliminate the population using the stream. On the other hand, species not vitally dependent on migration may adapt themselves, if uninterrupted long stretches of rivers are available to them. Even in such cases, the population upstream of the barrier may dwindle in time, as the fish may only travel downstream. For the downstream migrants, the barrier created by a fall in the water level is not absolute. The problem is one of mortality suffered during the fall and is negligible for dams below 100 ft high.

(2) Passage through turbines, over spillways or in the irrigation diversions involves physically hazardous conditions for the fish. In passing through the turbines, the fish are subject to injury by physical contact with the moving and fixed parts and by the pressure changes. During passage over spillways, the fish are subjected to high velocity, pressure and shear forces and in some types of stilling basins, they are liable to be killed by impact or by being trapped in eddies. Downstream of spillways and turbines, the fish may be stunned by their traumatic experience and may also become more susceptible to predation.

The diversion of fish in the irrigation channels becomes a problem, when they are passed onto the fields or when the canals go dry for part of the year. The whole population of fish in a canal system may die when the bed goes dry. In lift irrigation schemes, the passage of fish through the pumps can also be fatal for the fish.

In addition to the above factors, river utilization can alter the thermal and chemical regime of a stream. The thermal pollution is discussed in Chapter 11. The chemical pollution is outside the scope of this chapter and is not discussed.

Types of Facilities. Broadly, the facilities developed to alleviate the conflict between fishery and river development fall in three categories: (1) facilities for upstream migrants, (2) facilities for downstream migrants and (3) methods for artifical propagation.

The facilities for upstream migrants consist of fish passages and mechanical lifting devices. In fish passages, the flow conditions are arranged to enable the fish to swim through. The mechanical lifting devices consist of a collection device, where the fish are attracted and trapped and an arrangement to mechanically transport them upstream of the barrier.

For downstream migrants, the type of facility depends on the amount of fall. In dams of 100 ft or smaller heights, the danger by passage over spillways is small. The damage due to passage through turbines can also be reduced, if certain conditions are avoided. Fortunately, there is not much conflict between the conditions required for the safe conduct of fish and an efficient operation of the turbine. For higher dams and for turbines where the mortality rate may be high, the facilities consist of screening the fish and attracting, trapping and transporting the migrants downstream. The screening of fish is a difficult procedure on account of the large quantities of flow involved. The downstream migrants are generally the juveniles. The screen sizes required for the juveniles are also susceptible to blockage by trash. To prevent the downstream migrants from entering the irrigation diversions, screens and louvers are commonly used. In some instances, it may be possible to use storage tanks and outlets on irrigation canals where the fish may shift during closures.

Artificial means of fish propagation are used to enhance the fish population so that any damage caused by the river development can be compensated. Such means consist of hatcheries and artificially maintained spawning channels. These facilities are discussed in the following pages.

18.2 FISH LADDERS

A fish ladder is a structure that connects the water levels upstream and downstream of a barrier. The flow in the ladder is arranged to be such that the fish can negotiate it without extraordinary effort. A fish ladder has four main components; (1) The approach to the ladder entrance, (2) the entrance to the ladder, (3) the ladder proper and (4) the exit into the upstream reservoir.

Approach to Fishway Entrance. In medium and large rivers, the fish ladder entrance is a small fraction of the total width of the channel. The discharge through the ladder is likewise small compared to the total discharge in the stream. The fish have to locate the entrance to be able to use the ladder at all. The approach to the fishway entrance is therefore a critical component.

To help the fish locate the entrance, the fish ladder entrance should be placed in the path of the migrants if this path is well defined. Alternatively, more than one ladder may be provided, although it is an expensive solution. The specific requirements for the suitable approach will depend on the characteristics of the stream, fish and the structure. However, the approach should remain connected with the mainstream and not be blocked by sediment deposits, islands etc. It should also be free from slackwater, reverse currents and high velocities. Moreover, the current of the attraction flow through the fish ladder should be somehow distinct from the rest of the flow. The flow through the ladder should also be free from odors obnoxious to the fish. Some fish, like salmon, have an extremely keen sense of smell and are distracted by human odors.

At McNary dam, excavated approach channels, special guide wall design adjacent to the spillway and large volume of supplemental attraction flow are provided to create suitable hydraulic conditions in the approach channel (Von Gunten, et al., 1956).

In Pakistan, the fish ladders are located in the divide walls separating the undersluices and the main weir sections (Figs. 18-1, 18-2). This arrangement is economical as it combines

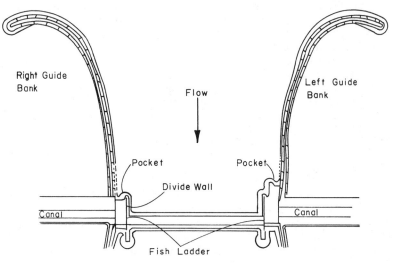

Fig. 18-1. Typical layout of a barrage (Pakistan).

two objectives in one structure. It also ensures that the approach to the fish ladder entrance is located on the same side as the better defined river channel.

The problem of maintaining a self-propagating approach to the entrance is more difficult when the entrance is located between two overflow sections of the dam. In such cases, unless the attraction flow is substantial, the entrance is likely to be lost to the fish. To maintain distinct flow conditions in the approach, the flow through the fish ladder has to be increased at higher flow stages. Model experiments can be particularly helpful for determining the approach conditions and the amount of attraction flow (Irrigation Research Institute, 1966). Investigation of the fish habits and migration characteristics may be necessary before the project design. The results of such an investigation on Frazer River at Hope in connection with Spuzzum Dam (Muir and Ruus, 1961) are shown in Fig. 18-3. The attraction flow can then be designed for the extreme conditions during periods when the ladder is most likely to be used.

There is some evidence that the spill-pattern over the spillway can be manipulated to guide the upstream migrants. Leman and Paulik (1966) report the effect of spill-pattern manipulation on the guidance of migrant salmon at Rock Island dam. This dam has three fish ladders, situated on the left,

18-4

middle and right side of the dam. They found that by passing the spill flow through the three gates adjacent to the right ladder they could increase the population of sockeye using this ladder in preference over the others. They also found that because of extreme turbulence generated close to the right fish ladder entrance, under certain gate openings, the entrance was not available to the fish. Leman and Paulik also found that the response time of the fish to adjust to the changed spill pattern was very small.

Entrance. The fish ladder entrance is the point at which the upstream migrants enter the ladder. The entrance may be in the form of weirs, orifices or slots. The requirements of a suitable entrance are that the fish having been attracted to it, should be able to negotiate it. For entrances, an average velocity of four fps is generally recommended (Von Gunten, et al., 1956, Banys and Leonardson, 1969).

In weir type entrances, the crest level is controlled to correspond to the tail water levels. The control may be automatic as in Priest Rapid fish ladder or manual as in most of the fish ladders in Pakistan. The orifice entrance consists of a rectangular opening controlled by a gate. The orifice is submerged 2-8 feet below the tail water elevation.

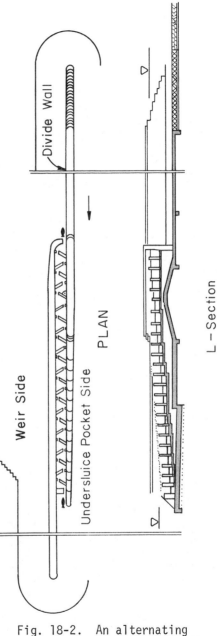

Fig. 18-2. An alternating baffle fish ladder located in the divide wall of a barrage.

18-5

The slot entrance consists of a vertical opening through which the flow is discharged usually under a head of 1 ft.

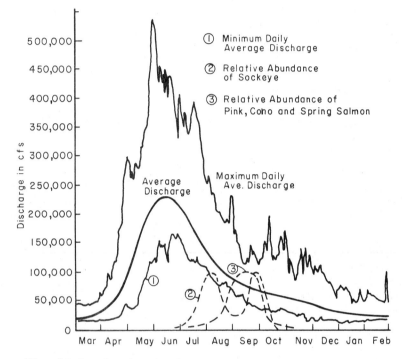

Fig. 18-3. Graphs showing the flow in Frazer River at Hope and the periods of migration of adult fish at Spuzzum (after Muir and Ruus, 1961).

A series of studies were conducted by the Corps of Engineers to determine the relative efficacies of weir and submerged orifice type of entrances under prototype conditions. These studies indicated (MacLean, 1961) that using similar quantities of water, the submerged orifice entrances were more efficient than overflow weirs. In these studies when the weir and orifice entrance were equally available more than 60 percent of the fish passed through the orifices and the remainder over the weirs. The orifices location at shallow (2.5 - 6.5 ft), medium (14.8 ft average) and deep (30 ft) submergence were also tested. By far the greatest proportion of the fish chose the orifice with shallow submergence. It was concluded that an orifice set from 2 - 8 ft below tail water level provides the most attractive conditions for the entrance.

With widely varying downstream flow discharges, the attraction flow in the approach has to be increased with increasing discharges. In these situations, a slot entrance may be more suitable, because it requires greater discharge for similar velocities at higher tail water levels. Auxiliary water supply has to be provided in these conditions.

The size of the entrance depends on the number of fish to be handled, although no quantitative criteria are available. At McNary Dam, 10-15 ft wide entrances have been used. The smallest slot to pass salmon is about 1 ft when few fish are attracted and a width of 4 ft or more is usually provided.

The water velocity and the location of the entrance with respect to the surrounding flow conditions are important factors in determining the success of the ladder design. The maximum water velocity that fish may be able to negotiate at the entrance will depend on the species and size of the fish. In the Corps of Engineers' experiments with 5 ft wide entrances it was found that fish preferred the higher velocity entrance over the lower velocity. This was found true even under conditions in which the fish could not negotiate the channel and were swept back (MacLean, 1961).

At McNary Dam four different entrances were provided. One on the Washington shore fish ladder between the navigation lock and the spillway and three on the Oregon shore fish ladder. The latter consisted of a powerhouse collection system on the Oregon shore side, an entrance between the powerhouse and spillway and one on the shoreline. On the Washington side, the entrance consists of four overflow weirs, three discharging longitudinally and one laterally in the spillway. The entrance from the spillway was placed at a point where the velocities in the stilling basin would be of the order of 10-12 fps. It was reasoned that at this point the fish would experience difficulty in penetrating the flow and would choose the entrance to the lateral fish ladder.

The location of entrance downstream of the powerhouse was found favorable from model tests for Tobique Narrows Dam in Canada (Mahaffy, 1954). In this dam, two entrances were provided in a gallery along the downstream face of the powerhouse and two additional entrances in the leg of the fish ladder parallel to the tail race. The operational experience in this fish ladder has indicated that during higher tail water levels, the salmon preferred the side entrances. For lower flows, the entrances in the gallery were preferred.

In the Pakistan fish ladders, the entrances are all axially located. A common characteristic of the more successful ladders is that the entrances are located on the undersluice side of the divide wall where the quantity and frequency of discharge is better. These entrances are located almost at the end of the stilling basin.

Deelder (1958) discussing the experience in Netherlands, states that entrances alongside the weirs that discharge parallel to the river flow are inefficient and difficult to be perceived by the migrating fish. He favors a lateral entrance that discharges normal to the river flow, placed just downstream

of the section where the turmoil of water passing over the
weir has finished.

The experience in USSR (Antonnikov, 1964) indicates:

(1) The fish move against the current and approach the
dam at places with the greatest water velocity. The movement
of the fish is thus primarily directed to the powerplant,
especially to the wing well between the powerplant and the
spillway.

(2) The fish prefer the flow situation below the powerplant where the velocities are more uniform than along the
spillways where energy losses cause rapid changes in velocity.

(3) The fishladder entrance are better located between the
powerhouse and the dam or on the bank next to the powerhouse.

(4) The water discharge from the entrance should be
directed at 22 - 25° to the axis of the main current.

(5) The depth at the entrance should be 0.6 to 0.8 times
the depth in the river channel near the entrance.

The Russian experience with the attraction of fish to the
powerhouse is also borne by the operating experience at McNary
dam. There five times more fish were collected in the
entrances across the downstream face of the powerhouse, than
in the Oregon shore entrance and the number of fish using the
entrance between the powerhouse and the spillway was negligible
even during periods of no spill.

Exits. The fish ladder exit is the upstream section of the
ladder where the fish leave the ladder. The exit has the
following functions:

(1) To deliver the fish to an appropriate location in
the reservoir.

(2) To admit correct discharge in the ladder and to
cater for reservoir level fluctuations.

(3) To prevent trash from entering the reservoir and
clogging the ladder.

If the exit is located within the zone of influence of the
spillway or other diversions, the fish, somewhat exhausted by
the journey through the ladder may be swept downstream or in
the canal. It is therefore necessary to locate the ladder
exits away from the spillway, the powerhouse and the irrigation
intakes. When the reservoir elevation is fluctuating, a fixed
level exit will introduce a smaller discharge in the fish
ladder at lower pool levels. On the other hand, during higher
pool elevations, the drop at the exit section may increase
beyond suitable limits. These conditions can be corrected by
installing automatically adjusting exit gates that respond to
the change in reservoir level and by providing adjustable weirs
downstream of the exit. It may also be necessary to introduce
supplemental flow to make up the discharge in the ladder. The
debris entering the fish ladder can clog channel passages and
render the ladder ineffective. For this reason trash racks
are provided.

In the Oregon shore fish ladder at McNary Dam, the exit releases the fish about 1300 ft from the powerhouse to prevent the fish from being drawn into the powerhouse intake. The debris is removed by 10 ft wide travelling screens that have a mean velocity of 1.4 fps through the net area at the maximum flow. An alarm system is installed to indicate excessive head on the screens. At Bonneville Dam, the pool level may fluctuate by about 10 ft. In the original design of the Bonneville fish ladder, a regulating gate was provided at the exit end to regulate the discharge and the continuation of the pool steps was made by stop-log weirs. This proved to be a cumbersome operation and consequently the weirs were modified to bulkhead gates that provide suitable control for pool fluctuations (MacLean, 1961).

At McNary dam, a series of automatically operated tilting weirs were used to provide the necessary continuation of the pool steps and a regulating weir to provide the control of flow for changing reservoir levels. These weirs are hinged at bottom and can be rotated from horizontal to the vertical position. The automatic weir system is considered to be expensive and requires considerable attention and maintenance. In subsequent projects the Corps has replaced the automatic weir system by a series of non-overflow bulkheads with orifices. The reduction in the discharge entering the fish ladder with a lower pool level is then made up by admitting required flow through the ladder floor immediately below the control section. The details of the exit control section for Ice Harbor Dam are shown in Fig. 18-4.

The fish ladders installed in the Pakistan barrages have different arrangements. Most are provided with a single exit controlled by stop logs on either the weir or the undersluice side of the divide wall. In some, multiple side ports at increasing elevation with distance from the entrance are provided. These ports can be manually closed by stop logs and thus the length of the fish ladder can be adjusted at the same time as the discharge adjustment for a varying pool level. In three latter fish ladders at Qadirabad, Chasma and Marala, the bulkhead arrangement similar to Ice Harbor Dam is provided with supplemental water supply.

Ladder. The ladder is the portion of the fish passage between the entrance and the exit. Generally if the fish have entered the ladder and the flow conditions are not too adverse, the fish will be able to swim up the ladder. The requirements of a suitable ladder are that the flow should not overtax the fish. It should also provide an unhampered passage without risk of injury. There should be no sharp projections and sufficient resting areas should be available to the fish. Some fish like salmon can surmount obstacles by leaping if they have sufficient length of take-off in deep water. A leap of 6 ft height is generally accepted as the maximum for salmon, although higher leaps have been recorded.

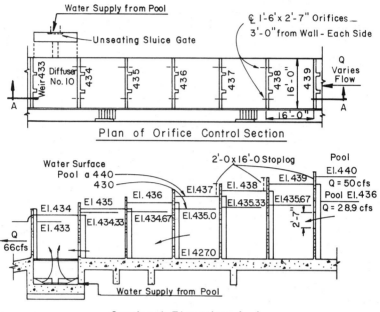

Fig. 18-4.   Ice Harbor Dam fish ladder control section (after McLean, 1961).

The tolerance to extreme flow conditions vary with the species and size of the fish. However, it is generally agreed that large scale turbulence in the ladder be reduced and that the pattern of flow should be even and repetitive from pool to pool.

The purpose of the ladder is to provide the change in elevation (equal to the difference in the water level between the entrance and the exit) with the flow conditions tolerable for the fish. This can be accomplished by various arrangements of obstacles and baffles. Consequently, many varieties of ladders have been tested and constructed. Some of the important types are:

(1) Denil type, (2) alternate obstacle type, (3) paired obstacle type and (4) overflow weir-submerged orifice baffle type. A Denil type fish ladder (Fig. 18-5), is a straight

Fig. 18-5. Denil type fish ladder.

channel with closely spaced baffles placed on the sides and
bottom. This type was evolved by Denil in Belgium and has been
extensively used in Europe. The first Denil type ladder in
USA was built in 1949 at Dryden Dam on the Wenatchee River,
Washington (Muir and Ruus, 1961). This type is generally
inadequate for varying water levels.

The alternate obstacle type produces a zig zag flow path
formed by vertical slots located on the alternate sides of the
ladder. The baffles forming the slots have been designed in
many different arrangements, shapes and angles. This type was
most commonly used in the fish ladder in Pakistan. A typical
arrangement at a barrage is shown in Fig. 18-2. The flow
through the slots can be controlled by stop logs. The experience in Pakistan (Ahmad and Ahmad, 1961) indicates that these
ladders are unsatisfactory because the high velocity flow is
localized. It is felt that the fish dislike the winding path
and would rather have a straight course even if it means
encountering greater velocities.

In the paired obstacle type ladders, the slots are
centrally located in the channel. The flow in these ladders is
again concentrated and is generally unstable.

The most important and successful type of ladder has been
evolved by the Corps of Engineers in the Columbia river dams.
The first of these, at Bonneville, consisted of vertical overflow baffles with two orifices at floor level, one adjacent to
each wall. The McNary Dam fish ladders were similar. The weir
baffles at McNary are 6 ft high with two orifices 23 inches
high by 21 inches wide placed with centerline 3 ft from wells
and the orifice bottom flush with the floor. Based on the
experience at Bonneville and McNary Dam fish ladders, the
design used at Ice Harbor Dam on Snake River was evolved. It
was also adopted at Wanapum and other dams. The Ice Harbor Dam
ladder is based on the same principle of overflow weir and
submerged orifice close to the floor but the width of the

overflow weir is restricted. The typical arrangement and
detail of a baffle is given in Fig. 18-6.

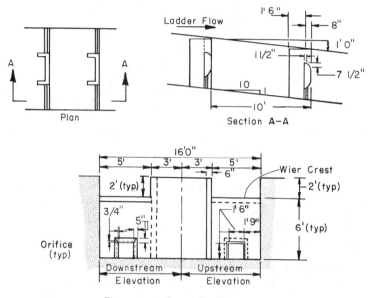

Fig. 18-6. Typical overflow weir-orifice baffle used in
the fish ladder at Wanapum Dam, Columbia River
(after Banys and Leonardson, 1969).

The Corps' overflow weir-submerged orifice fish ladders
are designed to work at about 1 ft head on each baffle. The
fish have a choice between swimming through the orifice or over
the weir. The pattern of flow in the pools has been found to
be attractive for the fish. The pools also provide sufficient
resting area. The hydraulics of the weir-orifice baffles is
such that if the head on the weirs is increased beyond 1 ft,
the falling jet streams over the pool surface. The best
operation is obtained at 10-12 inches head on the weirs. A
problem occurred at McNary fish ladders, when insufficient
head was experienced on the weirs. A resonant wave appeared
that periodically travelled down the ladder causing unsteady
flow conditions. Extensive laboratory and prototype studies
were made to prevent the surging effect. The Ice Harbor type
fish ladder (Fig. 18-4 and 18-6) was adopted at three barrages
constructed in Pakistan under the Indus Basin Project. The

writer working with a 1:6 scale model of the ladder could reproduce the surging. However, at 1 ft (prototype) head on the
weirs, no surging problem was experienced.

In USSR, a special design providing a conical grating
guide (PVA) on the upstream side of the orifices has been
developed (Antonnikov, 1964). The baffles are overflow weir-
submerged orifice types. The arrangement of PVR is shown in
Fig. 18-7. The comparison of velocity distribution obtained
with and without the PVR is shown in Fig. 18-7a. It is claimed
that the flow conditions in this type of ladder are more
attractive to the fish. It seems that the PVR would have
problems even in the presence of small debris.

An orifice baffle type of ladder, Fig. 18-8, was evolved
at the hydraulic laboratories of the Laval University (Michel
and Nadeau, 1965). The orifices have borda mount pieces, and
are staggered in the consecutive baffles. This arrangement was
adopted after observing the ascent of Atlantic Salmon in a 4-5
ft depth of flow in a 100 ft long rapid. It was noticed that
the salmon progressed upstream in a zigzag path punctuated by
rest behind the stones in the bed. The orifice with borda
mouth piece is supposed to duplicate the flow conditions chosen
by the ascending salmon and trout. It is also considered to be
more economical in construction cost compared to the overflow
weir type baffles. The prototype ladder was built in a steep
reach of the Nabisipi River estuary in France and is reported
to be working satisfactorily.

Apart from the shape and arrangement of baffles, design
criteria are needed for the spacing of baffles and slope and
width of the ladder.

Ladder Slope. The Bonneville and McNary fish ladders were
designed with a slope of 1 in 16 and 1 in 20 respectively. It
was thought that in long ladders, the fish travel would be
hampered by their exhaustion on extensive and steep slopes. A
series of experiments was performed by U.S. Fish and Wildlife
Bureau of Commercial Fisheries at the Bonneville Fish
Laboratory (Collins, et al., 1962), to test the ability of
salmon to ascend high fish ladders and the effect of ladder
slope on this ability. Two short fish ladders were constructed
with slopes 1 in 8 and 1 in 16. Experiments comparing the
performance of salmon in these fish ladders indicated a faster
rate of passage in the steeper ladder. Additional experiments
were undertaken using a pair of endless fish ladders with
slopes 1 in 8 and 1 in 16. In each ladder, the highest pool
was joined with the lowest through a fish lock. As the fish
reached the top pool, they were rapidly lowered to the bottom
pool to begin the ascent again. Most fish were tested for a
climb through 100 pools. Four of each species were allowed to
climb 1,000 pools. One sockeye salmon was able to climb
through an elevation of 6,648 feet in a 5-day period. This was

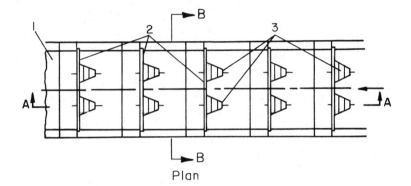

Plan

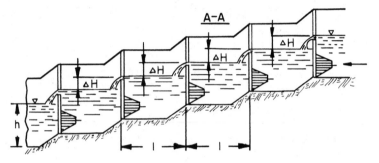

A-A

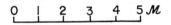

0   1   2   3   4   5 *M*

B-B

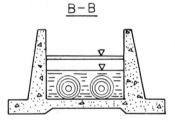

1. Concrete Compartment
2. Wood Partitions
3. PVR

Fig. 18-7.   Overflow weir-orifice type fish ladder baffles
with (PVR) grating (after Antonnikov, 1964).

18-14

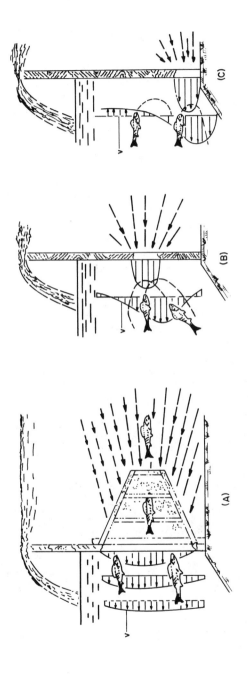

Fig. 18-7a. Effect of (PVR) grating on the flow pattern through submerged orifices and movement of fish (after Antonnikov, 1964).

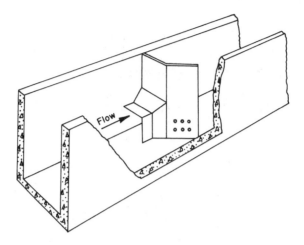

Fig. 18-8. Orifice baffles with borda mouthpieces.

not the ultimate climbing capability of the salmon since the
laboratory personnel gave up before the fish did.

The biochemical indices of fish fatigue were also used to
compare the performance of ladders. It was concluded that
ascent in a properly designed fish ladder was only a moderate
exercise for fish. The steeper slope was found equally efficient for the passage of salmon as the flatter slope. It
was also found that the rate of climb was independent of the
number of fish present in the ladder.

A comparison of some very steep and short fish ladders was
made by Ziemer and Behlke (1966). They compute the total
energy E spent by the fish in swimming through a ladder as

$$E = \frac{L}{V_f} \left\{ \frac{HW}{L} + C_d \frac{\rho \ell^2 (V_f + V_w)^2}{2} \right\} (V_f + V_w)$$

where V_f is the velocity of the fish of weight W , up the
ladder, V_w is the water velocity down the ladder, H is the
drop of water in the ladder of length L , C_d is the drag
coefficient of the fish in water and ρ is the mass density of
water. For yearling Sockeye Salmon, they found a value

$$C_d = \frac{3.3}{R^{.417}}$$

18-16

where R is the Reynolds number, $\ell(V_f + V_w)/\nu$, ℓ being the length of fish and ν the kinematic viscosity of water. Assuming that

$$C_d = \frac{a_o}{R^\alpha} = \frac{a_1}{\{\ell(V_f + V_w)\}^\alpha}$$

the power P required for the fish to swim in the ladder is

$$P = \frac{WH}{L} (V_f + V_w) + \frac{a_1 \rho}{2} \ell^{2-\alpha}(V_f + V_w)^{3-\alpha}$$

and

$$E = WH \frac{(V_f + V_w)}{V_f} + \frac{a_1 \rho}{2} \ell^{2-\alpha} \frac{(V_f + V_w)^{3-\alpha}}{V_f} \cdot L$$

For a given H, V_f , V_w , W and ℓ , P decreases with L and E increases with L . Thus in flatter slopes the fish need smaller power, but greater total energy expenditure. The critical values of P and E for different species and sizes are not known. These quantities are also effected by $(V_f + V_w)$, the velocity of fish relative to the current. The field of propulsion dynamics, critical P and adjustment of V_f by the fish is a fertile field for joint research by hydrodynamists and fishery biologists. The experience shows that the Ice Harbor type fish ladder design is conservative and it does not over tax the fish.

Baffle Spacing and Width. For a given head on the baffle weirs (1 ft in general) and the ladder slope, the spacing of baffles is automatically fixed. For a 1 in 10 slope, the baffle spacing is 10 ft. The space between baffles provides a storage area for the fish. The width and baffle spacing would be related to the number of fish in any compartment. Quantitative limits for the minimum compartment dimensions are not available. However, the existing fish ladders show that this is not a critical factor. The Corps of Engineers research showed (MacLean, 1961) that salmon passed in a 4 ft wide, 1 in 16 slope fish ladder at a rate of 3000 fish per hour without showing that capacity of the ladder has been reached. On the other hand, Killick (in Muir and Ruus, 1961) has recorded an unusual run of 2 million sockeye salmon, that did develop congestion at the Hell's Gate fishway causing a delay of about 4 days.

Auxiliary Water Supply. The flow conditions in the ladder are affected by the water levels at the two ends. With fixed

exit structures, the flow through the ladder will vary with
the upstream pool elevations. For a fixed discharge entering
the exit, the velocity of flow through the inlet decreases
with increasing downstream river stages. Under this condition
the entrance can lose its distinction to the fish unless the
ladder flow is also increased. For this reason, it is
necessary to provide some kind of control at the exit end of
the ladder and a supplemental water supply in the fish ladder.
The control at the exit of the ladder is easy to provide for
submerged orifice exits (see Fig. 18-4). For meeting the
requirements of design velocities in the lower end of the
ladder and for increasing the flow at the inlet, auxiliary
water supply is needed.

The supplemental water supply is added in such a way, that
it diffuses in the ladder flow evenly and without causing
large eddies. This is achieved by a manifold diffuser below
the ladder floor. The supply is transmitted to the diffuser
chambers either by conduit or through overflow wiers (chimneys)
in a supply channel parallel to the ladder (Fig. 18-9). The
locations where auxiliary water supply is added, depends on the
hydraulics of the ladder, but usually, additional supply will
be needed downstream of the exit control structure and in the
lower part of the ladder that is submerged at high river levels.

It is possible that the flow through the diffuser grating
may attract the fish towards the manifold chamber. For this
reason, the velocity through the gross area of the diffusion
grating is restricted to 0.25 - 0.30 fps. In the model studies
of the diffusion chamber in the Irrigation Research Institute,
Lahore (1967), it was found that the sediment load in the
ladder flow and the auxiliary supply tended to collect in the
diffusion chambers. Since many of the chambers may not be
operative over considerable lengths of time, the sediment
deposits could become permanent. Depending on the sediment
load in the flow the deposits were also formed in the operative chimneys. These deposits adversely affected the flow
pattern through the manifolds, causing a non-uniform distribution of inflow (Fig. 18-10). The model tests showed that the
deposits could not be adequately cleaned by reverse flow
through the chambers. A system of panels that could cover the
right half of the grating was found necessary to desilt the
chambers by reverse flow.

The auxilary flow can be obtained from the upstream pool
in low head diversion structures. In high head structures,
with power generation, it is more economical to pump water from
the tailrace. On the Washington shore fish ladder at McNary
Dam, a 6 by 8 ft gravity supply conduit controlled by a slide
gate provides as much as 2,000 cfs for the manifold below the
three downstream entrances. The flow in the manifold below the
side entrance into the spillway is controlled by 3-20 inches
roto-valves. Because of the disturbing effect of air bubbles
on salmon, air vents were not used on any control valve in the

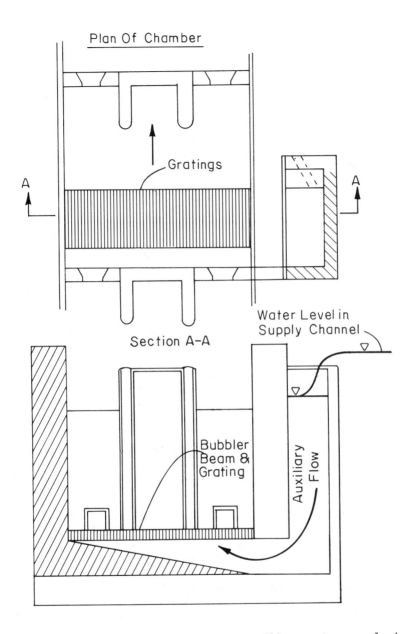

Fig. 18-9. Diffusion chambers for auxiliary water supply in Pakistan fish ladders.

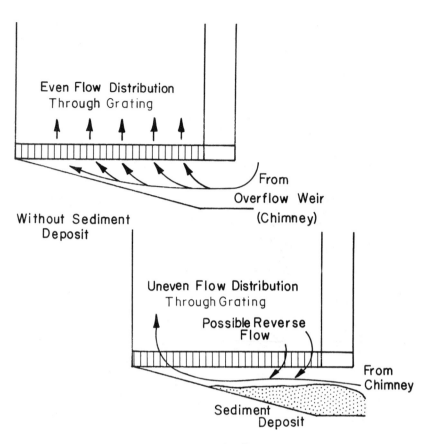

Fig. 18-10. Effect of sediment deposit on flow through
diffusion chamber.

auxilary water supply system. On the Oregon shore fish ladder,
the greater portion of the supplemental water is pumped from
the tail race. A pumphouse with three pumps, each capable of
providing 2,500 cfs at 6 ft of head, is located on the south
shore. The pumps discharge into a pressure conduit 22 by 24
feet, which is branched to feed the diffusion chambers. The
pumping requirements vary from 4,200 cfs to 5,500 with an
average value of 4,600 cfs. Gravity supplemental flow is also
provided on the Oregon shore ladder up to 1,000 cfs.

   Monitoring. The criteria of the most attractive flow conditions for fish are not known in detail. The true test of the
success of any fish ladder is the number of fish using it. A
fish ladder also provides a unique opportunity to monitor the
fish migration on a continuous basis because in the ladder they

are all confined within a small area. For these reasons,
counting stations are important adjuncts of fish ladders.

In this country, provisions have been made for counting
of migrants at all fish ladders constructed by the Corps of
Engineers. At Bonneville dam, a complete count was made of all
the fish until the fall of 1950. Since then counting has been
discontinued during winter months because of the rather small
migrations. At McNary Dam, the counting stations consists of
a V-trap. The fish are induced to rise to an opening on the
counting board by picket sections. A 4 by 4 by 8 ft enclosure
equipped with a 3 by 4 ft window overlooking the counting board
is provided. The counting board is controlled from within the
counting house. It is important to provide optimum flow and
light conditions at counting stations to prevent delay of the
fish passage and to be able to identify the fish.

The fish counting is an expensive procedure. It also
causes some obstruction to the fish passage. At McNary, the
counting section is operated during daylight hours during March
to September. No count is attempted during the remaining
months (Von Gunten, et al., 1956).

Delay in Migration of Adult Fish. The time taken by the fish
in locating the inlet of the fish ladder and swimming through
the ladder is greater than the time taken by the fish in
negotiating the same stretch of the river before the dam. In
anadromous fish, this is of concern to the biologist because
prolonged delay will deplete the energy reserves of the fish
proceeding to the spawning ground. Some earlier experiments
at Bonneville Dam had indicated an average delay of 2.6 to
3.0 days in the passage of fish (Muir and Ruus, 1961). On the
other hand, a reduction of the fish passage time has been
reported in certain situations. On the actual rate of travel
in the pools, the studies at McNary Dam have shown that the
average time required to move through each ladder pool (20 ft
long) was about 2.5 minutes.

18.3 FISHLOCKS

Fishlocks are similar to single lift navigation locks.
They work in intermittant cycles of "fishing" and "lifting". In
this country fishlocks have been constructed in some Columbia
river dams. The main advantage for fishlocks is that they are
more economical of water than fish ladders because their cycle
of operation can be adjusted to the fish run.

The general arrangement of the first fishlock constructed
and operated in Scotland (Anonymous, 1956) is shown in Fig.
18-11. This lock was constructed as a part of Torr Achilty
Dam. This dam is 50 ft high and the pool varies over a depth
of 10 ft. Similar locks have also been constructed at other
dams in Scotland, some with pool level fluctuations of 80 ft.

The cycle of operation of a fishlock is schematically
shown in Fig. 18-12. Flow through the exit weir enters with

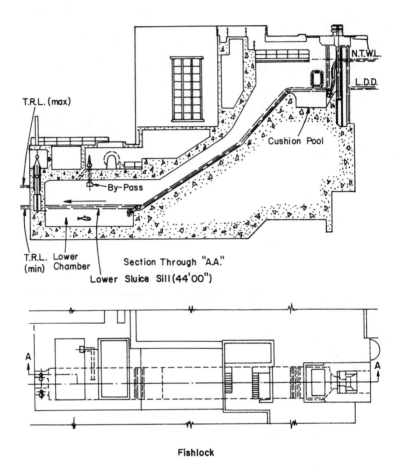

Fig. 18-11. General arrangement of fishlock at Torr Achilty
Dam (Scotland).

a head of about one ft on the weir. This water falls in a
cushion pool that is provided to avoid injury to fish that may
enter with the flow. From the cushion pool, the water flows
down a sloping shaft in the lower chamber. Flow from the lower
chamber can pass through the fish inlets or through a bypass.
In Torr Achilty lock, two inlets are provided, to cater for

the tail water level fluctuations, and one of them is used at a time. The fish are attracted by the flow through the lock and enter the lower chamber through the inlet. When sufficient number have been collected, the inlet is closed and the lock is filled. The bypass starts operating as soon as the lower chamber is filled and this induces a downward current in the shaft that guides the fish upstream. When the water level in the shaft equals the forebay level, a differential on the exit weir is still maintained due to the bypass flow and the fish exit into the reservoir over the weir. When all the fish have escaped the lock, the fish inlet gates are opened, first gradually, to empty the lock.

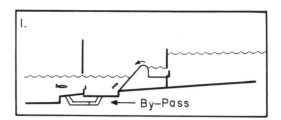

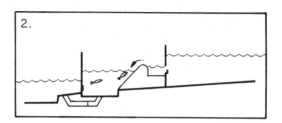

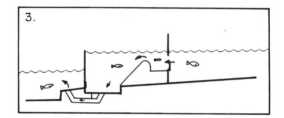

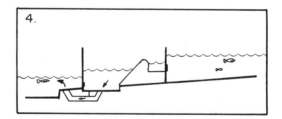

Fig. 18-12. Schematic operation of a fishlock.

One cycle at Torr Achilty lock extends over 4 hours; 3 hours for fishing, when fish collect in the lower chamber, 20 minutes for filling the shaft, 30 minutes for fish exit and 5 minutes for dewatering. Experience showed, that filling time could be reduced to 10 minutes without causing any discomfort to the fish.

Fishlocks have also been adopted to replace the existing
Denil type fish ladders on Meuse River in the Netherlands
(Deelder, 1958). The experience in Scotland and the Netherlands
has shown the fishlocks to be efficient fish passage structures.
The attraction flow in the fishlocks is necessarily smaller
than in fish ladders. In the Torr Achilty dam, the small
attraction flow is compensated by placing the fishlock directly
below a small powerplant. Other advantage claimed for the
fishlocks is that the total effort exerted by the fish in
surmounting a dam is nearly independent of the height of the
dam.

Fishlocks are also provided in Bonneville and McNary dams.
At McNary Dam, the gravity flow fish lock on the Washington
shore was constructed to provide an auxiliary method of passing fish in case of failure or closure of the main fish ladder.
It was also to provide an experimental facility of improved
design that would overcome the major deficiences experienced
in the fishlocks at Bonneville (Von Gunten et al., 1956), i.e.,
the inability to attract fish in the lock chamber. The
Washington shore fishlock at McNary Dam has been positioned,
so that the fish ladder entrance and the lower weirs can be
used as the fishlock entrance. This fishlock provides a 85 ft
lift and can be operated with or without the fish ladder being
in operation. Some other features of this fish lock are: (1)
the weir crest at the inlet to the lock is surmounted by an
arrangement of vertical steel rods curved upstream to form a
"finger-trap" that prevents the fish from escaping out of the
holding pool, (2) the fish are held in the holding pool (25 by
35 feet) between the entrance and the lock while the lock is
filling (3) a continuous flow through the entrance is provided
even when the lock is filling to attract the fish into the
holding basin, (4) the gate between the holding basin and the
fishlock chamber is made sharp crested (5) the flow enters the
lock chamber through a diffusion area that distributes the
inflow uniformly during filling operations (6) a movable
slatted lock chamber floor, called "brail" is provided to urge
the fish from the lock chamber into the exit channel. A
"finger-trap" is also attached to the brail on the entrance
weir side to prevent the escape of the fish.

An experimental pressure fishlock was constructed on the
Oregon shore to determine the efficacy of passing the migrants
directly from the tail race to the forebay. This lock is
similar to the Washington shore fishlock with the difference
that the lock chamber is connected to the forebay by a tunnel.

18.4 MECHANICAL LIFTING OF FISH

At McNary Dam, the fish ladders with a slope of 1 in 20
are about 2,000 ft long. At dams much higher than 100 ft,
conventional fish ladders become cumbersome. In such cases and

in other special situations, like fish passage during construction, mechanical means of lifting the fish over the dam are provided. In general, the mechanical lifting facilities consist of a barrier dam to halt the upstream migrants, a fish entrance and trapping facility and the collecting and lifting arrangement.

A good example of mechanical lifting of the fish is provided by the fish handling facilities at Baker River Project (Wayne, Jr., 1961). This project consists of two dams, the lower Baker Dam 285 ft high and the Upper Baker Dam 312 ft high. The lower dam was completed in 1927. The fish passage facilities at the lower dam consisted of a low diversion structure extending across the river and a concrete fish ladder extending from the tail race to a collecting pool. From the pool, the trapped fish were transported in small steel tanks through a 800 ft long cableway to upstream side of the dam. This system was never adequate and had largely deteriorated when the upper dam was planned in 1955. It was then decided to construct a new handling facility for both the dams.

The general arrangement of the barrier dam located 1/2 mile downstream of the Lower Baker Dam is shown in Figs. 18-13 and 18-14. In the design of barrier dams, provision has to be made for maintaining a minimum differential head on the dam at all times. This is to ensure that the fish cannot cross it except through the fish entrance in the collecting facility. For Baker River Project, a minimum differential of 8 ft was decided. To maintain this head at higher river flows without sacrificing the head on the powerplants, two radial gates (75 ft wide) were installed on the dam.

The fish trap is located along the river bank on one end of the barrier dam. This consists of a fish entrance, two holding ponds, a brail pond and a hopper pond (Fig. 18-15).

The attraction flow of 80 cfs is obtained from upstream of the dam by gravity flow and is fed to various points in the trap through diffusion chambers. The quantity and location of attraction flow in the trap are shown in Fig. 18-15. The average exit velocity through the diffusion chambers is 1/4 fps.

The weir gates in the trap are automatically controlled with the fluctuations in the tail water. A head of 10 ft is maintained on each weir. "Crowders" (grating) are used to clear the fish from the holding ponds. The brail is similar to those described for fishlocks and is used to transfer the fish to hoppers. The hoppers are 1,000 gallons steel tanks. After about 100 adult salmons have been collected in the hopper, the entrance to the hopper is closed and it is lifted by an overhead travelling crane. The fish are then transferred to steel tanks mounted on trucks. These trucks are provided with ice chambers to control the temperature, recirculating pumps and air injectors. The trucks travel about 14 miles to dump the fish upstream of the Upper Baker Dam. One cycle of

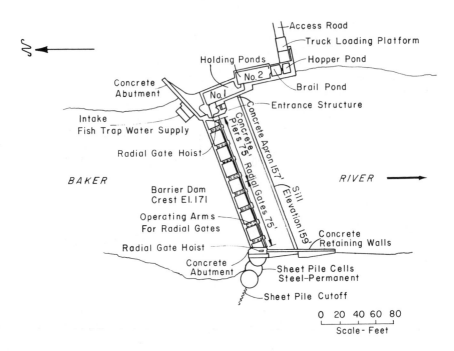

Fig. 18-13. Plan of barrier dam and fish trap at Baker River Project (after Wayne, Jr., 1961).

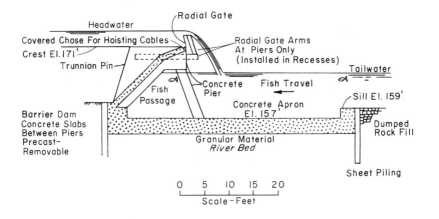

Fig. 18-14. Cross section of the barrier dam at Baker River Project (after Wayne, Jr., 1961).

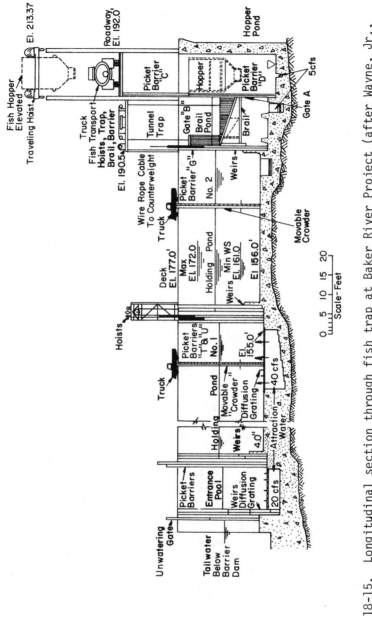

Fig. 18-15. Longitudinal section through fish trap at Baker River Project (after Wayne, Jr., 1961).

loading from the hoppers to the steel tanks takes about 8 minutes. Up to 10,000 adult salmon have been handled this way during a single month and up to 3,000 in a single day.

18.5 FISH PASSAGE DURING CONSTRUCTION

In streams, where the anadromous fish runs may be interrupted during the construction phase of a project, it is necessary to provide temporary fish passage facilities. The temporary facilities are probably more difficult to design because of the many uncertain conditions that can arise during construction.

At McNary Dam, temporary fish passage facilities were provided during the second phase of construction (Von Gunten et al., 1956). These comprised three separate temporary fish ladders with vertical slots in the baffles. Gated orifices were constructed in each baffle to regulate the fall between ladder compartments. One of these ladders failed during the construction and an emergency trap was constructed in the partially completed fish lock. The fish were collected from the trap and mechanically hauled over the coffer dam. As many as 5,000 fish were handled this way. Mechanical lowering of the fish was also used during a later phase of construction when the permanent Oregon fish ladder was operated by pumped water.

18.6 PASSAGE THROUGH HIGHWAY DRAINAGE STRUCTURES

The extension of highways into the spawning areas of anadromous fish may close some of the streams to the upstream migrants if the culverts are improperly designed. This subject has only recently been investigated by the State of California (Kay and Lewis, 1970). The investigation covered 40 culverts on streams which had a history of supporting anadromous fish populations.

In each culvert, the fish population above and below the culvert was sampled. If juvenile anadromous fish were found above the culvert, it was an indication that some adult fish had been able to pass the culvert. If no juveniles were found upstream, but were found in the population downstream, it was indicated that the culvert formed a barrier to the passage of the fish. A fish-passing rating was thus assigned to each of the culverts. It was found that the hydraulic characteristics of the culverts could be simply related to the fish passing ability of the culvert. This is shown in Fig. 18-16. For comparison, a curve developed by Ziemer (quoted in Kay and Lewis, 1970) is given in Fig. 18-17.

The following recommendations are given by Kay and Lewis for designing the highway culverts on spawning streams.

(1) Some oversizing of culverts is desirable.

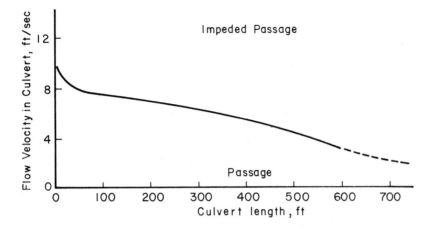

Fig. 18-16. Criterion for fish passing ability of culverts in California (after Kay and Lewis, 1970).

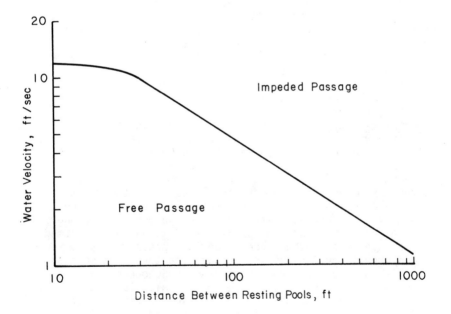

Fig. 18-17. Ziemer's criterion for swimming capability of migrating salmon for Alaskan conditions (after Kay and Lewis, 1970).

(2) The culvert grade line should be depressed below
    normal streambed to encourage gravel deposit in the
    culvert and to create a pool at the culvert.
(3) Due consideration be given to the channel degradation
    downstream of the culvert so that a physical barrier
    is not created.
(4) The darkness in the culverts seems to have no
    adverse effect on fish passage.
(5) The velocity in the culvert should be in the
    "Passage" range of Fig. 18-16 for a discharge that
    is equalled or exceeded 10 percent of the time
    during October to April. The criterion in Fig. 18-16
    can be replaced by others if available for the region
    concerned.

18.7 DOWNSTREAM MIGRANTS

The juvenile salmons in their seaward travel cannot
benefit from the facilities provided for upstream migrants.
The juveniles travel in the top 15-20 ft of the reservoir and
are probably distributed in the width of a stream in the same
proportion as the discharge. Those passing through the fish
ladders are therefore an insignificant proportion of the total
number of downstream migrants because of the small proportion
of the ladder to river discharge. Almost all the downstream
migrants, therefore, pass with the releases over the spillway
or through the turbines. Mortalities are caused either way.
A number of studies have been made on the mortality rates
of downstream migrants through spillways and turbines.
Facilities have been developed, that screen the young fish and
provide mechanical or other means for transferring them downstream of the dams.
Mortality Rates in Turbines. Extensive studies of the
mortality rates of downstream migrants have been made on the
Columbia river dams (Schoeneman et al., 1961, Hamilton and
Andrews, 1954, Von Gunten, 1961, Cramer and Oligher, 1969
among others). In passing through a turbine the injury is
suffered somewhere between the scroll case and the draft tube.
Although direct evidence is not available, cavitation and
direct physical contact with the wicket gates or the runner
probably cause most of the mortalities. It had been assumed
for many years that the sudden change of pressure that a young
salmon experiences in passing through the turbine also causes
mortalities. However, recent studies by Schoeneman and
Regenthal (1957, quoted in Schoeneman et al., 1961) and Rowley
(1955) indicate that the rate of release of pressure determines
the number of mortalities if there is a head space of air.
Without head space of air, salmon fingerlings are unable to
become accustomed to pressure and sudden release of pressure
does not effect them. Foye and Scott (1965) have reported
tests in which young fish of six species (including salmon and

lake trout 3-5 inches long) were subjected to 300 psi pressure
that was released in 10 minutes. They report no increased
mortality in tested salmon and trout over the control groups.
The effect of low pressure on the young salmon is discussed by
Muir (1959) in great detail. In his experiments, Muir studied
the effect of low pressure as well as of low pressure followed
by sudden high pressure as would happen in the cavitating zones
of a runner. His conclusion is that the high pressure waves
caused by the collapse of air bubbles are responsible for the
mortality of the young salmon.

The mortality ratio of young fish passing through the
turbines of McNary dam has been studied by Schoeneman et al.,
(1961). In their well designed experiments, test groups of
marked salmon yearlings were released through the turbines
and a control group downstream of the dam. Members of both
the groups were recovered farther downstream in the river and
the mortality rate was estimated. Similar tests were also
carried out at Big Cliff Dam, which has hydraulic characteristics pertinent to the mortality study, similar to McNary Dam.
In both cases a mortality rate of 11 percent was observed.
These results are valid for the McNary Dam turbines which are
Kaplan wheels operating under a head of about 90 ft. At lower
Baker Dam, which has Francis turbines operating under 250 ft
head, the mortality rate of the salmon fingerlings was of the
order of 30 percent. On the other hand, at the lower Elwha
Dam (Muir, 1959) with a head of 104 ft, the mortality rate of
fingerlings passing through the turbines is negligible.

The design and setting of turbines has been studied for
conditions of fingerling survival also. Such conditions in
general may also be conducive to the efficiency of the turbines,
e.g., the elimination of cavitation. The studies of mortality
rate at prototype structure were concerned with the percentage
of mortality and not with the causes. A program of investigation was initiated by Army Corps of Engineers with two
objectives: (1) To verify if model studies could be used in
the study and classification of cause of mortality in passage
through turbines and (2) To compare the results of model
studies with the prototype structures. These are discussed by
Von Gunten (1961) and by Cramer and Oligher (1964). The main
conclusions from these studies are:

(1) The research on fignerling mortality in passing
through turbines is practicable.

(2) With a small model turbine (12 in. in diameter)
having blade clearances less than the length of test fish
specimens, wide variations in survival can be obtained depending on speed and tailwater elevation.

(3) Mechanical injury to the fish can be distinguished
from pressure injury. In subsequent study (Cramer and Oligher,
1964), it was possible to further subdivide the cause of injury
to (a) mechanical, (b) pressure, (c) shearing action of water
and (d) cavitation.

(4)   Extremely high mortality prevails when cavitation is experienced in the turbine.

(5)   Survival of fingerlings as related to the turbine characteristics is consistent in model and prototype tests. Direct correlation between model tests and prototype results appears possible to a good degree of accuracy.

(6)   In the prototype studies, the maximum percentage of survival nearly coincides with the hydraulic conditions for the maximum efficiency of the turbine (Fig. 18-18 and 18-19).

(7)   At similar net heads, normal speeds and turbine settings, total mortality rates are similar for Kaplan and Francis runners.

(8)   Mechanical injuries to the fish increase with the speed of the runner.

(9)   Total mortality increases as the tailwater load is dropped; even though the point of general cavitation is not reached.

(10)   Mechanical injury to the fish is related with the physical features of the turbine such as blade spacing, clearance between blades and the wicket gate and the speed of the runner.   In the model turbine a relatively small increase (3/8 inches) in the clearance between the blade and the wicket gate markedly decreased the mortality.

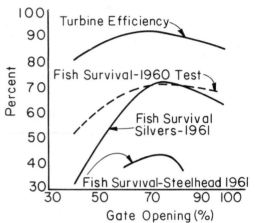

Fig. 18-18.   Correlation, fish survival with turbine efficiency, Cushman No. 2 hydroelectric project, 1960 and 1961 (after Cramer and Oligher, 1964).

(11)   Under favorable conditions the survival rate of yearlings is high.   This offers encouragement that through proper precautionary measures in turbine design and operation, successful fish passage through turbines can be achieved.

Mortality Rate Over Spillways.   The downstream migrants also cross the dams through flow over the spillways.   The fingerlings passing with the spill are subjected to high velocities generated near the spillway bottoms and to the action of flow

18-32

in the stilling basins. In hydraulic jump type basins and in strong back flow eddies, the fish are liable to be hurt by impact with the friction blocks and by their inability to escape the eddies.

At low dams, the mortality rates of yearlings even with hydraulic jump type stilling basins are not high. Mortality rate tests were made at McNary and Big Cliff Dam spillways. These tests showed that the mortality rate in passage over the spillways was about two percent (Schoeneman et al., 1961). Similar tests at the Lower Baker Dam from 1950 to 1952, with a total fall of about 250 ft showed mortality rates of 54 to 64 percent (Wayne, Jr., 1961).

Glines dam on Elwha

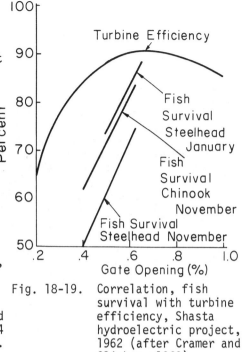

Fig. 18-19. Correlation, fish survival with turbine efficiency, Shasta hydroelectric project, 1962 (after Cramer and Oligher, 1969).

River Washington, has a free fall spillway. The jet drops 180 ft into a pool. Tests at this dam indicated almost negligble mortality rates in passage with the spill. At lower Baker Dam an experimental timber ski jump type spillway chute was installed for passing the salmon fingerlings between the forebay and the tailwater under conditions approximating free fall. A total of 240,000 fingerlings were passed over the ski jump and a mortality rate of only 15 percent was observed (compared to 54-64 percent over the hydraulic jump type spillway). A study of the effect of free fall into a pool of water was made at the University of Washington, Seattle, by dropping the fingerlings from various heights into a pool. In a free fall the fingerlings are reported to achieve a terminal fall velocity of about 40 fps in about 100 ft of descent. The mortality rate in these tests was reported to be negligible (Muir and Ruus, 1961). It appears that for dams up to 100 ft height, the mortality rate of downstream migrants passing over the spillways is small. For higher dams, a free-falling spill can considerably reduce the mortality rates.

Guidance System for Downstream Migrants. The total effect of mortality on the fish population due to passage through hydraulic turbines and over spillways can be estimated from the rates of mortality and proportion of the total downstream migrants using the two paths during periods of significant migration. If the migrants have to pass a number of dams, the total mortality is compounded. For example, if the average mortality at one dam is of the order of 20 percent and the fish encounter four such dams in their downstream migration, the population at the end of the last dam would have been reduced by 59 percent. Some other factors, like the susceptibility to predation of fish stunned by the impact in the spillway would possibly increase the net mortality estimates from tests. Several methods have been devised for guiding the downstream migrants away from the turbine entrances and spillways and for moving the fish downstream. Some of these methods are screens, louvers and electric screens.

Screens. The use of screens to remove fingerlings from the flow is subject to two problems. One, the limitation of velocity, so that the fish are not injuried by impact or entanglement in the screens and two, the clogging of screens by debris. For these reasons, the screens are limited in their use to comparatively smaller flows. They are generally not used in the forebays of large dams.

Fish screens of many types have been evolved and used in the past. There consists of duplicate screens and slots, rotating drum screens and vertically moving screens. In the duplicate screens, as the screens get clogged, clean screens are installed in the alternate slots and the clogged ones are removed and cleaned. In the rotating drum screens (Fig. 18-20), the debris problem is controlled by the self cleaning prop- erties of a drum rotating from upstream to downstream direc- tion. The floating debris is carried by the rotating drum and deposited in the downstream direction (Whalls, et al., 1956). A large number of rotating drum screens are in use especially for screening the fish from small irrigation diversions. In the vertically moving screens an endless belt of screen panels is used. The approach velocity to the screens is limited to about 1.5 fps to make the screens self cleaning and to avoid impingement of the fish on the screens.

A 100 ft deep screen has been provided at the Upper Baker Dam intakes to prevent the passage of fish. This screen con- sists of V-shape aluminum beams attached to a semicircular arch baffle formed of trusses and supported by 2 floating pontoons. The whole system (Fig. 18-21) rises or falls with the reservoir water level.

Louvers. A louver is a series of vertical slats spaced 1-4 inches apart and placed along a diagonal line across the flow (Figs. 18-22, 18-23). Louvers had been used in efforts to deflect moss in irrigation canals and this first suggested the possibility of their use in deflecting fish (Rhone, 1969). A system of louvers to deflect fish from the intake of Tracy pumping plant (Central Valley Project, California), was developed after extensive laboratory and field investigations. This plant has a flow capacity of about 5,000 cfs.

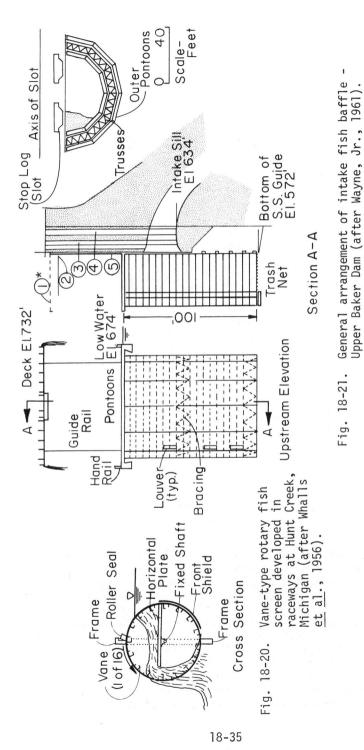

Fig. 18-20. Vane-type rotary fish screen developed in raceways at Hunt Creek, Michigan (after Whalls et al., 1956).

Fig. 18-21. General arrangement of intake fish baffle - Upper Baker Dam (after Wayne, Jr., 1961).

* 1. Top of baffle with full reservoir.
  2. Full reservoir elevation (724.00).
  3. Stop log slot.
  4. Intake gate slot.
  5. Guide rails.

18-35

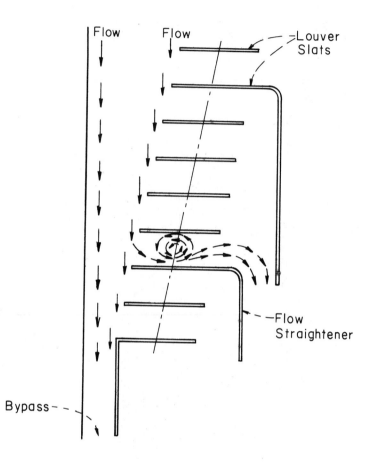

Fig. 18-22. Flow through the louvers (after USBR, 1957).

The flow approaching a louver is deflected both upstream and downstream. The fish approaching a louver tend to avoid it, probably due to the eddy formed between the slats (Fig. 18-22) and move along the louver. At the downstream end the louver terminates in a bypass, which the fish enter. Flow straighteners are introduced on the downstream side of the slats to correct the flow conditions. The reaction of the fish to the louvers is illustrated in Fig. 18-23. The fish can stay a constant distance from the louvres by maintaining a swimming velocity of $V_s = V_a$. Sin θ . Model studies show that for $\theta > 40°$, fish have difficulty in locating the bypass. The louvers are generally designed with a θ of $10° - 15°$. In

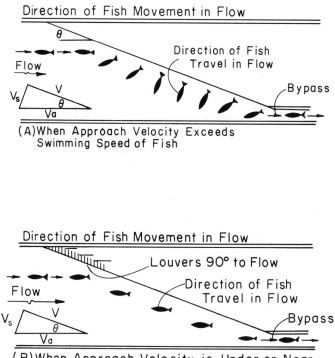

Fig. 18-23. Reaction of fish to louvers (after USBR, 1957).

wider channels, when the length of the louvers becomes too long, they may be placed in a series of contiguous V's with the bypass channel located at their downstream apexes (Fig. 18-24). This arrangement has been used at the intake of Tehama-Colusa Canal system in the Sacramento Valley (Striplin, Jr., 1968).

The louvers are liable to be choked with the debris in flow. Efficient trash removal facilities upstream are therefore needed.

The layout of the Tracy Fish Colleting facility is shown in Fig. 18-25. The main channels line of louvers is set at an angle of 15^0 to flow and is approximately 320 ft long. The

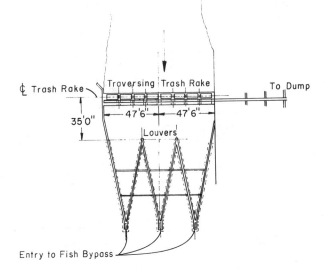

Fig. 18-24. Saw tooth louver design (after USBR, 1957).

louvers slats are 2 1/2 inches by 3/16 inch with 1 in clear
spacing. Four 6-inch wide bypasses are spaced 75 ft apart.
The bypasses are transitioned into 3 ft concrete pipes running
to the upstream end of the secondary louvers structure. The
secondary louver structure, located in a 120 ft long concrete
channel, has 2 parallel lines of louvers at an angle of
15° to the flow and a single 6-inch bypass. The discharge in
the secondary system is reduced from 120 cfs to 10 cfs. From
the bypass in the secondary system, the fish are transported
to holding tanks and moved by trucks.
      As a result of the model and prototype scale studies, the
following design criteria were evolved at the Tracy plant.
      (1) The angle of the louver system may vary between 10°
and 15° to the direction of approaching flow.
      (2) Individual louver slats should be placed normal to
the approaching flow.
      (3) The average maximum velocity of water in the channel
as it approaches the louver system should not exceed 5.3 fps.
      (4) A trashrack should be built ahead of the louver
system and there should be a minimum of 25 ft of non-turbulent
flow between the trashrack and the upstream end of the louver
system.

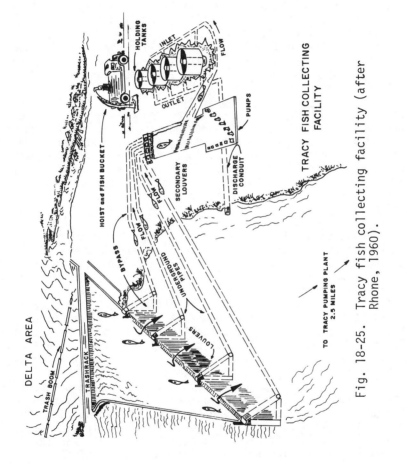

Fig. 18-25. Tracy fish collecting facility (after Rhone, 1960).

(5) Bypass for entry of fish diverted by the louvers should be about 75 ft apart because it is not certain that all fish would pass along the entire length of the system.

(6) Bypass openings should be 6 inches wide both to facilitate entry of fish and to minimize the possibility of clogging.

(7) The trashrack bars should have a clear opening of 2 inches.

The prototype structure at Tracy pumping plant has been tested in a number of ways. It has been shown that efficiencies of 93-100 percent can usually be obtained in deflecting the fish into bypasses.

Louvers have also been used in smaller channels with good results. A louver facility constructed in Maxwell Irrigation Canal in Oregon has (max. discharge 100 cfs) been reported by Bates and Jewett, Jr., (1961).

Bypassing Through Turbine Gatewells. The fish entering the turbine intakes generally travel near the ceilings of intake structures. Long (referred in Marquette and Long, 1971) showed that 70 percent of the downstream migrants were concentrated within 15 ft of the intaker ceiling. A research program was initiated by the National Marine Fishery Service to study, if this concentration of the fish could be utilized to bypass the migrants around the turbines at the expense of a small discharge. The gatewell openings in the turbine intake ceiling are ideally located for this purpose.

Marquette and Long (1971) studied the use of gatewells in the laboratory. They studied gatewells with two types of openings; type 1 as used in Priest Rapid Dam and type 2 used in Ice Harbor Dam (Fig. 18-26). The latter gatewell has an induced flow caused by the pressure differential between the two openings. Marquette and Long tried different kinds of screens intercepting 1/3 to 2/5 of the intake flow. The resulting effect in the flow just in gatewell intake is shown in Fig. 18-27. Each test was run with hatchery raised salmon fingerlings released in the model intake and the fish entering the gatewell were counted. These tests showed that

(1) For type 1 gatewells, about seven percent of the fish entered the gatewell, even without any flow being diverted through it. This was increased to about 15 percent with the introduction of a solid baffle projecting one-third into the flow. The guiding efficiency through the gatewell was increased by introducing screens instead of solid baffle and the increase of efficiency was more for more porous screens (87 percent for the greatest porosity tested).

(2) In type 1 gatewells, the guiding efficiency with the screen increased from 7 to 39 percent. It was noticed that about 60 percent of the fish entering the gatewell re-entered the intake through the downstream opening of the gatewell. The screening of this opening thus increased the guiding efficiency to 67 percent.

Tests made for the optimum placement of the orifices in the gatewell wall to bypass the fish entering the gatewells have been reported by Liscom (1971). He found that an orifice placed on the upstream wall and about 5 ft below the water level in the gatewell was the most efficient location. The bypassing of juvenile salmon and trout migrating through the turbine intakes is demonstrated by prototype studies also. The results of some prototype tests on the gatewell bypass at Ice Harbor Dam have been reported by Park and Farr (1972). At this dam, there are three operational turbines, each with three intake gatewells. In each gatewell an orifice about 6 in. in diameter has been installed. A total of 172,785 juvenile salmon and trout were trapped through these orifices in two month periods. Many other species were also trapped, including some adult salmons and trout.

Collection Through Barges.
A system of collection of downstream migrants through barges was installed at the Upper and Lower Baker Dams. This has been described by Wayne, Jr., (1961). A specially designed barge whose draft can be varied from 1 to 4 ft by varying the quantity of water in floation tanks, has two turbine pumps of 75 cfs capacity and a secondary pump with a capacity of 12 cfs. The fingerlings are attracted to the barge by the attraction current generated by the operation of the large pumps. The fingerlings are diverted by a timber skimmer into a flared steel

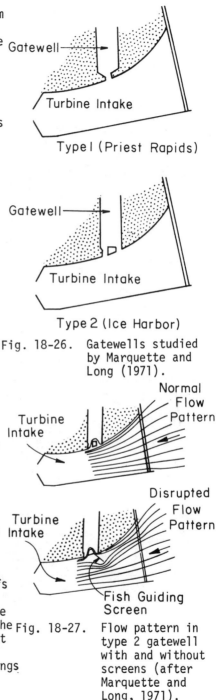

Fig. 18-26. Gatewells studied by Marquette and Long (1971).

Fig. 18-27. Flow pattern in type 2 gatewell with and without screens (after Marquette and Long, 1971).

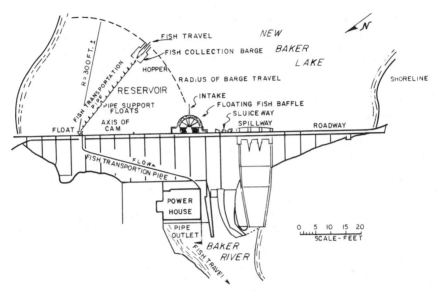

Fig. 18-28. General plan of downstream migrant's transportation -- Upper Baker Dam (after Wayne, Jr., 1961).

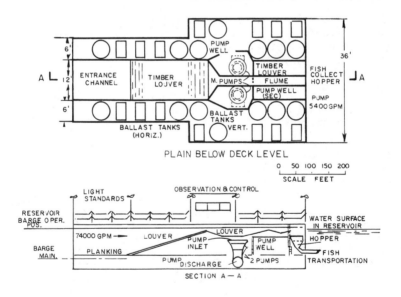

Fig. 18-29. General arrangement of Upper Baker fish collection barge (after Wayne, Jr., 1961).

chute along with about 13.3 cfs of water. The flow is
further reduced over another skimmer to 1.3 cfs. This flow
along with the fish is discharged through a hopper and a
flexible pipe to the tailrace. The transportation flow is
finally moving at about 40 fps before being discharged. The
general arrangement of the facility at Upper Baker Dam is
shown in Fig. 18-28 and the detail of the barge is shown in
Fig. 18-29.

Skimmer. Even after the fish have been guided away from the
spillway or the turbine inlet, the problem of handling a large
amount of flow remains to be solved. In power projects, it is
also necessary to economize the discharge used in fish transportation. A device is therefore needed at the end of the
downstream migrant guidance system that can remove the excess
water with the least possible head loss while providing favorable flow conditions for the safe passage of the fish. The
skimmer was developed for this purpose by E. P. Richey (1957)
at the University of Washington. The skimmer consists of an
inclined screen over which the total attraction flow is passed.
The screen removes most of the water with the fish passing at
the end with the quantity needed for downstream transportation.
The skimmer was originally developed for the Mayfield Dam.
Subsequently, it has been used on other projects also (Alder
Dam, Washington, Pelton Project, Oregon, etc.)

The facility developed on Mayfield Dam is shown in Fig. 18-
30. An attraction current of water is drawn through the
submerged orifice gate and over the adjustable weir gate that
regulates the flow to the skimmer screen. Two such screens
15 ft wide and 25 ft long each require a maximum attraction
flow of 200 cfs. A major portion of the flow falls through the
screens into a chamber from which the water is pumped into
the intake of the power tunnel. The remainder of the flow
(about 10 cfs) and the fingerlings flow over top of the screen
to the pool. A very small part of the originally diverted flow
is thus used for transporting the fingerlings. The skimmer
arrangement at the Pelton Project is shown in Fig. 18-31.

An alternative skimmer arrangement used on the North
Fork Project (Eicher, 1958) is shown in Fig. 18-32. In this
arrangement, the pumps are placed directly behind the screens
and the attraction flow is regulated by the quantity of water
pumped. It is claimed that this type of skimmer develops a
smaller head loss than the inclined screen type skimmer (Fig.
18-31). It is also less susceptible to the problem of trash
collection and the draw down in sump caused by a lag in the
fluctuation of reservoir level and corresponding adjustment of
inflow control weir.

Electric Screens. Another device which has been tested to
prevent the entry of fish into the turbine intakes or the
canals is the electric screen. The screens are made of
energized electrodes suspended from a cable across the channel.

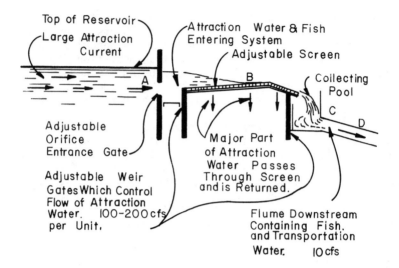

Fig. 18-30.   Schematic arrangement of the skimmer at Mayfield
Dam (after Muir, 1957).

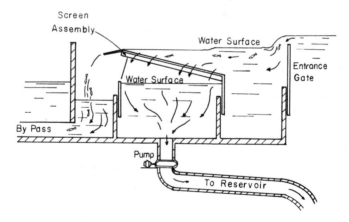

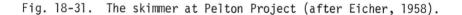

Fig. 18-31.   The skimmer at Pelton Project (after Eicher, 1958).

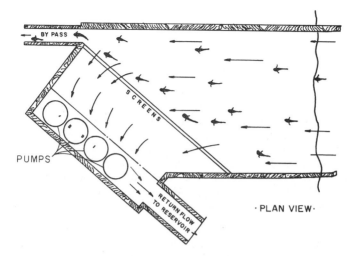

Fig. 18-32. The skimmer at North Fork Dam (after Eicher, 1958).

A typical arrangement for the turbine intakes consists of
electrodes located 15-25 ft upstream of the intake screens.
The electrodes and the screen are energized with opposite
polarity. Tests made by McMillan (1928) showed that the fish
are sensitive to the presence of voltage gradient in water and
in the presence of this gradient, they tend to align themselves
along the equipotential lines. The effect of voltage gradient
on fish is to cause discomfort to fatal paralysis depending on
the gradient. The tolerable value of gradient depends on the
conductivity of water and the size of fish. McMillan found
that the tolerable value of voltage gradient is larger for the
smaller fish and it decreases with an increase in the conductivity of water.

Large scale successful applications of electric screen are
not known. Electric screens were tried by the Colorado
Game and Fish Department (Nolting, 1962) in the Willow Creek
Reservoir diversion canal. The screen consisted of 6 pairs
of horizontal electrodes (1/4 inch diameter copper cable),
stretched across the canal about 300 ft upstream of the outlet
gates. Observations on this screen as well as a 1/6 scale
model showed that the fish upon approaching the electric field
reacted sharply but were unable to control their response. The
reaction was found as of uncontrolled panic without relation

to forewarning, direction or pattern. The electric screens at this site were not found effective in stopping the fish and were removed. The possible use of electric screen was also tested in connection with the downstream migrant facilities at Baker Dam but was found ineffective (Andrew et al., 1956).

18.8 ARTIFICIAL PROPAGATION OF FISH

The river developments reduce the fish population in streams in two ways. One, by causing additional mortality and hinderance in the spawning run and two, by drowning out the spawning channels or otherwise making them unfit for spawning. In addition to all the facilities designed to reduce the fish mortality and hinderance in spawning runs, methods of artificial propagation are also used. There are two such methods: the hatcheries and the spawning channels.

Hatcheries. The survival rate of eggs deposited under natural conditions is very low. Mortality is caused by many factors such as inefficient fertilization of the eggs, predatory animals, floods, adverse weather conditions and so on. In addition the young fry are subject to destruction by predators and diversion into channels that subsequently go dry. In the presence of obstructions in the passage of upstream migrants, overcrowding of smelt eggs takes place. This reduces the proportion of eggs that will hatch successfully. For these reasons, hatcheries are constructed where the survival rate can be enhanced.

The fish are trapped and retrieved from the streams and kept in the holding ponds. As they become sexually mature, they are stripped of their eggs. The eggs are fertilized and kept in incubation troughs. After hatching, the fries are put in rearing ponds until they are ready for stocking or release. Hatcheries for different species are in use in almost all areas of fishery importance. The hatchery fish are somewhat different from naturally raised fish and are also less able to survive than wild fish. However because of their large numbers, their population growth is better than in nature. With the current advances in bio-chemistry, it should be possible to improve the survival and food value of hatchery raised fish. Successful experiments on selective breeding of salmon have already been carried out (Donaldson and Menasveta, 1961).

Spawning Channels. The spawning channels are selected by fish for certain biologically suitable considerations, like the velocity, chemical content of water, porosity and inflow through the bed, shelter from predators etc. In the case of anadromous fish like salmon, of course, there is an instinctive compulsion for the fish to use the same channel where it was hatched. The man-made work can often change the characteristics of these channels. For example, a spawning channel may not be availble to the fish if it is drawned by an impoundment or it may become unsuitable for spawning, if the characteristics of the bed (porosity and seepage are altered). In river developments it is often necessary to make up for the spawning channels lost to the fish.

Spawning channels are artificially maintained channels that resemble natural channels and in which the environmental conditions are controlled. For salmon, the survival rate of eggs is very critically affected by the velocity of flow and sedimentation.

The spawning behavior of salmon is described by Idyll (1968) and Heard (1972) and of Steelhead Trout by Orcutt et al., (1964). After the eggs have been laid and fertilized, the female cover their eggs with gravel. For incubation the eggs require a constant percolation of oxygen-saturated water. The ideal conditions are provided by a bed of rounded gravel of 34-40 percent void ratio. Various investigations have shown that the survival of eggs is inversely related to the amount of foreign material covering them. Shelton and Pollock (1965) studied the effect of siltation in a 2,000 ft long, and 10 ft wide channel having a 12 inch gravel bed. In the absence of silt control in the channel they found a 50 percent survival rate in the salmon eggs compared to 95 percent survival when silt was eliminated from the incubation channels.

The deposition of suspended sediment in a gravel bed has been studied by Einstein (1968). He observed that the sus- pended particles slowly filter through the gravel interstices. Einstein also developed an analytical model for predicting the rate of deposition in the bed from a known concentration of the suspended material. Shelton and Pollock (1965) have recommended the use of silt traps suited to the type and amount of suspended load in the spawning or incubation channel.

Excessive sediment is also a problem in natural spawning streams. Many a time, this sediment is a result of man's activities in the watershed. This condition is treated by re- moving its cause and/or by cleaning the stream beds. In Alaska, the Forest Service have developed a streambed gravel cleaner called the "riffle sifter" (Meehan, 1971). This is a self powered amphibious vehicle that stirs up the streambed gravel, sucks up the sand and finer material and sprays them on the stream banks. In the absence of watershed treatment, the stream bed cleaning has probably to be repeated every year.

Efforts have been made in some watersheds to make fresh salmon pools and spawning beds by blasting pools in the rock bed of new streams and by transplanting gravel. In other streams, the flow is concentrated by temporary installations to produce salmon pools (Hardy, 1953).

The hydraulic design of spawning channel for salmon, has been described by Herbert (1965). The hydraulic roughness of the gravel bed increases after redds have been constructed by the fish and the Manning's may increase from 0.020 to 0.029 depending on the size of gravel and the redds. The criteria

used in the hydraulic design of salmon spawning channels are
given by Banys and Leonardson (1969) as:
(1)   Spawning - channels should have a bottom area of
about 60 ft^2 per pair of fish.
(2)   The channel width be about 25 ft.
(3)   The average channel velocity should be about 2.3 fps.
(4)   The minimum water depth over spawning gravels should
be 2.5 ft.
(5)   The spawning gravels should be at least 2.5 ft thick.
(6)   Resting areas for the fish then be provided at about
250-300 ft apart.
(7)   The holding pools should be about 20 cu ft of water
per fish.

Spawning channels have been constructed upstream of upper
Baker Dam Lake (Wayne, Jr., 1961), McNary Dam channel and many
other places. Additional advantages from the provision and
maintenance of spawning channel is that the anadromous fish
will come back to the channel for spawning. It is thus
possible to strategically locate the spawning channels so that
after about one life cycle of the fish the area continues to
be productive without additional stocking.

18.9   CONCLUSION

The fish passage facilities have been provided in Europe
as early as 17th century. In Pakistan, the fish ladders were
constructed in the barrages constructed by the British engineers at the turn of the century. Nevertheless the conflict
between the fishery and river development interests never
became as acute as in the case of Columbia River. This conflict, like many others, had its benefits. A need for a
multidisciplinary approach involving the hydraulic engineers,
the fishery biologists, and the naturalists emerged from
this controversy. This approach supported by the ingenuity of
research workers in the allied fields has contributed a great
deal to the understanding and the solution of the problem.
As Preston and Rydell (1957) put it, the situation has now
changed from "fish versus dams" to "fish and dams".

The adverse effects of river developments on the fisheries perhaps cannot be totally eliminated. Yet, the progress
over the last three decades has provided adequate tools so
that the fish resource can be maintained at the present levels,
if not enhanced.

There are many facilities in operation in the world today that do not serve their purpose. Almost all the fish
ladders in Pakistan, constructed prior to 1960, are not working
efficiently. The Indus River Hilsa (an anadromous fish) is
denied about two-thirds of its spawning area due to the
construction of barrages (Islam and Talbot, 1968). In Russia,
the consensus is that even the most efficient fish ladders
are only 10 percent as effective as the undisturbed river

(Antonnikov, 1964). The problem of screening the fish from the irrigation diversions in Pakistan, which has the largest contiguous system of irrigation canals, has not yet been dealt with. As a result millions of pounds of fish are destroyed in the dry beds of canals every year. An emphasis is needed on the monitoring of many existing structures and their improvement.

The Army Corps of Engineer's research on the Columbia basin facilities has evolved an outstanding design at Ice Harbor Dam. This type of ladder is very successful when the pool and tail water levels as well as the river discharges are varying in a year. This design had been adopted on three new barrages in Pakistan. Many other ingenious devices like the skimmer and the louver system have application in other places and locations. Research is continuing on screens formed by air bubbles, sound waves and other devices. The artificial means of fish propagation are useful in counterbalancing the effect of man-made works. Selective breeding of fish can probably more than compensate for what might be lost at some places.

In the total treatment of the problem at river development projects, the McNary Dam facilities, Portland General Electric facilities at North Fork and Pelton Projects and the Baker River Project facilities are among the most successful.

In dealing with fish, the designer is faced with the same problem as with any other animal. The habits and requirement of fish vary with the species and locations. It is probably difficult to transplant solutions obtained at one point to another, in toto. However, the spirit of cooperative research that was successful in the Columbia basin can be applied to other situations.

REFERENCES

Ahmad, M., and Ahmad, S., Fish Ladders or Fish Ways, Paper No. 346, Proceedings West Pakistan Engineering Congress, 1961.

Andrew, F. J., Johnson, P. C. and Kersey, L.R., Further Experiments with an Electric Screen for Downstream Migrant Salmon at Baker Dam, Int. Pac. Salmon Fish. Comm. Progress Report, 1956.

Anonymous, First Operational Fish Lift in Scotland, Civil Engineering and Public Works,Review, Vol. 51, No. 602, August, 1956.

Antonnikov, A. F., Hydroelectric Construction and the Problem of Fish Passage Facilities, Hydroelectric Construction No. 3, 1964, pp. 26-28. Translated by Ole A. Mathisen Fisheries Research Institute, Univ. of Washington, Seattle, Circular No. 225.

Banys, R. and Leonardson, K. R., Fishways at Dams, Section 23 of Handbook of Applied Hydraulics, Ed. Davis and Sorensen, 3rd Edition, McGraw-Hill, 1969.

Bates, D. W., and Jewett, Jr., S. G., Louver Efficiency in Deflecting Downstream Migrant Steelhead, Trans. Amer. Fish. Soc., Vol. 90(3), July, 1961.

Clay, Jr., C. H., The Engineer's Part in Fisheries Conservation, Engineering Journal, Vol. 34, No. 11, Nov. 1951.

Clay, Jr., C. H., Design of Fishways and Other Fish Facilities, The Queen's Printer, Ottawa, 1961.

Collins, G. B., Gauley, R. J., and Elling, C. H., Ability of Salmonids to Ascend High Fishways, Trans. Am. Fish. Soc. Vol. 91(1), Jan. 1962, pp. 1-7.

Cramer, F. K., and Oligher, R. C., Passing Fish Through Hydraulic Turbines, Trans. Amer. Fish. Soc., Vol. 93(3) July, 1964.

Deelder, C. L., Modern Fish Passes in the Netherlands, The Progressive Fish-Culturist, Vol. 20(4), October, 1958.

Donaldson, L. R., and Menasveta, D., Selective Breeding of Chinook Salmon, Trans. Amer. Fish. Soc., Vol. 90(2), April, 1961.

Eicher, G. J., Fish-Bypass Experience at PGE's New Hydro Projects, Electric Light and Power, Vol. 36(9), April 15, 1958.

Einstein, H. A., Deposition of Suspended Particles in a Gravel Bed, Proc. ASCE, Journal of Hydraulics Division, Vol. 94, No. HY5, September, 1968.

Foye, R. E., and Scott, M., Effects of Pressure on Survival of Six Species of Fish, Trans. Amer. Fish. Soc., Vol. 94(1), January, 1965.

Funk, John, L, Movement of Stream Fishes in Missouri, Trans. Am. Fish. Soc., September, 1955.

Hamilton, J. A. R., and Andrews, F. J., Investigation of the Effect of Baker Dam on Downstream Migrant Salmon, Inter. Pacific Salmon Fish. Comm., Bull. 6.

Hardy, Eric, Salmon Ladders and Fish Passes, Water Power (London), Vol. 5, No. 5, May, 1953.

Heard, W. R., Spawning Behavior of Pink Salmon on an Artificial Redd, Trans. Amer. Fish. Soc. Vol. 101(2), April, 1972.

Herbert, D. J., Hydraulic Design of a Channel Adapted to Use as a Salmon Spawning Facility, Paper presented to ASCE Hydraulics Division Conference, Tuscon, August, 1965.

Heman, M. L., Campbell, R. S., and Redmond, L. C., Manipulation of Fish Populations through Reservoir Drawdown, Trans. Am. Fish. Soc., Vol. 98(2), April, 1969.

Hubley, Jr., R. C., Movement of Tagged Channel Catfish in the Upper Mississippi River, Trans. Am. Fish Soc., 92(2) April, 1963.

Idyll, C. P., The Incredible Salmon, National Geographical Magazine, Vol. 134, No. 2, August, 1968.

Irrigation Research Institute, Qadirabad Barage (River Channel) Fish Ladder - Desilting, Technical Report No. 513/Hyd/1966 March, 1967, Lahore, Pakistan.

Islam, B. N., and Talbot, G. B., Fluvial Migration, Spawning and Fecundity of Indus River Hilsa, Hilsa ilisha, Trans. Amer. Fish. Soc., Vol. 97(4), October, 1968.

Kay, A. R., and Lewis, R. B., Passage of Anadromous Fish Through Highway Drainage Structures, Highway Research Report (NTIS No. PB 194 659), California State Division of Highways, June 1970.

Leman, B., and Paulik, G. J., Spill-Pattern Manipulation to Guide Migrant Salmon Upstream, Trans. Amer. Fish. Soc., Vol. 95(4), October, 1966.

Liscom, K. L., Orifice Placement in Gatewells of Turbine Intakes for Bypassing Juvenile Fish Around Dams, Trans. Amer. Fish. Soc., Vol. 100(2), March, 1971.

Mahaffy, H. L., Safe Conduct for Salmon, The Engineering Journal Vol. 37, No. 9, Sept. 1954, pp. 1092-1095.

Marquette, W. A., and Long, C. W., Laboratory Studies of Screens for Diverting Juvenile Salmon and Trout from Turbine Intakes, Trans. Amer. Fish. Soc., Vol. 100(3), July, 1971.

MacLean, B. M., Model and Prototype Research on Fish Ladders, Proc. ASCE, Journal of Power Division, Vol. 87, No. PO 2, July, 1961.

McMillan, F. O., Electric Fish Screen, Bull. of the Bureau of Fisheries, Vol. XLIV, 1928.

Michel, B., and Nadeau, R., A New-Type of Fishway Designed for Continuous Operation, Houille Blanche, Vol. 20, No. 6, October, 1965 (in French).

Meehan, W. R., Effect of Gravel Cleaning on Bottom Organisms in Three Southeast Alaska Streams, Progressive Fish-Culturist Vol. 33(2), April, 1971.

Muir, J. F., Passage of Adult and Young Fish over Proposed Low and High Head Dams Across the Fraser River, Civil Engineering Department, University of British Columbia, March, 1957.

Muir, J. F., Passage of Young Fish Through Turbines, Proc. ASCE, Journal of Power Division, Vol. 85, No. PO(1), 1959.

Muir, J. F., and Ruus, E., Engineering Research on the Fish and Power Problem, Paper presented to Annual General Meeting, Engineering Institute of Canada, May, 1961.

Nolting, D. H., Electric Fish Screen Efficiency, Willow Creek Reservoir, Tech. Bulletin, No. 11, Department of Game and Fish, Colorado, May, 1962.

Olson, D. E. and Scidmore, W. J., Homing Behavior of Spawning Walleyes, Trans. Am. Fish. Soc., 91(4), October, 1962.

Orcutt, D. R., Pulliam, B. R., and Arp, A, Characteristics of Steelhead Trout Redds in Idaho Stream, Trans. Amer. Fish. Soc., Vol. 97(1), January, 1968.

Park, D. L., and Farr, W. E., Collection of Juvenile Salmon and Steelhead Trout passing through Orifices in Gatewells of Turbine Intakes at Ice Harbor Dam, Trans. Amer. Fish. Soc., Vol. 101(2), April, 1972.

Preston, H. A. and Rydell, L. E., Coexistence of Fish and Dams, Proceedings ASCE Journal of Power Division, Vol. 83, No. PO5, October, 1957.

Raymond, H. L., Migration Rates of Yearling Chinook Salmon in Relation to Flows and Impoundments in the Columbia and Snake Rivers, Trans. Amer. Fish. Soc., Vol. 97(4), October, 1968.

Raymond, H. L., Effect of John Day Reservoir on the Migration Rate of Juvenile Chinook Salmon in the Columbia River, Trans. Amer. Fish. Soc., Vol. 98(3), July, 1969.

Rhone, T. J., Fish Protective Facilities at the Tracy Pumping Plant Central Valley Project, California, Presented at the 9th Hyd. Division Conferences, ASCE, Seattle, Washington, August, 1960.

Richey, E. P., A Model Study of Some Fish Facilities for the Proposed Mayfield Dam, The Trends in Engineering, Univ. of Washington, Seattle, January, 1957.

Rowley, W. E., Hydrostatic Pressure Tests on Rainbow Trout, California Fish and Game, Vol. 41(3), July, 1955.

Schoneman, D. E., Pressey, R. T. and Junge, Jr., C. O., Mortalities of Downstream Migrant Salmon at McNary Dam, Trans. Amer. Fish. Soc., Vol. 90(1), January, 1961.

Shelton, J. M., and Pollock, R. D., Siltation and Egg Survival in Incubation Channels, Trans. Amer. Fish. Soc., Vol. 94(2) January, 1965.

Striplin, Jr., W. M., Bio-Engineering--Now and in the Future, Civil Engineering, July, 1968.

United States Bureau of Reclamation, Fish Protection at the Tracy Pumping Plant, Central Valley Project, California, Report, February, 1957.

Von Gunten, G. H., Fish Passage Through Hydraulic Turbines, Proceedings ASCE, Journal of Hyd. Division, Vol. 87, No. HY3, May, 1961.

Von Gunten, G. H., Smith, Jr., H. A., and MacLean, B. M., Fish Passage Facilities at McNary Dam, Proc. Paper 895, Journal of Power Division, ASCE Vol. 82, PO1, February, 1956.

Wayne, Jr., W. W., Fish Handling Facilities for Baker River
    Project, Proceedings ASCE, Journal of Power Division, No.
    PO. 3, Vol. 87, November, 1961.

Whalls, M. J., Shetter, D. S. and Vondett, J. E., A Simplified
    Rotary Fish Screen and an Automatic Water Gate, Trans.
    Amer. Fish Soc., September, 1956.

Ziemer, G. L., and Behlke, C. E., Analysis of Salmon Capabilities
    Capabilities in Steep Fish Ladders, Proc. Second Annual
    American Water Resources Conference, Univ. of Chicago,
    Chicago, November, 1966.

Chapter 19

BASIN PLANNING CAN BE HAZARDOUS?

by

Robert Sadove, Director, Special Projects Department, Internati
national Bank for Reconstruction and Development

Chapter 19

BASIN PLANNING CAN BE HAZARDOUS?

19.1 INTRODUCTION

Proper exploitation and use of water resources can provide
a dynamic basis for economic growth. The potential of river
basin water resources can be enormous. When effectively
harnessed, they can dramatically increase the productivity of
millions of acres, provide a reliable source of domestic and
industrial water, result in production of large quantities of
electric power, give flood protection, help control erosion,
improve navigation, assist the development of fisheries and
often create important new recreation facilities.

To reap these benefits, there must be extensive and comprehensive planning. Imaginative and careful planning can assure
that anticipated benefits are transformed into solid realities,
and that these benefits are not vitiated by unintended harmful
side effects.

There have been mistakes in river basin planning and much
has been made recently of the social and ecological dangers of
dam building. But the fact that mistakes may have been made
in a few spectacular cases cannot deter us from future planning
for the development of water resources. The stakes are too
high. Many developing countries are confronted with the
problem of rapidly growing and desperately poor populations
but limited resources. Without development of water resources,
already deplorable economic and social conditions will
inevitable deteriorate at an ever increasing pace.

Ill considered water development -- based on haphazard
planning -- is dangerous to people and the environment. But
those who advocate a do-nothing policy because of the dangers
are wrong.

There are always dangers in any change and change always
has a price. According to a recent series of articles by
Sterling (1972), it is said that in Egypt the price was high.
It is argued that the clear water being provided by the Aswan
Dam is scouring the riverbed, eroding the delta coastline, and
causing the disappearance of fish; that prevention of natural
flooding by the dam has robbed the land of revitalizing fertile
silt deposits, that transpiration and silting in the reservoir
have reduced storage capacity; that heavy use of water and poor
drainage have caused underground water levels to rise, creating
serious problems of waterlogging and soil salinity; that overflows have disrupted the lives of many forcing them to move
and locate in strange and often destitute areas; and that the
constant supply of water in irrigation ditches has exacerbated
the spread of water-borne diseases.

But there were also gains from the dam. A large quantity
of hydroelectric power has generated new industries and
employment opportunities -- in a land of high unemployment and

underemployment. The dam has brought additional acres under cultivation and permitted greater intensification and diversification of cropping. It has enabled Egypt -- formerly a food short economy -- to reduce its dependency on cotton, and become a major exporter of such cash crops as rice, onions, and potatoes.

The losses and gains in this illustration highlight the trade-offs that are inherent in dam building. We must plan so that the gains far exceed the costs, financially, socially, and ecologically.

Moreover, the experience at Aswan and elsewhere has shown us where the costs are likely to arise, allowing us to plan to reduce or eliminate them. A responsible plan will provide housing for the displaced, drainage systems for disposal of overflows, anticipatory medical care to prevent disease and fertilizer for downstream land denied the enrichment of periodic flooding.

It is the thesis of this paper that careful, responsible, and successful planning is within our grasp, but that to achieve such success we must give more consideration to preservation of existing natural forces and established ways of indigenous people. The great gains to be achieved from success, and the desperate need for that success, double our responsibility to plan with vision and understnading.

If the basic objective of river basin development is to devise the most economical means of exploiting water and power resources to maximize productivity, the planning techniques can be relatively straightforward. They can deal primarily with the several key variables familiarly used in most hydrological, adricultural, and economic studies. Cost-benefit analysis, for example, can be made of such clear-cut water developemnt alternatives as canal improvement, surface water storage, or tubewells for groundwater. Because maximization of output is so important in the poorer developing countries where basic demand for food and shelter have yet to be met, most river basin analysis has traditionally emphasized the technical, engineering and cost-benefit analysis of dam construction and related irrigation developments. External or secondary effects have been analyzed mostly within the confines of isolated project analysis although they have rarely been quantified.

More recently, increasing emphasis has been placed on the environmental effects of river basin planning. Systematic programmins of socio-ecological factors into domprehensive mathematical models could add a new dimension in evaluating individual water resource projects or the series of projects that form an entire river basin program. Such models as these may also be modified to introduce additional elemants such as political considerations in weighing the potential benefits and inevitable costs. Known planning techniques -- systems analysis, mathematical programming, as well as physical planning -- may thus be used with much greater sophistication and sensitivity to social and ecological refinement.

In the past comprehensive mathematical models have been used in our river basin development work to represent entire investment programs. Such models were used to analyze a full scheme of development projects integrated on the basis of key economic relationships. This integration allowed the planner to take into consideration the singular as well as simultaneous effect of certain key variables and constraints on the overall program, and to trace the impact of any cahnge in variables and constraints. Model building, nevertheless, was limited by the modest number of variables which could be handled at any one time. Let me first illustrate the usefulness and limitations of the planning technique, in particular, a linear programming optimization model, which was used in the Indus River Basin Study in Pakistan, see Lieftinck (1969).

The Indus River Basin program was an outcome of the partition of the Indian sub-continent. This political act disrupted the existing irrigation systems and stood in the way of their continued development. A solution had to be found for rational allocation and use of the water and power resources of the rivers which divided India and Pakistan. After a decade of negotiations, aided by the good offices of the World Bank, these two countries signed the Indus Water Treaty in 1960 which provided for peaceful division of the waters of the Indus River and its six main tributaries.

The imaginative engineering concept which underlay the treaty was a system of "link" canals of unusually large capacity for transferring part of the substantial surplus water from the Indus to its "eastern" tributaries where it could meet the irrigation requirements of the eastern portions of West Pakistan. This area had hitherto been served by the water of three rivers which according to the provisions of the Indus Treaty were to be diverted upstream and made available to India. The plans for diverting water flows from the main Indus across the Punjab to the natural basins in the east were regarded by some as "pie in the sky reverie" because of the boldness of the concept and the large sum of money required.

Fortunately, however, the participants, as well as the aid-giving community, were geared for the challenge. An international agreement was signed in 1960 by seven countries and the World Bank to establish the Indus Basin Development Fund in order to provide funds to implement this conceptual framework and the related works. The donors initially contributed $895 million.

Over the next several years, the works on the link canals, the Mangla Dam as well as several large barrages were carried our expeditiously but significant cost overruns and the difficulties of financing all of them necessitated a supplemental agreement in 1964 providing $315 million to complete all the works except the Dam on the Indus. The agreement also established a Special Study Group to determine the economic and technical feasibility of constructing the large multi-purpose dam and

reservoir on the mainstem of the Indus at Tarbela with the understanding that if it were economic the Bank would help raise the
funds needed. If the Study Group found such a dam uneconomic,
an alternative approach to water development eliminating this
major dam was to be proposed and any remaining funds owuld be
used for such a program. The decision regarding Tarbela was
to be undertaken within the context of a detailed survey of all
the water and power resources of West Pakistan and a related
investment program.

To test the economic efficiency of this Action Program
which was designed to develop fully the entire water and power
resources in the Indus Basin a systems analysis was employed
through the use of linear programming techniques. The major
criterion for selecting the specific investments for the Action
Program was the maximization of the rate of return whereas the
test used in the linear program was the return for the whole
program rather than that for any one project. The ultimate
objective was to design a comprehensive program to provide a
basis for development planning within the context of successive
Five-Year Plans.

The task of formulating actual agriculture and water
investments was a very complex one as the different parts of
the vast Basin area varied a great deal in their socio-economic
characterisitcs. Soils vary, land holding change, ground
quality differs, to name a few and consequently the development
potential of each area differs. This planning task was made
even more complex by the overriding regional constraint on
Basin development -- uneven distribution and uncertainty of
water supply. While the volume of water supply from the Basin
and its subdivisions is substantial, eighty percent of annual
flows occur in the five months, May to September. Water was
scarce in the other months because rainfall is short and major
groundwater resources were largely untapped.

Moreover, the development schemes to be proposed for the
near term (i.e. 1965-75) had to be designed to promote development of a modern, self-sufficient agricultural economy in the
area where traditional agriculture has ruled for centuries.

For the purpose of program formulation the Basin area was
broken into a number of different natural territorial subdivisions -- the canal command areas -- covering some 33 million
acres of irrigated land and comprising the largest single
irrigation system in the world. For each designated zone,
various combinations of water development activities were
simulated, and their relative advantages analyzed in terms of
estimated irrigation requirements. In the linear program, a
series of hypothetical water development schemes were aggregated
and analyzed in terms of the greatest returns expected to be
realized from each simulated pattern of development for the
irrigation system as a whole. Projects (about 500 projects
considered for execution in two different time periods)
selected on the basis of the simulations were in turn tested

to verify each project's efficiency in the use of limited regional resources -- foreign exchange, surface water, public development funds, implementation capacity. The linear program revealed simultaneously the effects of alternative levels of these and other regional conditions on investment plans and generated an optimum internally consistent water development program for the whole Basin. The actual program which had been formulated by the Study Group was "tested" by comparing it with the program generated by the systems analysis.

Systems analysis and the use of mathematical models helped to confirm the areas of the greatest development potential, to define the range of alternatives, to establish specific investment priorities, to determine the timing of various investment projects, and find the most efficient means of implementing the recommended projects.

The planning procedure undertaken for the Basin development was a significant step forward from the traditional approach under which development programs were composed of a number of projects developed in relative isolation. The development program for the Indus Basin, on the other hand, was designed as a complete system of projects drawn together on the basis of pertinent interrelationships and developed in light of one another. The various large projects, particularly the Tarbela dam, were from the ouset never intended to be considered in isolation but as the major component of a larger scheme designed not only to meet West Pakistan's needs for electric power but also for additional supplies of irrigation water through the integration of surface and groundwater.

The special advantage of systems analysis is its capability of taking into account a wide variety of economic, political and social factors and examining the simultaneous effects of these factors for given areas under alternative schemes. However, in the Indus case, the study group deliberately limited the number of variables employed by using an optimizing linear program in order to focus on the relative merits of those several technical and economic variables which appeared directly related to maximizing agricultural production in the specific areas. As large quantities of diverse varibales were introduced, the model used quickly became combersome in the analysis of 500 projects and some 54 canal commands. The primary objective of devising an economically optimum investment program was in conflict with the introduction of substantially greater complexity into the analysis.

In any case, the voluminous technical studies and economic reports did not systematically incorporate such nonquantifiable data as political, cultural, social, and ecological factors which must also enter into the judgments of decision-makers. In retrospect, one could contend that the focus on economic and technical variables to the exclusion of vital social, political or health data was a severe limitation of the model.

This was where the "technical" analysis ended, and policy formulation began.

Close coordination is essential between technicians of diverse fields of discipline and policy-makers who determine public sector investments as well as influency private sector inputs. Cooperation and coordinated effort between planner and policy-maker was well demonstrated in the case of the Indus Basin enterprise. Here an unusual blend of expertise was assembled to articulate an effective course of action.

International experts of high technical competence prepared the extensive studies and analyses on which the water and power development programs were based. This work then served as a framework for the Pakistani policy-makers in executing the country's development projects. The government leaders of Pakistan and especially the chairman and chief engineers of the West Pakistan Water and Power Development Authority knew what had to be done and were determined to do it. River basin planning truly becomes a dynamic process when the traditional gap between the technical planner and the policy-maker has been bridged.

One example of the caliber of these technical inputs which proved so valuable to the success of the Basin Plan was the report on Land and Water Development in the Indus Plan by the U. S. White House Panel, usually referred to as the Revelle Report (1964). This study needs emphasis not only because of its contributions to the achievement of greater agricultural productivity, but also because it reflected the work of some 20 leading experts from all parts of the world covering 15 major scientific disciplines.

These experts proposed a massive program of public groundwater development as a means of increasing irrigation supplies and overcoming the problems of waterlogging and salinity. They proposed a large-scale attack involving a major ecological change. A number of tubewell and drainage projects each covering one million acres were designed to exploit the large acquifer of some 300 million acre feet underlying the Indus Basin to increase irrigation supplies while also providing extensive drainage.

The Revelle recommendations were of lasting significance -- tubewells eventually proved to be one of the most forceful propellants of the "Green Revolution." As a result of continued exploitation of groundwater irrigation by tubewell development throughout the Basin, soil depleted by waterlogging and salinity was once again made highly productive. This major achievement was reflected in the accelerated growth of agricultural production between 1960 and 1969. During this period the volume of wheat production, the most important foodgrain in West Pakistan, increased from the annual average level of 3.4 million tons in the fifties to 7.2 million tons in 1969-70. Most of this improvement took place in Punjab Province where three-quarters of Pakistan's wheat is grown and which was the main beneficiary of the Indus water development scheme.

Rice production, the second most important foodgrain, similarly increased from about one million tons to 2.3 million tons during the same period. A combination of irrigation from over 70,000 new tubewells, public and private, and use of Mexi-Pak Wheat varieties contributed to this increased production. For instance, in one year between 1967-68 and 1968-69, the cultivated acreage increased two and a half times from 2.4 million to 6 million.

In retrospect, however, the outcome of the Indus Basin Planning was not without flaws and distortions which could serve as lessons to future river planners.

First, the focus was almost entirely on the maximization of agricultural output and secondarily on the use of water as a power resource. Important factors such as the role of the private sector or the problem of regional balance were more or less neglected. Better distribution of income, both regionally and by classes, and of the benefits from the expected expansion of output were included in the preparatory studies but were hardly considered when it came to actual allocation of funds and execution of projects. Projects were developed with little regard for the need to increase employment and tended to be heavily capital intensive.

It has been argued that the Indus project required a disproportionate share of Pakistan's internal financial resources. To illustrate the magnitude of the program, the total combined expenditures on canals, private and public tube-well development and dam construction represented about 6-7% of the country's Gross National Product.

Some have argued that the enormous investment expenditures devoted to water and agricultural development resulted in gross neglect of the country's urban sector. Without sufficient resources or an adequate development effort it stagnated and ultimately a violent demonstration of dissatisfaction with this situation erupted. Even if a more balanced resource allocation might not have altered the course of history, such an allegation does point up the need to have river basin analysis more cogni-zant of the "other" dimensions of the problem -- in this case the social impact of program development. Overly ambitious programs straining too harshly human and financial resources must be avoided.

Second, the Indus development scheme failed to take certain contingencies into account. Although difficult, attempts should be made to make plans flexible enough to accommodate some of the mutations of technical innovations. For instance, the Indus scheme greatly underestimated the poten-tial of Mexi-Pak wheat varieties. It was only envisaged that by 1975 a million acres of new varieties would be planted. As noted above, by 1970, some six million acres were being planted.

The prevailing attitude of those involved in the studies had been somewhat pessimistic toward the role of "miracle seeds" as many felt that farmers would resist accepting and growing the new varieties; after all, they needed more careful planting, better water control, and better land preparation. Had the expected level of crop yields from the new varieties been accepted, rate of return calculations for certain projects might have shown somewhat differnet results.

It is difficult to judge whether such miscalculations were a factor in too much resources going into capital intensive water projects and too small an effort being directed to farm modern-ization. In any case, the point is clear that precision in economic analysis is a worthy goal, but rates of return -- particularly extending longer than two to three decades -- can indeed lead one into a false sense of knowledge and security in decision-making.

Finally, another interesting aspect of this experience deserves mentioning as it illustrates the danger of built-in rigidity which often arises from any "plan." It is often said that once a plan is formulated it tends to be regarded as some-thing sacred and policy-makers may become wedded to the objectives expressed in it. What looks good on paper may not be the best thing in realizing desired goals.

In the Indus studies, the Revelle proposal to build large-scale public tubewells as a way to overcome salinity, drainage, and irrigation problems was a brilliant approach to the long term problem, but it created an initial bias against private tubewell development. To the great surprise of many planners, a vigorous private sector investment in tubewells took place without public help. The 66,000 wills which were not forecast until 1971, had been achieved by 1968, and it was indeed fortu-nate because public sector resources proved so scarce. This again illustrated there was a job for everyone, public and private alike, since the task of developing an extensive system of tubewells covering such a large Basin was a great and costly one.

The lesson to be learned was that it might have been more appropriate to have planned from the outset to take more effec-tive advantage of the private initiative which combined the activities of those primarily responsible for introducing the "miracle"seeds with water development. Instead, the private sector in agriculture had to fight somewhat of an uphill battle, although Pakistan had through most of this period enthusiastically endorsed private sector initiative in other areas such as industry.

Planning techniques now available could have better high-lighted this kind of a problem for policy-makers to focus on. Since the mathematical programming activities applied in the Indus case, see Lieftinck (1969). More sophisticated models have been developed in our work in Bangladesh, see International Bank Reports A & B (1972), which can help broaden the frame of analysis. Let me illustrate this point by discussing a particular mathematical model that was used in the planning of the Ganges-Brahmaputra River basin system in Bangladesh. As an initial stage of a comprehensive planning effort, a group working with the World Bank, developed a macro-economic model with a thirty-year time horizon under the guidance of Professor Robert Dorfman of Harvard University in order to provide Basin studies with a proper economic framework. The main objectives of Professor Dorfman's model were to see (1) what burden the agriculture sector would have to carry if Bangladesh were to be a viable economy which would be able to absorb productively expected future population growth; (2) whether, in fact, Bangladesh could remain and/or become a viable economy; and (3) what the financial resource implications of a viable economy would be over a thirty-year time period. The purpose of the model was not to present planning targets or projections based on past figures. Instead, the objective was to provide a tool for analysis which could then be used to judge whether the achievements outlined for agriculture were consistent with overall plans for the country's future.

Technically, this model was very sophisticated in its imaginative use of international data and application of economic theory. It, in effect, took data from the development experience of other countries which have undergone modernization during this half century and applied them to Bangladesh.

The initial computer runs produced some interesting and important data although they were preliminary results. The model showed that Bangladesh, if it followed certain patterns, could become a viable economy over a thirty-period but this would necessitate external financial assistance in the magnitude of $500-700 million per annum which may not be realistic. It also showed that the role of agriculture would have to decline from 55% of GNP at the beginning of the 70's to 33% of GNP in the year 2000 if unemployment were to be kept at an acceptable level of say 10%. It also showed that the extent of resource mobilization would have to improve from a historical savings rate of 11% of GNP to some 15% by the mid-seventies and stay at that level over some 30 years. Under these assumptions, the investment-savings gap would decrease from 9.3% of GDP in the mid-seventies to less than 0.5% of GDP by 2000. Substantial injection of foreign capital would be needed to close the gap.

The model is, of course, designed to be run over and over again under different sets of assumptions. That is the whole purpose of such an exercise. One can measure the sensitivity of a system of variables. One can both isolate and interrelate variables. Then, presumable, the study of "implementation" can be limited to those variables which appear most "sensitive." The question is how serious are the omissions. I would say for macro analysis -- not serious at this level of aggregation.

In principle, then, through the use of this kind of a model, the level of agriculture production necessary for growth to meet certain objectives could be related to the level of investments

in water resource development which appears necessary.
Furthermore, some indication could also be given of the optimum
level of external assistance and domestic savings if the economy
were to become viable, and accordingly a very rough consistency
check could be made to see whether sufficient resources would
be available to finance required water control investments.
All of this would then become a framework, the intensive
implementation evaluation would be related to this prospective.
For most of us this is a "starting point."

Despite the obvious usefulness of such models, many are
disturbed by their creation. Some feel that most countries
cannot really afford the luxury of such models. There are more
important things to do. In non-academic circles, some would
say such models are dangerous, don't use them, play ostrich,
because model results can give ammunition to irresponsible
individuals. Other state that it is more important to work on
specific policy measures. Still others fear any comprehensive
set of numbers because the numbers would tend to freeze positions.
Some question the relevance of the data since much of it had
been drawn from the experience of other nations at similar
stages of development.

In short, the general feeling often is that with this kind
of exercise damage occurs very quickly since the preliminary
results can be misinterpreted as constituting a foundation for
a plan of action. Others, of course, feel that a valuable
tool for general economic analysis and for river basin planning
can be created and that running models under various assumptions permit the drawing of conclusions concerning both the
limits of investment and the parameters of policy for sound
socio-economic river basin planning. But there can be no
doubt that within these limits, much more work needs to be done
by both experienced policy-makers and technicians of many
disciplines.

Another model, used in the Bangladesh work illustrated
this. For example, a sector-project simulation model was
designed as a tool for aggregating specific project proposals
into investment programs for the achievement of certain water
and agricultural targets. It was, in the first instance,
specifically geared to calculating the agricultural production
which would result from certain proposed programs. Using the
data obtained from the exhaustive research conducted over a
10-year period by a United Nations Development Program Soil
Survey team, the area of Bangladesh was broken down into 50
land development units. A sample program was designed based
on the best estimates of constraints: (1) present land use
and availability of irrigation water (surface and groundwater)
and (2) capacities for administration, engineering, and training
needed for implementation. Using 12% as a minimum discount rate,
the model excluded all investments without a positive net present
worth. In other words, a 12% rate of return cut-off point was
used. The model then formulated a tentative investment program

for water and agriculture development based on projects in the order of their greatest returns over a thirty-year span. Since the model was a simulation, it would be possible to introduce many more variables than that used in the Indus Study.

Nevertheless, the model -- an inanimate tool for analysis -- however erroneously became the center of controversy within our own group. The model had printed out some preliminary results which were not only being taken very seriously but also taken out of context. It was indeed a very complex calculating model but it calculated only on the assumptions fed in. The assumptions employed were perhaps socio-economically untenable in some cases. This remains to be tested.

A critical input, for example, that was deliberately omitted was the effect and importance of flood control on the quality of life of the people of Bangladesh. Such a major omission deserves an explanation. First, the Bangladesh Government must determine the importance of flood control but this Government only came into existence when the first runs of the model were made. Second, with the creation of Bangladesh, the whole approach to flood control could be broadened to consider potential friendly relations between the two riparian parties. In fact, only with the creation of Bangladesh did it become possible to examine optimum solutions to the Ganges-Brahmaputra-Meghna river basin.

Thus, in this particular model, we did not choose to quantify a qualitative judgment. We left out a dummy variable or made it zero. But we were fully aware of the need to take this factor into account before planning decisions could be made. However, since models are made to be run under different sets of assumptions, we could accept the decision not to quantify the unquantifiable, i.e. the importance of the quality of life.

Despite our careful reservations on the preliminary results of the model runs, the output was taken by some as an absolute and not discounted by the context in which they were derived. Thus, the preliminary results of this model in some discussions we have had presented more of threat than a contribution to planning.

The instrument (the model) should not fall in disrepute because it is misused. Many of us -- and let us be very open -- particularly economists and engineers -- like absolute answers, and absolute answers dictate very static cross-sections ...e.g., a table enumerating a list of projects, a set of numbers, a series of activities which are then taken seriously and analyzed in and of themselves. Instead, these data might look entirely different if carefully interpreted in the full complexity of a dynamic context and tested under completely different sets of assumptions. The models we have developed allow us to do just that -- but with a far greater degree of precision than in the past. Our obligation must be to use them with full knowledge of their and our own limitations and to develop action alternatives for those charged with decision making responsibility.

To the use of these new tools we have added another, but equally essential, dimension to the planning process. We have begun to look at river basin planning with new eyes -- the eyes of the potential beneficiary -- the farmer who plants the seed and uses the water.

Regional and national goals must be translated into changes of mind and behavior of the village people affected by river basin development. Otherwise, the development effort misses the mark. This means that planners and public officials must become sensitive to the needs and desires of the people for whom the fruits of development are directed.

To obtain this perspective, the Bank is making an analysis of cultural determinants of farmers' response. Attempts are being made to view the anticipated changes in production and village environment from the viewpoint of farmers that will ultimately determine project viability.

We are undertaking careful analyses of enormous changes that have taken place in selected villages located in the Mekong Basin in order to see what caused tham and what it takes to make a farmer respond to new investment with new levels of production. For instance, an anthropologist who lived in the village of Pa Ao in Northeast Thailand was sent back to the same village some 18 years later to assess the changed lives of the villagers who had benefited from market access roads and agricultural development programs. The changes were all pervasive. The diet had substantially improved with more food available and new food items such as fresh vegetables and fruits. Improved marketing, credit, education, and sanitation bacilities were also observed. These physical changes reflect new mental attitudes and all of the changes, physical and mental, taken together indicate that a foundation has been laid for breaking out of the rigid hold of traditional poverty -- and this is the key to self-sustained economic development.

19.2 CONCLUSION

In terms of methodology we have come a long way from the mathematical sophistication of the linear programming model used in the Indus case to the simpler tools of simulation now being used in our Ganges-Brahmaputra work which are extremely sophisticated in their being capable of handling diverse variables. With such simple techniques as these, we can now do a better job of river basin planning. We know there are going to be costs -- social and ecological, as well as financial. In the past we were aware of these costs, but systematic and integrated mathematical analysis was not applied. The new analytical tools can now help us quantify environmental and social costs and measure them against expected economic returns with greater accuracy. We can give policy makers a clear picture of the gains to be achieved and the losses to be borne, and with knowledge of the costs we can plan to eliminate or minimize them.

The Indus Basin Works succeeded in its objectives partly because of the close relations between those who were technically competent in planning and execution and those responsible for policy formulation. With improved methods of analysis, we must discharge our responsibility by the clearest possible articulation of goals, assumptions, and constraints. We must also be frank about the reliability and accuracy which can be accorded to our results.

For valid reasons, the technicians are rarely the decision makers. The technician must understand his role. He exists to define options and not to prescribe policy. Conversely, the policy-maker bears a heavy responsibility. He must study the options laid before him and make a decision affecting millions of people. He cannot responsibly park the decision on the computer or the technician.

We thus arrive at some very simple fundamentals. River basin planning like penicillin can be hazardous. It requires certain compromises and sacrifices of resources whether ecological or social. With responsible use it could revolutionize the lives of the river's people as dramatically as a Salk vaccine. Without planning, many may have to remain destitute. Thus, the great responsibility rests on the members of the planning profession. Their task is to recognize the errors made in the past, reappraise their roles, respect the views of their critics, and minimize the immediate losses while maximizing the long-term gains.

REFERENCES

International Bank for Reconstruction and Development, A, 1972, East Pakistan Land and Water Resources Sector Study; Vol. III, Sector Economics Technical Report; No. 3, Special Projects Department.

International Bank for Reconstruction and Development, B, 1972, Bangladesh: Land, Water, and Power Studies: Final Report; center for Population Studies, see p. 5 of this report for the list of 18 models being studied.

Lieftinck, Pieter, 1969, A Linear Programming Analysis of Potential Irrigation Developments; Johns Hopkins Press, paper IV.

Lieftinck, Pieter, 1969, Water and Power Resources of West Pakistan: A study in Sector Planning; Vol. III - Background and methodology, World Bank Study Group, Johns Hopkins Press.

Revelle, Roger, 1964, Report on Land and Water Development in the Indus Plain; White House Panel on Waterlogging and Salinity in West Pakistan.

Sterling, Claire, 1972, Superdams: The Perils of Progress; The Atlantic.

Chapter 20

FEDERAL GUIDELINES FOR WATER RESOURCE PROJECT EVALUATION

by

H. P. Caulfield, Jr., Professor of Political Science, Colorado
State University, Fort Collins, Colorado

Chapter 20

FEDERAL GUIDELINES FOR WATER RESOURCE PROJECT EVALUATION

Probably most of those who will be reading these remarks have come to the field of water and related land resource use and development from highly technical backgrounds of expertise in hydraulics, hydrology and sediment movement. Topics within those fields are covered by most of the papers in this volume. My academic background is in economics and political science. For much of my career I have related to the field of water and related land resource use and development from the perspective of the Federal government and there at the level of policy development, program planning and review. Thus my relationship to this field that we share is at the opposite end of the spectrum of its problems and related disciplines from those that preoccupy you.

Federal guidelines for water resource project evaluation spring from the Flood Control Act of 1936 wherein the Congress of the United States directed that flood control projects should be undertaken "if the benefits to whomsoever they may accrue are in excess of the estimated costs, and if the lives and social security of people are otherwise adversely affected." The application of this legislative provision has been far wider than to just flood control projects. Either by statute or by administrative order, the general purport of this provision has been made broadly applicable to all water resource projects of the Corps of Engineers, Bureau of Reclamation and the Soil Conservation Service.

The seeming import of this provision, which apparently was adopted at the suggestion of the then National Resources Planning Board, brought a particular point of view to the professional application of this mandate from Congress to look into "benefits" and "costs", namely, that of economics. The normative theoretical branch of the discipline of economics that had been developed up to then, and has been subsequently further developed, known as "welfare economics" became the intellectual underpinning for this endeavor. Professor Pigou's "Economics of Welfare", first published in 1922, was the take-off point in this general development of economic thought. The opportunity afforded by the Congress to apply this normative theory to the field of water and related land resource use and development was apparently welcomed by economists, and it has been substantially exploited by them within the Federal government with outside support from academic economists. Because of this unusual opportunity to apply a normative theory, economists have taken a very special interest in the water resource area, in my opinion, more so than in most other areas of public policy and action. This is why economists have been intruding in an area that engineers, hydrologists and other technical experts have thought is, or should be, peculiarly theirs.

The first official product of this interest of economists in trying to implement the statute of 1936 was popularly known as the Green Book, a report of the Subcommittee on Benefits and Costs of the Federal Inter-Agency River Basin Committee. Bearing the title, "Proposed Practices for Economic Analysis of River Basin Projects," this report embodying Pigouvian theory was published in 1950. With slight additions and changes, a revised edition was published in 1958. The Green Book is well known among planning practitioners and academicians in this field.

The Proposed Practices set forth "criteria and principles" of "general economic welfare" for "application by agencies within the framework of their particular programs and responsibilities." Thus goals or objectives other than "general economic welfare," defined as economic efficiency from a "comprehensive public viewpoint," were still recognized as relevant. For example, the proposed practices were intended to apply to economic analysis within the 160-acre rule in Reclamation Law to implement the "family farm" concept. This rule, it was understood, reflected an objective other than "general economic welfare" as defined.

The Proposed Practices, moreover, called for identification of all beneficial or adverse effects of a project in both tangible (i.e., monetary) terms or intangible terms. An "intangible" beneficial effect of a flood control project, an effect which the Congress clearly had in mind when it established flood control as a national, largely non-reimbursable project purpose, is the saving of human life. However, because of the subsequent great weight that has been given by the Office of Management and Budget (formerly the Bureau of the Budget) and the Congress to a B/C ratio in terms of tangible values (e.g., savings in property damage) and to a ratio of 1.0/1, or greater, as the basic criterion of authorization and funding of a water development project, all other goals were made secondary. For example, regional development per se, that is provision of settlement opportunities or improvement of underdeveloped areas, a major objective of the Congress in passage of the Reclamation Act of 1902, and the TVA Act of 1933, was made secondary to the goal of national economic efficiency.

The Green Book (1950 or 1958) was never adopted by the Federal Inter-Agency River Basin Committee or its successor committees. However, the basic philosophy and many of the criteria and principles of the Green Book, explicitly or implicitly, were embodied in Budget Circular A-47 issued by the U.S. Bureau of the Budget on December 31, 1952.

Its most fundamental standards and procedures were these:
(a) The most economical means of meeting needs in a region were to be set forth as an important consideration in reviewing of proposed projects.
(b) The relative economy of alternative means available on a national basis for meeting needs was to be set forth for consideration.

(c) Benefits and costs, in total and separately for each
purpose, were to be set forth. Where benefits and costs
could not be estimated in monetary terms their relative
significance was to be stated in as precise and quantitative terms as possible; and lastly, in the words of the
circular itself,
(d) "While it is recognized that a comparison of estimated benefits with estimated costs does not provide a
precise measure of the absolute merits of any particular
program or project, one essential criterion in justifying
any program or project will, except in unusual cases where
adequate justification is presented, be that its estimated
benefits to whomsoever they may accrue exceed its estimated
costs."
In contrast to the Green Book, which called for the
application of its criteria and principles within the framework of an agency's particular programs and responsibilities,
"A-47" called for analyses of proposed water projects in terms
of its standards and procedures by sponsoring departments and
agencies and then an indication where a requirement of law
or official agency views were at variance.
The upshot of these standards and procedures was this:
a program or project proposed for authorization or funding had
to have a benefit to cost ratio greater than 1.0 to 1 in terms
of tangible benefits and tangible costs from a national point
of view. By implication, changes in law inconsistent with the
standards and procedures of "A-47" would be sought. Contrary
views of departments and agencies would be accepted only in
unusual cases that were adequately justified. What was being
done by "A-47" was rigorous adoption of one objective of water
projects: "national economic efficiency." In effect, other
possible objectives of water projects were being denied. This
action flew in the face of a good deal of American history
with regard to what the objectives of these water projects
were in terms of long accepted public policy. This historical
congressionally accepted public policy is what caused, in my
opinion, a great deal of difficulty for the Bureau of the
Budget in trying to implement rigorously Budget Bureau Circular
A-47 during the 1950's and until the advent of the Kennedy
Administration in 1961.
What, in brief, are some of the historically developed
objectives of public policy that are still operative in support
of water resource projects? Multiple goals, or objectives,
have been involved throughout our Nation's long concern with
the use of its water and related land resources. In Secretary
of the Treasury Gallatin's Report on Roads and Canals of 1808,
which proposed a comprehensive plan of canals and other navi-
gable waterways to provide low-cost transport covering the
whole of a largely unpopulated and undeveloped United States,
the goals were these: economic development, furthering political unity, and military defense. This proposal was made
before the advent of the railroad and after the Louisiana

Purchase of 1803. Gallatin envisioned, incidentally, that comprehensive development under the plan, as distinct from piecemeal development of parts, would induce sufficient economic development to pay for the waterway system with interest through levy of toll charges.

When Federal authority to undertake navigation projects at Federal expense became clearly established after the Civil War, economic development of the Middle West with the aid of cheap waterway transportation of grain and other bulk commodities was a basic national policy objective. But such projects were conceived as providing not only waterway transportation but also competition to railroads with the socio-economic objective of regulating their freight rates.

With enactment in 1902 of the Reclamation Act, the Federal government pushed its responsibility for economic development further West through provision of agricultural water developments that extended the possibilities of Western settlement. Thus it was Western settlement, not increased agricultural production, that was the primary objective of the Reclamation program. As a secondary objective, that of promoting a Nation of family farms, the Act also provided that no Federally developed water could be supplied to lands in excess of 160 acres in any one landholder. And the landholder was required to be a "bonafide resident on such land..."

Multiple-purpose development increasingly became a national goal of water and related land resource development under the aegis of the Conservation Movement after the turn of the century. In addition to navigation and irrigation, hydroelectric power, flood control, domestic and industrial water, land stabilization, drainage, watershed protection and enhancement of outdoor recreation and fish and wildlife all became, eventually, purposes of such development. Each of these developmental purposes was not established with economic development as its sole objective, but its furtherance was a widely-supported objective that they all had in common.

When the Congress legislated in the Flood Control Act of 1936 on procedures to be followed in the evaluation of flood control projects to be submitted to Congress for authorization, the Nation was in the midst of the Great Depression. Federal support of "economic development" was indeed a major national objective then and in post World War II fears of recession. Analysis of "benefits" and "costs" of water resource plans in terms of criteria of "national economic efficiency" was the way the economics profession and discipline looked at the problem of obtaining "economic development" in the most efficient way. Thus, in preparation of the Green Book and of Budget Bureau Circular A-47, it is not surprising that the normative ideology of economists, with its central focus upon "national economic efficiency," became the dominant mode of thought in those documents.

The Bureau of the Budget attempted rigorously to apply "A-47" to all projects presented to it for review in the 1950's.

It did not go so far, for example, as to ask Congress to abandon the "family farm" objective in Reclamation projects by repeal of the "160 acre rule" in the interests of national economic efficiency. But it did adopt a general negative stance toward all Reclamation projects. Moreover, its professional staff did everything it informally could to block new authorizations. Presumably, it saw no national need for Reclamation projects in an era of widespread surpluses in agricultural production.

The general strategy of the Bureau of the Budget, applicable to all proposed water projects of the Corps of Engineers and Soil Conservation Service as well as the Bureau of Reclamation, was to make a positive B/C ratio in terms of tangible benefits and costs an absolute requirement in order to obtain its approval. This effort led to great dissatisfaction with "A-47" within the Congress beginning about 1956. Few, if any, in the Congress called for abandonment of benefit-cost analysis per se, but there was a widespread call for its "liberalization", chiefly through specific changes in evaluation procedures: change of the period of analysis from 50 to 100 years, recognition of secondary or regional benefits of water projects, treatment of opportunities for enhancement of recreation and fish and wildlife as one of the primary purposes of water projects, and elimination of "taxes foregone" in costs allocated to public electric power. These proposed specific changes in evaluation procedures were an indirect means, in my opinion, to achieve more general objectives which were taken by various proponents of water resource projects to be eminently valid. The dissatisfaction of Congress with the then applicable evaluation procedures was also shown by its various attempts, then and since, to authorize water resource projects of the three planning agencies even though the projects did not have approval of the Bureau of the Budget or its successor, the Office of Management and Budget. Often, but not always, these attempts have been successful.

"Policies, Standards and Procedures in the Formulation, Evaluation and Review of Plans for Use and Development of Water and Related Land Resources," an interdepartmental agreement approved by the President for application by the Federal departments concerned and the Bureau of the Budget, replaced Budget Bureau Criteria A-47 on May 15, 1962. Although a document of the Executive Branch and never approved formally by the Congress, Senator Clinton Anderson, then Chairman of the Senate Committee on Interior and Insular Affairs, saw to publication of the agreement by the Senate on May 29, 1962. In an introductory statement, he indicated the mood at the time of many in the Congress:

"The new policies and standards, established in an agreement of the four Department heads, replace Budget Bureau Circular A-47 which caused considerable contention, both as to content and as to the propriety of its source."

The new policies and standards have become widely known, and with misunderstanding of their origins by some, as "Senate Document 97." They were prepared by the Interdepartmental Staff Committee, ad hoc, U.S. Water Resource Council[1]/.

The basic objective in the formulation of plans, according to "Senate Document 97," is to provide the "best use, or combination of uses, of water and related land resources to meet all foreseeable short or long-term needs." In pursuit of this basic objective, full consideration is to be given to the following multiple objectives and "reasoned choices made between them when they conflict:"

Development. Water and related land resource development and management are taken to be essential to economic development and growth for all the various multiple-purposes including outdoor recreational and fish and wildlife enhancement. (Previously in "A-47," full consideration of outdoor recreation and fish and wildlife had not been given in project formulation with respect to possible specific enhancement measures involving joint facilities and in project analysis through estimation of tangible benefits and allocation of joint as well as separable costs.)

Preservation. Proper stewardship of the Nation's natural bounty is taken to require preservation in "particular instances" of open space; green space; wild areas of rivers, lakes, beaches and mountains; and areas of unique natural beauty, historical and scientific interest. (To highlight "preservation" as an objective of water and related land "use", as distinct from "development," was then new to water planning standards. This newness was despite the fact that conflicts between "development" and "preservation" had occurred in the past, initially in a great debate in 1913 between Gifford Pinchot and John Muir in the Hetch Hetchy controversy involving Yosemite National Park in California.)

Well-being of People. Hardship and basic needs of particular groups are to be of concern, but development for the benefit of the few or the disadvantage of the many is to be avoided. In accord with this objective, socio-economic policy requirements established by the Congress are to be observed (e.g., the 160-acre rule in relation to Federal supply of water for irrigation and "preference clauses" relating to the sale of Federal power to local bodies public and rural electric cooperatives.) Also, "well-being of people" was an objective that could take into account the saving of life by a flood control project while savings from property damage would be taken to be a benefit in furtherance of the developmental objective.

Planning, according to "Senate Document 97," is to include all relevant means to achieve proposed project objectives

[1]/ The author was the chairman of this Committee when he was Assistant Director and then Director, Resource Program Staff, Office of the Secretary, Department of the Interior; 1961-1966.

and purposes (including non-structural as well as structural means) singly, in combination or in "alternative combinations reflecting different basic choice patterns."

Comprehensive plans are to be formulated initially to include all units and purposes which satisfy national economic efficiency criteria in terms of tangible benefits and costs:

(a) Tangible benefits exceed project economic costs.

(b) Each separable unit or purpose provides benefits at least equal to its costs.

(c) The scope of development is such as to provide the maximum net benefits.

(d) There is no more economical means, evaluated on a comparable basis, of accomplishing the same purpose or purposes which would be precluded from development if the plan were undertaken.

The discount rate to be used in calculating the present value of benefits and costs is the weighted average of the "coupon rates" on outstanding long-term Federal bands. In the nineteen sixties this was about 3 1/4 percent.

Thus "Senate Document 97" clearly provides that optimum plans in terms of criteria of national economic efficiency (assuming one agrees with the provision on the discount rate), are to be presented for consideration within the Executive Branch and to the Congress. In addition, however, such optimum plans are to provide baselines from which alternative plans reflecting intangible values reflecting different objectives can be judged (e.g., by determining the developmental benefits foregone if preservation of a scenic river is relevant as an alternative to multiple purpose development). And, according to "Senate Document 97," when major differences arise among technically possible plans conceived as desirable for a river basin on the basis of intangible benefits and costs, in comparison to optimum plans based on tangible benefits and costs, alternative plans giving expression to these major differences are to be presented for consideration within the Executive Branch and to the Congress.

Regional, state and local points of view or objectives are to be considered as well as national points of view in terms of criteria of national economic efficiency or other national policy. A comparison of differences arising from these various points of view is also to be included in reports.

Finally, "Senate Document 97" provides that general and specific judgments are to be made upon comprehensive plans, programs and project proposals as a basis for recommendation to the Congress. Review aimed at arriving at such judgments is to be based upon the provisions of "Senate Document 97" itself, applicable laws, their legislative intent and Executive policies and orders as well as recognized technical standards. In contrast to "A-47" no requirement is set forth that projects, generally, must have a benefit-cost ratio greater than 1.0 to 1 as a basis for recommendation to the Congress. On the other hand, "Senate Document 97" did not bar the Bureau of the Budget, nor does it bar the Office of Management and Budget today, from adopting such benefit-cost ratio requirement as its own administrative standard. And this requirement has been the unwritten rule since promulgation of "Senate Document 97" on May 15, 1962.

The proposal of the Water Resources Council in July 1968 to amend "Senate Document 97" to change the formula for determination of discount the rate used in the calculation of benefits and costs precipitated a new Congressional call for liberalization supported by various developmental interest groups. Raising the discount rate, which would be the effect of the formula change, would result in a lower B/C ratio and make infeasible borderline projects that formerly were considered feasible. Initially, Council efforts in response to this pressure were directed toward developing specific improvements in analytical procedures for carrying out policies and objectives of "Senate Document 97" that had not been well developed in that document. It also adopted in December 1968, a new formula for the annual determination of the discount rate based upon the "yield rate" on outstanding long-term Federal bonds rather than the "coupon rate." This action changed the discount rate then from 3 1/4 percent to 4 5/8 percent. After this action, and in view of the obligation of the Council under Section 103 of the Water Resources Planning Act of 1965 to promulgate with the approval of the President its own "principle, standards and procedures" for application by all Federal water and related land planning agencies and all reviewing agencies within the Executive Branch, the Council began to direct its attention to this much larger task of replacing Senate Document 97 in its entirety, initially through the work of a Special Task Force.

To serve as a basis for public hearings, a report of June 1969 from the Special Task Force to the Council was published and became known as the Blue Book. Subsequently, after the hearings and in June 1970, reports of the Special Task Force on "Principles" and "Standards" for planning water and land resources were made available, informally, to the interested public. A third report, "Procedures" for planning water and land resources, was to be developed later. The first two, duplicated on orange paper, became known as the Orange Books.

"The overall purpose of water and land planning", the Special Task Force asserted in the report on Principles, "is to reflect society's preferences for attainment of the objectives defined below:

"A. To enhance national economic development by increasing the value of the Nation's output of goods and services and improving national economic efficiency.
"B. To enhance the quality of the environment by the management, conservation, preservation, creation, restoration, or improvement of the quality of certain natural and cultural resources and ecological systems.

"C. To enhance social well-being by the equitable distribution of real income, employment, and population, with special concern for the incidence of the consequences of a plan on affected persons or groups; by contributing to the security of life and health; by providing educational, cultural, and recreational opportunities; and by contributing to national security.

"D. To enhance regional development through increases in a region's income; increases in employment; and improvements of its economic base, environment, social well-being, and other specified components of the regional objective."

"No one objective," the Special Task Force further asserted, "has any inherently greater claim on water and land use than any other. These Principles do not imply the relative priorities to be assigned among the multiobjectives in plan formulation and evaluation."

In these general statements the Special Task Force sets forth its conception of appropriate objectives of water and land resource planning. But it also makes clear its position, here and in subsequent more detailed provisions, that national economic efficiency should no longer be considered the primary objective. There should be a national objective account for each objective. The beneficial effects and costs of a particular plan, within a set of alternatives, should be evaluated in terms of each objective. Opportunities foregone by adopting one plan in comparison to each other plan should be indicated and then considered.

With respect to the matter of evaluating benefits and costs in terms of a common time period, the Task Force adopted the view that the discount rate to be used should be one reflecting "social time preference." On this basis, it recommended that a rate of 5 1/2 percent be adopted.

The Orange Books prepared by the Special Task Force were never adopted by the Water Resources Council, with the approval of the President, to replace "Senate Document 97," as supplemented and amended. Instead the Water Resources Council issued in December 1971 its own "Proposed Principles and Standards for Planning Water and Related Land Resources" for purposes of public review and hearing.

The proposed Principles and Standards of December 1971 differed significantly from those proposed by the Special Task Force and reflected substantial influence exerted by the Office of Management and Budget.

Major changes were these:
(a) As an objective for plan formulation, the objective of enhancing "social well-being" was dropped. Plans formulated in terms of other objectives, however, could still be evaluated in terms of beneficial and adverse effects on "social well-being."

(b)   The regional development objective in plan formulation was made contingent upon advance approval in each case.
(c)   An explicit requirement was made that one alternative plan must be formulated reflecting optimum contributions to the national economic efficiency objective and that at least one be formulated reflecting contributions to the environmental quality objective.   In other words, the other two objectives are downgraded and emphasis is centered on the making of trade-offs only between national economic efficiency and environmental quality in deciding upon plans.
(d)   The concept of the discount rate as reflecting "social time preference" was explicitly replaced by one reflecting "the opportunity cost of all Federal investment activities, including water resource projects" and this cost is "recognized to be the real rate of return on non-Federal investments."   This rate is now taken to be 10 percent.   But, due to an alleged preference in the Federal political process to "subsidize" water projects, the discount rate is placed at 7 percent for five years.

In 1972, hearings on the proposed Principles and Standards of December 1971, have been held both in Washington and in a few major cities across the land.   In terms of both statements submitted for the record and in actual testimony, the response to the call for advice was very great indeed and reflected marked divergence in points of view by different groups and interests.   The changes between the Orange Books and the proposed Principles and Standards of December 1971 were both praised and condemned.   The Water Resources Council has prepared recently a full analysis of this public input to its decision processes.   It is understood that much of the input relates to the areas where changes had been made.   Thus, they relate to major issues which deserve some explication and analysis.

Elimination of "enhancement of social well-being" as an objective in plan formation could turn out to be politically difficult for the Nixon Administration.   This change would appear to rule out Reclamation irrigation plans expressly formulated on the basis of, and constrained by, the "160-acre" rule to provide "family farms," as now provided in law.   Also it would appear to rule out plans expressly formulated to achieve a particular probability of saving human life, a particular concern of Congressional critics with respect to current application of "Senate Document 97."   Moreover, the general idea of consciously using public investments to enhance social well-being, not permitted by the proposed Principles and Standards of December 1971, evokes substantial interest, both positive and negative, in American society.   To the extent projects could be expressly formulated, for example, to achieve a possibly desirable "redistribution of income," such formulation for public consideration would not be permitted.   It should be noted, in this connection, that the Congress has not yet

shown any inclination to give planners a general license to
formulate plans on the basis of any social enhancement that
may occur to them as desirable. Experience with Congress during
the nineteen sixties on the issue of "area redevelopment benefits" tends to bear out this observation. Clearly specific
aspects of the enhancement of social well-being, as now provided by law or which have a possibility of acceptance by the
Congress (e.g., the saving of human life), in considering plans
for authorization, will need to be permitted to serve as objectives of plan formulation. This more limited conception of
the social well-being objective, would appear to have greater
political practicality than the Task Force proposal. On the
other hand, the current Council proposal is an invitation to
needless political embarrassment.

Certain environmentalist critics of the proposed
Principles and Standards of December 1971 did not feel that
they gave adequate standing to ecological concerns. Should
"quality of the environment" have a built-in higher standing
in the Principles and Standards than, say "national economic
development?" Or should they have only an equal built-in
standing in considering specific alternative plans as proposed?
What some environmentalists want is an a priori policy decision
that in effect rules out the formulation and consideration of
projects that would violate some conception of a standard of
environmental quality. This is a very fundamental issue.
Parallel to it is the issue backed by much of the economics professional fraternity, whether "national economic development"
should be the overriding objective. There is an increasing
group of economists, however, who favor the multi-objective
planning approach, along the general lines proposed by the
Council's Special Task Force. This shift in academic opinion
has its center at M.I.T. and Harvard. At Colorado State
University and elsewhere, research is also going foreward on
the presumption that the general idea of a multi-objective
approach is here to stay.

Another major issue has to do with the long standing
argument over "secondary benefits[2]. The report of the Special
Task Force of the Water Resources Council of June 1969, devoted
substantial attention to this matter. The Orange Books treated
the issue under two headings: (1) "increases in output resulting from external economics, and (2)" utilization of unem-
ployed or underemployed resources." The Council's Proposed
Principles and Standards of December 1971 recognize the possibility of added benefits due to the (1) but do not recognize
such possibility due to (2). This is both a philosophical and

2/ See Caulfield, H.P., Jr., 1971, A National-Regional Impact
   Evaluation System--Discussion; Proceedings of the Business
   and Economics Statistics Section, American Statistical
   Association, August 23-26, 1971; pp. 211-214 for a detailed
   discussion on this issue.

empirical measurement issue within the fraternity of professional economists. It can be said to be another substantial issue between the Harvard and Chicago schools of economics, the former generally siding with the position taken in the Orange Books and the latter with that in the Proposed Principles and Standards of December 1971. The Chicago school has had predominant influence in the Nixon Administration.

The final major issue is the "discount rate." The issue on the conceptual level among professional economists is between a rate believed to represent "social time preference" versus a rate reflecting "the opportunity cost of capital." The former concept is based on the view that collective concern and decision with respect to valuation of benefits accruing in the future for public projects is superior to a determination based upon a statistical analysis of individual time preferences determined individually. As a Nation, according to "social time preference" doctrine, we would and should collectively, value benefits accruing to generations yet unborn more highly, compared to the benefits for us today, than individually we would value future benefits in relation to an opportunity to obtain personal benefits today. Opportunity cost doctrine reflects belief in individual decision-making in the economic marketplace or "consumer sovereignty," as the appropriate determinant. Such decision-making in the investment of individual savings (denial of consumption benefits now), in relation to investment opportunities available, establishes through the competitive process "the real rate of return on non-Federal investments," or the opportunity cost of capital.

With regard to empirical calculation, the opportunity cost of capital concept has the advantage of being calculable, even though there is plenty of room for argument as to method. Social time preference, so far, has not been found to be calculable. It must be based upon general judgment within the political market-place with little to guide that judgment. Insufficient research effort, in my opinion, has been devoted to the formulation of normative and procedural guidelines that might be acceptable in arriving at a politically-determined discount rate in accord with the concept of social time preference.

The Council's decision in 1968 establishing a formula for the annual calculation of the discount rate based on the yield rate of return on long-term Federal bonds endeavored to bridge the gulf between these two opposing conceptions, as well as take into account the "cost of money" concept held widely by Congressmen and by non-economists in the Executive Branch. The yield rate on Federal bonds can be argued, and I so argued as Executive Director of the U.S. Water Resources Council, to be the minimum rate that is consistent with marginal (not average) opportunity-cost. On the other hand, it can be argued to be a high rate from the point of view of social time preference. If one is an environmentalist and argues intellectually (rather than in short-run political terms, as

environmentalists are doing today; see below), then each
generation ought to value benefits accruing to future
generations to be of equal value, at least, to benefits accruing
to us today. The discount rate would then be zero. A "more
hair-shirt" environmental idealism might even be said to call
for valuing benefits for future generations more highly than
benefits for our generation. The discount rate would then be
negative. Finally, the yield rate can be said to be an adequate approximation of the "cost of money" to the Federal
government[3].

Today on the political level of concern, environmentalists
generally, plus the "consumer sovereignty" economists, have
squared off against the water developers who feel that recognition of the long-term benefits of water development should
be reflected in a low discount rate. But water developers are
willing to accept the 1968 discount rate formula which currently
works out to a discount rate of 5 1/2 percent. The environmentalists see a high discount rate, like 10 percent, as providing a built-in means of preventing many water developments
from ever being proposed for public consideration. It would
save them, as they see it, from engaging in many project-by-
project arguments. They are on-the-offensive to the extent
that the Environmental Defense Fund has brought suit against
the Water Resources Council to try to have the Judicial Branch
set aside the Council's decision in 1968 with respect to the
discount rate. The Fund says that the Council's decision was
arbitrary and capricious because it had no proper theoretical
basis. In its prayer to the Federal Court, the Fund suggests
that the proper concept is that of the "opportunity cost of
capital," the proper expression of that is 10 percent, and the
Council should be forced by the Judicial Branch to adopt this
position. No court decision has been rendered. Whether such
aggressiveness by environmentalists as this suit, together with
other aggressiveness, will make or break the current environmental movement remains to be seen.

On the other hand, the former members of the Mississippi
Valley Association and the Rivers and Harbors Congress (who
now comprise the Water Resources Congress), the former National
Reclamation Association (now called the National Water Resources
Association), and the National Association or Soil Conservation
Districts, appear to be in complete disarray, politically.
These are the traditional interests in favor of water and
related land resource developments. They appear to be thrown
back politically, on their haunches. They do not seem to know
how to defend themselves against this unprecedented threat to
the developments they have taken to be in the public good.

3/ See testimony by the author and others in Hearings before
the Subcommittee on Economy in Government of the Joint
Economic Committee, 90th Congress, 2nd Session, July 30 and
August 1, 1968, particularly pages 1-48, especially pages
46-47.

Whether they will recover some semblance of their former strength also remains to be seen.

Where do Federal guidelines for Water Project Evaluation stand, as of mid-1972, in the Executive Branch and with respect to the Congress? In the Executive Branch there has been no change of position since publication by the Water Resources Council in December 1971 of its Proposed Principles and Standards. As noted previously, hearings have been held during 1972; and later in the year the Council published a detailed "Summary/Analysis of Public Response to the Proposed Principles and Standards for Planning Water and Related Land Resources."

The Congress, in passing the Omnibus Rivers and Harbors Act of 1970, instructed the Corps of Engineers to undertake multi-objective planning in accord generally with the report of the Special Task Force of the Water Resources Council of July 1970 (i.e., the Orange Books). Moreover, bills have been introduced in the Congress which imply that if the Water Resources Council, with the approval of the President, does not settle satisfactorily the current major issues, the Congress will. Finally, both the House and Senate Appropriation Committees in their 1972 reports on public works appropriations have come out strongly against the opportunity-cost concept or the discount rate which has been proposed by the Administration.

Right now, in September 1972, it looks as though the Nixon Administration does not intend to settle current major issues in this field before the November election. And, it also looks as though there will be no congressional action until after the new Congress convenes in January 1973, if then. In the meantime, planners within the Executive Branch are uncertain and confused as to the guidelines within which they should perform their professional role, especially with respect to "new planning starts." Also, the professional staff of the Water Resource Council is held up in its development of the "Procedures" to be utilized in carrying out the "Principles" and "Standards."

All of this discussion, it should be noted, can be said to point to the fact that the ultimate optimization in planning and action with respect to water and related land resource use and development is a political optimization within the current structure of Federal policy decision-making. All other optimizations, economic or otherwise, are sub-optimizations.

REFERENCES

Caulfield, H.P. Jr., 1961, Welfare, economics and resource development; in land and water planning for economic growth: University of Colorado.

Caulfield, H.P. Jr., 1971, A national regional impact evaluation system--discussion: Proceedings of the Business and Economic Statistics Section, American Statistical Association, August 23-26, 1971, p. 211-214.

Gallatin, A., 1968, (1808) Report on roads and canals: Augusta M. Kelley Co., New York.

Holmes, B. H., 1972, A history of federal water resources programs, 1800-1960: U.S. Department of Agriculture, Economic Research Service, Washington, D.C., Misc. Publication No. 1233.

Joint Economic Committee, Subcommittee on Economy in Government, 1968, Economic analysis of public investment decisions: Interest rate policy and discounting analysis: Hearings July 30,31 and August 1, 1968, Government Printing Office, Washington, D.C.

Maass, A., et al., 1962, Design of water resource systems: Harvard University Press, Cambridge, Massachusetts.

Pigou, A. C., 1922, The economics of welfare: 4th Ed. London, Macmillan and Co., Ltd., 1932.

Subcommittee on Benefits and Costs, Federal Inter-agency River Basin Committee, 1950, Proposed practices for economic analysis of river basin projects ("The Green Book"): Government Printing Office, Washington, D.C.

Subcommittee on Evaluation Standards, Inter-agency Committee on Water Resources, 1958, Proposed practices for economic analysis of river basin projects ("The Green Book"): Government Printing Office, Washington, D.C.

Technical Committee of the Water Resources Centers of the Thirteen Western States, 1971, Water resources planning and social goals: conceptualization toward a new methodology: Final Research Report for the Office of Water Resources Research on Project C-2194 and published by the Utah Water Research Laboratory (Publication PRWG-94-1), Logan, Utah.

U.S. Bureau of the Budget, 1952, Circular A-47: Washington, D.C., December 31.

U.S. Water Resources Council (ad hoc), 1962, Policies, standards and procedures in the formulation, evaluation and review of plans for use and development of water and related land resources: Senate Document 97, 87th Congress, 2nd Session, U.S. Government Printing Office, Washington, D.C., May.

U.S. Water Resources Council, Special Task Force, 1969, Procedures for evaluation of water and related land resource projects ("The Blue Book"): Washington, D.C.

U.S. Water Resources Council, Special Task Force, 1970, Federal agency technical comments on the special Task Force report entitled: Procedures for evaluation of water and related land resource projects: Washington, D.C.

U.S. Water Resource Council, Special Task Force, 1970, Public response to the special Task Force report entitled: Procedures for evaluation of water and related land resource projects: Washington, D.C.

U.S. Water Resources Council, Special Task Force, 1970, Principles for planning water and land resources: and Standards for planning water and land resources: Informally made available as "The Orange Books", reprinted as Committee Print, Serial No. 92-20 of the Senate Committee on Public Works, 1971.

U.S. Water Resources Council, 1971, Proposed principles and standards for planning water and related land resources: Federal Register, Washington, D.C., Vol. 36, No. 245, December 21.

U.S. Water Resources Council, 1972, Summary/Analysis of public response to the proposed principles and standards for planning water and related land and resources: Washington, D.C.

Appendix A

THOUGHTS ON RIVER BASIN PLANNING

Rolland Kasser, Vice President of Harza Engineering Company,
150 South Wacker Drive, Chicago, Illinois

Appendix A

THOUGHTS ON RIVER BASIN PLANNING

A.1 INTRODUCTION

During the process of listing significant experiences
with river basin plans and problems in preparation for this
paper, the dominant thought that emerged was the need for plans
to be adjustable for changing conditions. It is a matter of
record that plan after plan have matured to various degrees of
inadequacy or even failure. In most cases, the inadequacies or
failures are the result of imposing a static plan on dynamic
natural and economic conditions. Flexibility for change is,
then, the central theme for our observations.

A.2 HISTORICAL

Of the five earlier known areas of civilization, Egypt,
Crete, Mesopotamia, Indus and the Yellow River, four were
located in river basins. Two of these, the Nile Basin in Egypt
and Indus in West Pakistan, are currently undergoing a renais-
sance of development works which promise to achieve a level of
productivity far greater than ever hoped for in the past. To
a lesser degree, the Tigris and Euphrates Rivers in Iraq and
the Yellow River in China are undergoing measures which will
enhance the basic economy of the areas they support. The only
non-river basin early cultural center, the Island of Crete, has
receded to a level of semiobscurity while other areas have
surged forward to economic and cultural prominence.

The four above mentioned river basin areas have, down
through the years, alternately flourished and then receded to
obscurity. One of the earliest examples of environmental mis-
management is presented by the Tigris-Euphrates River Basin.
Historical records show that the earliest civilizations in this
area were located near the mouth and along the lower reaches of
these rivers. Perhaps the best known of these is Babylon. Seed
and other organic debris captured in successive annual layers
of flood deposited silt suggest that the earliest crops were
those that flourished in sweet water and soil. These crops were
gradually replaced by a succession each more tolerant of salinity than its predecessor leading to the most salt tolerant
crops and eventually no crops at all. The lesson that salinity
must be flushed out of the soil had not yet been learned.

Lower reaches of the river became less productive and the
area of habitation slowly moved upstream seeking new areas of
sweet water and soil with no salinity. This retreat from salinity continued and by the year 1000 the center of population
was centered around what is now called Baghdad. Some time

around the year 1200, an invasion from the north destroyed not
only the greater part of the population but also much of what
then was highly sophisticated irrigation works. These works
were never rebuilt and much of what is operating today was
constructed during the last fifty years. Nevertheless, as one
flies over the previously irrigated area it is possible to
detect many patterns of irrigation canals and other features.
The more clearly defined are generally associated with Roman
and post-Roman times, but there are also indications of what
would appear to be much earlier works. One could scarcely place
the blame for the late 12th century invasion on inadequate river
basin planning, but the criss-crossing scars of abandoned,
redirected and reconstructed works leaves little doubt but that
the planning that existed in those days falls somewhere between
the expeditious and the whimisical.

A.3 PLANNING CRITERIA

Today we are fascinated by the thesis that current river
basin planning is substantially more sophisticated than in the
past. We not only strive to avoid detrimental results of river
development but go a step beyond by hoping to optimize the beneficial effects of such development. Starting with the assets
of land, water, vegetation, animal life, and culture, we catalog, appraise, evaluate, and eventually evolve these components
into a plan which will, in some compromised manner, provide an
optimum combination of beneficial fulfillment. Until recently,
this fulfillment was measured on technical, financial, and
sometimes political scales. Now it must also be measured on
the environmental scale.

The question now is "For whose benefit and for whose use
do we plan the development of a river basin?" Heretofore, the
planning and development of a river basin usually resulted in
such great economic gains that little or no thought was given
to ecological or environmental spin out and much less whether
such spin out was good or bad. To improve the economic level
of a thousand or one hundred thousand human beings was considered justification for such works; and, in most instances the
short term gain was the sole measuring stick. Little thought
was given to the possibility that plans conceived for one objective may turn out ultimately to be exceedingly wasteful. Let
us examine one of our major U.S. rivers.

A.4 COLORADO RIVER

The plans for utilization of the waters of the Colorado
River have had the benefit of dedication and sincerity of the
highest levels of expertise. When different groups with essentially equivalent dedication, sincerity and expertise disagreed,
resolution has been sought and found in court. Short-range
objectives were to assure a dependable supply of municipal and

industrial waters for Los Angeles metropolitan area. Long-range objectives were to establish the rights of the states in the basin to develop and use the water resource. The keynote was to plan a development which would assure equitable use. This is reflected in the full range of states' rights extending to the point of entitling some states to deplete river flow by consumptive use or diversion out of a basin but at the same time assuring that part of the resource would be reserved for later use in areas of slower development.

The principles governing planning and development of the Colorado River have evolved through a series of documentary actions. The Colorado River Compact signed in Santa Fe in 1922 established equal entitlements to the upper and lower basins and provided for a later allocation to Mexico. The entitlements were based on the assessment of water availability from flow records available in 1922 which indicated an average annual flow of about 17 million acre/feet. Two years later saw the implementation of the LaRue Plan for development of storage and power by the staged construction of about twelve low dams.

The Boulder Canyon Project Act ratified initially by six of the seven interested states, established limits for consumptive use of Colorado River water in California and authorized the construction of a dam in Black Canyon or Boulder Canyon to store not less than 20 million acre/feet. It also authorized construction of the All American Canal Project to serve the Imperial and Coachella Valleys. The Secretary of the Interior was established as the authority controlling distribution of water to the lower river.

A water treaty was executed with Mexico in 1944 for annual delivery of 1.5 million acre/feet. Davis Dam was then authorized for power and river regulation and to meet the Mexican Treaty obligations. Thus, by 1946, over a period of some 24 years the principles and allocations were established for the Lower Colorado River development.

In 1948 the Upper Colorado River Compact was approved and established entitlements to each of the Upper Basin states. Also, a commission of federal and state representatives was activated. In about 1954, the Colorado River Storage Project, including Glen Canyon Dam and Reservoir as the principal storage facility, was authorized to provide upper basin water uses and to provide the storage capacity necessary to comply with requirements for deliveries of water to the lower basin. This program included construction of not only Glen Canyon Dam but also Flaming Gorge Dam on the Green River and the Navajo Dam on the San Juan River plus several dams on the Gunnison River.

In the early 1960's, comprehensive studies were made of the filling of the Glen Canyon Reservoir, now identified as

Lake Powell. Those studies revealed that the water supply on the Colorado River was much less than it was thought to be in 1922 and recognized that filling of Lake Powell could only be accomplished in high runoff years. This necessitated establishing criteria for downstream releases and, when possible, increases in storage. Subsequently, a settlement of the Supreme Court suit between Arizona and California established rights of both states to use Colorado River water. This was followed by the authorization of the Central Arizona Project.

A. 5 UNANTICIPATED PROBLEMS

A number of problems have emerged during the last 50 years. As previously indicated, the water allocations established in 1922 promised more water than the Colorado River can supply on a long time average basis, but needed and sensible adjustments are thwarted by prescribed finite and inflexible allocations.

Although water quality was not mentioned in the various documentary activities, it has since developed that drainage waters from the Wellton-Mohawk Project have created problems with Mexico. Also, industrial wastes originating in the Upper Colorado River Basin have created water quality problems in the upper and also lower areas. This injects a new and unanticipated criterion with which existing plans are incapable of dealing.

One of the earliest works, Lake Mead, formed by the construction of the dam authorized by the Boulder Canyon Project Act (now called Hoover Dam) is no longer needed fully for storage for river regulation, since Lake Powell performs most of that function. It would appear that Lake Mead provides a valuable reserve of water supply but any advantage offered by such a reserve is more than offset by the loss through evaporation of some 850,000 acre/feet per year. At some point in time, this evaporation loss must be apportioned to the entitlements of Nevada, Arizona, and California. This loss could be greatly reduced by lowering the level of Lake Mead Reservoir, but this would be injurious to power rights established by contracts with the Hoover power allotees.

It is apparent that a greater amount of regulatory storage will be required for the Upper Colorado River basin to use its allocated portion of the water supply and to comply with the provisions of the Colorado River Compact than would have been necessary if the water supply were greater. This situation is further complicated by the current suit filed by environmentalists seeking to prevent filling of the upper half of Lake Powell so as to prevent submergence of the Rainbow Bridge.

The foregoing undoubtedly gives a negative, unbalanced picture of the Colorado River development. You may be approaching the conclusion that the net result of planning has been detrimental. This is not true. There are many beneficial results of lasting value. To mention a few of such benefits the Metropolitan Water District of Southern California receives annually some 1.2 million acre-feet of water for domestic and industrial consumption. In the states of California and Arizona, irrigation is provided for over 750,000 acres and the powerstation at Hoover Dam provides a capacity in excess of 1.3 million kilowatts which is utilized in the adjacent and surrounding four states. Without these and the many other primary and secondary benefits the economy of the area would have remained inert.

A.6 CONCLUSIONS

Experience on the Colorado River and elsewhere serves to highlight several areas in which expertise and past practice have gone astray. It becomes increasingly obvious that plans for basin development must be kept flexible so as to avoid, insofar as possible, committments in perpetuity for unnecessary water losses or prevlusion of changes which future generations may find desirable or necessary. It now appears that one of the earlier plans, the LaRue Plan, put forth about 1924 would have provided a sounder basis for river development, offering a more efficient conservation of water resources and providing for a more equitable development of hydroelectric power and energy. It now appears unfortunate that subsequent planning and actions have eliminated the possibility of adopting the flexible concepts of LaRue.

One of the major as yet unresolved problems in the Colorado River Basin stems from the now established fact that the early plans were based on questionable hydrologic determinations which promised substantially more water than now appears available. Considering the high level of technical expertise invoked during the earlier studies, it is difficult to understand how such a gross overestimation of water availability could have occurred. Nevertheless, this serves to emphasize the necessity for multiple independent evaluations of this basic area of information and also the desirability of limiting water allocations and development plans to assured supplies and to defer decisions on doubtful portions of the water resource until a dependable analysis can be made. We now know that in many basins in the West water conservation measures have reduced appreciably the runoff at downstream points and water allocations must be made in anticipation of the effects of such independent programs **or**, alternatively, organizational controls must be provided to assure compatability of all water control measures with legal allocations.

The concept of the basin planning must extend not only to include the entire area encompassed in such basin but should consider the basin as a natural unit. In devising plans for water allocations as the basis for development of the Colorado River, the basin was divided first into upper and lower sections which were fragmented by political boundaries. Partly as a political expendiency, water entitlements were based on state or other boundaries which led to inefficient location of storage reservoirs. For example, Lake Mead could physically have performed the storage function for which the Glen Canyon Dam was built. Or possibly a smaller reservoir at Lake Mead could have met the needs of the lower basin so long as storage was required in the Upper Basin, thereby minimizing the duplication of capabilities at Lake Powell.

The question of water quality was generally ignored in the various compacts and agreements which served as a basis for the Colorado River Basin planning. Water quality problems have emerged in the lower reaches of the river from the discharge of saline drainage effluents from irrigated areas in the United States which result in damaging levels of salinity in water delivered to Mexico. Certainly future plans must give full recognition to the protection of water quality rather than to ignore what could become a major source of trouble.

Although of great concern at the present, the term "environmental impact" and vocabulary related thereto had not been invented during the early days of the Colorado River Basin development. Obviously, consideration of environmental impacts are now essential. The fact that water quality and environmental impact were both generally overlooked during the formative stages of the Colorado River Basin planning serves to emphasize that advances in the state of the art can well bring to significant or controlling levels aspects which today are of little or no concern. Flexibility then becomes an even more necessary criterion.

In addition to flexibility, a basin plan must include specific provisions for periodic review and appraisal against the constantly changing background of needs, aims, and state of the art. The primary purpose of such review and reevaluation is that of avoiding unnecessary construction, and most of all, wastage of valuable resources.

The foregoing conclusions are obviously based on hindsight and are aimed specifically at experiences gained in the Colorado River Basin. Nevertheless, in spite of their limitations they point to broader principles which will serve to avoid some or possibly all of the problems encountered in the Colorado River Basin. The most significant of these are flexibility and periodic reevaluation. In other words, the plan must be made to be changed and planning must be thought of as an on-going

and continous process. "In summary, we must develop a technique
for planning which allows us to do something today that we won't
regret tommorrow."

Appendix B

SEDIMENT AND PHOSPHORUS CONTENT OF STREAM FLOWS

by

A. W. Taylor, Chemist, U.S. Soils Laboratory
Beltsville, Maryland

Contribution from the
Soil and Water Conservation Research Division,
Agricultural Research Service, USDA.

Appendix B

SEDIMENT AND PHOSPHORUS CONTENT OF STREAM FLOWS

B.1 ABSTRACT

The phosphate carried by a stream can be classified in three forms -- that in free solution, that on the sediment in adsorption equilibrium with the solution, and that in fixed or unavailable forms. The biologically available fraction can be identified as the sum of the first two. The third, inert, fraction often comprises 90% of the total. For this reason, measurements of the total carried by the sediments is biologically meaningless.

The amount present in true solution is easily measured by analysis of filtered or clarified samples. The distinction between available and unavailable adsorbed forms is less easily drawn. Methods for measuring available phosphate in soils have included extraction procedures with a variety of salts and acid solutions, anion exchange resin and isotopic dilution techniques using ^{32}P. Different procedures rarely give the same result: criteria for their evaluation are operational and the data must be judged in terms of the use to which it is to be put.

The distribution of available phosphate between water and sediment can be represented as a system approaching adsorption desorbtion equilibrium. Studies on the Mahantango Creek, a tributary of the Susquehanna River in central Pennsylvania, have shown that the changes in distribution of phosphate between the water and sediments can be interpreted in terms of the adsorption isotherms characteristic of the sediments and the soils from which they are derived. The system is highly dynamic. Soluble phosphate in runoff from the more fertile soils is continously adsorbed by the phosphate-deficient sediments of the streambed so that the P concentration in solution is reduced to less than 15 ppb within a few hours. The extent to which sediments act as a scavenger for dissolved phosphate can be predicted if the adsorption characteristics are known.

Appendix C

TABLE OF CONTENTS - FROM VOLUMES I & II
RIVER MECHANICS

by

Hsieh W. Shen, Professor of Civil Engineering, Colorado State
University, Fort Collins, Colorado

Appendix C

TABLE OF CONTENTS - FROM VOLUMES I & II
RIVER MECHANICS

C.1   VOLUME I

Chapter